NFPA 72®

National Fire Alarm and Signaling Code

2013 Edition

This edition of NFPA 72, *National Fire Alarm and Signaling Code*, was prepared by the Technical Committees on Fundamentals of Fire Alarm and Signaling Systems, Testing and Maintenance of Fire Alarm and Signaling Systems, Initiating Devices for Fire Alarm and Signaling Systems, Notification Appliances for Fire Alarm and Signaling Systems, Protected Premises Fire Alarm and Signaling Systems, Emergency Communication Systems, Supervising Station Fire Alarm and Signaling Systems, Public Emergency Reporting Systems, and Single- and Multiple-Station Alarms and Household Fire Alarm Systems, released by the Technical Correlating Committee on Signaling Systems for the Protection of Life and Property, and acted on by NFPA at its June Association Technical Meeting held June 11–14, 2012, in Las Vegas, NV. It was issued by the Standards Council on August 9, 2012, with an effective date of August 29, 2012, and supersedes all previous editions.

Five tentative interim amendments (TIAs), indicated by boxed notices at the appropriate areas within the document, were issued on August 9, 2012. For further information on tentative interim amendments, see Section 5 of the NFPA Regulations Governing Committee Projects available at: http://www.nfpa.org/assets/files/PDF/CodesStandards/TIAErrataFI/TIARegs.pdf.

This edition of NFPA 72 was approved as an American National Standard on August 29, 2012.

Origin and Development of NFPA 72

The development of NFPA's signaling standards dates back to 1898 with the appointment of the Committee on Thermo-Electric Fire Alarms. The 1905 edition of NBFU 71A, *Rules and Requirements of the National Board of Fire Underwriters for the Construction, Installation, and Use of Signaling Systems Used for the Transmission of Signals Affecting the Fire Hazard as Recommended by the National Fire Protection Association*, and related documents dating back to 1903 were among the first of numerous signaling standards published in conjunction with the National Fire Protection Association. The descendants of these earlier standards have been consolidated into the *National Fire Alarm Code, NFPA 72*.

The first edition of the *National Fire Alarm Code*, published in 1993, was a consolidation of the 1989 edition of NFPA 71, *Standard for the Installation, Maintenance, and Use of Signaling Systems for Central Station Service*; the 1990 edition of NFPA 72, *Standard for the Installation, Maintenance, and Use of Protective Signaling Systems*; the 1990 edition of NFPA 72E, *Standard on Automatic Fire Detectors*; the 1989 edition of NFPA 72G, *Guide for the Installation, Maintenance, and Use of Notification Appliances for Protective Signaling Systems*; the 1988 edition of NFPA 72H, *Guide for Testing Procedures for Local, Auxiliary, Remote Station, and Proprietary Protective Signaling Systems*; and the 1989 edition of NFPA 74, *Standard for the Installation, Maintenance, and Use of Household Fire Warning Equipment*. Many of the requirements of these standards were identical or very similar. The recommendations that were taken from the guides (NFPA 72G and NFPA 72H) were changed to mandatory requirements.

The 1996 edition of *NFPA 72* incorporated many changes of a technical nature. These changes related to issues such as the Americans with Disabilities Act, software testing, fire modeling, and communications.

The 1999 edition represented a major change in code content and organization. The chapters were arranged to facilitate user friendliness and provide a logical structure. A new chapter on public fire reporting was added, and many technical revisions were made. Annex B (formerly Appendix B) was streamlined to facilitate ease of use, many unenforceable terms were removed, and Chapter 3 was reorganized to facilitate a more logical approach.

The 2002 edition reflected an extensive editorial revision of the Code to comply with the latest edition of the *Manual of Style for NFPA Technical Committee Documents*. These revisions included the addition of three administrative chapters at the beginning of the Code: "Administration," "Referenced Publications," and "Definitions." Eight technical chapters followed the administrative chapters in the same sequence as in the 1999 edition. Other editorial revisions included the breakout of paragraphs with multiple requirements into individually numbered paragraphs for each requirement, the minimization of use of exceptions, the use of consistent headings for sections and section subdivisions, and reorganization to limit paragraph numbering to six digits.

The 2002 edition contained a number of technical revisions throughout the Code. These included a major revision of the power supply requirements; a new requirement addressing impairments to fire alarm systems; additional requirements concerning the review and approval of performance-based detection system designs; revision of the rules for system survivability from attack by fire; the introduction of rules for an alternate approach for audible signaling; the addition of requirements to address performance-based designs for visible signaling; the relocation of testing and maintenance requirements for single- and multiple-station alarms and household fire alarm systems to the testing and maintenance chapter; and revisions to re-establish the prescriptive rules for household fire-warning equipment from the 1996 edition of the Code.

The 2007 edition contained a number of technical revisions including many to accommodate new technology and to take advantage of new research. Changes were made to better address the integration of mass notification systems and other systems with fire alarm systems. Revisions were also made in several areas of the Code for clarity and to enhance its usability.

Some of the more significant revisions in the 2007 edition addressed protection of fire alarm control units, personnel qualification, heat detector response time, smoke detector spacing, smoke detection in ducts, detectors that use multiple sensing inputs, video image smoke and flame detection, synchronization of visible notification appliances, exit marking audible notification appliances, tactile notification appliances, different types of protected premises fire alarm system, and in-building enhancement systems for firefighter radio communications.

The 2007 edition also included significant changes to the requirements for smoke alarms in residential applications, revisions to require the interconnection of smoke alarms for existing occupancies, revisions to require additional smoke alarms for larger dwelling units, and revisions to allow voice messages to be included as a part of the smoke alarm notification signal.

Revisions in the 2007 edition to enhance and clarify the Code included those that address suppression system inputs to the fire alarm system, emergency/voice alarm communications systems, fire alarm system interface with elevator systems, and the means to indicate central station service. In addition, a complete revision of the Record of Completion Form along with examples of filled-out forms were provided.

The 2007 edition also included the addition of two new annexes — one to provide guidance for the design of mass notification systems and one to replace previous annex material for the design of fire service interfaces with a separate industry standard.

The 2010 edition of the Code presented a major change in the scope and organization of the document. This was reflected in the new title, *National Fire Alarm and Signaling Code*. The broader scope of the Code included emergency communications systems in addition to the traditional scope of fire alarm systems. A new chapter on emergency communications systems (ECS) was added to provide requirements for a variety of systems used for communication of information in various emergency situations. The ECS chapter included new systems such as in-building mass notification systems, wide-area mass notification systems, distributed recipient mass notifications systems, two-way radio communications enhancement system, and area of refuge emergency communications systems. The ECS chapter also included two systems formerly located in the chapter on protected premises fire alarm systems: (in-building fire) emergency voice/alarm communications systems, and two-way in-building wired (telephone) emergency services communication systems.

Two other new chapters were added in the 2010 edition. The new chapter on circuits and pathways included requirements and information formerly from the chapters on fundamentals of fire alarm systems and from the chapter on protected premises fire alarm systems. This new chapter provided circuit and pathway performance (class) designations and pathway survivability level designations as well as general wiring requirements presented in a format that allowed use by any type of system covered in the Code. The new chapter on emergency control functions and interfaces included requirements and information formerly contained in the chapter of protected premises fire alarm systems. In this chapter the term *fire safety function* generally was replaced with the term *emergency control function* to reflect the potentially broader application beyond just fire alarm systems. This new chapter also included new provisions for first-responder-use elevators and elevators for occupant-controlled evacuation.

The 2010 edition was substantially reorganized to accommodate the new chapters in a logical order with reserved chapter numbers included to minimize the potential for further renumbering in the future. The overall organization included administrative chapters, support chapters, and system chapters as well as numerous annexes for usability.

Significant revisions were also made throughout the 2010 edition to reflect the broader application of the Code to emergency communication systems. These included revisions within the chapter on fundamentals to address power supply requirements, signal priorities, signal distinction and documentation requirements; revisions to the protected premises chapter to better accommodate non–fire alarm systems in combination systems; revisions to the supervising stations chapter and public emergency reporting system chapter to allow their use for emergency communications systems; and revisions to the testing and maintenance chapter to incorporate requirements for the inspection, testing, and maintenance of mass notification systems and two-way radio communications enhancement systems.

In addition to the content of the new chapters, the 2010 edition included significant technical changes. These included new requirements for signaling to the deaf and hard of hearing, new requirements and guidance for the design, installation, and testing of voice communications systems to ensure voice intelligibility, and extensive revision of requirements for the installation of smoke detectors in both level and sloped joist and beam ceiling applications.

Revisions to the supervising station chapter in the 2010 edition included the retirement of four legacy transmission technologies no longer being installed: active multiplex transmission systems, McCulloh systems, directly connected noncoded systems, and private microwave systems. The subsection on "Other Transmission Technologies" was relocated to become the default subsection for supervising stations communications methods.

Modifications in the 2010 edition to the chapter on single- and multiple-station alarms and household fire alarms systems included new provisions to address the interconnection of smoke alarms using wireless technology, new provisions for signaling to those with hearing loss, and new requirements and guidance for the placement of smoke alarms and smoke detectors.

The 2010 edition included two new guidance annexes, Annex C on system performance and design, and Annex D on speech intelligibility.

Prior editions of this document have been translated into languages other than English, including Spanish.

The 2013 edition of the Code builds on the organizational changes made in the 2010 edition. New Chapter 7, "Documentation," has been added to improve the usability of the document. The chapter provides a central location for all the documentation requirements of the Code. In some cases the documentation provisions are contained directly in the new chapter. In other cases references are provided to the locations of documentation requirements contained in other chapters. As an example, the new chapter contains the minimum documentation requirements that apply to any system covered by the Code while additional document requirements that might apply from other parts of the Code or from other governing laws, codes, or standards are listed with an appropriate reference. The Record of Completion and Record of Inspection, Testing, and Maintenance forms are included at the end of the chapter and have been completely revised so they are easier to use with a basic form for straightforward systems and supplemental forms for more complex systems.

Chapter 10, "Fundamentals," has been reorganized for the 2013 edition to provide a more user-friendly flow of requirements. In addition, requirements for circuit monitoring found in the previous edition of Chapter 10 have been relocated to Chapter 12, "Circuits and Pathways," a more logical location.

Extensive usability changes have also been made in the inspection and testing tables of Chapter 14, "Inspection, Testing, and Maintenance." The visual inspection table has been updated, adding new inspection methods for each component along with the inspection frequency. The test methods and test frequency tables have been combined into a single table so that the test method appears along with the test frequency for each component. The component listings in both tables have reorganized and coordinated so that components and equipment are easier to find.

The 2013 edition of the Code also includes many technical updates. Among these are changes in Chapter 10, "Fundamentals," requiring supervising stations operators and fire alarm system service providers to report to the authority having jurisdiction certain conditions of system impairment. Requirements for inspection, testing, and service personnel qualifications have been updated to better reflect the level of qualification needed for each type of activity. Changes have also been made in Chapter 18, "Notification Appliances," requiring documentation of the locations that require audible notification appliances as well as documentation of the audibility levels that must be produced. Area of coverage requirements were also added for visible notification appliances. Changes have been made in Chapter 21, "Emergency Control Function Interfaces," to address requirements for elevator recall when sprinklers are installed in elevator pits. The requirements for occupant evacuation elevators have also been completely revised to coordinate with changes being made in ASME A.17.1/B44, *Safety Code for Elevators and Escalators.* Changes have been made in Chapter 24, "Emergency Communications Systems," to address the use of microphones, to address the use of textual and graphical visible notification appliances for primary or supplemental notification, and to update the requirements for emergency command centers. Changes have been made in Chapter 26, "Supervising Station Alarm Systems," to address alarm signal verification, alarm signal content, and restoration of signals. These changes have been made in part to help emergency responders better manage issues related to unwanted alarms. In addition, new definitions for unwanted alarms have been added to more precisely identify the sources of these alarms. Changes have also been made to update the communications methods addressed in Chapter 26. Among these are changes to the supervision interval requirements for communications paths and changes to the types of transmission means that can be used for the second channel of a DACT. Changes have been made in Chapter 29, "Single- and Multiple-Station Alarms and Household Fire Alarm Systems," to address the connection of sprinkler waterflow switches to multiple-station alarms and to add new requirements addressing the smoke alarm resistance to common nuisance sources.

Technical Correlating Committee on Signaling Systems for the Protection of Life and Property (SIG-AAC)

Robert P. Schifiliti, *Chair*
R. P. Schifiliti Associates, Inc., MA [SE]

Lee F. Richardson, *Secretary*
National Fire Protection Association, MA

Douglas M. Aiken, Lakes Region Mutual Fire Aid, NH [U]
    Rep. International Municipal Signal Association
Andrew G. Berezowski, Honeywell Inc., CT [M]
    Rep. National Electrical Manufacturers Association
Art Black, Carmel Fire Protection Associates, CA [E]
J. Robert Boyer, UTC/Edwards Company, NJ [M]
John C. Fannin III, SafePlace Corporation, DE [U]
Louis T. Fiore, L. T. Fiore, Inc., NJ [IM]
    Rep. Central Station Alarm Association
Bruce Fraser, Fraser Fire Protection Services, MA [SE]
Vic Humm, Vic Humm & Associates, TN [SE]
David F. Klein, Las Vegas Fire & Rescue, NV [E]
    Rep. International Association of Fire Chiefs
Peter A. Larrimer, U.S. Department of Veterans Affairs, PA [U]

Fred M. Leber, LRI Fire Protection Engineering, Canada [SE]
James M. Mundy, Jr., Asset Protection Associates, Ltd., NY [M]
    Rep. Automatic Fire Alarm Association, Inc.
Lynn Nielson, City of Henderson, NV [E]
Thomas F. Norton, Norel Service Company, Inc., MA [IM]
    Rep. U.S. Naval Historical Center
    (VL to Document: 72)
Rodger Reiswig, Tyco/SimplexGrinnell, FL [M]
Lawrence J. Shudak, Underwriters Laboratories Inc., IL [RT]
Tom G. Smith, Cox Systems Technology, OK [IM]
    Rep. National Electrical Contractors Association
Lawrence J. Wenzel, Hughes Associates, Inc., CT [SE]

Alternates

Jeffrey R. Brooks, SimplexGrinnell, MA [M]
    (Alt. to R. Reiswig)
Richard W. Bukowski, The RJA Group, Inc., MD [SE]
    (Alt. to B. Fraser)
Louis Chavez, Underwriters Laboratories Inc., IL [RT]
    (Alt. to L. J. Shudak)
Thomas P. Hammerberg, Automatic Fire Alarm Association, Inc., GA [M]
    (Alt. to J. M. Mundy, Jr.)

Jack McNamara, Bosch Security Systems, NY [M]
    (Alt. to A. G. Berezowski)
Earl P. Valois, City of New Orleans Fire Department, LA [E]
    (Alt. to D. F. Klein)
Frank L. Van Overmeiren, FP&C Consultants, Inc., IN [SE]
    (Alt. to V. Humm)

Nonvoting

Benjamin B. Aycock, Charlotte-Mecklenburg , NC
    (Member Emeritus)
Merton W. Bunker, Jr., U.S. Department of State, VA [U]
    Rep. TC on Protected Premises Fire Alarm Systems
Shane M. Clary, Bay Alarm Company, CA [IM]
    Rep. TC on Fundamentals of Fire Alarm Systems
Laurence J. Dallaire, U.S. Architect of the Capitol, DC [E]
    Rep. TC on Household Fire Alarm Systems
Raymond A. Grill, Arup Fire, DC [SE]
    Rep. TC on Notification Appliances for Fire Alarm Systems
Jeffrey G. Knight, City of Newton Fire Department, MA [U]
    Rep. TC on Public Fire Reporting Systems
J. Jeffrey Moore, Hughes Associates, Inc., OH [SE]
    Rep. TC on Testing & Maintenance of Fire Alarm Systems

Wayne D. Moore, Hughes Associates, Inc., RI [SE]
    Rep. TC on Emergency Communication Systems
Daniel J. O'Connor, Aon Fire Protection Engineering, IL [I]
    Rep. TC on Initiating Devices for Fire Alarm Systems
Warren E. Olsen, Fire Safety Consultants, Inc., IL [E]
    Rep. TC on Supervising Station Fire Alarm Systems
Martin H. Reiss, The RJA Group, Inc., MA [SE]
    Rep. Safety to Life Correlating Committee
Evan E. Stauffer, Jr., U.S. Department of the Navy, PA
    Rep. TC Public Emergency Service Communications
Dean K. Wilson, Hughes Associates, Inc., PA [SE]
    (Member Emeritus)

Lee F. Richardson, NFPA Staff Liaison

This list represents the membership at the time the Committee was balloted on the final text of this edition. Since that time, changes in the membership may have occurred. A key to classifications is found at the back of the document.

NOTE: Membership on a committee shall not in and of itself constitute an endorsement of the Association or any document developed by the committee on which the member serves.

Committee Scope: This Committee shall have primary responsibility for documents on the installation, performance, maintenance, testing, and use of signaling components and signaling systems for the protection of life, property, and mission continuity.

Technical Committee on Fundamentals of Fire Alarm and Signaling Systems (SIG-FUN)
(Chapters 1 and 10)

Shane M. Clary, *Chair*
Bay Alarm Company, CA [IM]

Jeffrey S. Hancock, *Secretary*
Valero Energy Corporation, TX [U]

William R. Ball, National Joint Apprentice & Training Committee, IN [L]
    Rep. International Brotherhood of Electrical Workers
Andrew G. Berezowski, Honeywell Inc., CT [M]
    Rep. National Electrical Manufacturers Association
Robert A. Bonifas, Alarm Detection Systems, Inc., IL [IM]
    Rep. Central Station Alarm Association
Manuelita E. David, Aon Fire Protection Engineering, CA [I]
Daniel G. Decker, Safety Systems, Inc., MI [IM]
James Ditaranto, Commercial Electrical Systems, FL [IM]
Sanford E. Egesdal, Egesdal Associates PLC, MN [SE]
David W. Frable, U.S. General Services Administration, IL [U]
Daniel J. Gauvin, Tyco/SimplexGrinnell, MA [M]
David Goodyear, Seneca College, Canada [SE]
Kevin M. Green, Pyro-Comm Systems, Inc., CA [IM]
Scott Jacobs, ISC Electronic Systems, Inc., CA [IM]
Jon Kapis, The RJA Group, Inc., CA [SE]
Walter J. Kessler, Jr., FM Approvals, MA [I]
Fred M. Leber, LRI Fire Protection Engineering, Canada [SE]

Chester S. Maciaszek, Savannah River Nuclear Solutions, LLC, SC [U]
Richard A. Malady, Fire Fighter Sales & Service Company, PA [IM]
    Rep. National Association of Fire Equipment Distributors
Jack McNamara, Bosch Security Systems, NY [M]
James M. Mundy, Jr., Asset Protection Associates, Ltd., NY [M]
    Rep. Automatic Fire Alarm Association, Inc.
Louis Nash, U.S. Coast Guard, DC [E]
Thomas F. Norton, Norel Service Company, Inc., MA [IM]
    Rep. U.S. Naval Historical Center
David J. Stone, Underwriters Laboratories Inc., IL [RT]
Emily Troyanski, Intertek Testing Services, NJ [RT]
Ed Vaillancourt, E & M International, Inc., NM [M]
    Rep. Fire Suppression Systems Association
Todd W. Warner, Brooks Equipment Company, Inc., NC [M]
    Rep. Fire Equipment Manufacturers' Association
William F. Wayman, Jr., Hughes Associates, Inc., MD [SE]

Alternates

Eric J. Apolenis, The RJA Group, Inc., CA [SE]
    (Alt. to J. Kapis)
Bob Elliott, FM Approvals, MA [I]
    (Alt. to W. J. Kessler, Jr.)
Kimberly A. Gruner, Fike Corporation, MO [M]
    (Alt. to E. Vaillancourt)
Robert M. Hill, Robert Hill & Associates, MA [M]
    (Alt. to J. M. Mundy, Jr.)
Daniel M. Kester, Battelle, WA [U]
    (Alt. to J. S. Hancock)
Edward Loughney, Southwestern Idaho Electrical JATC, ID [L]
    (Alt. to W. R. Ball)

Maria Marks, Siemens Industry, MD [M]
    (Alt. to A. G. Berezowski)
Vincent B. Mori, Intertek, IL [RT]
    (Alt. to E. Troyanski)
Allan Sanedrin, Underwriters Laboratories Inc., IL [RT]
    (Alt. to D. J. Stone)
Richard A. Savicki, Safety Systems, Inc., MI [IM]
    (Alt. to D. G. Decker)
Robert A. Williams, II, Vector Security Inc., VA [IM]
    (Alt. to R. A. Bonifas)
Dennis R. Yanek, Tyco/ADT Security Systems, NJ [M]
    (Alt. to D. J. Gauvin)

Lee F. Richardson, NFPA Staff Liaison

This list represents the membership at the time the Committee was balloted on the final text of this edition. Since that time, changes in the membership may have occurred. A key to classifications is found at the back of the document.

NOTE: Membership on a committee shall not in and of itself constitute an endorsement of the Association or any document developed by the committee on which the member serves.

Committee Scope: This Committee shall have primary responsibility for documents on common system fundamentals for fire alarm and signaling systems, requirements for approvals, power supplies, equipment performance, system documentation, and compatibility.

Technical Committee on Testing and Maintenance of Fire Alarm and Signaling Systems (SIG-TMS)
(Chapter 14, Annex D, and Annex G)

J. Jeffrey Moore, *Chair*
Hughes Associates, Inc., OH [SE]

Mark L. Rochholz, *Secretary*
Aon Fire Protection Engineering Corporation, IL [I]

Kevin J. Breen, Breen Electrical Contractors Inc., NY [IM]
     Rep. Independent Electrical Contractors, Inc.
Charles E. Brockett, XL Global Asset Protection Services, TX [I]
Jeffrey R. Brooks, Tyco/SimplexGrinnell, MA [M]
Robert E. Butchko, Siemens Industry, Inc., NJ [M]
Steve Carter, Orr Protection Systems, Inc., KY [M]
     Rep. Fire Suppression Systems Association
Louis Chavez, Underwriters Laboratories, Inc., IL [RT]
Scott D. Corrin, University of California-Riverside, CA [U]
Scott R. Edwards, Gentex Corporation, MI [M]
     Rep. National Electrical Manufacturers Association
Peter C. Harrod, The RJA Group, Inc., MA [SE]
Herbert B. Hurst, Jr., Savannah River Nuclear Solutions, LLC, SC [U]
William E. Johannsen, AFA Protective Systems, Inc., FL [IM]
Robert H. Kelly, Fire Defense Equipment Company, Inc., MI [IM]
J. David Kerr, Plano Fire Department, TX [E]
     Rep. NFPA Fire Service Section
David E. Kipley, AREVA NP, Inc., IL [U]
     Rep. Edison Electric Institute

Chuck Koval, U.S. General Services Administration, WA [U]
Peter A. Larrimer, U.S. Department of Veterans Affairs, PA [U]
Joseph B. McCullough, Western Technical Services, Inc., CO [IM]
James Murphy, Vector Security Inc., PA [IM]
     Rep. Central Station Alarm Association
Michael J. Reeser, Santa Rosa Fire Equipment Service Inc., CA [IM]
     Rep. California Automatic Fire Alarm Association Inc.
James R. Schifiliti, Fire Safety Consultants, Inc., IL [SE]
Joe Scibetta, BuildingReports, GA [M]
George E. Seymour, Total Safety US, Inc., TX [IM]
     Rep. National Association of Fire Equipment Distributors
Derek Shackley, Pacific Auxiliary Fire Alarm, CA [M]
     Rep. Automatic Fire Alarm Association, Inc.
Timothy M. Soverino, Nantucket, MA [U]
     Rep. International Municipal Signal Association
Frank L. Van Overmeiren, FP&C Consultants, Inc., IN [SE]

Alternates

Timothy E. Adams, American Society for Healthcare Engineering, IN [U]
     (Voting Alt. to ASHE Rep.)
Leonard Belliveau, Jr., Hughes Associates, Inc., RI [SE]
     (Alt. to J. J. Moore)
Anthony Bloodworth, Siemens Industries, Inc., TX [M]
     (Alt. to R. E. Butchko)
Scott D. Carlson, Fire Defense Equipment Company, Inc., MI [IM]
     (Alt. to R. H. Kelly)
Larry R. Dischert, Tyco/ADT Security Services, Inc., NJ [M]
     (Alt. to J. R. Brooks)
Joshua W. Elvove, U.S. General Services Administration, CO [U]
     (Alt. to C. Koval)
John F. Gudmundson, Underwriters Laboratories, Inc., , CA [RT]
     (Alt. to L. Chavez)
Rick Heffernan, SDi, NJ [M]
     (Alt. to S. R. Edwards)
Vic Humm, Vic Humm & Associates, TN [SE]
     (Alt. to F. L. Van Overmeiren)

Bill Isemann, Guardian Fire Protection Services LLC, MD [IM]
     (Alt. to G. E. Seymour)
Jon Kapis, The RJA Group, Inc., CA [SE]
     (Alt. to P. C. Harrod)
Peter Leszczak, U.S. Department of Veterans Affairs, CT [U]
     (Alt. to P. A. Larrimer)
Jay Levy, Hochiki America Corporation, CA [IM]
     (Alt. to M. J. Reeser)
Chester S. Maciaszek, Savannah River Nuclear Solutions, LLC, SC [U]
     (Alt. to H. B. Hurst, Jr.)
Joseph L. Palmieri, Carter Brothers Fire & Life Safety LLC, MA [M]
     (Alt. to D. Shackley)
Michael D. Sides, XL Global Asset Protection Services, FL [I]
     (Alt. to C. E. Brockett)
Michael J. Slattery, AFA Protective Systems, Inc., MA [IM]
     (Alt. to W. E. Johannsen)

Lee F. Richardson, NFPA Staff Liaison

This list represents the membership at the time the Committee was balloted on the final text of this edition. Since that time, changes in the membership may have occurred. A key to classifications is found at the back of the document.

NOTE: Membership on a committee shall not in and of itself constitute an endorsement of the Association or any document developed by the committee on which the member serves.

Committee Scope: This Committee shall have primary responsibility for documents and requirements for the proper inspection, testing, and maintenance of fire alarm and emergency communications systems and associated components, for both new and existing systems.

Technical Committee on Initiating Devices for Fire Alarm and Signaling Systems (SIG-IDS)
(Chapter 17 and Annex B)

Daniel J. O'Connor, *Chair*
Aon Fire Protection Engineering, IL [I]

William P. Adams, *Secretary*
Apollo Fire Detectors North America, GA [M]
Rep. National Electrical Manufacturers Association

Wayne J. Aho, Xtralis, Inc., MA [M]

Mark S. Boone, Dominion Resources Services Inc., VA [U]
Rep. Edison Electric Institute

John A. Chetelat, Honeywell Life Safety Group, CT [M]
Rep. Fire Suppression Systems Association

John M. Cholin, J. M. Cholin Consultants Inc., NJ [SE]

Kenneth W. Dungan, Risk Technologies, LLC, TN [SE]

Gary P. Fields, The Protectowire Company, Inc., MA [M]

Cheryl A. Gagliardi, FM Approvals, MA [I]

Robert A. Hall, R. A. Hall & Associates, NJ [SE]

Robert L. Langer, Amerex Corporation, AL [M]
Rep. Fire Equipment Manufacturers' Association

Loren L. Leimer, Hochiki America Corporation, CA [M]
Rep. Automatic Fire Alarm Association, Inc.

Norbert W. Makowka, National Association of Fire
Equipment Distributors, IL [IM]

Chris Marrion, Marrion Fire & Risk Consulting, NY [SE]

Samuel M. Miller, BP Exploration (Alaska) Inc., AK [U]

Ovid E. Morphew, Jr., Design/Systems Group, TX [IM]
Rep. National Independent Fire Alarm Distributors Assn.

James W. Mottorn, II, Bosch Security Systems, NY [M]

Lynn Nielson, City of Henderson, NV [E]

Ronald D. Ouimette, Siemens Building Technologies, Inc., NJ [M]

John L. Parssinen, Underwriters Laboratories Inc., IL [RT]

Martin H. Reiss, The RJA Group, Inc., MA [SE]

David L. Royse, Potter Electric Signal Company, MO [M]

James R. Schario, Electrical Industry Training Center (IBEW/NECA), MO [L]
Rep. International Brotherhood of Electrical Workers

Kenneth R. Schneider, Sprinkler Fitters LU 268 JAC, MO [L]
Rep. United Assn. of Journeymen & Apprentices of the Plumbing & Pipe Fitting Industry

Michael D. Sides, XL Global Asset Protection Services, FL [I]

Mark Swerdin, Zurich Services Corporation, NY [I]

Lawrence J. Wenzel, Hughes Associates, Inc., CT [SE]

Alternates

Mark E. Agar, Fire Equipment Company Inc., MI [IM]
(Alt. to N. W. Makowka)

Michael B. Baker, Automatic Fire Alarm Association, Inc., OR [M]
(Alt. to L. L. Leimer)

Jan Braam, UTC Fire & Security Company/Edwards, FL [M]
(Alt. to W. P. Adams)

Charles E. Brockett, XL Global Asset Protection Services, TX [I]
(Alt. to M. D. Sides)

Thomas C. Brown, The RJA Group, Inc., MD [SE]
(Alt. to M. H. Reiss)

Michael Earl Dillon, Dillon Consulting Engineers, Inc., CA [SE]
(Alt. to R. A. Hall)

Scott M. Golly, Hughes Associates, Inc., MD [SE]
(Alt. to L. J. Wenzel)

Michael A. Henke, Potter Electric Signal Company, MO [M]
(Alt. to D. L. Royse)

Noura Milardo, FM Global, MA [I]
(Alt. to C. A. Gagliardi)

David E. Mills, Underwriters Laboratories Inc., IL [RT]
(Alt. to J. L. Parssinen)

David M. Nelson, Volunteer Technology Systems, TN [IM]
(Alt. to O. E. Morphew, Jr.)

Brian E. Swanick, Siemens Building Technologies, Inc., NJ [M]
(Alt. to R. D. Ouimette)

Jerry Trotter, City of Henderson, NV [E]
(Alt. to L. Nielson)

Michael Yakine, UTC/Kidde-Fenwal, Inc., MA [M]
(Alt. to J. A. Chetelat)

Lee F. Richardson, NFPA Staff Liaison

This list represents the membership at the time the Committee was balloted on the final text of this edition. Since that time, changes in the membership may have occurred. A key to classifications is found at the back of the document.

NOTE: Membership on a committee shall not in and of itself constitute an endorsement of the Association or any document developed by the committee on which the member serves.

Committee Scope: This Committee shall have primary responsibility for documents on the installation and operation of initiating devices for fire alarm and signaling systems.

Technical Committee on Notification Appliances for Fire Alarm and Signaling Systems (SIG-NAS)
(Chapter 18 and Annex E)

Raymond A. Grill, *Chair*
Arup Fire, DC [SE]

David E. Becker, *Secretary*
Fire Equipment Service Company, KY [IM]
Rep. National Association of Fire Equipment Distributors

Robert F. Bitter, Honeywell, Inc., MO [M]
Thomas Carrie, Jr., Aon/Schirmer Engineering Corporation, IL [I]
Michael L. Edwards, U.S. Architect of the Capitol, DC [U]
Daniel M. Grosch, Underwriters Laboratories Inc., IL [RT]
Jeffrey M. Klein, System Sensor, IL [M]
  Rep. Automatic Fire Alarm Association, Inc.
David L. Klepitch, Whitman, Requardt & Associates, LLP, MD [SE]
Neal W. Krantz, Sr., Krantz Systems & Associates, LLC, MI [IM]
  Rep. NFPA Industrial Fire Protection Section
Daniel F. Laurich, Warminster Township, Fire Marshal, PA [E]
Steven P. Lewis, RFI Enterprises, CA [IM]

David O. Lowrey, City of Boulder Fire Rescue, CO [E]
Bob D. Morgan, Fort Worth Fire Department, TX [E]
David Newhouse, Gentex Corporation, MI [M]
  Rep. National Electrical Manufacturers Association
Maurice M. Pilette, Mechanical Designs Ltd., MA [SE]
Jack Poole, Poole Fire Protection, Inc., KS [SE]
Sam P. Salwan, Environmental Systems Design, Inc., IL [SE]
Robert P. Schifiliti, R. P. Schifiliti Associates, Inc., MA [SE]
Michael T. Schmitt, Long Grove Fire Protection District, IL [E]
Daniel L. Seibel, Wolverine Fire Protection Company, MI [IM]
Morris L. Stoops, UTC Fire & Security, FL [M]
Paul R. Strelecki, Siemens Building Technologies, Inc., NJ [M]

Alternates

Robert F. Accosta, Jr., Arup, NY [SE]
  (Alt. to R. A. Grill)
Brendan F. Donnelly, Poole Fire Protection, OK [SE]
  (Alt. to J. Poole)
Doug Kline, Nowak Supply Fire Systems, IN [M]
  (Voting Alt. to FSSA Rep.)
Michael J. Knoras, Jr., Aon/Schirmer Engineering Corporation, GA [I]
  (Alt. to T. Carrie, Jr.)
Neal W. Krantz, Jr., Krantz Systems & Associates, LLC, MI [IM]
  (Alt. to N. W. Krantz, Sr.)

James Mongeau, Space Age Electronics, Inc., MA [M]
  (Alt. to J. M. Klein)
Leon Newsome, Cooper Notification, FL [M]
  (Alt. to D. Newhouse)
Robert M. Pikula, Reliable Fire Equipment Company, IL [IM]
  (Alt. to D. E. Becker)
Marlon Erthal Vieira, Siemens Building Technologies, Inc., NJ [M]
  (Alt. to P. R. Strelecki)

Lee F. Richardson, NFPA Staff Liaison

This list represents the membership at the time the Committee was balloted on the final text of this edition. Since that time, changes in the membership may have occurred. A key to classifications is found at the back of the document.

NOTE: Membership on a committee shall not in and of itself constitute an endorsement of the Association or any document developed by the committee on which the member serves.

Committee Scope: This Committee shall have primary responsibility for documents on the installation and operation of notification appliances for fire alarm and signaling systems.

Technical Committee on Protected Premises Fire Alarm and Signaling Systems (SIG-PRO)
(Chapters 12, 21, 23 and Annex C)

Merton W. Bunker, Jr., *Chair*
U.S. Department of State, VA [U]

Leonard Belliveau, Jr., *Secretary*
Hughes Associates, Inc., RI [SE]

Scott Barrett, World Electronics, Inc., FL [M]
James G. Bisker, U.S. Department of Energy, DC [U]
David J. Burkhart, Code Consultants, Inc., MO [SE]
Anthony J. Capowski, Tyco/SimplexGrinnell, MA [M]
Henry M. Corson, IV Siemens Fire Safety, NJ [M]
Paul F. Crowley, FM Approvals, MA [I]
Keith W. Dix, West Metro Fire Department, CO [E]
Joshua W. Elvove, U.S. General Services Administration, CO [U]
Thomas P. Hammerberg, Automatic Fire Alarm Association, Inc., GA [M]
Scott D. Harris, AFA Protective Systems, Inc., NY [IM]
Mark D. Hayes, Aon Fire Protection Engineering Corporation, TX [I]
William K. Hopple, Hopple & Company, CA [IM]
Daniel J. Horon, CADgraphics, Incorporated, MN [M]
Vic Humm, Vic Humm & Associates, TN [SE]
Jim R. Kern, Kern Technical Services, TN [SE]

Thomas E. Kuhta, Willis Corporation, NJ [I]
Peter Leszczak, U.S. Department of Veterans Affairs, CT [U]
Fletcher MacGregor, Marsh USA Inc., MI [I]
Scott T. Martorano, The Viking Corporation, MI [M]
 Rep. National Fire Sprinkler Association
Jebediah J. Novak, Cedar Rapids Electrical JATC, IA [L]
 Rep. International Brotherhood of Electrical Workers
John R. Olenick, Vector Security Inc., MD [IM]
 Rep. Central Station Alarm Association
Kurt A. Ruchala, FIREPRO Incorporated, MA [SE]
Yogesh B. Shah, Honeywell Life Safety/Notifier, CT [M]
 Rep. Fire Suppression Systems Association
Lawrence J. Shudak, Underwriters Laboratories Inc., IL [RT]
Ralph E. Transue, The RJA Group, Inc., IL [SE]
Bogue M. Waller, Mazzett Nash Lipsey Burch, TN [U]
 Rep. American Society for Healthcare Engineering
Carl F. Willms, Fire Security Technologies, Inc., NJ [SE]

Alternates

Donald C. Birchler, FP&C Consultants, Inc., MO [SE]
 (Alt. to V. Humm)
Shane M. Clary, Bay Alarm Company, CA [IM]
 (Alt. to W. K. Hopple)
Lee C. DeVito, FIREPRO Incorporated, MA [SE]
 (Alt. to K. A. Ruchala)
Diane P. Doliber, Wilmington, NC [SE]
 (Alt. to J. R. Kern)
Gary Girouard, Tyco/SimplexGrinnell, MA [M]
 (Alt. to A. J. Capowski)
Jacob P. Hemke, Code Consultants, Inc., MO [SE]
 (Alt. to D. J. Burkhart)
Theodore Ivers, Underwriters Laboratories Inc., NY [RT]
 (Alt. to L. J. Shudak)
Walter J. Kessler, Jr., FM Approvals, MA [I]
 (Alt. to P. F. Crowley)
Peter A. Larrimer, U.S. Department of Veterans Affairs, PA [U]
 (Alt. to P. Leszczak)

Timothy J. Lawyer, Aon Fire Protection Engineering Corporation, CA [I]
 (Alt. to M. D. Hayes)
David J. LeBlanc, The RJA Group, Inc., MA [SE]
 (Alt. to R. E. Transue)
Michael D. Mann, American Professional Services, Inc., OK [IM]
 (Alt. to J. R. Olenick)
Wayne D. Moore, Hughes Associates, Inc., RI [SE]
 (Alt. to L. Belliveau, Jr.)
Joseph Ranaudo, AFA Protective Systems, Inc., NY [IM]
 (Alt. to S. D. Harris)
Scott F. Ruland, Fike Corporation, MO [M]
 (Alt. to Y. B. Shah)
Donald Struck, Siemens Fire Safety, NJ [M]
 (Alt. to H. M. Corson, IV)
Jeffery G. Van Keuren, UTC Fire & Security, FL [M]
 (Alt. to T. P. Hammerberg)

Nonvoting

Benjamin B. Aycock, Charlotte-Mecklenburg , NC
(Member Emeritus)

Lee F. Richardson, NFPA Staff Liaison

This list represents the membership at the time the Committee was balloted on the final text of this edition. Since that time, changes in the membership may have occurred. A key to classifications is found at the back of the document.

NOTE: Membership on a committee shall not in and of itself constitute an endorsement of the Association or any document developed by the committee on which the member serves.

Committee Scope: This Committee shall have primary responsibility for documents on the installation and operation of protected premises fire alarm and signaling systems, including their interconnection with initiating devices, notification appliances, and other related building control equipment, within the protected premises.

Technical Committee on Emergency Communication Systems (SIG-ECS) (Chapter 24)

Wayne D. Moore, *Chair*
Hughes Associates, Inc., RI [SE]

Daniel P. Finnegan, *Secretary*
Siemens Industry, Inc., NJ [M]
Rep. National Electrical Manufacturers Association

Steven D. Admire, Communication Concepts, TX [IM]
Christopher Afuwah, Fire Department City of New York, NY [E]
Oded Aron, Port Authority of New York & New Jersey, NJ [U]
Peter Binkley, Evax Systems, Inc., CT [M]
Daniel Bridgett, U.S. Department of the Navy, CA [E]
Whit Chaiyabhat, Georgetown University, MD [U]
Thomas M. Chambers, Vector Security Inc., PA [IM]
    Rep. Central Station Alarm Association
Joe L. Collins, Dallas/Fort Worth International Airport, TX [U]
Joseph Dafin, U.S. General Services Administration, DC [U]
John C. Fannin III, SafePlace Corporation, DE [U]
Bruce Fraser, Fraser Fire Protection Services, MA [SE]
John S. Fuoto, AMEC Environment & Infrastructure, VA [SE]

Charles E. Hahl, The Protection Engineering Group, Inc., VA [SE]
Raymond N. Hansen, U.S. Department of the Air Force, FL [U]
Waymon Jackson, University of Texas at Austin, TX [U]
Scott Lacey, Lacey Fire Protection Engineering, AR [SE]
Robert J. Libby, The RJA Group, Inc., GU [SE]
Derek D. Mathews, Underwriters Laboratories Inc., IL [RT]
James Mongeau, Space Age Electronics, Inc., MA [M]
    Rep. Automatic Fire Alarm Association, Inc.
Joseph Ranaudo, AFA Protective Systems, Inc., NY [IM]
Rodger Reiswig, Tyco/SimplexGrinnell, FL [M]
Sean C. Remke, FP&C Consultants, Inc., IN [SE]
Aviv Siegel, AtHoc, Inc., CA [M]
James P. Simpson, National Joint Apprentice & Training Committee, MN [L]
    Rep. International Brotherhood of Electrical Workers
Andrew B. Woodward, Arup Fire, MA [SE]

Alternates

Laura E. Doyle, U.S. General Services Administration, DC [U]
    (Alt. to J. Dafin)
Jon M. Evenson, The RJA Group, Inc., IL [SE]
    (Alt. to R. J. Libby)
Raymond A. Grill, Arup Fire, DC [SE]
    (Alt. to A. B. Woodward)
Paul E. Macknis, U.S. Department of the Navy, CA [E]
    (Alt. to D. Bridgett)
J. Jeffrey Moore, Hughes Associates, Inc., OH [SE]
    (Alt. to W. D. Moore)
Denise L. Pappas, Valcom, Inc., VA [M]
    (Alt. to D. P. Finnegan)

Thomas J. Parrish, Telgian Corporation, MI [IM]
    (Alt. to S. D. Admire)
Yatin J. Patel, Underwriters Laboratories Inc., IL [RT]
    (Alt. to D. D. Mathews)
Todd C. Shearer, Tyco/SimplexGrinnell, NJ [M]
    (Alt. to R. Reiswig)
Garland L. Waldrop, University of Texas at Austin, TX [U]
    (Alt. to W. Jackson)
Larry D. Watson, American Professional Services, Inc., OK [IM]
    (Alt. to T. M. Chambers)
Piper P. Wick, Cooper Notification, TX [M]
    (Alt. to J. Mongeau)

Lee F. Richardson, NFPA Staff Liaison

This list represents the membership at the time the Committee was balloted on the final text of this edition. Since that time, changes in the membership may have occurred. A key to classifications is found at the back of the document.

NOTE: Membership on a committee shall not in and of itself constitute an endorsement of the Association or any document developed by the committee on which the member serves.

Committee Scope: This committee shall have primary responsibility for documents on the risk analysis, design, application, installation, and performance of emergency communications systems and their components. Public emergency services communications systems covered by NFPA 1221 are outside the scope of this committee except where they interface with in-building bi-directional amplifiers and where trouble and supervisory signals are intended to be monitored by the building fire alarm system.

Technical Committee on Supervising Station Fire Alarm and Signaling Systems (SIG-SSS) (Chapter 26)

Warren E. Olsen, *Chair*
Fire Safety Consultants, Inc., IL [E]
Rep. Illinois Fire Inspectors Association

Anthony Mucci, *Secretary*
Tyco/ADT Security Services, Inc., FL [M]

Geoffrey Aus, Menlo Park Fire Protection District, CA [E]
Raymond E. Bigelow, Town of Needham, MA Fire Department, MA [U]
    Rep. International Municipal Signal Association
Art Black, Carmel Fire Protection Associates, CA [E]
Edward R. Bonifas, Alarm Detection Systems, Inc., IL [IM]
J. Robert Boyer, UTC/Edwards Company, NJ [M]
    Rep. National Electrical Manufacturers Association
Thomas C. Brown, The RJA Group, Inc., MD [SE]
Robert F. Buckley, Signal Communications Corporation, MA [M]
Paul M. Carroll, Central Signal Corporation, MA [M]
    Rep. Automatic Fire Alarm Association, Inc.
Scott Colby, Colby Fire & Security Systems, Inc., LA [IM]
Thomas F. Connaughton, Intertek Testing Services, NJ [RT]
Lawrence E. Coveny, Chicago Metropolitan Fire Prevention Company, IL [IM]

James S. Crews, Fireman's Fund Insurance Company, GA [I]
Patrick M. Egan, Select Security, PA [IM]
Bob Elliott, FM Approvals, MA [I]
Louis T. Fiore, L. T. Fiore, Inc., NJ [SE]
Harvey M. Fox, Keltron Corporation, MA [M]
Xianxu Hu, Insurance Services Office, Inc., NJ [I]
James Keighley, Wayne Alarm Systems, MA [IM]
    Rep. Central Station Alarm Association
Richard Kleinman, AFA Protective Systems Inc., NY [IM]
Ronald Marts, Telcordia Technologies, NJ [U]
Gene Monaco, Monaco Enterprises, Inc., WA [M]
Donald C. Pannell, City of Memphis, TN [E]
Isaac I. Papier, Honeywell, Inc., IL [M]
Steven A. Schmit, Underwriters Laboratories Inc., IL [RT]
Sean P. Titus, Fike Corporation, MO [M]
    Rep. Fire Suppression Systems Association

Alternates

Douglas M. Aiken, Lakes Region Mutual Fire Aid, NH [U]
    (Alt. to R. E. Bigelow)
Jeffrey A. Betz, AT&T Corporation, NJ [U]
    (Alt. to R. Marts)
David A. Blanken, Keltron Corporation, MA [M]
    (Alt. to H. Fox)
Cheryl A. Gagliardi, FM Approvals, MA [I]
    (Alt. to B. Elliott)
Gordon G. Hope, Jr., Honeywell, Inc., NY [M]
    (Alt. to I. I. Papier)
Michael Johnson, The RJA Group, Inc., WA [SE]
    (Alt. to T. C. Brown)
Larry W. Mann, Central Station, Inc., AL [M]
    (Alt. to P. M. Carroll)

Derek D. Mathews, Underwriters Laboratories Inc., IL [RT]
    (Alt. to S. A. Schmit)
Scott M. May, Bosch Security Systems, NY [M]
    (Alt. to J. R. Boyer)
Robert Mitchell, Bay Alarm Company, CA [IM]
    (Alt. to J. Keighley)
Rodger Reiswig, Tyco/SimplexGrinnell, FL [M]
    (Alt. to A. Mucci)
Robert V. Scholes, Fireman's Fund Insurance Company, CA [I]
    (Alt. to J. S. Crews)
Frank J. Tokarz, Monaco Enterprises, Inc., WA [M]
    (Alt. to G. Monaco)

Lee F. Richardson, NFPA Staff Liaison

This list represents the membership at the time the Committee was balloted on the final text of this edition. Since that time, changes in the membership may have occurred. A key to classifications is found at the back of the document.

NOTE: Membership on a committee shall not in and of itself constitute an endorsement of the Association or any document developed by the committee on which the member serves.

Committee Scope: This Committee shall have primary responsibility for documents on the installation and operation of equipment for the transmission and receipt of signals from a protected premises to a supervising station, including the supervising station facilities.

Technical Committee on Public Emergency Reporting Systems (SIG-PRS) (Chapter 27)

Jeffrey G. Knight, *Chair*
City of Newton Fire Department, MA [U]
Rep. International Municipal Signal Association

Leo F. Martin, Jr., *Secretary*
Martin Electrical Code Consultants, MA [SE]

Bruce L. Abell,　U.S. Army Corps of Engineers, VA [U]
Douglas M. Aiken,　Lakes Region Mutual Fire Aid, NH [E]
George W. Allen,　R. B. Allen Company, Inc., NH [IM]
Robert J. Campbell,　Braintree, MA [SE]
Anthony W. Cole,　Wal-Mart Stores, Inc., CA [U]
Daniel R. Dinwiddie,　L W Bills Company, MA [M]
Romeo G. Dupuis,　U.S. Department of Veterans Affairs, MI [U]
Sidney M. Earley,　TLC Systems, MA [IM]
Emerson B. Fisher,　Intelligent Systems Services, IL [IM]
John K. Guhl,　California State Fire Marshal, CA [E]
　Rep. International Association of Fire Chiefs

Paul T. Kahle,　Code Consultants, Inc., MO [SE]
Robert E. Lapham,　Signal Communications Corporation, MA [M]
Robert Malanga,　Fire and Risk Engineering, NJ [SE]
　Rep. Fairmount Fire Company No. 1
Max McLeod,　Siemens Industry, Inc., AL [M]
Isa Y. Saah,　The Protection Engineering Group, VA [SE]
Stephen Smith,　Advanced Signal Corporation, MA [IM]
Michael Strube,　King-Fisher Company, Inc., MA [M]
Cindy G. Tate,　Fort A.P. Hill Fire & Emergency Services, VA [U]
Frank J. Tokarz,　Monaco Enterprises, Inc., WA [M]

Alternates

Charles E. Hahl,　The Protection Engineering Group, Inc., VA [SE]
　(Alt. to I. Y. Saah)
Nathaniel M. Johnson,　City of Laconia Fire Department, NH [U]
　(Alt. to J. G. Knight)

Gregory D. Lapin,　King-Fisher Company, Inc., MA [M]
　(Alt. to M. Strube)
Gene Monaco,　Monaco Enterprises, Inc., WA [M]
　(Alt. to F. J. Tokarz)
Allen J. Uhrine,　Siemens Industry, Inc., PA [M]
　(Alt. to M. McLeod)

Lee F. Richardson, NFPA Staff Liaison

This list represents the membership at the time the Committee was balloted on the final text of this edition. Since that time, changes in the membership may have occurred. A key to classifications is found at the back of the document.

NOTE: Membership on a committee shall not in and of itself constitute an endorsement of the Association or any document developed by the committee on which the member serves.

Committee Scope: This Committee shall have primary responsibility for documents on the proper configuration, performance, installation, and operation of public emergency alarm reporting systems and auxiliary alarm systems. The Committee scope shall include systems that use a communication infrastructure that is publicly owned, operated, and controlled. Reporting of alarms by voice over the public switched telephone network utilizing the Universal Emergency Number 9-1-1, or any other telephone number that can be dialed, is outside the scope of this committee.

Technical Committee on Single- and Multiple-Station Alarms and Household Fire Alarm Systems (SIG-HOU) (Chapter 29)

Laurence J. Dallaire, *Chair*
U.S. Architect of the Capitol, DC [E]

H. Wayne Boyd, U.S. Safety & Engineering Corporation, CA [IM]
  Rep. California Automatic Fire Alarm Association Inc.
Dan Cantrell, Broadview Security, TX [IM]
David E. Christian, Gentex Corporation, MI [M]
  Rep. Automatic Fire Alarm Association, Inc.
Thomas G. Cleary, National Institute of Standards & Technology, MD [RT]
James J. Convery, Aon/Schirmer Engineering Corporation, NY [I]
Darrell Dantzler, U.S. Department of State, MD [U]
Timothy K. Dedear, City of Farmers Branch Fire Department, TX [E]
Edward M. Fraczkowski, EBL Engineers, LLC, MD [SE]
Robert B. Fuller, Fire Code Analysts, Inc., CA [C]
Justin A. Geiman, U.S. Bureau of Alcohol, Tobacco, Firearms & Explosives, MD [RT]
Wendy B. Gifford, Consultant, IL [SE]

Daniel T. Gottuk, Hughes Associates, Inc., MD [SE]
Mark A. Kittle, Town of Snowmass Village, CO [E]
Anna Kryagin, Port Authority of New York & New Jersey, NJ [U]
Thomas J. McNelis, Jarden Safety and Security, IL [M]
  Rep. National Electrical Manufacturers Association
David E. Mills, Underwriters Laboratories Inc., IL [RT]
Kim R. Mniszewski, FX Engineering, Inc., IL [SE]
Cory Ogle, Code Consultants, Inc., MO [SE]
Jeffrey L. Okun, Nuko Security, Inc., LA [IM]
Stephen M. Olenick, Combustion Science & Engineering, Inc., MD [SE]
Steven Orlowski, National Association of Home Builders, DC [U]
Forrest J. Pecht, U.S. Access Board, DC [C]
Larry Ratzlaff, UTC/Kidde Safety, IL [M]
Richard M. Simpson, Vector Security Inc., PA [IM]
  Rep. Central Station Alarm Association

Alternates

Oded Aron, Port Authority of New York & New Jersey, NJ [U]
  (Alt. to A. Kryagin)
Edward J. Babczak, U.S. Department of State, MD [U]
  (Alt. to D. Dantzler)
Lawrence Brown, National Association of Home Builders, DC [U]
  (Alt. to S. Orlowski)
David A. Bush, UTC/Kidde Safety, CO [M]
  (Alt. to L. Ratzlaff)
Manuelita E. David, Aon Fire Protection Engineering, CA [I]
  (Alt. to J. J. Convery)
Richard T. Long, Jr., Exponent, Inc., MD [SE]
  (Voting Alt. for Exponent)

Jeffery P. McBride, EBL Engineers, LLC, MD [SE]
  (Alt. to E. M. Fraczkowski)
Christopher L. Mealy, Hughes Associates, Inc., MD [SE]
  (Alt. to D. T. Gottuk)
John L. Parssinen, Underwriters Laboratories Inc., IL [RT]
  (Alt. to D. E. Mills)
Richard Jay Roberts, Honeywell Life Safety, IL [M]
  (Alt. to D. E. Christian)
Samuel T. (Ted) Stoler, Vector Security Inc., PA [IM]
  (Alt. to R. M. Simpson)
Emily Troyanski, Intertek Testing Services, NJ [RT]
  (Voting Alt. to Intertek Rep.)

Nonvoting

Arthur S. Lee, U.S. Consumer Product Safety Commission, MD [C]

Maurice M. Pilette, Mechanical Designs Ltd., MA [SE]
  Rep. TC on Residential Sprinkler Systems

Lee F. Richardson, NFPA Staff Liaison

This list represents the membership at the time the Committee was balloted on the final text of this edition. Since that time, changes in the membership may have occurred. A key to classifications is found at the back of the document.

NOTE: Membership on a committee shall not in and of itself constitute an endorsement of the Association or any document developed by the committee on which the member serves.

Committee Scope: This Committee shall have primary responsibility for documents on the performance, installation, operation, and use of single- and multiple-station alarms and household alarm systems for fire warning.

Contents

NFPA 72

National Fire Alarm and Signaling Code

2013 Edition

IMPORTANT NOTE: This NFPA document is made available for use subject to important notices and legal disclaimers. These notices and disclaimers appear in all publications containing this document and may be found under the heading "Important Notices and Disclaimers Concerning NFPA Documents." They can also be obtained on request from NFPA or viewed at www.nfpa.org/disclaimers.

NOTICE: An asterisk (*) following the number or letter designating a paragraph indicates that explanatory material on the paragraph can be found in Annex A.

Changes other than editorial are indicated by a vertical rule beside the paragraph, table, or figure in which the change occurred. These rules are included as an aid to the user in identifying changes from the previous edition. Where one or more complete paragraphs have been deleted, the deletion is indicated by a bullet (•) between the paragraphs that remain.

A reference in brackets [ ] following a section or paragraph indicates material that has been extracted from another NFPA document. As an aid to the user, the complete title and edition of the source documents for extracts in mandatory sections of the document are given in Chapter 2 and those for extracts in informational sections are given in Annex G. Extracted text may be edited for consistency and style and may include the revision of internal paragraph references and other references as appropriate. Requests for interpretations or revisions of extracted text shall be sent to the technical committee responsible for the source document.

A reference in parentheses ( ) following a paragraph indicates the committee responsibility for that section or paragraph. Committee acronyms are keyed to the acronyms shown with the committee lists at the front of the document.

Information on referenced publications can be found in Chapter 2 and Annex G.

Chapter 1 Administration

1.1 Scope.

1.1.1 *NFPA 72* covers the application, installation, location, performance, inspection, testing, and maintenance of fire alarm systems, supervising station alarm systems, public emergency alarm reporting systems, fire warning equipment and emergency communications systems (ECS), and their components.

1.1.2 The provisions of this chapter apply throughout the Code unless otherwise noted.

1.2* Purpose.

1.2.1 The purpose of this Code is to define the means of signal initiation, transmission, notification, and annunciation; the levels of performance; and the reliability of the various types of fire alarm systems, supervising station alarm systems, public emergency alarm reporting systems, fire warning equipment, emergency communications systems, and their components.

1.2.2 This Code defines the features associated with these systems and also provides information necessary to modify or upgrade an existing system to meet the requirements of a particular system classification.

1.2.3 This Code establishes minimum required levels of performance, extent of redundancy, and quality of installation but does not establish the only methods by which these requirements are to be achieved.

1.2.4* This Code shall not be interpreted to require a level of protection that is greater than that which would otherwise be required by the applicable building or fire code.

1.3 Application.

1.3.1 Alarm systems shall be classified as follows:

(1) Fire alarm systems
  (a) Household fire alarm systems
  (b) Protected premises (local) fire alarm systems
(2) Supervising station alarm systems
  (a) Central station (service) alarm systems
  (b) Remote supervising station alarm systems
  (c) Proprietary supervising station alarm systems
(3) Public emergency alarm reporting systems
  (a) Auxiliary alarm systems — local energy type
  (b) Auxiliary alarm systems — shunt type

1.3.2 Emergency communications systems shall be classified as follows:

(1) One-way emergency communications systems
  (a) Distributed recipient mass notification systems
  (b) In-building fire emergency voice/alarm communications systems
  (c) In-building mass notification systems
  (d) Wide area mass notification systems
(2) Two-way emergency communications systems
  (a) In-building emergency communications systems

1.3.3 Any reference or implied reference to a particular type of hardware shall be for the purpose of clarity and shall not be interpreted as an endorsement.

1.3.4 The intent and meaning of the terms used in this Code shall be, unless otherwise defined herein, the same as those of *NFPA 70, National Electrical Code*®.

1.4 Retroactivity.

1.4.1 Unless otherwise noted, it is not intended that the provisions of this document be applied to facilities, equipment, structures, or installations that were existing or approved for construction or installation prior to the effective date of the document.

1.4.2 In those cases where it is determined by the authority having jurisdiction that the existing situation involves a distinct hazard to life or property, retroactive application of the provisions of this document shall be permitted.

1.5 Equivalency.

1.5.1 Nothing in this Code shall prevent the use of systems, methods, devices, or appliances of equivalent or superior quality, strength, fire resistance, effectiveness, durability, and safety over those prescribed by this Code.

1.5.2 Technical documentation shall be submitted to the authority having jurisdiction to demonstrate equivalency.

1.5.3 The systems, methods, devices, or appliances that are found equivalent shall be approved.

1.6 Units and Formulas.

1.6.1 The units of measure in this Code are presented in U.S. Customary Units (inch-pound units).

1.6.2 Where presented, the International System (SI) of Units follow the inch-pound units in parentheses.

1.6.3 Where both systems of units are presented, either system shall be acceptable for satisfying the requirements in this Code.

1.6.4 Where both systems of units are presented, users of this Code shall apply one set of units consistently and shall not alternate between units.

1.6.5* The values presented for measurements in this Code are expressed with a degree of precision appropriate for practical application and enforcement. It is not intended that the application or enforcement of these values be more precise than the precision expressed.

1.6.6 Where extracted text contains values expressed in only one system of units, the values in the extracted text have been retained without conversion to preserve the values established by the responsible technical committee in the source document.

1.7 Code Adoption Requirements. This Code shall be administered and enforced by the authority having jurisdiction designated by the governing authority. *(See Annex E for sample wording for enabling legislation.)*

Chapter 2   Referenced Publications

2.1 General. The documents or portions thereof listed in this chapter are referenced within this Code and shall be considered part of the requirements of this document.

2.2 NFPA Publications. National Fire Protection Association, 1 Batterymarch Park, Quincy, MA 02169-7471.

NFPA 10, *Standard for Portable Fire Extinguishers,* 2010 edition.
NFPA 13, *Standard for the Installation of Sprinkler Systems,* 2013 edition.
NFPA 25, *Standard for the Inspection, Testing, and Maintenance of Water-Based Fire Protection Systems,* 2011 edition.
NFPA 37, *Standard for the Installation and Use of Stationary Combustion Engines and Gas Turbines,* 2010 edition.
NFPA 70®, *National Electrical Code®,* 2011 edition.
NFPA 75, *Standard for the Fire Protection of Information Technology Equipment,* 2013 edition.
NFPA 90A, *Standard for the Installation of Air-Conditioning and Ventilating Systems,* 2012 edition.
NFPA 101®, *Life Safety Code®,* 2012 edition.
NFPA 110, *Standard for Emergency and Standby Power Systems,* 2013 edition.
NFPA 111, *Standard on Stored Electrical Energy Emergency and Standby Power Systems,* 2013 edition.
NFPA 170, *Standard for Fire Safety and Emergency Symbols,* 2012 edition.
NFPA 601, *Standard for Security Services in Fire Loss Prevention,* 2010 edition.
NFPA 720, *Standard for the Installation of Carbon Monoxide (CO) Detection and Warning Equipment,* 2012 edition.
NFPA 1221, *Standard for the Installation, Maintenance, and Use of Emergency Services Communications Systems,* 2013 edition.
NFPA 1600®, *Standard on Disaster/Emergency Management and Business Continuity Programs,* 2010 edition.
NFPA 1620, *Standard for Pre-Incident Planning,* 2010 edition.

2.3 Other Publications.

2.3.1 ANSI Publications. American National Standards Institute, Inc., 25 West 43rd Street, 4th Floor, New York, NY 10036.

ANSI A-58.1, *Building Code Requirements for Minimum Design Loads in Buildings and Other Structures.*

ANSI S1.4a, *Specifications for Sound Level Meters,* 1985, reaffirmed 2006.

ANSI S3.41, *American National Standard Audible Emergency Evacuation Signal,* 1990, reaffirmed 2008.

ANSI/ASME A17.1/CSA B44–10, *Safety Code for Elevators and Escalators,* 2010.

ANSI/IEEE C2, *National Electrical Safety Code,* 2007.

ANSI/TIA-568-C.3, *Optical Fiber Cabling Components Standard,* June 2008.

ANSI/UL 217, *Standard for Single and Multiple Station Smoke Alarms,* 2006, revised 2012.

ANSI/UL 268, *Standard for Smoke Detectors for Fire Alarm Systems,* 2009.

ANSI/UL 827, *Standard for Central-Station Alarm Services,* 2008.

ANSI/UL 864, *Standard for Control Units and Accessories for Fire Alarm Systems,* 2003, revised 2011.

ANSI/UL 985, *Standard for Household Fire Warning System Units,* 2000, revised 2008.

ANSI/UL 1638, *Visual Signaling Appliances — Private Mode Emergency and General Utility Signaling,* 2008.

ANSI/UL 1730, *Standard for Smoke Detector Monitors and Accessories for Individual Living Units of Multifamily Residences and Hotel/Motel Rooms,* 2006, revised 2007.

ANSI/UL 1971, *Standard for Signaling Devices for the Hearing Impaired,* 2002, revised 2008.

ANSI/UL 1981, *Central Station Automation Systems,* 2003.

UL 2017, *Standard for General-Purpose Signaling Devices and Systems,* 2008, revised 2011.

ANSI/UL 2572, *Mass Notification Systems,* 2011.

ANSI/UL 60950, *Information Technology Equipment — Safety — Part 1: General Requirements,* 2007.

2.3.2 EIA Publications. Electronic Industries Alliance, 2500 Wilson Boulevard, Arlington, VA 22201-3834.

EIA Tr 41.3, *Telephones.*

2.3.3 IMSA Publication. International Municipal Signal Association, 165 East Union Street, Newark, NY 14513-0539.

"IMSA Official Wire and Cable Specifications," 1998.

2.3.4 ISO Publications. International Organization for Standardization, 1, ch. de la Voie-Creuse, Case postale 56, CH-1211 Geneva 20, Switzerland.

ISO 7731, *Danger signals for work places — Auditory danger signals.*

2.3.5 Telcordia Publications. Telcordia Technologies, One Telcordia Drive, Piscataway, NJ 08854.

GR-506-CORE, *LATA Switching Systems Generic Requirements: Signaling for Analog Interface,* 2006.

GR-909-CORE, Fiber in the Loop Systems Generic Requirements, 2004.

2.3.6 Other Publications.

Merriam-Webster's Collegiate Dictionary, 11th edition, Merriam-Webster, Inc., Springfield, MA, 2003.

2.4 References for Extracts in Mandatory Sections.

NFPA 70®, *National Electrical Code*®, 2011 edition.

NFPA 96, *Standard for Ventilation Control and Fire Protection of Commercial Cooking Operations,* 2011 edition.

NFPA 101®, *Life Safety Code*®, 2012 edition.

NFPA 654, *Standard for the Prevention of Fire and Dust Explosions from the Manufacturing, Processing, and Handling of Combustible Particulate Solids,* 2013 edition.

NFPA 720, *Standard for the Installation of Carbon Monoxide (CO) Detection and Warning Equipment,* 2012 edition.

NFPA 1221, *Standard for the Installation, Maintenance, and Use of Emergency Services Communications Systems,* 2013 edition.

NFPA 5000®, *Building Construction and Safety Code*®, 2012 edition.

Chapter 3   Definitions

3.1 General. The definitions contained in this chapter shall apply to the terms used in this Code. Where terms are not defined in this chapter or within another chapter, they shall be defined using their ordinarily accepted meanings within the context in which they are used. *Merriam-Webster's Collegiate Dictionary,* 11th edition, shall be the source for the ordinarily accepted meaning.

3.2 NFPA Official Definitions.

3.2.1* Approved. Acceptable to the authority having jurisdiction.

3.2.2* Authority Having Jurisdiction (AHJ). An organization, office, or individual responsible for enforcing the requirements of a code or standard, or for approving equipment, materials, an installation, or a procedure.

3.2.3* Code. A standard that is an extensive compilation of provisions covering broad subject matter or that is suitable for adoption into law independently of other codes and standards.

3.2.4 Labeled. Equipment or materials to which has been attached a label, symbol, or other identifying mark of an organization that is acceptable to the authority having jurisdiction and concerned with product evaluation, that maintains periodic inspection of production of labeled equipment or materials, and by whose labeling the manufacturer indicates compliance with appropriate standards or performance in a specified manner.

3.2.5* Listed. Equipment, materials, or services included in a list published by an organization that is acceptable to the authority having jurisdiction and concerned with evaluation of products or services, that maintains periodic inspection of production of listed equipment or materials or periodic evaluation of services, and whose listing states that either the equipment, material, or service meets appropriate designated standards or has been tested and found suitable for a specified purpose.

3.2.6 Shall. Indicates a mandatory requirement.

3.2.7 Should. Indicates a recommendation or that which is advised but not required.

3.3 General Definitions.

3.3.1 Accessible (as applied to equipment). Admitting close approach; not guarded by locked doors, elevation, or other effective means. [**70,** 2011] (SIG-FUN)

3.3.2 Accessible (as applied to wiring methods). Capable of being removed or exposed without damaging the building structure or finish or not permanently closed in by the structure or finish of the building. [**70,** 2011] (SIG-FUN)

3.3.3 Accessible, Readily (Readily Accessible). Capable of being reached quickly for operation, renewal, or inspections without requiring those to whom ready access is requisite to climb over or remove obstacles or to resort to portable ladders, and so forth. [**70,** 2011] (SIG-FUN)

3.3.4 Accessible Spaces (as applied to detection coverage in Chapter 17). Spaces or concealed areas of construction that can be entered via openable panels, doors hatches, or other readily movable elements (e.g., ceiling tiles). (SIG-IDS)

3.3.5 Acknowledge. To confirm that a message or signal has been received, such as by the pressing of a button or the selection of a software command. (SIG-SSS)

3.3.6* Acoustically Distinguishable Space (ADS). An emergency communications system notification zone, or subdivision thereof, that might be an enclosed or otherwise physically defined space, or that might be distinguished from other spaces because of different acoustical, environmental, or use characteristics, such as reverberation time and ambient sound pressure level. (SIG-NAS)

3.3.7 Active Multiplex System. A multiplexing system in which signaling devices such as transponders are employed to transmit status signals of each initiating device or initiating device circuit within a prescribed time interval so that the lack of receipt of such a signal can be interpreted as a trouble signal. (SIG-SSS)

3.3.8 Addressable Device. A fire alarm system component with discrete identification that can have its status individually identified or that is used to individually control other functions. (SIG-IDS)

3.3.9 Adverse Condition. Any condition occurring in a communications or transmission channel that interferes with the proper transmission or interpretation, or both, of status change signals at the supervising station. *(See also 3.3.257.10, Trouble Signal.)* (SIG-SSS)

3.3.10 Air Sampling–Type Detector. See 3.3.66, Detector.

3.3.11 Alarm. A warning of danger. (SIG-FUN)

3.3.12 Alarm Box.

3.3.12.1 *Auxiliary Alarm Box.* An alarm box that can only be operated from one or more remote initiating devices or an auxiliary alarm system used to send an alarm to the communications center. (SIG-PRS)

3.3.12.2 *Combination Fire Alarm and Guard's Tour Box.* A manually operated box for separately transmitting a fire alarm signal and a distinctive guard patrol tour supervisory signal. (SIG-IDS)

3.3.12.3 *Manual Fire Alarm Box.* A manually operated device used to initiate a fire alarm signal. (SIG-IDS)

3.3.12.4 *Master Alarm Box.* A publicly accessible alarm box that can also be operated by one or more remote initiating devices or an auxiliary alarm system used to send an alarm to the communications center. (SIG-PRS)

3.3.12.5 *Publicly Accessible Alarm Box.* An enclosure, accessible to the public, housing a manually operated transmitter used to send an alarm to the communications center. (SIG-PRS)

3.3.13 Alarm Service. The service required following the receipt of an alarm signal. (SIG-SSS)

3.3.14 Alarm Signal. See 3.3.257, Signal.

3.3.15 Alarm System. See 3.3.105, Fire Alarm System; 3.3.284, Supervising Station Alarm System; 3.3.215, Public Emergency Alarm Reporting System; 3.3.87.1.2, In-Building Fire Emergency Voice/Alarm Communication System; and 3.3.87.1.3, In-Building Mass Notification System.

3.3.16 Alarm Verification Feature. A feature of automatic fire detection and alarm systems to reduce unwanted alarms wherein smoke detectors report alarm conditions for a minimum period of time, or confirm alarm conditions within a given time period after being reset, in order to be accepted as a valid alarm initiation signal. (SIG-PRO)

3.3.17 Alert Tone. An attention-getting signal to alert occupants of the pending transmission of a voice message. (SIG-PRO)

3.3.18 Analog Initiating Device (Sensor). See 3.3.132, Initiating Device.

3.3.19 Ancillary Functions. Ancillary functions are those non-emergency activations of the fire alarm or mass notification audible, visual, and textual output circuits allowed. Ancillary functions can include general paging, background music, or other non-emergency signals. (SIG-ECS)

3.3.20 Annunciator. A unit containing one or more indicator lamps, alphanumeric displays, or other equivalent means in which each indication provides status information about a circuit, condition, or location. (SIG-FUN)

3.3.21 Apartment Building. A building or portion thereof containing three or more dwelling units with independent cooking and bathroom facilities. (SIG-HOU) [**5000**, 2012]

3.3.22 Audible Notification Appliance. See 3.3.173, Notification Appliance.

3.3.23 Automatic Extinguishing System Supervisory Device. See 3.3.132, Initiating Device.

3.3.24 Automatic Fire Detector. See 3.3.66, Detector.

3.3.25 Automatic Fire Extinguishing or Suppression System Operation Detector. See 3.3.66, Detector.

3.3.26 Autonomous Control Unit (ACU). See 3.3.59, Control Unit.

3.3.27 Auxiliary Alarm System. See 3.3.215, Public Emergency Alarm Reporting System.

3.3.28 Auxiliary Box. See 3.3.12, Alarm Box.

3.3.29* Average Ambient Sound Level. The root mean square, A-weighted, sound pressure level measured over the period of time that any person is present, or a 24-hour period, whichever time period is the lesser. (SIG-NAS)

3.3.30 Beam Construction. See 3.3.37, Ceiling Surfaces.

3.3.31 Building Fire Alarm System. See 3.3.105, Fire Alarm System.

3.3.32 Building Fire Safety Plan. Documentation that provides information on the use of alarms, transmission of alarms, response to alarms, evacuation of immediate area, evacuation of smoke compartment, preparation of floors and building for evacuation and extinguishment of fire. (SIG-ECS)

3.3.33 Carrier. High-frequency energy that can be modulated by voice or signaling impulses. (SIG-SSS)

3.3.34 Carrier System. A means of conveying a number of channels over a single path by modulating each channel on a different carrier frequency and demodulating at the receiving point to restore the signals to their original form. (SIG-SSS)

3.3.35 Ceiling. The upper surface of a space, regardless of height. Areas with a suspended ceiling have two ceilings, one visible from the floor and one above the suspended ceiling. (SIG-IDS)

3.3.35.1 *Level Ceilings.* Ceilings that are level or have a slope of less than or equal to 1 in 8. (SIG-IDS)

3.3.35.2 *Sloping Ceiling.* A ceiling that has a slope of more than 1 in 8. (SIG-IDS)

3.3.35.3* *Sloping Peaked-Type Ceiling.* A ceiling in which the ceiling slopes in two directions from the highest point. Curved or domed ceilings can be considered peaked with the slope figured as the slope of the chord from highest to lowest point. (SIG-IDS)

3.3.35.4* *Sloping Shed-Type Ceiling.* A ceiling in which the high point is at one side with the slope extending toward the opposite side. (SIG-IDS)

3.3.36 Ceiling Height. The height from the continuous floor of a room to the continuous ceiling of a room or space. (SIG-IDS)

3.3.37 Ceiling Surfaces.

3.3.37.1 *Beam Construction.* Ceilings that have solid structural or solid nonstructural members projecting down from the ceiling surface more than 4 in. (100 mm) and spaced more than 36 in. (910 mm), center to center. (SIG-IDS)

3.3.37.2 *Girder.* A support for beams or joists that runs at right angles to the beams or joists. If the top of the girder is within 4 in. (100 mm) of the ceiling, the girder is a factor in determining the number of detectors and is to be considered a beam. If the top of the girder is more than 4 in. (100 mm) from the ceiling, the girder is not a factor in detector location. (SIG-IDS)

3.3.37.3* *Smooth Ceiling.* A ceiling surface uninterrupted by continuous projections, such as solid joists, beams, or ducts, extending more than 4 in. (100 mm) below the ceiling surface. (SIG-IDS)

3.3.37.4 *Solid Joist Construction.* Ceilings that have solid structural or solid nonstructural members projecting down from the ceiling surface for a distance of more than 4 in. (100 mm) and spaced at intervals of 36 in. (910 mm) or less, center to center. (SIG-IDS)

3.3.38 Central Station. See 3.3.283.1, Central Supervising Station.

3.3.39 Central Station Alarm System. See 3.3.284.1, Central Station Service Alarm System.

3.3.40 Central Station Service. See 3.3.285, Supervising Station Service.

3.3.41 Central Station Service Alarm System. See 3.3.284, Supervising Station Alarm System.

3.3.42 Central Supervising Station. See 3.3.283, Supervising Station.

3.3.43 Channel. A path for voice or signal transmission that uses modulation of light or alternating current within a frequency band. (SIG-SSS)

3.3.43.1 Communications Channel. A circuit or path connecting a subsidiary station(s) to a supervising station(s) over which signals are carried. (SIG-SSS)

3.3.43.2 Derived Channel. A signaling line circuit that uses the local leg of the public-switched network as an active multiplex channel while simultaneously allowing that leg's use for normal telephone communications. (SIG-SSS)

3.3.43.3* Radio Channel. A band of frequencies of a width sufficient to allow its use for radio communications. (SIG-SSS)

3.3.43.4 Transmission Channel. A circuit or path connecting transmitters to supervising stations or subsidiary stations on which signals are carried. (SIG-SSS)

3.3.44 Circuit. Either a means of providing power or a connection path between locations *(see 3.3.190)*. (SIG-PRO)

3.3.45 Circuit Interface. See 3.3.137, Interface.

3.3.46 Cloud Chamber Smoke Detection. See 3.3.269, Smoke Detection.

3.3.47* Coded. An audible or visible signal that conveys several discrete bits or units of information. (SIG-NAS)

3.3.48 Combination Detector. See 3.3.66, Detector.

3.3.49 Combination Emergency Communications Systems. See 3.3.88, Emergency Communications Systems — Combination.

3.3.50 Combination Fire Alarm and Guard's Tour Box. See 3.3.12, Alarm Box.

3.3.51 Combination System. See 3.3.105, Fire Alarm System.

3.3.52 Common Talk Mode. See 3.3.294, Talk Mode.

3.3.53* Communications Center. A building or portion of a building that is specifically configured for the primary purpose of providing emergency communications services or public safety answering point (PSAP) services to one or more public safety agencies under the authority or authorities having jurisdiction. [**1221,** 2013] (SIG-PRS)

3.3.54 Communications Channel. See 3.3.43, Channel.

3.3.55 Communications Circuit. Any signaling path of an emergency communications system that carries voice, audio, data, or other signals. (SIG-ECS)

3.3.56 Communications Cloud. The area in the communications path that is supported by providers of communication services not governed under the scope of *NFPA 72* in which signals travel between a protected property and a monitoring station. Depending on the type of transmission that is used, signals can travel on a single defined route or through various routes depending on what is available when the signal is initiated. (SIG-SSS)

3.3.57* Condition. A situation, environmental state, or equipment state of a fire alarm or signaling system. (SIG-FUN)

3.3.57.1 Abnormal (Off-Normal) Condition. A situation, environmental state, or equipment state that warrants some type of signal, notification, communication, response, action, or service. (SIG-FUN)

3.3.57.1.1* Alarm Condition. An abnormal condition that poses an immediate threat to life, property, or mission. (SIG-FUN)

3.3.57.1.2* Pre-Alarm Condition. An abnormal condition that poses a potential threat to life, property, or mission, and time is available for investigation. (SIG-FUN)

3.3.57.1.3* Supervisory Condition. An abnormal condition in connection with the supervision of other systems, processes, or equipment. (SIG-FUN)

3.3.57.1.4* Trouble Condition. An abnormal condition in a system due to a fault. (SIG-FUN)

3.3.57.2 Normal Condition. Circuits, systems, and components are functioning as designed and no abnormal condition exists. (SIG-FUN)

3.3.58 Contiguous Property. See 3.3.207, Property.

3.3.59 Control Unit. A system component that monitors inputs and controls outputs through various types of circuits. (SIG-PRO)

3.3.59.1* Autonomous Control Unit (ACU). The primary control unit for an in-building mass notification system. (SIG-ECS)

3.3.59.2 Emergency Communications Control Unit (ECCU). A system capable of sending mass notification messages to individual buildings, zones of buildings, individual outdoor speaker arrays, or zones of outdoor speaker arrays; or a building, multiple buildings, outside areas, or a combination of these. (SIG-ECS)

3.3.59.3 Fire Alarm Control Unit. See 3.3.102, Fire Alarm Control Unit.

3.3.59.4 Wireless Control Unit. A component that transmits/receives and processes wireless signals. (SIG-PRO)

3.3.60 Day-Care Home. A building or portion of a building in which more than 3 but not more than 12 clients receive care, maintenance, and supervision, by other than their relative(s) or legal guardian(s), for less than 24 hours per day. [**101,** 2012] (SIG-HOU)

3.3.61 Dedicated Function Fire Alarm Control Unit. See 3.3.102, Fire Alarm Control Unit.

3.3.62 Dedicated Function Fire Alarm System. See 3.3.105, Fire Alarm System.

3.3.63 Deficiency. A condition that interferes with the service or reliability for which the part, system, or equipment was intended. (SIG-TMS)

3.3.64 Delinquency Signal. See 3.3.257, Signal.

3.3.65 Derived Channel. See 3.3.43, Channel.

3.3.66 Detector. A device suitable for connection to a circuit that has a sensor that responds to a physical stimulus such as gas, heat, or smoke. (SIG-IDS)

3.3.66.1 Air Sampling–Type Detector. A detector that consists of a piping or tubing distribution network that runs from the detector to the area(s) to be protected. An aspiration fan in the detector housing draws air from the protected area back to the detector through air-sampling ports, piping, or tubing. At the detector, the air is analyzed for fire products. (SIG-IDS)

3.3.66.2 Automatic Fire Detector. A device designed to detect the presence of a fire signature and to initiate action. For the purpose of this Code, automatic fire detectors are classified as follows: Automatic Fire Extinguishing or Suppression System Operation Detector, Fire–Gas Detector, Heat Detector, Other Fire Detectors, Radiant Energy–Sensing Fire Detector, and Smoke Detector. (SIG-IDS)

3.3.66.3 Automatic Fire Extinguishing or Suppression System Operation Detector. A device that automatically detects the operation of a fire extinguishing or suppression system by means appropriate to the system employed. (SIG-IDS)

3.3.66.4* Combination Detector. A device that either responds to more than one of the fire phenomena or employs more than one operating principle to sense one of these phenomena. Typical examples are a combination of a heat detector with a smoke detector or a combination rate-of-rise and fixed-temperature heat detector. This device has listings for each sensing method employed. (SIG-IDS)

3.3.66.5 Electrical Conductivity Heat Detector. A line-type or spot-type sensing element in which resistance varies as a function of temperature. (SIG-IDS)

3.3.66.6 Fire–Gas Detector. A device that detects gases produced by a fire. (SIG-IDS)

3.3.66.7* Fixed-Temperature Detector. A device that responds when its operating element becomes heated to a predetermined level. (SIG-IDS)

3.3.66.8* Flame Detector. A radiant energy–sensing fire detector that detects the radiant energy emitted by a flame. *(Refer to A.17.8.2.)* (SIG-IDS)

3.3.66.9 Gas Detector. A device that detects the presence of a specified gas concentration. Gas detectors can be either spot-type or line-type detectors. (SIG-IDS)

3.3.66.10 Heat Detector. A fire detector that detects either abnormally high temperature or rate-of-temperature rise, or both. (SIG-IDS)

3.3.66.11 Line-Type Detector. A device in which detection is continuous along a path. Typical examples are rate-of-rise pneumatic tubing detectors, projected beam smoke detectors, and heat-sensitive cable. (SIG-IDS)

3.3.66.12* Multi-Criteria Detector. A device that contains multiple sensors that separately respond to physical stimulus such as heat, smoke, or fire gases, or employs more than one sensor to sense the same stimulus. This sensor is capable of generating only one alarm signal from the sensors employed in the design either independently or in combination. The sensor output signal is mathematically evaluated to determine when an alarm signal is warranted. The evaluation can be performed either at the detector or at the control unit. This detector has a single listing that establishes the primary function of the detector. (SIG-IDS)

3.3.66.13* Multi-Sensor Detector. A device that contains multiple sensors that separately respond to physical stimu-

lus such as heat, smoke, or fire gases, or employs more than one sensor to sense the same stimulus. A device capable of generating multiple alarm signals from any one of the sensors employed in the design, independently or in combination. The sensor output signals are mathematically evaluated to determine when an alarm signal is warranted. The evaluation can be performed either at the detector or at the control unit. This device has listings for each sensing method employed. (SIG-IDS)

3.3.66.14 Other Fire Detectors. Devices that detect a phenomenon other than heat, smoke, flame, or gases produced by a fire. (SIG-IDS)

3.3.66.15 Pneumatic Rate-of-Rise Tubing Heat Detector. A line-type detector comprising small-diameter tubing, usually copper, that is installed on the ceiling or high on the walls throughout the protected area. The tubing is terminated in a detector unit containing diaphragms and associated contacts set to actuate at a predetermined pressure. The system is sealed except for calibrated vents that compensate for normal changes in temperature. (SIG-IDS)

3.3.66.16 Projected Beam–Type Detector. A type of photoelectric light obscuration smoke detector wherein the beam spans the protected area. (SIG-IDS)

3.3.66.17 Radiant Energy–Sensing Fire Detector. A device that detects radiant energy, such as ultraviolet, visible, or infrared, that is emitted as a product of combustion reaction and obeys the laws of optics. (SIG-IDS)

3.3.66.18* Rate Compensation Detector. A device that responds when the temperature of the air surrounding the device reaches a predetermined level, regardless of the rate-of-temperature rise. (SIG-IDS)

3.3.66.19* Rate-of-Rise Detector. A device that responds when the temperature rises at a rate exceeding a predetermined value. (SIG-IDS)

3.3.66.20 Smoke Detector. A device that detects visible or invisible particles of combustion. (SIG-IDS)

3.3.66.21 Spark/Ember Detector. A radiant energy–sensing fire detector that is designed to detect sparks or embers, or both. These devices are normally intended to operate in dark environments and in the infrared part of the spectrum. (SIG-IDS)

3.3.66.22 Spot-Type Detector. A device in which the detecting element is concentrated at a particular location. Typical examples are bimetallic detectors, fusible alloy detectors, certain pneumatic rate-of-rise detectors, certain smoke detectors, and thermoelectric detectors. (SIG-IDS)

3.3.67 Digital Alarm Communicator Receiver (DACR). A system component that accepts and displays signals from digital alarm communicator transmitters (DACTs) sent over the public switched telephone network. (SIG-SSS)

3.3.68 Digital Alarm Communicator System (DACS). A system in which signals are transmitted from a digital alarm communicator transmitter (DACT) located at the protected premises through the public-switched telephone network to a digital alarm communicator receiver (DACR). (SIG-SSS)

3.3.69 Digital Alarm Communicator Transmitter (DACT). A system component at the protected premises to which initiating devices or groups of devices are connected. The DACT seizes the connected telephone line, dials a preselected number to connect to a DACR, and transmits signals indicating a status change of the initiating device. (SIG-SSS)

3.3.70 Digital Alarm Radio Receiver (DARR). A system component composed of two subcomponents: one that receives and decodes radio signals, the other that annunciates the decoded data. These two subcomponents can be coresident at the central station or separated by means of a data transmission channel. (SIG-SSS)

3.3.71 Digital Alarm Radio System (DARS). A system in which signals are transmitted from a digital alarm radio transmitter (DART) located at a protected premises through a radio channel to a digital alarm radio receiver (DARR). (SIG-SSS)

3.3.72 Digital Alarm Radio Transmitter (DART). A system component that is connected to or an integral part of a digital alarm communicator transmitter (DACT) that is used to provide an alternate radio transmission channel. (SIG-SSS)

3.3.73 Display. The visual representation of output data, other than printed copy. (SIG-NAS)

3.3.74 Distributed Recipient Mass Notification System (DRMNS). See 3.3.87, Emergency Communications System.

3.3.75 Donor Antenna. The outside antenna on the building where a public safety radio enhancement system operates. (SIG-ECS)

3.3.76 Donor Site. The repeater or base station site with which the public safety radio enhancement system communicates. (SIG-ECS)

3.3.77 Dormitory. A building or a space in a building in which group sleeping accommodations are provided for more than 16 persons who are not members of the same family in one room, or a series of closely associated rooms, under joint occupancy and single management, with or without meals, but without individual cooking facilities. [*101*, 2012] (SIG-HOU)

3.3.78* Double Doorway. A single opening that has no intervening wall space or door trim separating the two doors. (SIG-IDS)

3.3.79 Downlink. The radio signal from the base station transmitter to the portable public safety subscriber receiver. (SIG-ECS)

3.3.80 Dual Control. The use of two primary trunk facilities over separate routes or different methods to control one communications channel. (SIG-SSS)

3.3.81 Dwelling Unit. One or more rooms arranged for complete, independent housekeeping purposes with space for eating, living, and sleeping; facilities for cooking; and provisions for sanitation. [*5000*, 2012] (SIG-HOU)

    3.3.81.1 *Multiple Dwelling Unit.* A building containing three or more dwelling units. (SIG-HOU)

    3.3.81.2 *Single Dwelling Unit.* A building consisting solely of one dwelling unit. (SIG-HOU)

3.3.82 Effective Masked Threshold. The minimum sound level at which the tone signal is audible in ambient noise. (SIG-NAS)

3.3.83 Electrical Conductivity Heat Detector. See 3.3.66, Detector.

3.3.84* Ember. A particle of solid material that emits radiant energy due either to its temperature or the process of combustion on its surface. (*See also 3.3.275, Spark.*) (SIG-IDS)

3.3.85 Emergency Command Center. See 3.3.89, Emergency Communications System — Emergency Command Center.

3.3.86 Emergency Communications Control Unit (ECCU). See 3.3.59, Control Unit.

3.3.87 Emergency Communications System. A system for the protection of life by indicating the existence of an emergency situation and communicating information necessary to facilitate an appropriate response and action. (SIG-ECS)

    3.3.87.1 *One-Way Emergency Communications System.* One-way emergency communications systems are intended to broadcast information, in an emergency, to people in one or more specified indoor or outdoor areas. It is intended that emergency messages be conveyed either by audible, visible, or textual means, or any combination thereof. (SIG-ECS)

    3.3.87.1.1 *Distributed Recipient Mass Notification System (DRMNS).* A distributed recipient mass notification system is a system meant to communicate directly to targeted individuals and groups that might not be in a contiguous area. (SIG-ECS)

    3.3.87.1.2 *In-Building Fire Emergency Voice/Alarm Communications System.* Dedicated manual or automatic equipment for originating and distributing voice instructions, as well as alert and evacuation signals pertaining to a fire emergency, to the occupants of a building. (SIG-ECS)

    3.3.87.1.3 *In-Building Mass Notification System.* A system used to provide information and instructions to people in a building(s) or other space using intelligible voice communications and including visible signals, text, graphics, tactile, or other communication methods. (SIG-ECS)

    3.3.87.1.4 *Wide-Area Mass Notification System.* Wide-area mass notification systems are generally installed to provide real-time information to outdoor areas and could have the capability to communicate with other notification systems provided for a campus, military base, municipality, or similar single or multiple contiguous areas. (SIG-ECS)

    3.3.87.2 *Two-Way Emergency Communications System.* Two-way emergency communications systems are divided into two categories, those systems that are anticipated to be used by building occupants and those systems that are to be used by fire fighters, police, and other emergency services personnel. Two-way emergency communications systems are used to both exchange information and to communicate information such as, but not limited to, instructions, acknowledgement of receipt of messages, condition of local environment, and condition of persons, and to give assurance that help is on the way. (SIG-ECS)

3.3.88 Emergency Communications Systems — Combination. Various emergency communication systems such as fire alarm, mass notification, fire fighter communications, area of refuge communications, elevator communications, or others and that can be served through a single control system or through an interconnection of several control systems. (SIG-ECS)

3.3.89* Emergency Communications System — Emergency Command Center. The room(s) or area(s) staffed during any emergency event by assigned emergency management staff. The room or area contains system communications and control equipment serving one or more buildings where responsible authorities receive information from premises sources or systems or from (higher level) regional or national sources or systems and then disseminate appropriate information to individuals, a building, multiple buildings, outside campus areas, or a combination of these in accordance with the emergency response plan established for the premises. The room or area contains the controls and indicators from which the ECS systems located in the room or area can be manually controlled as required by the emergency response plan and the emergency management coordinator. (SIG-ECS)

3.3.90* Emergency Control Function Interface Device. A listed fire alarm or signaling system component that directly interfaces with the system that operates the emergency control function. (SIG-PRO)

3.3.91* Emergency Control Functions. Building, fire, and emergency control elements or systems that are initiated by the fire alarm or emergency communications system and either increase the level of life safety for occupants or control the spread of the harmful effects of fire or other dangerous products. (SIG-PRO)

3.3.92* Emergency Response Facility (ERF). A structure or a portion of a structure that houses emergency response agency equipment or personnel for response to alarms. [**1221,** 2013] (SIG-PRS)

3.3.93 Emergency Response Plan. A documented set of actions to address response to natural, technological, and man-made disasters and other emergencies prepared by the stakeholders from information obtained during the risk analysis. (SIG-ECS)

3.3.94* Evacuation. The withdrawal of occupants from a building. (SIG-PRO)

3.3.95 Evacuation Signal. See 3.3.257, Signal.

3.3.96 Evacuation Signaling Zone. See 3.3.320, Zone.

3.3.97 Executive Software. See 3.3.272, Software.

3.3.98 Exit Marking Audible Notification Appliance. See 3.3.173, Notification Appliance.

3.3.99 False Alarm. See 3.3.307, Unwanted Alarm.

3.3.100 Field of View. The solid cone that extends out from the detector within which the effective sensitivity of the detector is at least 50 percent of its on-axis, listed, or approved sensitivity. (SIG-IDS)

3.3.101 Fire Alarm Control Interface (FACI). See 3.3.137, Interface.

3.3.102* Fire Alarm Control Unit (FACU). A component of the fire alarm system, provided with primary and secondary power sources, which receives signals from initiating devices or other fire alarm control units, and processes these signals to determine part or all of the required fire alarm system output function(s). (SIG-PRO)

    3.3.102.1 *Master Fire Alarm Control Unit.* A fire alarm control unit that serves the protected premises or portion of the protected premises as a local fire alarm control unit and accepts inputs from other fire alarm control units. (SIG-PRO)

    3.3.102.2 *Protected Premises (Local) Control Unit.* A fire alarm control unit that serves the protected premises or a portion of the protected premises. (SIG-PRO)

    3.3.102.2.1* *Dedicated Function Fire Alarm Control Unit.* A protected premises fire alarm control unit which is intended to provide operation of a specifically identified emergency control function. (SIG-PRO)

    3.3.102.2.2 *Releasing Service Fire Alarm Control Unit.* A protected premises fire alarm control unit specifically listed for releasing service that is part of a fire suppression system and which provides control outputs to release a fire suppression agent based on either automatic or manual input. (SIG-PRO)

3.3.103 Fire Alarm/Evacuation Signal Tone Generator. A device that produces a fire alarm/evacuation tone upon command. (SIG-PRO)

3.3.104 Fire Alarm Signal. See 3.3.257, Signal.

3.3.105 Fire Alarm System. A system or portion of a combination system that consists of components and circuits arranged to monitor and annunciate the status of fire alarm or supervisory signal-initiating devices and to initiate the appropriate response to those signals. (SIG-FUN)

    3.3.105.1* *Combination System.* A fire alarm system in which components are used, in whole or in part, in common with a non-fire signaling system. (SIG-PRO)

    3.3.105.2 *Household Fire Alarm System.* A system of devices that uses a fire alarm control unit to produce an alarm signal in the household for the purpose of notifying the occupants of the presence of a fire so that they will evacuate the premises. (SIG-HOU)

    3.3.105.3 *Municipal Fire Alarm System.* A public emergency alarm reporting system. (SIG-PRS)

    3.3.105.4* *Protected Premises (Local) Fire Alarm System.* A fire alarm system located at the protected premises. (SIG-PRO)

    3.3.105.4.1 *Building Fire Alarm System.* A protected premises fire alarm system that includes any of the features identified in 23.3.3.1 and that serves the general fire alarm needs of a building or buildings and that provides fire department or occupant notification or both. (SIG-PRO)

    3.3.105.4.2 *Dedicated Function Fire Alarm System.* A protected premises fire alarm system installed specifically to perform emergency control function(s) where a building fire alarm system is not required. (SIG-PRO)

    3.3.105.4.3 *Releasing Fire Alarm System.* A protected premises fire alarm system that is part of a fire suppression system and/or that provides control inputs to a fire suppression system related to the fire suppression system's sequence of operations and outputs for other signaling and notification. (SIG-PRO)

3.3.106* Fire Command Center. The principal attended or unattended room or area where the status of the detection, alarm communications, control systems, and other emergency systems is displayed and from which the system(s) can be manually controlled. (SIG-ECS)

3.3.107 Fire Extinguisher Electronic Monitoring Device. A device connected to a control unit that monitors the fire extinguisher in accordance with the requirements of NFPA 10, *Standard for Portable Fire Extinguishers.* (SIG-IDS)

3.3.108 Fire Warden. A building staff member or a tenant trained to perform assigned duties in the event of a fire emergency. (SIG-PRO)

3.3.109 Fire Warning Equipment. Any detector, alarm, device, or material related to single- and multiple-station alarms or household fire alarm systems. (SIG-HOU)

3.3.110 Fire–Gas Detector. See 3.3.66, Detector.

3.3.111 Fixed-Temperature Detector. See 3.3.66, Detector.

3.3.112 Flame. A body or stream of gaseous material involved in the combustion process and emitting radiant energy at specific wavelength bands determined by the combustion chemistry of the fuel. In most cases, some portion of the emitted radiant energy is visible to the human eye. (SIG-IDS)

3.3.113 Flame Detector. See 3.3.66, Detector.

3.3.114 Flame Detector Sensitivity. The distance along the optical axis of the detector at which the detector can detect a fire of specified size and fuel within a given time frame. (SIG-IDS)

3.3.115 Frequency. Minimum and maximum time between events. (SIG-TMS)

3.3.115.1 *Weekly Frequency.* Fifty-two times per year, once per calendar week.

3.3.115.2 *Monthly Frequency.* Twelve times per year, once per calendar month.

3.3.115.3 *Quarterly Frequency.* Four times per year with a minimum of 2 months, maximum of 4 months.

3.3.115.4 *Semiannual Frequency.* Twice per year with a minimum of 4 months, maximum of 8 months.

3.3.115.5 *Annual Frequency.* Once per year with a minimum of 9 months, maximum 15 months.

3.3.116 Gateway. A device that is used in the transmission of serial data (digital or analog) from the fire alarm control unit to other building system control units, equipment, or networks and/or from other building system control units to the fire alarm control unit. (SIG-PRO)

3.3.117 Girder. See 3.3.37, Ceiling Surfaces.

3.3.118 Guard's Tour Reporting Station. A device that is manually or automatically initiated to indicate the route being followed and the timing of a guard's tour. (SIG-IDS)

3.3.119 Guard's Tour Supervisory Signal. See 3.3.257, Signal.

3.3.120 Guest Room. An accommodation combining living, sleeping, sanitary, and storage facilities within a compartment. [*101*, 2012] (SIG-HOU)

3.3.121 Guest Suite. An accommodation with two or more contiguous rooms comprising a compartment, with or without doors between such rooms, that provides living, sleeping, sanitary, and storage facilities. [*101*, 2012] (SIG-HOU)

3.3.122* Hearing Loss. A full or partial decrease in the ability to detect or comprehend sounds. (SIG-NAS)

3.3.122.1 *Profound Hearing Loss.* A hearing threshold of greater than 90 dB.

3.3.123 Heat Alarm. A single- or multiple-station alarm responsive to heat. (SIG-IDS)

3.3.124 Heat Detector. See 3.3.66, Detector.

3.3.125 High Power Speaker Array (HPSA). High power speaker arrays provide capability for voice and tone communications to large outdoor areas. (SIG-ECS)

3.3.126 Hotel. A building or groups of buildings under the same management in which there are sleeping accommodations for more than 16 persons and primarily used by transients for lodging with or without meals. [*101*, 2012] (SIG-HOU)

3.3.127 Household Fire Alarm System. See 3.3.105, Fire Alarm System.

3.3.128 Hunt Group. A group of associated telephone lines within which an incoming call is automatically routed to an idle (not busy) telephone line for completion. (SIG-SSS)

3.3.129* Identified (as Applied to Equipment). Recognizable as suitable for the specific purpose, function, use, environment, application, and so forth, where described in a particular *Code* requirement. [*70*, 2011] (SIG-PRS)

3.3.130* Impairment. An abnormal condition where a system, component, or function is out of order, and the condition can result in the system or unit not functioning when required. (SIG-FUN)

3.3.130.1* *Emergency Impairment.* An abnormal condition where a system, component, or function is out of order due to an unexpected deficiency. (SIG-FUN)

3.3.130.2* *Planned Impairment.* An abnormal condition where a system, component, or function is out of service due to work that has been planned in advance. (SIG-FUN)

3.3.131 In-Building Mass Notification System. See 3.3.87, Emergency Communications System.

3.3.132 Initiating Device. A system component that originates transmission of a change-of-state condition, such as in a smoke detector, manual fire alarm box, or supervisory switch. (SIG-IDS)

3.3.132.1 *Analog Initiating Device (Sensor).* An initiating device that transmits a signal indicating varying degrees of condition as contrasted with a conventional initiating device, which can only indicate an on–off condition. (SIG-IDS)

3.3.132.2 *Automatic Extinguishing System Supervisory Device.* A device that responds to abnormal conditions that could affect the proper operation of an automatic sprinkler system or other fire extinguishing system(s) or suppression system(s), including, but not limited to, control valves, pressure levels, liquid agent levels and temperatures, pump power and running, engine temperature and overspeed, and room temperature. (SIG-IDS)

3.3.132.3 *Nonrestorable Initiating Device.* A device in which the sensing element is designed to be destroyed in the process of operation. (SIG-IDS)

3.3.132.4 *Restorable Initiating Device.* A device in which the sensing element is not ordinarily destroyed in the process of operation, whose restoration can be manual or automatic. (SIG-IDS)

3.3.132.5 *Supervisory Signal Initiating Device.* An initiating device such as a valve supervisory switch, water level indicator, or low air pressure switch on a dry pipe sprinkler system in which the change of state signals an off-normal condition and its restoration to normal of a fire protection or life safety system; or a need for action in connection with guard tours, fire suppression systems or equipment, or maintenance features of related systems. (SIG-IDS)

3.3.133 Initiating Device Circuit. A circuit to which automatic or manual initiating devices are connected where the signal received does not identify the individual device operated. (SIG-PRO)

3.3.134 Inspection Personnel. See 3.3.193, Personnel.

3.3.135 Intelligibility. The quality or condition of being intelligible. (SIG-NAS)

3.3.136* Intelligible. Capable of being understood; comprehensible; clear. (SIG-NAS)

3.3.137 Interface.

3.3.137.1 *Circuit Interface.* A circuit component that interfaces initiating devices or control circuits, or both; notification appliances or circuits, or both; system control outputs; and other signaling line circuits to a signaling line circuit. (SIG-PRO)

3.3.137.1.1 *Signaling Line Circuit Interface.* A system component that connects a signaling line circuit to any combination of initiating devices, initiating device circuits, notification appliances, notification appliance circuits, system control outputs, and other signaling line circuits. (SIG-PRO)

3.3.137.1.2* *Emergency Control Function Interface.* The interface between the fire alarm system emergency control function interface device and the component controlling the emergency control function. (SIG-PRO)

3.3.137.2* *Fire Alarm Control Interface.* The fire alarm control interface coordinates signals to and from the fire alarm system and other systems. (SIG-ECS)

3.3.138 Ionization Smoke Detection. See 3.3.269, Smoke Detection.

3.3.139 Leg Facility. The portion of a communications channel that connects not more than one protected premises to a primary or secondary trunk facility. The leg facility includes the portion of the signal transmission circuit from its point of connection with a trunk facility to the point where it is terminated within the protected premises at one or more transponders. (SIG-SSS)

3.3.140 Level Ceilings. See 3.3.35, Ceiling.

3.3.141 Life Safety Network. A type of combination system that transmits fire safety control data through gateways to other building system control units. (SIG-PRO)

3.3.142 Line-Type Detector. See 3.3.66, Detector.

3.3.143 Living Area. Any normally occupiable space in a residential occupancy, other than sleeping rooms or rooms that are intended for combination sleeping/living, bathrooms, toilet compartments, kitchens, closets, halls, storage or utility spaces, and similar areas. [*101*, 2012] (SIG-HOU)

3.3.144 Loading Capacity. The maximum number of discrete elements of fire alarm systems permitted to be used in a particular configuration. (SIG-SSS)

3.3.145 Local Energy Type Auxiliary Alarm System. See 3.3.215, Public Emergency Alarm Reporting System.

3.3.146* Local Operating Console (LOC). Equipment used by authorized personnel and emergency responders to activate and operate an in-building mass notification system. (SIG-ECS)

3.3.147 Lodging or Rooming House. A building or portion thereof that does not qualify as a one- or two-family dwelling, that provides sleeping accommodations for a total of 16 or fewer people on a transient or permanent basis, without personal care services, with or without meals, but without separate cooking facilities for individual occupants. [*101*, 2012] (SIG-HOU)

3.3.148 Loss of Power. The reduction of available voltage at the load below the point at which equipment can function as designed. (SIG-FUN)

3.3.149 Low-Power Radio Transmitter. Any device that communicates with associated control/receiving equipment by low-power radio signals. (SIG-PRO)

3.3.150 Maintenance. Work, including, but not limited to, repair, replacement, and service, performed to ensure that equipment operates properly. (SIG-TMS)

3.3.151 Malicious Alarm. See 3.3.307.1, Unwanted Alarm.

3.3.152* Managed Facilities-Based Voice Network (MFVN). A physical facilities-based network capable of transmitting real time signals with formats unchanged that is managed, operated, and maintained by the service provider to ensure service quality and reliability from the subscriber location to public-switched telephone network (PSTN) interconnection points or other MFVN peer networks. (SIG-SSS)

3.3.153 Manual Fire Alarm Box. See 3.3.12, Alarm Box.

3.3.154* Manufacturer's Published Instructions. Published installation and operating documentation provided for each product or component. The documentation includes directions and necessary information for the intended installation, maintenance, and operation of the product or component. (SIG-TMS)

3.3.155* Mass Notification Priority Mode. The mode of operation whereby all fire alarm occupant notification is superseded by emergency mass notification action. (SIG-ECS)

3.3.156* Mass Notification System. See 3.3.87.1.3, In-Building Mass Notification System. (SIG-PRO)

3.3.157 Master Box. See 3.3.12, Alarm Box.

3.3.158 Master Fire Alarm Control Unit. See 3.3.102, Fire Alarm Control Unit.

3.3.159 Multi-Criteria Detector. See 3.3.66, Detector.

3.3.160 Multiple Dwelling Unit. See 3.3.81, Dwelling Unit.

3.3.161 Multiple-Station Alarm. A single-station alarm capable of being interconnected to one or more additional alarms so that the actuation of one causes the appropriate alarm signal to operate in all interconnected alarms. (SIG-HOU)

3.3.162 Multiple-Station Alarm Device. Two or more single-station alarm devices that can be interconnected so that actuation of one causes all integral or separate audible alarms to operate; or one single-station alarm device having connections to other detectors or to a manual fire alarm box. (SIG-HOU)

3.3.163 Multiplexing. A signaling method characterized by simultaneous or sequential transmission, or both, and reception of multiple signals on a signaling line circuit, a transmission channel, or a communications channel, including means for positively identifying each signal. (SIG-SSS)

3.3.164 Multi-Sensor Detector. See 3.3.66, Detector.

3.3.165 Municipal Fire Alarm Box (Street Box). A publicly accessible alarm box. (See 3.3.12, Alarm Box.)

3.3.166 Municipal Fire Alarm System. See 3.3.105, Fire Alarm System.

3.3.167 Net-Centric Alerting System (NCAS). A net-centric alerting system incorporates web-based management and alert activation application through which all operators and administrators could gain access to the system's capabilities based on the users' permissions and the defined access policy. (SIG-ECS)

3.3.168 Network.

3.3.168.1 *Wireless Network.* The method of communications used in a public emergency alarm reporting system when it consists of a wireless type of communications infrastructure. (SIG-PRS)

3.3.168.2 *Wired Network.* The method of communications used in a public emergency alarm reporting system when it consists of a wired type of communications infrastructure. (SIG-PRS)

3.3.169 Network Architecture. The physical and logical design of a network, and the inherent ability of the design to carry data from one point to another. (SIG-ECS)

3.3.170 Noncontiguous Property. See 3.3.207, Property.

3.3.171* Nonrequired. A system component or group of components that is installed at the option of the owner, and is not installed due to a building or fire code requirement. (SIG-FUN)

3.3.172 Nonrestorable Initiating Device. See 3.3.132, Initiating Device.

3.3.173 Notification Appliance. A fire alarm system component such as a bell, horn, speaker, light, or text display that provides audible, tactile, or visible outputs, or any combination thereof. (SIG-NAS)

3.3.173.1 *Audible Notification Appliance.* A notification appliance that alerts by the sense of hearing. (SIG-NAS)

3.3.173.1.1 *Exit Marking Audible Notification Appliance.* An audible notification appliance that marks building exits and areas of refuge by the sense of hearing for the purpose of evacuation or relocation. (SIG-NAS)

3.3.173.1.2* *Textual Audible Notification Appliance.* A notification appliance that conveys a stream of audible information. (SIG-NAS)

3.3.173.2 *Tactile Notification Appliance.* A notification appliance that alerts by the sense of touch or vibration. (SIG-NAS)

3.3.173.3 *Visible Notification Appliance.* A notification appliance that alerts by the sense of sight. (SIG-NAS)

3.3.173.3.1 *Textual Visible Notification Appliance.* A notification appliance that conveys a stream of visible information that displays an alphanumeric or pictorial message. Textual visible notification appliances provide temporary text, permanent text, or symbols. Textual visible notification appliances include, but are not limited to, annunciators, monitors, CRTs, displays, and printers. (SIG-NAS)

3.3.174 Notification Appliance Circuit. A circuit or path directly connected to a notification appliance(s). (SIG-PRO)

3.3.175 Notification Zone. See 3.3.320, Zone.

3.3.176 Nuisance Alarm. See 3.3.307.2, Unwanted Alarm.

3.3.177* Occupiable. A room or enclosed space designed for human occupancy. (SIG-FUN)

3.3.178 Occupiable Area. An area of a facility occupied by people on a regular basis. (SIG-FUN)

3.3.179* Octave Band. The bandwidth of a filter that comprises a frequency range of a factor of 2. (SIG-NAS)

3.3.179.1 *One-Third Octave Band.* The bandwidth of a filter that comprises a frequency range of a factor of $2^{1/3}$. (SIG-NAS)

3.3.180 Off-Hook. To make connection with the public-switched telephone network in preparation for dialing a telephone number. (SIG-SSS)

3.3.181 One-Third Octave Band. See 3.3.179, Octave Band.

3.3.182 One-Way Emergency Communications System. See 3.3.87, Emergency Communications System.

3.3.183 On-Hook. To disconnect from the public-switched telephone network. (SIG-SSS)

3.3.184 Open Area Detection (Protection). Protection of an area such as a room or space with detectors to provide early warning of fire. (SIG-IDS)

3.3.185 Operating Mode.

3.3.185.1 *Private Operating Mode.* Audible or visible signaling only to those persons directly concerned with the implementation and direction of emergency action initiation and procedure in the area protected by the fire alarm system. (SIG-NAS)

3.3.185.2 *Public Operating Mode.* Audible or visible signaling to occupants or inhabitants of the area protected by the fire alarm system. (SIG-NAS)

3.3.186 Other Fire Detectors. See 3.3.66, Detector.

3.3.187* Ownership. Any property or building or its contents under legal control by the occupant, by contract, or by holding of a title or deed. (SIG-SSS)

3.3.188 Paging System. A system intended to page one or more persons by such means as voice over loudspeaker, coded audible signals or visible signals, or lamp annunciators. (SIG-PRO)

3.3.189 Parallel Telephone System. A telephone system in which an individually wired circuit is used for each fire alarm box. (SIG-SSS)

3.3.190 Path (Pathways). Any circuit, conductor, optic fiber, radio carrier, or other means connecting two or more locations. (SIG-PRO)

3.3.191 Pathway Survivability. The ability of any conductor, optic fiber, radio carrier, or other means for transmitting system information to remain operational during fire conditions. (SIG-ECS)

3.3.192 Permanent Visual Record (Recording). An immediately readable, not easily alterable, print, slash, or punch record of all occurrences of status change. (SIG-SSS)

3.3.193 Personnel.

3.3.193.1 *Inspection Personnel.* Individuals who conduct a visual examination of a system or portion thereof to verify that it appears to be in operating condition, in proper location, and is free of physical damage or conditions that impair operation. (SIG-TMS)

3.3.193.2 *Service Personnel.* Individuals who perform those procedures, adjustments, replacement of components, system programming, and maintenance as described in the manufacturer's service instructions that can affect any aspect of the performance of the system. (SIG-TMS)

3.3.193.3 *System Designer.* Individual responsible for the development of fire alarm and signaling system plans and specifications in accordance with this Code. (SIG-FUN)

3.3.193.4 *System Installer.* Individual responsible for the proper installation of fire alarm and signaling systems in accordance with plans, specifications, and manufacturer's requirements. (SIG-FUN)

3.3.193.5 *Testing Personnel.* Individuals who perform procedures used to determine the status of a system as intended by conducting acceptance, reacceptance, or periodic physical checks on systems. (SIG-TMS)

3.3.194 Photoelectric Light Obscuration Smoke Detection. See 3.3.269, Smoke Detection.

3.3.195 Photoelectric Light-Scattering Smoke Detection. See 3.3.269, Smoke Detection.

3.3.196 Plant. One or more buildings under the same ownership or control on a single property. (SIG-SSS)

3.3.197 Pneumatic Rate-of-Rise Tubing Heat Detector. See 3.3.66, Detector.

3.3.198 Positive Alarm Sequence. An automatic sequence that results in an alarm signal, even when manually delayed for investigation, unless the system is reset. (SIG-PRO)

3.3.199 Power Supply. A source of electrical operating power, including the circuits and terminations connecting it to the dependent system components. (SIG-FUN)

3.3.200 Primary Battery (Dry Cell). A nonrechargeable battery requiring periodic replacement. (SIG-FUN)

3.3.201 Primary Trunk Facility. That part of a transmission channel connecting all leg facilities to a supervising or subsidiary station. (SIG-SSS)

3.3.202 Prime Contractor. The one company contractually responsible for providing central station services to a subscriber as required by this Code. The prime contractor can be either a listed central station or a listed alarm service–local company. (SIG-SSS)

3.3.203 Private Operating Mode. See 3.3.185, Operating Mode.

3.3.204 Private Radio Signaling. A radio system under control of the proprietary supervising station. (SIG-SSS)

3.3.205 Profound Hearing Loss. See 3.3.122, Hearing Loss.

3.3.206 Projected Beam–Type Detector. See 3.3.66, Detector.

3.3.207 Property.

3.3.207.1 *Contiguous Property.* A single-owner or single-user protected premises on a continuous plot of ground, including any buildings thereon, that is not separated by a public thoroughfare, transportation right-of-way, property owned or used by others, or body of water not under the same ownership. (SIG-SSS)

3.3.207.2 *Noncontiguous Property.* An owner- or user-protected premises where two or more protected premises, controlled by the same owner or user, are separated by a public thoroughfare, body of water, transportation right-of-way, or property owned or used by others. (SIG-SSS)

3.3.208 Proprietary Supervising Station. See 3.3.283, Supervising Station.

3.3.209 Proprietary Supervising Station Alarm System. See 3.3.284, Supervising Station Alarm System.

3.3.210 Proprietary Supervising Station Service. See 3.3.285, Supervising Station Service.

3.3.211 Protected Premises. The physical location protected by a fire alarm system. (SIG-PRO)

3.3.212 Protected Premises (Local) Control Unit. See 3.3.102, Fire Alarm Control Unit.

3.3.213 Protected Premises (Local) Fire Alarm System. See 3.3.105, Fire Alarm System.

3.3.214 Public Address System. An electronic amplification system with a mixer, amplifier, and loudspeakers, used to reinforce a given sound and distributing the "sound" to the general public around a building. (SIG-ECS)

3.3.215 Public Emergency Alarm Reporting System. A system of alarm-initiating devices, transmitting and receiving equipment, and communication infrastructure (other than a public telephone network) used to communicate with the communications center to provide any combination of manual or auxiliary alarm service. (SIG-PRS)

3.3.215.1* *Auxiliary Alarm System.* A protected premises fire alarm system or other emergency system at the protected premises and the system used to connect the protected premises system to a public emergency alarm reporting system for transmitting an alarm to the communications center. (SIG-PRS)

3.3.215.1.1 *Local Energy Type Auxiliary Alarm System.* An auxiliary system that employs a locally complete arrangement of parts, initiating devices, relays, power supply, and associated components to automatically activate a master box or auxiliary box over circuits that are electrically isolated from the public emergency alarm reporting system circuits. (SIG-PRS)

3.3.215.1.2 *Shunt-Type Auxiliary Alarm System.* An auxiliary system electrically connected to the public emergency alarm reporting system extending a public emergency alarm reporting circuit to interconnect initiating devices within a protected premises, which, when operated, opens the public emergency alarm reporting circuit shunted around the trip coil of the master box or auxiliary box. The master box or auxiliary box is thereupon energized to start transmission without any assistance from a local source of power. (SIG-PRS)

3.3.215.2 *Type A Public Emergency Alarm Reporting System.* A system in which an alarm from an alarm box is received and is retransmitted to fire stations either manually or automatically. (SIG-PRS)

3.3.215.3 *Type B Public Emergency Alarm Reporting System.* A system in which an alarm from an alarm box is automatically transmitted to fire stations and, if used, is transmitted to supplementary alerting devices. (SIG-PRS)

3.3.216 Public Operating Mode. See 3.3.185, Operating Mode.

3.3.217 Public Safety Agency. A fire, emergency medical services, or law enforcement agency. (SIG-ECS)

3.3.218 Public Safety Radio Enhancement System. A system installed to assure the effective operation of radio communication systems used by fire, emergency medical services, or law enforcement agencies. (SIG-ECS)

3.3.219 Public Safety Radio System. A radio communication system used by fire, emergency medical services, or law enforcement agencies. (SIG-ECS)

3.3.220 Public Switched Telephone Network. See 3.3.290, Switched Telephone Network.

3.3.221 Publicly Accessible Fire Alarm Box. See 3.3.12, Fire Alarm Box.

3.3.222* Qualified. A competent and capable person or company that has met the requirements and training for a given field acceptable to the authority having jurisdiction. [**96,** 2011] (SIG-TMS)

3.3.223 Radiant Energy–Sensing Fire Detector. See 3.3.66, Detector.

3.3.224 Radio Alarm Repeater Station Receiver (RARSR). A system component that receives radio signals and resides at a repeater station that is located at a remote receiving location. (SIG-SSS)

3.3.225 Radio Alarm Supervising Station Receiver (RASSR). A system component that receives data and annunciates that data at the supervising station. (SIG-SSS)

3.3.226 Radio Alarm System (RAS). A system in which signals are transmitted from a radio alarm transmitter (RAT) located at a protected premises through a radio channel to two or more radio alarm repeater station receivers (RARSR) and that are annunciated by a radio alarm supervising station receiver (RASSR) located at the central station. (SIG-SSS)

3.3.227 Radio Alarm Transmitter (RAT). A system component at the protected premises to which initiating devices or groups of devices are connected that transmits signals indicating a status change of the initiating devices. (SIG-SSS)

3.3.228 Radio Channel. See 3.3.43, Channel.

3.3.229* Radio Frequency. The number of electromagnetic wave frequency cycles transmitted by a radio in 1 second. [**1221,** 2013] (SIG-PRS)

3.3.230 Rate Compensation Detector. See 3.3.66, Detector.

3.3.231 Rate-of-Rise Detector. See 3.3.66, Detector.

3.3.232 Record Drawings. Drawings (as-built) that document the location of all devices, appliances, wiring sequences, wiring methods, and connections of the components of the system as installed. (SIG-FUN)

3.3.233 Record of Completion. A document that acknowledges the features of installation, operation (performance), service, and equipment with representation by the property owner, system installer, system supplier, service organization, and the authority having jurisdiction. (SIG-FUN)

3.3.234 Releasing Fire Alarm System. See 3.3.105, Fire Alarm System.

3.3.235 Releasing Service Fire Alarm Control Unit. See 3.3.102, Fire Alarm Control Unit.

3.3.236 Relocation. The movement of occupants from a fire zone to a safe area within the same building. (SIG-PRO)

3.3.237 Remote Supervising Station. See 3.3.283, Supervising Station.

3.3.238 Remote Supervising Station Alarm System. See 3.3.284, Supervising Station Alarm System.

3.3.239 Remote Supervising Station Service. See 3.3.285, Supervising Station Service.

3.3.240 Repeater Station. The location of the equipment needed to relay signals between supervising stations, subsidiary stations, and protected premises. (SIG-SSS)

3.3.241 Reset. A control function that attempts to return a system or device to its normal, nonalarm state. (SIG-FUN)

3.3.242 Residential Board and Care Occupancy. An occupancy used for lodging and boarding of four or more residents, not related by blood or marriage to the owners or operators, for the purpose of providing personal care services. [**101,** 2012] (SIG-HOU)

3.3.243 Residential Occupancy. An occupancy that provides sleeping accommodations for purposes other than health care or detention and correctional. [**101,** 2012] (SIG-HOU)

3.3.244* Response. Actions performed upon the receipt of a signal. (SIG-FUN)

> **3.3.244.1* *Alarm Response.*** The response to the receipt of an alarm signal. (SIG-FUN)

> **3.3.244.2* *Pre-Alarm Response.*** The response to the receipt of a pre-alarm signal. (SIG-FUN)

> **3.3.244.3* *Supervisory Response.*** The response to the receipt of a supervisory signal. (SIG-FUN)

> **3.3.244.4* *Trouble Response.*** The response to the receipt of a trouble signal. (SIG-FUN)

3.3.245 Restorable Initiating Device. See 3.3.132, Initiating Device.

3.3.246 Risk Analysis. A process to characterize the likelihood, vulnerability, and magnitude of incidents associated with natural, technological, and manmade disasters and other emergencies that address scenarios of concern, their probability, and their potential consequences. (SIG-ECS)

3.3.247 Runner. A person other than the required number of operators on duty at central, supervising, or runner stations (or otherwise in contact with these stations) available for prompt dispatching, when necessary, to the protected premises. (SIG-SSS)

3.3.248 Runner Service. The service provided by a runner at the protected premises, including restoration, resetting, and silencing of all equipment transmitting fire alarm or supervisory or trouble signals to an off-premises location. (SIG-SSS)

3.3.249 Scanner. Equipment located at the telephone company wire center that monitors each local leg and relays status changes to the alarm center. Processors and associated equipment might also be included. (SIG-SSS)

3.3.250 Secondary Trunk Facility. That part of a transmission channel connecting two or more, but fewer than all, leg facilities to a primary trunk facility. (SIG-SSS)

3.3.251 Selective Talk Mode. See 3.3.294, Talk Mode.

3.3.252 Separate Sleeping Area. The area of a dwelling unit where the bedrooms or sleeping rooms are located. [**720,** 2012] (SIG-HOU)

3.3.253 Service Personnel. See 3.3.193, Personnel.

3.3.254 Shapes of Ceilings. The shapes of ceilings can be classified as sloping or smooth. (SIG-IDS)

3.3.255 Shop Drawings. Documents that provide information pertaining to the system, such as property location, scaled floor plans, equipment wiring details, typical equipment installation details, riser details, conduit/conductor size and routing information, and other information necessary for the installer to complete the fire alarm installation. (SIG-FUN)

3.3.256 Shunt-Type Auxiliary Alarm System. See 3.3.215, Public Emergency Alarm Reporting System.

3.3.257* Signal. A message indicating a condition, communicated by electrical, visible, audible, wireless, or other means. (SIG-FUN)

> **3.3.257.1* *Alarm Signal.*** A signal that results from the manual or automatic detection of an alarm condition. (SIG-FUN)

> **3.3.257.2 *Carbon Monoxide Alarm Signal.*** A signal indicating a concentration of carbon monoxide at or above the alarm threshold that could pose a risk to the life safety of the occupants and that requires immediate action. [**720,** 2012] (SIG-FUN)

> **3.3.257.3 *Delinquency Signal.*** A signal indicating a supervisory condition and the need for action in connection with the supervision of guards or system attendants. (SIG-PRO)

> **3.3.257.4 *Evacuation Signal.*** A distinctive alarm signal intended to be recognized by the occupants as requiring evacuation of the building. (SIG-PRO)

> **3.3.257.5* *Fire Alarm Signal.*** A signal that results from the manual or automatic detection of a fire alarm condition. (SIG-FUN)

> **3.3.257.6* *Guard's Tour Supervisory Signal.*** A signal generated when a guard on patrol has activated a guard's tour reporting station. (SIG-PRO)

> **3.3.257.7* *Pre-Alarm Signal.*** A signal that results from the detection of a pre-alarm condition. (SIG-FUN)

> **3.3.257.8 *Restoration Signal.*** A signal that results from the return to normal condition of an initiating device, system element, or system. (SIG-FUN)

> **3.3.257.9* *Supervisory Signal.*** A signal that results from the detection of a supervisory condition. (SIG-FUN)

> **3.3.257.10* *Trouble Signal.*** A signal that results from the detection of a trouble condition. (SIG-FUN)

3.3.258 Signal Transmission Sequence. A DACT that obtains dial tone, dials the number(s) of the DACR, obtains verification that the DACR is ready to receive signals, transmits the signals, and receives acknowledgment that the DACR has accepted that signal before disconnecting (going on-hook). (SIG-SSS)

3.3.259 Signaling Line Circuit. A circuit path between any combination of addressable appliances or devices, circuit interfaces, control units, or transmitters over which multiple system input signals or output signals or both are carried. (SIG-PRO)

3.3.260 Signaling Line Circuit Interface. See 3.3.137, Interface.

3.3.261 Single Dwelling Unit. See 3.3.81, Dwelling Unit.

3.3.262 Single-Station Alarm. A detector comprising an assembly that incorporates a sensor, control components, and an alarm notification appliance in one unit operated from a power source either located in the unit or obtained at the point of installation. (SIG-HOU)

3.3.263 Single-Station Alarm Device. An assembly that incorporates the detector, the control equipment, and the alarm-sounding device in one unit operated from a power supply either in the unit or obtained at the point of installation. (SIG-HOU)

3.3.264 Site-Specific Software. See 3.3.272, Software.

3.3.265 Sloping Ceiling. See 3.3.35, Ceiling.

3.3.266 Sloping Peaked-Type Ceiling. See 3.3.35, Ceiling.

3.3.267 Sloping Shed-Type Ceiling. See 3.3.35, Ceiling.

3.3.268 Smoke Alarm. A single or multiple-station alarm responsive to smoke. (SIG-HOU)

3.3.269 Smoke Detection.

> **3.3.269.1 *Cloud Chamber Smoke Detection.*** The principle of using an air sample drawn from the protected area into a high-humidity chamber combined with a lowering of chamber pressure to create an environment in which the resultant moisture in the air condenses on any smoke particles present, forming a cloud. The cloud density is measured by a photoelectric principle. The density signal is processed and used to convey an alarm condition when it meets preset criteria. (SIG-IDS)

> **3.3.269.2* *Ionization Smoke Detection.*** The principle of using a small amount of radioactive material to ionize the air between two differentially charged electrodes to sense the presence of smoke particles. Smoke particles entering the ionization volume decrease the conductance of the air by reducing ion mobility. The reduced conductance signal is processed and used to convey an alarm condition when it meets preset criteria. (SIG-IDS)

> **3.3.269.3* *Photoelectric Light Obscuration Smoke Detection.*** The principle of using a light source and a photosensitive sensor onto which the principal portion of the source emissions is focused. When smoke particles enter the light path, some of the light is scattered and some is absorbed, thereby reducing the light reaching the receiving sensor. The light reduction signal is processed and used to convey an alarm condition when it meets preset criteria. (SIG-IDS)

> **3.3.269.4* *Photoelectric Light-Scattering Smoke Detection.*** The principle of using a light source and a photosensitive sensor arranged so that the rays from the light source do not normally fall onto the photosensitive sensor. When smoke particles enter the light path, some of the light is scattered by reflection and refraction onto the sensor. The light signal is processed and used to convey an alarm condition when it meets preset criteria. (SIG-IDS)

> **3.3.269.5* *Video Image Smoke Detection (VISD).*** The principle of using automatic analysis of real-time video images to detect the presence of smoke. (SIG-IDS)

3.3.270 Smoke Detector. See 3.3.66, Detector.

3.3.271 Smooth Ceiling. See 3.3.37, Ceiling Surfaces.

3.3.272 Software. Programs, instruments, procedures, data, and the like that are executed by a central processing unit of a product and that influences the functional performance of that product. For the purpose of this Code, software is one of two types: executive software and site-specific software. (SIG-TMS)

3.3.272.1 *Executive Software.* Control and supervisory program that manages the execution of all other programs and directly or indirectly causes the required functions of the product to be performed. Executive software is sometimes referred to as firmware, BIOS, or executive program. (SIG-TMS)

3.3.272.2 *Site-Specific Software.* Program that is separate from, but controlled by, the executive software that allows inputs, outputs, and system configuration to be selectively defined to meet the needs of a specific installation. Typically it defines the type and quantity of hardware, customized labels, and the specific operating features of a system. (SIG-TMS)

3.3.273 Solid Joist Construction. See 3.3.37, Ceiling Surfaces.

3.3.274 Spacing. A horizontally measured dimension related to the allowable coverage of fire detectors. (SIG-IDS)

3.3.275* Spark. A moving particle of solid material that emits radiant energy due either to its temperature or the process of combustion on its surface. [654, 2013] (SIG-IDS)

3.3.276 Spark/Ember Detector. See 3.3.66, Detector.

3.3.277 Spark/Ember Detector Sensitivity. The number of watts (or the fraction of a watt) of radiant power from a point source radiator, applied as a unit step signal at the wavelength of maximum detector sensitivity, necessary to produce an alarm signal from the detector within the specified response time. (SIG-IDS)

3.3.278 Spot-Type Detector. See 3.3.66, Detector.

3.3.279 Stakeholder. Any individual, group, or organization that might affect, be affected by, or perceive itself to be affected by the risk. (SIG-ECS)

3.3.280 Stratification. The phenomenon where the upward movement of smoke and gases ceases due to the loss of buoyancy. (SIG-IDS)

3.3.281 Subscriber. The recipient of a contractual supervising station signal service(s). In case of multiple, noncontiguous properties having single ownership, the term refers to each protected premises or its local management. (SIG-SSS)

3.3.282 Subsidiary Station. A subsidiary station is a normally unattended location that is remote from the supervising station and is linked by a communications channel(s) to the supervising station. Interconnection of signals on one or more transmission channels from protected premises with a communications channel(s) to the supervising station is performed at this location. (SIG-SSS)

3.3.283 Supervising Station. A facility that receives signals from protected premises fire alarm systems and at which personnel are in attendance at all times to respond to these signals. (SIG-SSS)

3.3.283.1 *Central Supervising Station.* A supervising station that is listed for central station service and that also commonly provides less stringent supervising station services such as remote supervising services. (SIG-SSS)

3.3.283.2 *Proprietary Supervising Station.* A supervising station under the same ownership as the protected premises fire alarm system(s) that it supervises (monitors) and to which alarm, supervisory, or trouble signals are received and where personnel are in attendance at all times to supervise operation and investigate signals. (SIG-SSS)

3.3.283.3 *Remote Supervising Station.* A supervising station to which alarm, supervisory, or trouble signals or any combination of those signals emanating from protected premises fire alarm systems are received and where personnel are in attendance at all times to respond. (SIG-SSS)

3.3.284 Supervising Station Alarm Systems.

3.3.284.1 *Central Station Service Alarm System.* A system or group of systems in which the operations of circuits and devices are transmitted automatically to, recorded in, maintained by, and supervised from a listed central station that has competent and experienced servers and operators who, upon receipt of a signal, take such action as required by this Code. Such service is to be controlled and operated by a person, firm, or corporation whose business is the furnishing, maintaining, or monitoring of supervised alarm systems. (SIG-SSS)

3.3.284.2 *Proprietary Supervising Station Alarm System.* An installation of an alarm system that serves contiguous and noncontiguous properties, under one ownership, from a proprietary supervising station located at the protected premises, or at one of multiple noncontiguous protected premises, at which trained, competent personnel are in constant attendance. This includes the protected premises fire alarm system(s); proprietary supervising station; power supplies; signal-initiating devices; initiating device circuits; signal notification appliances; equipment for the automatic, permanent visual recording of signals; and equipment for initiating the operation of emergency building control services. (SIG-SSS)

3.3.284.3 *Remote Supervising Station Alarm System.* A protected premises fire alarm system (exclusive of any connected to a public emergency reporting system) in which alarm, supervisory, or trouble signals are transmitted automatically to, recorded in, and supervised from a remote supervising station that has competent and experienced servers and operators who, upon receipt of a signal, take such action as required by this Code. (SIG-SSS)

3.3.285 Supervising Station Service.

3.3.285.1 *Central Station Service.* The use of a system or a group of systems including the protected premises fire alarm system(s) in which the operations of circuits and devices are signaled to, recorded in, and supervised from a listed central station that has competent and experienced operators who, upon receipt of a signal, take such action as required by this Code. Related activities at the protected premises, such as equipment installation, inspection, testing, maintenance, and runner service, are the responsibility of the central station or a listed alarm service local company. Central station service is controlled and operated by a person, firm, or corporation whose business is the furnishing of such contracted services or whose properties are the protected premises. (SIG-SSS)

3.3.285.2 *Proprietary Supervising Station Service.* The use of a system or a group of systems including the protected premises fire alarm system(s) in which the operations of circuits and devices are signaled to, recorded in, and supervised from a supervising station under the same ownership as the protected premises that has competent and experienced operators who, upon receipt of a signal, take such action as required by this Code. Related activities at the protected premises, such as equipment installation, inspection, testing, maintenance, and runner service, are the responsibility of the owner. Proprietary supervising station service is controlled and operated by the entity whose properties are the protected premises. (SIG-SSS)

3.3.285.3 Remote Supervising Station Service. The use of a system including the protected premises fire alarm system(s) in which the operations of circuits and devices are signaled to, recorded in, and supervised from a supervising station that has competent and experienced operators who, upon receipt of a signal, take such action as required by this Code. Related activities at the protected premises, such as equipment installation, inspection, testing, and maintenance, are the responsibility of the owner. (SIG-SSS)

3.3.286 Supervisory Service. The service required to monitor performance of guard tours and the operative condition of fixed suppression systems or other systems for the protection of life and property. (SIG-PRO)

3.3.287 Supervisory Signal. See 3.3.257, Signal.

3.3.288 Supervisory Signal Initiating Device. See 3.3.132, Initiating Device.

3.3.289 Supplementary. As used in this Code, *supplementary* refers to equipment or operations not required by this Code and designated as such by the authority having jurisdiction. (SIG-FUN)

3.3.290 Switched Telephone Network.

3.3.290.1 Loop Start Telephone Circuit. A loop start telephone circuit is an analog telephone circuit that supports loop start signaling as specified in either Telcordia *GR-506-CORE, LATA Switching Systems Generic Requirements: Signaling for Analog Interface,* or Telcordia *GR-909-CORE, Fiber in the Loop Systems Generic Requirements.* (SIG-SSS)

3.3.290.2 Public Switched Telephone Network. An assembly of communications equipment and telephone service providers that utilize managed facilities-based voice networks (MFVN) to provide the general public with the ability to establish communications channels via discrete dialing codes. (SIG-SSS)

3.3.291 System Operator. An individual trained to operate and/or initiate a mass notification system. (SIG-ECS)

3.3.292 System Unit. The active subassemblies at the supervising station used for signal receiving, processing, display, or recording of status change signals; a failure of one of these subassemblies causes the loss of a number of alarm signals by that unit. (SIG-SSS)

3.3.293 Tactile Notification Appliance. See 3.3.173, Notification Appliance.

3.3.294 Talk Mode. A means of communications within a building normally dedicated to emergency functions. Commonly referred to as fire fighters' phones, but can also be used for communications with fire fighters and/or fire wardens, including occupants, during an emergency, such as between a fire command center and a designated location, such as a stair, stairwell, or location of emergency equipment. (SIG-ECS)

3.3.294.1 Common Talk Mode. The ability to conference multiple telephones in a single conversation. This is similar to what was referred to as a party line. (SIG-ECS)

3.3.294.2 Selective Talk Mode. The ability for personnel at the fire command center to receive indication of incoming calls and choose which call to answer. This includes the ability to transfer between incoming calls and conference multiple phone locations. Selective calling can include the ability to initiate calls to emergency phone locations. (SIG-ECS)

3.3.295 Testing Personnel. See 3.3.193, Personnel.

3.3.296 Textual Audible Notification Appliance. See 3.3.173, Notification Appliance.

3.3.297 Textual Visible Notification Appliance. See 3.3.173, Notification Appliance.

3.3.298 Transmission Channel. See 3.3.43, Channel.

3.3.299 Transmitter. A system component that provides an interface between signaling line circuits, initiating device circuits, or control units and the transmission channel. (SIG-SSS)

3.3.300 Transponder. A multiplex alarm transmission system functional assembly located at the protected premises. (SIG-SSS)

3.3.301 Trouble Signal. See 3.3.257, Signal.

3.3.302 Two-Way Emergency Communications System. See 3.3.87, Emergency Communications System.

3.3.303 Type A Public Emergency Alarm Reporting System. See 3.3.215, Public Emergency Alarm Reporting System.

3.3.304 Type B Public Emergency Alarm Reporting System. See 3.3.215, Public Emergency Alarm Reporting System.

3.3.305 Unintentional Alarm. See 3.3.307.3.

3.3.306 Unknown Alarm. See 3.3.307.4.

3.3.307* Unwanted Alarm. Any alarm that occurs that is not the result of a potentially hazardous condition. (SIG-FUN)

3.3.307.1 Malicious Alarm. An unwanted activation of an alarm initiating device caused by a person acting with malice. (SIG-FUN)

3.3.307.2* Nuisance Alarm. An unwanted activation of a signaling system or an alarm initiating device in response to a stimulus or condition that is not the result of a potentially hazardous condition. (SIG-FUN)

3.3.307.3 Unintentional Alarm. An unwanted activation of an alarm initiating device caused by a person acting without malice. (SIG-FUN)

3.3.307.4 Unknown Alarm. An unwanted activation of an alarm initiating device or system output function where the cause has not been identified. (SIG-FUN)

3.3.308 Uplink. The radio signal from the portable public safety subscriber transmitter to the base station receiver. (SIG-ECS)

3.3.309* Video Image Flame Detection (VIFD). The principle of using automatic analysis of real-time video images to detect the presence of flame. (SIG-IDS)

3.3.310 Video Image Smoke Detection (VISD). See 3.3.269, Smoke Detection.

3.3.311 Visible Notification Appliance. See 3.3.173, Notification Appliance.

3.3.312 Voice Message Priority. A scheme for prioritizing mass notification messages. (SIG-ECS)

3.3.313 WATS (Wide Area Telephone Service). Telephone company service allowing reduced costs for certain telephone call arrangements. In-WATS or 800-number service calls can be placed from anywhere in the continental United States to the called party at no cost to the calling party. Out-WATS is a service whereby, for a flat-rate charge, dependent on the total duration of all such calls, a subscriber can make an unlimited number of calls within a prescribed area from a particular telephone terminal without the registration of individual call charges. (SIG-SSS)

3.3.314* Wavelength. The distance between the peaks of a sinusoidal wave. All radiant energy can be described as a wave having a wavelength. Wavelength serves as the unit of measure for distinguishing between different parts of the spectrum. Wavelengths are measured in microns (µm), nanometers (nm), or angstroms (Å). (SIG-IDS)

3.3.315 Wide-Area Mass Notification System. See 3.3.87, Emergency Communications System.

3.3.316 Wide-Area Signaling. Signaling intended to provide alerting or information to exterior open spaces, such as campuses, neighborhood streets, a city, a town, or a community. (SIG-NAS)

3.3.317 Wireless Control Unit. See 3.3.59, Control Unit.

3.3.318 Wireless Protection System. A system or a part of a system that can transmit and receive signals without the aid of interconnection wiring. It can consist of either a wireless control unit or a wireless repeater. (SIG-PRO)

3.3.319 Wireless Repeater. A component used to relay signals among wireless devices, appliances, and control units. (SIG-PRO)

3.3.320 Zone. A defined area within the protected premises. A zone can define an area from which a signal can be received, an area to which a signal can be sent, or an area in which a form of control can be executed. (SIG-FUN)

3.3.320.1* *Evacuation Signaling Zone.* An area consisting of one or more notification zones where signals are actuated simultaneously. (SIG-ECS)

3.3.320.2 *Notification Zone.* A discrete area of a building, bounded by building outer walls, fire or smoke compartment boundaries, floor separations, or other fire safety subdivisions, in which occupants are intended to receive common notification. (SIG-PRO)

Chapter 4   Reserved

Chapter 5   Reserved

Chapter 6   Reserved

Chapter 7   Documentation

7.1 Application. (SIG-FUN)

7.1.1 The documentation of the design, acceptance, and completion of new systems required under this Code shall comply with the minimum requirements of this chapter.

7.1.2 The documentation of the alteration, maintenance, and testing of existing systems previously installed under this Code shall comply with the minimum requirements of this chapter.

7.1.3* Where required by governing laws, codes, or standards, or other parts of this Code, the requirements of this chapter, or portions thereof, shall apply.

7.1.4 Unless required by other governing laws, codes, or standards, the documentation requirements of this chapter shall not apply to Chapter 29.

7.1.5 This chapter outlines documentation requirements but does not prohibit additional documentation from being provided.

7.1.6 The requirements of other chapters shall also apply unless they are in conflict with this chapter.

7.2* Minimum Required Documentation. (SIG-FUN)

7.2.1 Where documentation is required by the enforcing authority, the following list shall represent the minimum documentation required for all fire alarm and emergency communications systems, including new systems and additions or alterations to existing systems:

(1) *Written narrative providing intent and system description
(2) Riser diagram
(3) Floor plan layout showing location of all devices and control equipment
(4) Sequence of operation in either an input/output matrix or narrative form
(5) Equipment technical data sheets
(6) Manufacturers published instructions, including operation and maintenance instructions
(7) Battery calculations (where batteries are provided)
(8) Voltage drop calculations for notification appliance circuits
(9) *Completed record of inspection and testing in accordance with 7.6.6 and 7.8.2
(10) Completed record of completion in accordance with 7.5.6 and 7.8.2
(11) Copy of site-specific software, where applicable
(12) Record (as-built) drawings
(13) Periodic inspection, testing, and maintenance documentation in accordance with Section 7.6
(14) Records, record retention, and record maintenance in accordance with Section 7.7

7.2.2* The person responsible for system design (layout) shall be identified on the system design documents.

7.2.3 All fire alarm drawings shall use symbols described in NFPA 170, *Standard for Fire Safety and Emergency Symbols*, or other symbols acceptable to the authority having jurisdiction.

7.3 Design (Layout) Documentation.

7.3.1* The requirements of Section 7.3 shall apply only where required by other governing laws, codes, or standards; by other parts of this Code; or by project specifications or drawings. (SIG-FUN)

7.3.2* Where required by governing laws, codes, or standards, or other parts of this Code, design (layout) documents shall be prepared prior to installing new systems. (SIG-ECS)

7.3.3* Where required by governing laws, codes, or standards, or other parts of this Code, preliminary plans shall be created. (SIG-ECS)

7.3.4 Notification. (SIG-NAS)

7.3.4.1* The requirements of 7.3.4 shall apply only where required by other governing laws, codes, or standards, or by other parts of this Code.

7.3.4.2 The documentation specified in 7.3.4 shall be required in whole or in part by other governing laws, codes, or standards, or by other parts of this Code.

7.3.4.3 Design documents shall include ambient sound pressure levels and audible design sound pressure levels in accordance with 18.4.1.4.3.

7.3.4.4 Analysis and design documentation for narrow band tone signaling shall be in accordance with 18.4.6.4.

7.3.4.5 The documentation of acoustically distinguishable spaces (ADS) shall be in accordance with 18.4.10.

7.3.4.6 Design documents shall specify the rooms and spaces that will have visible notification and those where visible notification will not be provided in accordance with 18.5.2.1.

7.3.4.7 Performance-based design alternatives for strobe design shall be in accordance with 18.5.5.6.2.

7.3.5 Detection. (SIG-IDS)

7.3.5.1 Heat-Sensing Fire Detectors. Heat detection design documentation shall be provided in accordance with Section 17.6.

7.3.5.2 Smoke-Sensing Fire Detectors. Smoke detection design documentation shall be provided in accordance with Section 17.7.

7.3.5.3 Radiant Energy-Sensing Fire Detectors. Radiant energy detection design documentation shall be provided in accordance with Section 17.8.

7.3.6 Risk Analysis Documentation. (SIG-ECS)

7.3.6.1 When a risk analysis is required to be prepared, findings and considerations of the risk analysis shall be documented.

7.3.6.2 When determined by the stakeholders, security and protection of the risk analysis documentation shall be in accordance with 7.3.7 and Section 7.7.

7.3.6.3 The risk analysis documentation shall list the various scenarios evaluated and the anticipated outcomes.

7.3.6.4 Risk analyses for mass notification systems shall be documented in accordance with 7.3.6 and 24.3.11.

7.3.7* Performance-Based Design Documentation.

7.3.7.1 Performance-based design documentation for fire detection shall be in accordance with Section 17.3. (SIG-IDS)

7.3.7.2 Performance-based design documentation for strobes shall be in accordance with 18.5.5.6.2. (SIG-NAS)

7.3.7.3 A copy of approval documentation resulting from performance-based designs shall be included with the record drawings in accordance with 7.5.6. (SIG-FUN)

7.3.8 Emergency Response Plan Documentation. (SIG-ECS)

7.3.8.1 When an emergency response plan is required to be prepared, such as for a mass notification system, findings of the plan shall be documented.

7.3.8.2 When identified by the stakeholders, security and protection of the emergency response plan documentation shall be in accordance with 7.7.3.

7.3.8.3 The emergency response plan shall document the various scenarios evaluated and the anticipated outcomes.

7.3.9 Evaluation Documentation. (SIG-FUN)

7.3.9.1* Evaluation documentation, such as identified in 23.4.3.1 and 24.4.3.24.2, shall include a signed statement(s) by the person responsible for the design attesting to the evaluation and the resultant technical decision and deeming it reliable and acceptable for the particular application.

7.3.9.2 A copy of the evaluation documentation shall be retained for the life of the system and be maintained with the documents required by 7.7.1.6.

7.4 Shop Drawings (Installation Documentation). (SIG-FUN)

7.4.1* The requirements of Section 7.4 shall apply only where required by other governing laws, codes, or standards; by other parts of this Code; or by project specifications or drawings.

7.4.2* Shop drawings shall be drawn to an indicated scale, on sheets of uniform size, with a plan of each floor.

7.4.3 Shop drawings for fire alarm and emergency communications systems shall provide basic information and shall provide the basis for the record (as-built) drawings required in accordance with 7.5.2.

7.4.4 Shop drawings shall include the following information:

(1) Name of protected premises, owner, and occupant (where applicable)
(2) Name of installer or contractor
(3) Location of protected premises
(4) Device legend and symbols in accordance with NFPA 170, or other symbols acceptable to the authority having jurisdiction
(5) Date of issue and any revision dates

7.4.5 Floor plan drawings shall be drawn to an indicated scale and shall include the following information, where applicable for the particular system:

(1) Floor or level identification
(2) Point of compass (indication of North)
(3) Graphic scale
(4) All walls and doors
(5) All partitions extending to within 15 percent of the ceiling height (where applicable and when known)
(6) Room and area descriptions
(7) System devices/component locations
(8) Locations of fire alarm primary power disconnecting means
(9) Locations of monitor/control interfaces to other systems
(10) System riser locations
(11) Type and number of system components/devices on each circuit, on each floor or level
(12) Type and quantity of conductors and conduit (if used) for each circuit
(13) Identification of any ceiling over 10 ft (3.0 m) in height where automatic fire detection is being proposed
(14) Details of ceiling geometries, including beams and solid joists, where automatic fire detection is being proposed
(15) Where known, acoustic properties of spaces

7.4.6 System riser diagrams shall be coordinated with the floor plans and shall include the following information:

(1) General arrangement of the system in building cross-section
(2) Number of risers
(3) Type and number of circuits in each riser
(4) Type and number of system components/devices on each circuit, on each floor or level
(5) Number of conductors for each circuit

7.4.7 Control unit diagrams shall be provided for all control equipment (i.e., equipment listed as either a control unit or control unit accessory), power supplies, battery chargers, and annunciators and shall include the following information:

(1) Identification of the control equipment depicted
(2) Location(s) of control equipment
(3) All field wiring terminals and terminal identifications
(4) All circuits connected to field wiring terminals and circuit identifications
(5) All indicators and manual controls
(6) Field connections to supervising station signaling equipment, releasing equipment, or emergency safety control interfaces, where provided

7.4.8 Typical wiring diagrams shall be provided for all initiating devices, notification appliances, remote indicators, annunciators, remote test stations, and end-of-line and power supervisory devices.

7.4.9* A narrative description or input/output matrix of operation shall be provided to describe the sequence of operation.

7.4.10 System calculations shall be included as follows:

(1) Battery calculations
(2) Notification appliance circuit voltage drop calculations
(3) Other required calculations, such as line resistance calculations, where required

7.5 Completion Documentation.

7.5.1* The requirements of Section 7.5 shall apply only where required by other governing laws, codes, or standards; by other parts of this Code; or by project specifications or drawings. (SIG-FUN)

7.5.2 Before requesting final approval of the installation, if required by the authority having jurisdiction, the installing contractor shall furnish a written statement stating that the system has been installed in accordance with approved plans and tested in accordance with the manufacturer's published instructions and the appropriate NFPA requirements. (SIG-FUN)

7.5.3 All systems including new systems and additions or alterations to existing systems shall include the following documentation, which shall be delivered to the owner or the owner's representative upon final acceptance of the system:

(1)*An owner's manual and manufacturer's published instructions covering all system equipment
(2) Record (as-built) drawings in accordance with 7.5.5
(3) A completed record of completion form in accordance with 7.5.6
(4) For software-based systems, record copy of the site-specific software in accordance with 7.5.7

(SIG-FUN)

7.5.4 Owner's manuals for emergency communications systems shall be in accordance with Section 24.8. (SIG-ECS)

7.5.5 Record Drawings (As-Builts). (SIG-FUN)

7.5.5.1 Record drawings shall consist of current updated and shop drawings reflecting the actual installation of all system equipment, components, and wiring.

7.5.5.2* A sequence of operations in input/output matrix or narrative form shall be provided with the record drawings to reflect actual programming at the time of completion.

7.5.5.3 Where necessary, revised calculations in accordance with 7.4.10 shall be provided depicting any changes due to installation conditions.

7.5.5.4 Record drawings shall be turned over to the owner with a copy placed inside the documentation cabinet in accordance with Section 7.7.

7.5.5.5* Record drawings shall include approval documentation resulting from variances, performance-based designs, risk analyses, and other system evaluations or variations.

7.5.6 Record of Completion. (SIG-FUN)

7.5.6.1* The record of completion shall be documented in accordance with 7.5.6 using either the record of completion forms, Figure 7.8.2(a) through Figure 7.8.2(f), or an alternative document that contains only the elements of Figure 7.8.2(a) through Figure 7.8.2(f) applicable to the installed system.

7.5.6.2* The record of completion documentation shall be completed by the installing contractor and submitted to the enforcing authority and the owner at the conclusion of the job. The record of completion documentation shall be permitted to be part of the written statement required in 7.5.2 and part of the documents that support the requirements of 7.5.8. When more than one contractor has been responsible for the installation, each contractor shall complete the portions of the documentation for which that contractor has responsibility.

7.5.6.3* The preparation of the record of completion documentation shall be the responsibility of the qualified and experienced person in accordance with 10.5.2.

7.5.6.4 The record of completion documentation shall be updated to reflect all system additions or modifications and maintained in a current condition at all times.

7.5.6.5 The updated copy of the record of completion documents shall be maintained in a documentation cabinet in accordance with 7.7.2.

7.5.6.6 Revisions.

7.5.6.6.1 All fire alarm and/or signaling system modifications made after the initial installation shall be recorded on a revised version of the original completion documents.

7.5.6.6.2 The revised record of completion document shall include a revision date.

7.5.6.6.3* Where the original or the latest overall system record of completion cannot be obtained, a new system record of completion shall be provided that documents the system configuration as discovered during the current project's scope of work.

7.5.6.7 Electronic Record of Completion.

7.5.6.7.1 Where approved by the authority having jurisdiction, the record of completion shall be permitted to be filed electronically instead of on paper.

7.5.6.7.2 If filed electronically, the record of completion document shall be accessible with standard software and shall be backed up.

7.5.7 Site-specific software documentation shall be in accordance with 14.6.1.2. (SIG-TMS)

7.5.8* Verification of Compliant Installation. (SIG-FUN)

7.5.8.1 Where required by the authority having jurisdiction, compliance of the completed installation with the requirements of this Code, as implemented via the referring code(s), specifications, and/or other criteria applicable to the specific installation, shall be certified by a qualified and impartial third-party organization acceptable to the authority having jurisdiction.

7.5.8.2 Verification of compliant installation shall be performed according to testing requirements and procedures specified in 14.4.1 and 14.4.2.

7.5.8.3 Verification shall ensure that:

(1) All components and functions are installed and operate per the approved plans and sequence of operation.
(2) All required system documentation is complete and is archived on site.
(3) For new supervising station systems, the verification shall also ascertain proper arrangement, transmission, and receipt of all signals required to be transmitted off-premises and shall meet the requirements of 14.4.1 and 14.4.2.
(4) For existing supervising station systems that are extended, modified, or reconfigured, the verification shall be required for the new work only, and reacceptance testing in accordance with Chapter 14 shall be acceptable.
(5) Written confirmation has been provided that any required corrective actions have been completed

7.5.9 Documentation of central station service shall be in accordance with 26.3.4. (SIG-SSS)

7.5.10 Documentation of remote station service shall be in accordance with 26.5.2. (SIG-SSS)

7.6 Inspection, Testing, and Maintenance Documentation. (SIG-TMS)

7.6.1 Test plan documentation shall be provided in accordance with 14.2.10.

7.6.2 Acceptance testing documentation shall be provided in accordance with 14.6.1.

7.6.3 Reacceptance test documentation shall be provided in accordance with 14.6.1.

7.6.4 Periodic inspection and testing documentation shall be provided in accordance with 14.6.2 through 14.6.4.

7.6.5 Impairment documentation shall be provided in accordance with Section 10.21.

7.6.6 Record of Inspection and Testing. The record of all inspections, testing, and maintenance as required by 14.6.2.4 shall be documented using either the record of inspection and testing forms, Figure 7.8.2(g) through Figure 7.8.2(l), or an alternative record that includes all the applicable information shown in Figure 7.8.2(g) through Figure 7.8.2(l).

7.7 Records, Record Retention, and Record Maintenance.

7.7.1 Records. (SIG-FUN)

7.7.1.1 A complete record of the tests and operations of each system shall be kept until the next test and for 1 year thereafter

unless more stringent requirements are required elsewhere in this Code.

7.7.1.2* The records shall be available for examination and, if required, reported to the authority having jurisdiction. Archiving of records by any means shall be permitted if hard copies of the records can be provided promptly when requested.

7.7.1.3 If off-premises monitoring is provided, records of all signals, tests, and operations recorded at the supervising station including public emergency alarm reporting system shall be maintained for not less than 1 year unless more stringent requirements are required elsewhere in this Code.

7.7.1.4 Required documents regarding system design and function shall be maintained for the life of the system.

7.7.1.5 Revisions and alterations to systems shall be recorded and records maintained with the original system design documents.

7.7.1.6* System documents shall be housed in the documentation cabinet as required by 7.7.2.

7.7.2 Document Accessibility. (SIG-FUN)

7.7.2.1 With every new system, a documentation cabinet shall be installed at the system control unit or at another approved location at the protected premises.

7.7.2.2* All record documentation shall be stored in the documentation cabinet.

7.7.2.3 Where the documentation cabinet is not in the same location as the system control unit, its location shall be identified at the system control unit.

7.7.2.4 The documentation cabinet shall be prominently labeled SYSTEM RECORD DOCUMENTS.

7.7.2.5 The contents of the cabinet shall be accessible by authorized personnel only.

7.7.3 Document Security. (SIG-ECS)

7.7.3.1 Security for system's documentation shall be determined by the stakeholders.

7.7.3.2* Where such documents cannot be protected from public access, it shall be permitted to remove sensitive information from record documents provided the owner retains complete documentation that will be made accessible to the authority having jurisdiction at an owner designated location.

7.8 Forms.

7.8.1 General.

7.8.1.1* The requirements of Section 7.8 shall apply only where required by other governing laws, codes, or standards; by other parts of this Code; or by project specifications or drawings. (SIG-FUN)

7.8.1.2 Where specific forms are required by other governing laws, codes, or standards; by other parts of this Code; or by project specifications or drawings, form layouts and content that differ from those in Section 7.8 shall be permitted provided that the minimum required content is included. (SIG-FUN)

7.8.2* Forms for Record of Completion, Record of Inspection and Testing, and Risk Analysis. Unless otherwise permitted or required in 7.5.6, 7.6.6, or 7.8.1.2, Figure 7.8.2(a) through Figure 7.8.2(l) shall be used to document the record of completion and record of inspection and testing. (SIG-FUN)

SYSTEM RECORD OF COMPLETION

This form is to be completed by the system installation contractor at the time of system acceptance and approval.
It shall be permitted to modify this form as needed to provide a more complete and/or clear record.
Insert N/A in all unused lines.
Attach additional sheets, data, or calculations as necessary to provide a complete record.

Form Completion Date: _____ Supplemental Pages Attached: _____

1. PROPERTY INFORMATION

Name of property: _____

Address: _____

Description of property: _____

Name of property representative: _____

Address: _____

Phone: _____ Fax: _____ E-mail: _____

2. INSTALLATION, SERVICE, TESTING, AND MONITORING INFORMATION

Installation contractor: _____

Address: _____

Phone: _____ Fax: _____ E-mail: _____

Service organization: _____

Address: _____

Phone: _____ Fax: _____ E-mail: _____

Testing organization: _____

Address: _____

Phone: _____ Fax: _____ E-mail: _____

Effective date for test and inspection contract: _____

Monitoring organization: _____

Address: _____

Phone: _____ Fax: _____ E-mail: _____

Account number: _____ Phone line 1: _____ Phone line 2: _____

Means of transmission: _____

Entity to which alarms are retransmitted: _____ Phone: _____

3. DOCUMENTATION

On-site location of the required record documents and site-specific software: _____

4. DESCRIPTION OF SYSTEM OR SERVICE

This is a: ❑ New system ❑ Modification to existing system Permit number: _____

NFPA 72 edition: _____

4.1 Control Unit

Manufacturer: _____ Model number: _____

4.2 Software and Firmware

Firmware revision number: _____

4.3 Alarm Verification   ❑ This system does not incorporate alarm verification.

Number of devices subject to alarm verification: _____ Alarm verification set for _____ seconds

NFPA 72 (p. 1 of 3)

FIGURE 7.8.2(a) System Record of Completion. (SIG-FUN)

SYSTEM RECORD OF COMPLETION *(continued)*

5. SYSTEM POWER

5.1 Control Unit

5.1.1 Primary Power

Input voltage of control panel:_____   Control panel amps:_____

Overcurrent protection: Type:_____   Amps:_____

Branch circuit disconnecting means location:_____   Number:_____

5.1.2 Secondary Power

Type of secondary power:_____

Location, if remote from the plant:_____

Calculated capacity of secondary power to drive the system:

In standby mode (hours):_____   In alarm mode (minutes):_____

5.2 Control Unit

❏ This system does not have power extender panels

❏ Power extender panels are listed on supplementary sheet A

6. CIRCUITS AND PATHWAYS

Pathway Type	Dual Media Pathway	Separate Pathway	Class	Survivability Level
Signaling Line				
Device Power				
Initiating Device				
Notification Appliance				
Other (specify):				

7. REMOTE ANNUNCIATORS

Type	Location

8. INITIATING DEVICES

Type	Quantity	Addressable or Conventional	Alarm or Supervisory	Sensing Technology
Manual Pull Stations				
Smoke Detectors				
Duct Smoke Detectors				
Heat Detectors				
Gas Detectors				
Waterflow Switches				
Tamper Switches				

© 2012 National Fire Protection Association   NFPA 72 (p. 2 of 3)

FIGURE 7.8.2(a) *Continued*

SYSTEM RECORD OF COMPLETION *(continued)*

9. NOTIFICATION APPLIANCES

Type	Quantity	Description
Audible		
Visible		
Combination Audible and Visible		

10. SYSTEM CONTROL FUNCTIONS

Type	Quantity
Hold-Open Door Releasing Devices	
HVAC Shutdown	
Fire/Smoke Dampers	
Door Unlocking	
Elevator Recall	
Elevator Shunt Trip	

11. INTERCONNECTED SYSTEMS

❏ This system does not have interconnected systems.

❏ Interconnected systems are listed on supplementary sheet _____ .

12. CERTIFICATION AND APPROVALS

12.1 System Installation Contractor

This system as specified herein has been installed according to all NFPA standards cited herein.

Signed: _____ Printed name: _____ Date: _____

Organization:_____ Title: _____ Phone: _____

12.2 System Operational Test

This system as specified herein has tested according to all NFPA standards cited herein.

Signed: _____ Printed name: _____ Date: _____

Organization:_____ Title: _____ Phone: _____

12.3 Acceptance Test

Date and time of acceptance test:_____

Installing contractor representative: _____

Testing contractor representative: _____

Property representative: _____

AHJ representative: _____

NFPA 72 (p. 3 of 3)

FIGURE 7.8.2(a) *Continued*

EMERGENCY COMMUNICATIONS SYSTEMS
SUPPLEMENTARY RECORD OF COMPLETION

This form is a supplement to the System Record of Completion. It includes systems and components specific to emergency communications systems.
This form is to be completed by the system installation contractor at the time of system acceptance and approval. It shall be permitted to modify this form as needed to provide a more complete and/or clear record. Insert N/A in all unused lines.

Form Completion Date: _____ Number of Supplemental Pages Attached: _____

1. PROPERTY INFORMATION

Name of property: _____

Address: _____

2. DESCRIPTION OF SYSTEM OR SERVICE

❏ Fire alarm with in-building fire emergency voice alarm communication system (EVAC)

❏ Mass notification system

❏ Combination system, with the following components:

    ❏ Fire alarm   ❏ EVACS   ❏ MNS   ❏ Two-way, in-building, emergency communications system

❏ Other (specify): _____

NFPA 72 edition: _____ Additional description of system(s): _____

_____

2.1 In-Building Fire Emergency Voice Alarm Communications System

Manufacturer: _____ Model number: _____

Number of single voice alarm channels: _____ Number of multiple voice alarm channels: _____

Number of speakers: _____ Number of speaker circuits: _____

Location of amplification and sound processing equipment: _____

_____

_____

Location of paging microphone stations:

Location 1: _____

Location 2: _____

Location 3: _____

2.2 Mass Notification System

2.2.1 System Type:

❏ In-building MNS–combination

❏ In-building MNS   ❏ Wide-area MNS   ❏ Distributed recipient MNS

❏ Other (specify): _____

NFPA 72 (p. 1 of 3)

FIGURE 7.8.2(b) Emergency Communications System Supplementary Record of Completion. (SIG-FUN)

EMERGENCY COMMUNICATIONS SYSTEMS
SUPPLEMENTARY RECORD OF COMPLETION *(continued)*

2. DESCRIPTION OF SYSTEM OR SERVICE *(continued)*

2.2.2 System Features:

❏ Combination fire alarm/MNS   ❏ MNS autonomous control unit   ❏ Wide-area MNS to regional national alerting interface

❏ Local operating console (LOC)   ❏ Distributed-recipient MNS (DRMNS)   ❏ Wide-area MNS to DRMNS interface

❏ Wide-area MNS to high power speaker array (HPSA) interface   ❏ In-building MNS to wide-area MNS interface

❏ Other (specify): _____

2.2.3 MNS Local Operating Consoles

Location 1: _____

Location 2: _____

Location 3: _____

2.2.4 High Power Speaker Arrays

Number of HPSA speaker initiation zones: _____

Location 1: _____

Location 2: _____

Location 3: _____

2.2.5 Mass Notification Devices

Combination fire alarm/MNS visual devices: _____   MNS-only visual devices: _____

Textual signs: _____   Other (describe): _____

Supervision class: _____

2.2.6 Special Hazard Notification

❏ This system does not have special suppression predischarge notification.

❏ MNS systems DO NOT override notification appliances required to provide special suppression predischarge notification.

3. TWO-WAY EMERGENCY COMMUNICATIONS SYSTEMS

3.1 Telephone System

Number of telephone jacks installed: _____   Number of warden stations installed: _____

Number of telephone handsets stored on site: _____

Type of telephone system installed: ❏ Electrically powered   ❏ Sound powered

3.2 Two-Way Radio Communications Enhancement System

Percentage of area covered by two-way radio service: Critical areas _____ %   General building areas _____ %

Amplification component locations: _____

_____

Inbound signal strength _____ dBm   Outbound signal strength _____ dBm

Donor antenna isolation is _____ dB above the signal booster gain.

Radio frequencies covered: _____

Radio system monitor panel location: _____

      NFPA 72 (p. 2 of 3)

FIGURE 7.8.2(b) *Continued*

EMERGENCY COMMUNICATIONS SYSTEMS
SUPPLEMENTARY RECORD OF COMPLETION *(continued)*

3. TWO-WAY EMERGENCY COMMUNICATIONS SYSTEMS *(continued)*

3.3 Area of Refuge (Area of Rescue Assistance) Emergency Communications Systems

Number of stations: _____   Location of central control point: _____

Days and hours when central control point is attended: _____

Location of alternate control point: _____

Days and hours when alternate control point is attended: _____

3.4 Elevator Emergency Communications Systems

Number of elevators with stations: _____   Location of central control point: _____

Days and hours when central control point is attended: _____

Location of alternate control point: _____

Days and hours when alternate control point is attended: _____

3.5 Other Two-Way Communications System

Describe: _____

4. CONTROL FUNCTIONS

This system activates the following control functions specific to emergency communications systems:

Type	Quantity
Mass Notification Override of Alarm Signaling Systems or Appliances	

See Main System Record of Completion for additional information, certifications, and approvals.

NFPA 72 (p. 3 of 3)

FIGURE 7.8.2(b) *Continued*

POWER SYSTEMS
SUPPLEMENTARY RECORD OF COMPLETION

This form is a supplement to the System Record of Completion. It includes systems and components specific to power systems that incorporate generators, UPS systems, remote battery systems, or other complex power systems. This form is to be completed by the system installation contractor at the time of system acceptance and approval. It shall be permitted to modify this form as needed to provide a more complete and/or clear record. Insert N/A in all unused lines.

Form Completion Date: _____ Number of Supplemental Pages Attached: _____

1. PROPERTY INFORMATION

Name of property: _____

Address: _____

2. SYSTEM POWER

2.1 Control Unit

2.1.1 Primary Power

Input voltage of control panel: _____ Control panel amps: _____

Overcurrent protection: Type: _____ Amps: _____

Location (of primary supply panelboard): _____

Disconnecting means location: _____

2.1.2 Engine-Driven Generator

Location of generator: _____

Location of fuel storage: _____ Type of fuel: _____

2.1.3 Uninterruptible Power System

Equipment powered by UPS system: _____

Location of UPS system: _____

Calculated capacity of UPS batteries to drive the system components connected to it:

In standby mode (hours): _____ In alarm mode (minutes): _____

2.1.4 Batteries

Location: _____ Type: _____ Nominal voltage: _____ Amp/hour rating: _____

Calculated capacity of batteries to drive the system:

In standby mode (hours): _____ In alarm mode (minutes): _____

2.2 In-Building Fire Emergency Voice Alarm Communications System or Mass Notification System

2.2.1 Primary Power

Input voltage of EVACS or MNS panel: _____ EVACS or MNS panel amps: _____

Overcurrent protection: Type: _____ Amps: _____

Location (of primary supply panelboard): _____

Disconnecting means location: _____

NFPA 72 (p. 1 of 2)

FIGURE 7.8.2(c) Power Systems Supplementary Record of Completion. (SIG-FUN)

POWER SYSTEMS
SUPPLEMENTARY RECORD OF COMPLETION *(continued)*

2. SYSTEM POWER *(continued)*

2.2.2 Engine-Driven Generator

Location of generator:_____

Location of fuel storage:_____   Type of fuel:_____

2.2.3 Uninterruptible Power System

Equipment powered by UPS system: _____

Location of UPS system:_____

Calculated capacity of UPS batteries to drive the system components connected to it:

In standby mode (hours):_____   In alarm mode (minutes):_____

2.2.4 Batteries

Location:_____   Type:_____   Nominal voltage:_____   Amp/hour rating:_____

Calculated capacity of batteries to drive the system:

In standby mode (hours):_____   In alarm mode (minutes):_____

2.3 Notification Appliance Power Extender Panels

❏ This system does not have power extender panels.

2.3.1 Primary Power

Input voltage of power extender panel(s): _____   Power extender panel amps:_____

Overcurrent protection: Type:_____   Amps:_____

Location (of primary supply panelboard): _____

Disconnecting means location: _____

2.3.2 Engine Driven Generator

Location of generator:_____

Location of fuel storage:_____   Type of fuel:_____

2.3.3 Uninterruptible Power System

Equipment powered by UPS system: _____

Location of UPS system:_____

Calculated capacity of UPS batteries to drive the system components connected to it:

In standby mode (hours):_____   In alarm mode (minutes):_____

2.3.4 Batteries

Location:_____   Type:_____   Nominal voltage:_____   Amp/hour rating:_____

Calculated capacity of batteries to drive the system:

In standby mode (hours):_____   In alarm mode (minutes):_____

See Main System Record of Completion for additional information, certifications, and approvals.

© 2012 National Fire Protection Association   NFPA 72 (p. 2 of 2)

FIGURE 7.8.2(c) *Continued*

NOTIFICATION APPLIANCE POWER PANEL
SUPPLEMENTARY RECORD OF COMPLETION

This form is a supplement to the System Record of Completion. It includes a list of types and locations
of notification appliance power extender panels.
This form is to be completed by the system installation contractor at the time of system acceptance and approval.
It shall be permitted to modify this form as needed to provide a more complete and/or clear record.
Insert N/A in all unused lines.

Form Completion Date: _____   Number of Supplemental Pages Attached: _____

1. PROPERTY INFORMATION

Name of property: _____

Address: _____

2. NOTIFICATION APPLIANCE POWER EXTENDER PANELS

Make and Model	Location	Area Served	Power Source

See Main System Record of Completion for additional information, certifications, and approvals.

© 2012 National Fire Protection Association   NFPA 72

FIGURE 7.8.2(d) Notification Appliance Power Panel Supplementary Record of Completion. (SIG-FUN)

INTERCONNECTED SYSTEMS
SUPPLEMENTARY RECORD OF COMPLETION

This form is a supplement to the System Record of Completion. It includes a list of types and locations
of systems that are interconnected to the main system.
This form is to be completed by the system installation contractor at the time of system acceptance and approval.
It shall be permitted to modify this form as needed to provide a more complete and/or clear record.
Insert N/A in all unused lines.

Form Completion Date: _____   Number of Supplemental Pages Attached: _____

1. PROPERTY INFORMATION

Name of property: _____

Address: _____

2. INTERCONNECTED SYSTEMS

Description	Location	Purpose

See Main System Record of Completion for additional information, certifications, and approvals.

NFPA 72

FIGURE 7.8.2(e)   Interconnected Systems Supplementary Record of Completion. (SIG-FUN)

DEVIATIONS FROM ADOPTED CODES AND STANDARDS
SUPPLEMENTARY RECORD OF COMPLETION

This form is a supplement to the System Record of Completion. It enables the designer and/or installer
to document and justify deviations from accepted codes or standards.
This form is to be completed by the system installation contractor at the time of system acceptance and approval.
It shall be permitted to modify this form as needed to provide a more complete and/or clear record.
Insert N/A in all unused lines.

Form Completion Date: _____   Number of Supplemental Pages Attached: _____

1. PROPERTY INFORMATION

Name of property: _____

Address: _____

2. DEVIATIONS FROM ADOPTED CODES OR STANDARDS

Description	Purpose

See Main System Record of Completion for additional information, certifications, and approvals.

© 2012 National Fire Protection Association   NFPA 72

FIGURE 7.8.2(f) Deviations from Adopted Codes and Standards Supplementary Record of Completion. (SIG-FUN)

SYSTEM RECORD OF INSPECTION AND TESTING

This form is to be completed by the system inspection and testing contractor at the time of a system test.
It shall be permitted to modify this form as needed to provide a more complete and/or clear record.
Insert N/A in all unused lines.
Attach additional sheets, data, or calculations as necessary to provide a complete record.

Inspection/Test Start Date/Time: _____   Inspection/Test Completion Date/Time: _____

Supplemental Form(s) Attached: _____ (yes/no)

1. PROPERTY INFORMATION

Name of property: _____

Address: _____

Description of property: _____

Name of property representative: _____

Address: _____

Phone: _____   Fax: _____   E-mail: _____

2. TESTING AND MONITORING INFORMATION

Testing organization: _____

Address: _____

Phone: _____   Fax: _____   E-mail: _____

Monitoring organization: _____

Address: _____

Phone: _____   Fax: _____   E-mail: _____

Account number: _____   Phone line 1: _____   Phone line 2: _____

Means of transmission: _____

Entity to which alarms are retransmitted: _____   Phone: _____

3. DOCUMENTATION

Onsite location of the required record documents and site-specific software: _____

4. DESCRIPTION OF SYSTEM OR SERVICE

4.1 Control Unit

Manufacturer: _____   Model number: _____

4.2 Software Firmware

Firmware revision number: _____

4.3 System Power

4.3.1 Primary (Main) Power

Nominal voltage: _____   Amps: _____   Location: _____

Overcurrent protection type: _____   Amps: _____   Disconnecting means location: _____

         NFPA 72 (p. 1 of 4)

FIGURE 7.8.2(g) System Record of Inspection and Testing. (SIG-TMS)

SYSTEM RECORD OF INSPECTION AND TESTING *(continued)*

4. DESCRIPTION OF SYSTEM OR SERVICE *(continued)*

4.3.2 Secondary Power

Type: _____ Location: _____

Battery type (if applicable): _____

Calculated capacity of batteries to drive the system:

In standby mode (hours): _____ In alarm mode (minutes): _____

5. NOTIFICATIONS MADE PRIOR TO TESTING

Monitoring organization   Contact: _____   Time: _____

Building management   Contact: _____   Time: _____

Building occupants   Contact: _____   Time: _____

Authority having jurisdiction   Contact: _____   Time: _____

Other, if required   Contact: _____   Time: _____

6. TESTING RESULTS

6.1 Control Unit and Related Equipment

Description	Visual Inspection	Functional Test	Comments
Control unit	❑	❑	
Lamps/LEDs/LCDs	❑	❑	
Fuses	❑	❑	
Trouble signals	❑	❑	
Disconnect switches	❑	❑	
Ground-fault monitoring	❑	❑	
Supervision	❑	❑	
Local annunciator	❑	❑	
Remote annunciators	❑	❑	
Remote power panels	❑	❑	
	❑	❑	

6.2 Secondary Power

Description	Visual Inspection	Functional Test	Comments
Battery condition	❑	❑	
Load voltage	❑	❑	
Discharge test	❑	❑	
Charger test	❑	❑	
Remote panel batteries	❑	❑	

     NFPA 72 (p. 2 of 4)

FIGURE 7.8.2(g) *Continued*

SYSTEM RECORD OF INSPECTION AND TESTING *(continued)*

6. TESTING RESULTS *(continued)*

6.3 Alarm and Supervisory Alarm Initiating Device

Attach supplementary device test sheets for all initiating devices.

6.4 Notification Appliances

Attach supplementary appliance test sheets for all notification appliances.

6.5 Interface Equipment

Attach supplementary interface component test sheets for all interface components.

Circuit Interface / Signaling Line Circuit Interface / Fire Alarm Control Interface

6.6 Supervising Station Monitoring

Description	Yes	No	Time	Comments
Alarm signal	❏	❏		
Alarm restoration	❏	❏		
Trouble signal	❏	❏		
Trouble restoration	❏	❏		
Supervisory signal	❏	❏		
Supervisory restoration	❏	❏		

6.7 Public Emergency Alarm Reporting System

Description	Yes	No	Time	Comments
Alarm signal	❏	❏		
Alarm restoration	❏	❏		
Trouble signal	❏	❏		
Trouble restoration	❏	❏		
Supervisory signal	❏	❏		
Supervisory restoration	❏	❏		

FIGURE 7.8.2(g) *Continued*

SYSTEM RECORD OF INSPECTION AND TESTING *(continued)*

7. NOTIFICATIONS THAT TESTING IS COMPLETE

Monitoring organization   Contact: _____   Time: _____

Building management   Contact: _____   Time: _____

Building occupants   Contact: _____   Time: _____

Authority having jurisdiction   Contact: _____   Time: _____

Other, if required   Contact: _____   Time: _____

8. SYSTEM RESTORED TO NORMAL OPERATION

Date: _____   Time: _____

9. CERTIFICATION

This system as specified herein has been inspected and tested according to NFPA 72, 2013 edition, Chapter 14.

Signed: _____   Printed name: _____   Date: _____

Organization: _____   Title: _____   Phone: _____

Qualifications (refer to 10.5.3): _____

10. DEFECTS OR MALFUNCTIONS NOT CORRECTED AT CONCLUSION OF SYSTEM INSPECTION, TESTING, OR MAINTENANCE

_____

_____

_____

_____

_____

_____

_____

_____

_____

_____

_____

_____

_____

_____

_____

_____

_____

_____

10.1 Acceptance by Owner or Owner's Representative:

The undersigned accepted the test report for the system as specified herein:

Signed: _____   Printed name: _____   Date: _____

Organization: _____   Title: _____   Phone: _____

      NFPA 72 (p. 4 of 4)

FIGURE 7.8.2(g) *Continued*

NOTIFICATION APPLIANCE
SUPPLEMENTARY RECORD OF INSPECTION AND TESTING

This form is a supplement to the System Record of Inspection and Testing.
It includes a notification appliance test record.
This form is to be completed by the system inspection and testing contractor at the time of the inspection and/or test.
It shall be permitted to modify this form as needed to provide a more complete and/or clear record.
Insert N/A in all unused lines.

Inspection/Test Start Date/Time: _____   Inspection/Test Completion Date/Time: _____

Number of Supplemental Pages Attached: _____

1. PROPERTY INFORMATION

Name of property: _____

Address: _____

2. NOTIFICATION APPLIANCE TEST RESULTS

Appliance Type	Location/Identifier	Test Results

NFPA 72 (p. 1 of 2)

FIGURE 7.8.2(h) Notification Appliance Supplementary Record of Inspection and Testing. (SIG-TMS)

NOTIFICATION APPLIANCE
SUPPLEMENTARY RECORD OF INSPECTION AND TESTING *(continued)*

2. NOTIFICATION APPLIANCE TEST RESULTS *(continued)*

Appliance Type	Location/Identifier	Test Results

See main System Record of Inspection and Testing for additional information, certifications, and approvals.

NFPA 72 (p. 2 of 2)

FIGURE 7.8.2(h) *Continued*

INITIATING DEVICE
SUPPLEMENTARY RECORD OF INSPECTION AND TESTING

This form is a supplement to the System Record of Inspection and Testing.
It includes an initiating device test record.
This form is to be completed by the system inspection and testing contractor at the time of the inspection and/or test.
It shall be permitted to modify this form as needed to provide a more complete and/or clear record.
Insert N/A in all unused lines.

Inspection/Test Start Date/Time: _____   Inspection/Test Completion Date/Time: _____

Number of Supplemental Pages Attached: _____

1. PROPERTY INFORMATION

Name of property: _____

Address: _____

2. INITIATING DEVICE TEST RESULTS

Device Type	Address	Location	Test Results

NFPA 72 (p. 1 of 2)

FIGURE 7.8.2(i)   Initiating Device Supplementary Record of Inspection and Testing. (SIG-TMS)

INITIATING DEVICE
SUPPLEMENTARY RECORD OF INSPECTION AND TESTING *(continued)*

2. INITIATING DEVICE TEST RESULTS *(continued)*

Device Type	Address	Location	Test Results

See main System Record of Inspection and Testing for additional information, certifications, and approvals.

© 2012 National Fire Protection Association

NFPA 72 (p. 2 of 2)

FIGURE 7.8.2(i) *Continued*

MASS NOTIFICATION SYSTEM
SUPPLEMENTARY RECORD OF INSPECTION AND TESTING

This form is a supplement to the System Record of Inspection and Testing.
It includes a mass notification system test record.
This form is to be completed by the system inspection and testing contractor at the time of the inspection and/or test.
It shall be permitted to modify this form as needed to provide a more complete and/or clear record.
Insert N/A in all unused lines.

Inspection/Test Start Date/Time: _____   Inspection/Test Completion Date/Time: _____

Number of Supplemental Pages Attached: _____

1. PROPERTY INFORMATION

Name of property: _____

Address: _____

2. MASS NOTIFICATION SYSTEM

2.1 System Type

❑ In-building MNS—combination

❑ In-building MNS—stand alone   ❑ Wide-area MNS   ❑ Distributed recipient MNS

❑ Other (specify): _____

2.2 System Features

❑ Combination fire alarm/MNS   ❑ MNS ACU only   ❑ Wide-area MNS to regional national alerting interface

❑ Local operating console (LOC)   ❑ Direct recipient MNS (DRMNS)   ❑ Wide-area MNS to DRMNS interface

❑ Wide-area MNS to high-power speaker array (HPSA) interface   ❑ In-building MNS to wide-area MNS interface

❑ Other (specify): _____

3. IN-BUILDING MASS NOTIFICATION SYSTEM

3.1 Primary Power

Input voltage of MNS panel: _____   MNS panel amps: _____

3.2 Engine-Driven Generator   ❑ This system does not have a generator.

Location of generator: _____

Location of fuel storage: _____   Type of fuel: _____

3.3 Uninterruptible Power System   ❑ This system does not have a UPS.

Equipment powered by a UPS system: _____

Location of UPS system: _____

Calculated capacity of UPS batteries to drive the system components connected to it:

In standby mode (hours): _____   In alarm mode (minutes): _____

3.4 Batteries

Location: Type: _____   Nominal voltage: _____   Amp/hour rating: _____

Calculated capacity of batteries to drive the system:

In standby mode (hours): _____   In alarm mode (minutes): _____

❑ Batteries are marked with date of manufacture.

NFPA 72 (p. 1 of 2)

FIGURE 7.8.2(j)   Mass Notification System Supplementary Record of Inspection and Testing. (SIG-TMS)

MASS NOTIFICATION SYSTEM
SUPPLEMENTARY RECORD OF INSPECTION AND TESTING *(continued)*

4. MASS NOTIFICATION EQUIPMENT TEST RESULTS

Description	Visual Inspection	Functional Test	Comments
Functional test			
Reset/power down test			
Fuses			
Primary power supply			
UPS power test			
Trouble signals			
Disconnect switches			
Ground-fault monitoring			
CCU security mechanism			
Prerecorded message content			
Prerecorded message activation			
Software backup performed			
Test backup software			
Fire alarm to MNS interface			
MNS to fire alarm interface			
In-building MNS to wide-area MNS			
MNS to direct recipient MNS			
Sound pressure levels Occupied ❏ Yes ❏ No Ambient dBA:_____ Alarm dBA:_____ (attach supplementary notification appliance form(s) with locations, values, and weather conditions)			
System intelligibility Test method:_____ Score:_____ CIS value:_____ (attach supplementary notification appliance form(s) with locations, values, and weather conditions)			
Other (specify):			

See main System Record of Inspection and Testing for additional information, certifications, and approvals.

NFPA 72 (p. 2 of 2)

FIGURE 7.8.2(j) *Continued*

EMERGENCY COMMUNICATIONS SYSTEMS
SUPPLEMENTARY RECORD OF INSPECTION AND TESTING

This form is a supplement to the System Record of Inspection and Testing.
It includes systems and components specific to emergency communication systems.
This form is to be completed by the system inspection and testing contractor at the time of the inspection and/or test.
It shall be permitted to modify this form as needed to provide a more complete and/or clear record.
Insert N/A in all unused lines.

Inspection/Test Start Date/Time: _____　　　Inspection/Test Completion Date/Time: _____

Number of Supplemental Pages Attached: _____

1. PROPERTY INFORMATION

Name of property: _____

Address: _____

2. DESCRIPTION OF SYSTEM OR SERVICE

❏ Fire alarm with in-building fire emergency voice alarm communication system (EVAC)

❏ Mass notification system

❏ Combination system, with the following components:

　❏ Fire alarm　　❏ EVACS　　❏ MNS　　❏ Two-way, in-building, emergency communication system

❏ Other (specify): _____

Additional description of system(s): _____

_____

2.1 In-Building Fire Emergency Voice Alarm Communication System

Manufacturer: _____　　Model number: _____

Number of single voice alarm channels: _____　　Number of multiple voice alarm channels: _____

Number of speakers: _____　　Number of speaker circuits: _____

Location of amplification and sound processing equipment: _____

_____

_____

Location of paging microphone stations:

Location 1: _____

Location 2: _____

Location 3: _____

2.2 Mass Notification System

2.2.1 System Type:

❏ In-building MNS—combination

❏ In-building MNS　　❏ Wide-area MNS　　❏ Distributed recipient MNS

❏ Other (specify): _____

　　　　　　　　　　　　　　　　　　NFPA 72 (p. 1 of 5)

FIGURE 7.8.2(k)　Emergency Communications Systems Supplementary Record of Inspection and Testing. (SIG-TMS)

EMERGENCY COMMUNICATIONS SYSTEMS
SUPPLEMENTARY RECORD OF INSPECTION AND TESTING *(continued)*

2. DESCRIPTION OF SYSTEM OR SERVICE *(continued)*

2.2.2 System Features:

❏ Combination fire alarm/MNS   ❏ MNS autonomous control unit   ❏ Wide-area MNS to regional national alerting interface

❏ Local operating console (LOC)   ❏ Distributed-recipient MNS (DRMNS)   ❏ Wide-area MNS to DRMNS interface

❏ Wide-area MNS to high-power speaker array (HPSA) interface   ❏ In-building MNS to wide-area MNS interface

❏ Other (specify): _____

2.2.3 MNS Local Operating Consoles

Location 1: _____

Location 2: _____

Location 3: _____

2.2.4 High-Power Speaker Arrays

Number of HPSA speaker initiation zones: _____

Location 1: _____

Location 2: _____

Location 3: _____

2.2.5 Mass Notification Devices

Combination fire alarm/MNS visual devices: _____   MNS-only visual devices: _____

Textual signs: _____   Other (describe): _____

Supervision class: _____

2.2.6 Special Hazard Notification

❏ This system does not have special suppression pre-discharge notification

❏ MNS systems DO NOT override notification appliances required to provide special suppression pre-discharge notification

3. TWO-WAY EMERGENCY COMMUNICATION SYSTEMS

3.1 Telephone System

Number of telephone jacks installed: _____   Number of warden stations installed: _____

Number of telephone handsets stored on site: _____

Type of telephone system installed: ❏ Electrically powered   ❏ Sound powered

3.2 Two-Way Radio Communications Enhancement System

Percentage of area covered by two-way radio service: Critical areas _____ %   General building areas _____ %

Amplification component locations: _____

_____

Inbound signal strength _____ dBm   Outbound signal strength _____ dBm

Donor antenna isolation is _____ dB above the signal booster gain

Radio frequencies covered: _____

Radio system monitor panel location: _____

NFPA 72 (p. 2 of 5)

FIGURE 7.8.2(k)   *Continued*

EMERGENCY COMMUNICATIONS SYSTEMS
SUPPLEMENTARY RECORD OF INSPECTION AND TESTING *(continued)*

3. TWO-WAY EMERGENCY COMMUNICATIONS SYSTEMS *(continued)*

3.3 Area of Refuge (Area of Rescue Assistance) Emergency Communications Systems

Number of stations:_____ Location of central control point:_____

Days and hours when central control point is attended:_____

Location of alternate control point:_____

Days and hours when alternate control point is attended:_____

3.4 Elevator Emergency Communications Systems

Number of elevators with stations:_____ Location of central control point:_____

Days and hours when central control point is attended:_____

Location of alternate control point:_____

Days and hours when alternate control point is attended:_____

3.5 Other Two-Way Communication System

Describe:_____

4. TESTING RESULTS

4.1 Control Unit and Related Equipment

Description	Visual Inspection	Functional Test	Comments
Control unit	❏	❏	
Lamps/LEDs/LCDs	❏	❏	
Fuses	❏	❏	
Trouble signals	❏	❏	
Disconnect switches	❏	❏	
Ground fault monitoring	❏	❏	
Supervision	❏	❏	
Local annunciator	❏	❏	
Remote annunciators	❏	❏	
Remote power panels	❏	❏	
Other:	❏	❏	

4.2 Secondary Power

Description	Visual Inspection	Functional Test	Comments
Battery condition	❏	❏	
Load voltage	❏	❏	
Discharge test	❏	❏	
Charger test	❏	❏	
Remote panel batteries	❏	❏	

NFPA 72 (p. 3 of 5)

FIGURE 7.8.2(k) *Continued*

EMERGENCY COMMUNICATIONS SYSTEMS
SUPPLEMENTARY RECORD OF INSPECTION AND TESTING *(continued)*

4. TESTING RESULTS *(continued)*

4.3 Emergency Communications Equipment

Description	Visual Inspection	Functional Test	Comments
Control unit	❏	❏	
Lamps/LEDs/LCDs	❏	❏	
Fuses	❏	❏	
Secondary power supply	❏	❏	
Trouble signals	❏	❏	
Disconnect switches	❏	❏	
Ground fault monitoring	❏	❏	
Panel supervision	❏	❏	
System performance	❏	❏	
System audibility	❏	❏	
System intelligibility	❏	❏	
Other:	❏	❏	

4.4 Mass Notification Equipment

Description	Visual Inspection	Functional Test	Comments
Functional test	❏	❏	
Reset/Power down test	❏	❏	
Fuses	❏	❏	
Primary power supply	❏	❏	
UPS power test	❏	❏	
Trouble signals	❏	❏	
Disconnect switches	❏	❏	
Ground fault monitoring	❏	❏	
CCU security mechanism	❏	❏	
Prerecorded message content	❏	❏	
Prerecorded message activation	❏	❏	
Software backup performed	❏	❏	
Test backup software	❏	❏	
Fire alarm to MNS Interface	❏	❏	
MNS to fire alarm interface	❏	❏	
In-building MNS to wide-area MNS	❏	❏	
MNS to direct recipient MNS	❏	❏	

FIGURE 7.8.2(k) *Continued*

**EMERGENCY COMMUNICATIONS SYSTEMS
SUPPLEMENTARY RECORD OF INSPECTION AND TESTING** *(continued)*

4. TESTING RESULTS *(continued)*

4.4 Mass Notification Equipment *(continued)*

Description	Visual Inspection	Functional Test	Comments
Sound pressure levels (attach report with locations, values, and weather conditions)	❏	❏	
System intelligibility ❏ CSI ❏ STI (attach report with locations, values, and weather conditions)	❏	❏	
Other:	❏	❏	

4.5 Two-Way Communication Equipment

Description	Visual Inspection	Functional Test	Comments
Phone handsets	❏	❏	
Phone jacks	❏	❏	
Off-hook indicator	❏	❏	
Call-in signal	❏	❏	
System performance	❏	❏	
System audibility	❏	❏	
System intelligibility	❏	❏	
Other:	❏	❏	

See main System Record of Inspection and Testing for additional information, certifications, and approvals.

NFPA 72 (p. 5 of 5)

FIGURE 7.8.2(k) *Continued*

INTERFACE COMPONENT
SUPPLEMENTARY RECORD OF INSPECTION AND TESTING

This form is a supplement to the System Record of Inspection and Testing.
It includes an interface component test record for circuit interfaces, signaling line circuit interfaces, and fire alarm control interfaces.
This form is to be completed by the system inspection and testing contractor at the time of the inspection and/or test.
It shall be permitted to modify this form as needed to provide a more complete and/or clear record.
Insert N/A in all unused lines.

Inspection/Test Start Date/Time: _____   Inspection/Test Completion Date/Time: _____

Number of Supplemental Pages Attached: _____

1. PROPERTY INFORMATION

Name of property: _____

Address: _____

2. INTERFACE COMPONENT TEST RESULTS

Interface Component Type	Address	Location	Test Results

NFPA 72 (p. 1 of 2)

FIGURE 7.8.2(l) Interface Component Supplementary Record of Inspection and Testing. (SIG-TMS)

INTERFACE COMPONENT
SUPPLEMENTARY RECORD OF INSPECTION AND TESTING *(continued)*

2. INTERFACE COMPONENT TEST RESULTS *(continued)*

Interface Component Type	Address	Location	Test Results

See main System Record of Inspection and Testing for additional information, certifications, and approvals.

© 2012 National Fire Protection Association

NFPA 72 (p. 2 of 2)

FIGURE 7.8.2(l) *Continued*

Chapter 8 Reserved

Chapter 9 Reserved

Chapter 10 Fundamentals

10.1 Application.

10.1.1 The basic functions of a complete fire alarm and/or signaling system shall comply with the requirements of this chapter.

10.1.2 The requirements of this chapter shall apply to systems, equipment, and components addressed in Chapters 12, 14, 17, 18, 21, 23, 24, 26, and 27.

10.1.3 The requirements of Chapter 7 shall apply where referenced in Chapter 10.

10.2 Purpose. The purpose of fire alarm and signaling systems shall be primarily to provide notification of alarm, supervisory, and trouble conditions; to alert the occupants; to summon aid; and to control emergency control functions.

10.3 Equipment.

10.3.1 Equipment constructed and installed in conformity with this Code shall be listed for the purpose for which it is used.

10.3.2 System components shall be installed, tested, inspected, and maintained in accordance with the manufacturer's published instructions and this Code.

10.3.3* All devices and appliances that receive their power from the initiating device circuit or signaling line circuit of a control unit shall be listed for use with the control unit.

10.3.4 All apparatus requiring rewinding or resetting to maintain normal operation shall be restored to normal as promptly as possible after each abnormal condition and maintained in normal condition for operation.

10.3.5 Equipment shall be designed so that it is capable of performing its intended functions under the following conditions:

(1)*At 85 percent and at 110 percent of the nameplate primary (main) and secondary (standby) input voltage(s)
(2) At ambient temperatures of 0°C (32°F) and 49°C (120°F)
(3) At a relative humidity of 85 percent and an ambient temperature of 30°C (86°F)

10.4 Installation and Design.

10.4.1* All systems shall be installed in accordance with the specifications and standards approved by the authority having jurisdiction.

10.4.2 Devices and appliances shall be located and mounted so that accidental operation or failure is not caused by vibration or jarring.

10.4.3 Equipment shall be installed in locations where conditions do not exceed the voltage, temperature, and humidity limits specified in the manufacturer's published instructions.

10.4.4* In areas that are not continuously occupied, automatic smoke detection shall be provided at the location of each fire alarm control unit(s), notification appliance circuit power extenders, and supervising station transmitting equipment to provide notification of fire at that location.

Exception: Where ambient conditions prohibit installation of automatic smoke detection, automatic heat detection shall be permitted.

10.4.5 Initiating Devices.

10.4.5.1 Initiating devices of the manual or automatic type shall be selected and installed so as to minimize nuisance and unintentional alarms.

10.4.5.2 Initiating devices shall comply with the requirements of Chapter 17 and Chapter 23.

10.4.5.3 All manual alarms shall be initiated by means of a listed manual fire alarm box or by means that is key operated or located within a locked cabinet or arranged to provide equivalent protection against unauthorized use.

10.5 Personnel Qualifications.

10.5.1 System Designer.

10.5.1.1 Fire alarm system and emergency communications system plans and specifications shall be developed in accordance with this Code by persons who are experienced in the proper design, application, installation, and testing of the systems.

10.5.1.2 State or local licensure regulations shall be followed to determine qualified personnel. Depending on state or local licensure regulations, qualified personnel shall include, but not be limited to, one or more of the following:

(1) Personnel who are registered, licensed, or certified by a state or local authority
(2) Personnel who are certified by a nationally recognized certification organization acceptable to the authority having jurisdiction
(3) Personnel who are factory trained and certified for fire alarm system design and/or emergency communication system design of the specific type and brand of system and who are acceptable to the authority having jurisdiction

10.5.1.3 The system designer shall be identified on the system design documents.

10.5.1.4 The system designer shall provide evidence of their qualifications and/or certifications when required by the authority having jurisdiction.

10.5.2 System Installer.

10.5.2.1 Fire alarm systems and emergency communications systems installation personnel shall be qualified or shall be supervised by persons who are qualified in the installation, inspection, and testing of the systems.

10.5.2.2 State or local licensure regulations shall be followed to determine qualified personnel. Depending on state or local licensure regulations, qualified personnel shall include, but not be limited to, one or more of the following:

(1) Personnel who are registered, licensed, or certified by a state or local authority
(2) Personnel who are certified by a nationally recognized certification organization acceptable to the authority having jurisdiction
(3) Personnel who are factory trained and certified for fire alarm system installation and/or emergency communications system installation of the specific type and brand of system and who are acceptable to the authority having jurisdiction

10.5.2.3 The system installer shall provide evidence of their qualifications and/or certifications when requested by the authority having jurisdiction.

10.5.3* Inspection, Testing, and Service Personnel. (SIG-TMS) Personnel, either individually or through their affiliation with an organization that is registered, licensed, or certified by a state or local authority, shall be recognized as qualified and experienced in the inspection, testing, and maintenance of systems addressed within the scope of this Code.

10.5.3.1* Inspection Personnel. Inspections shall be performed by personnel who have developed competence through training and experience acceptable to the authority having jurisdiction or meet the requirement of 10.5.3.3.

10.5.3.2* Testing Personnel. Testing personnel shall have knowledge and experience of the testing requirements for fire alarm and signaling equipment of this Code acceptable to the authority having jurisdiction or meet the requirement of 10.5.3.3.

10.5.3.3 Service Personnel. Service personnel shall be qualified in the maintenance and servicing of systems addressed within the scope of this Code. Qualified personnel shall include, but not be limited to, one or more of the following:

(1)*Personnel who are factory trained and certified for the specific type and brand of system being serviced
(2)*Personnel who are certified by a nationally recognized certification organization acceptable to the authority having jurisdiction
(3)*Personnel, either individually or through their affiliation with an organization that is registered, licensed, or certified by a state or local authority to perform service on systems addressed within the scope of this Code
(4) Personnel who are employed and qualified by an organization listed by a nationally recognized testing laboratory for the servicing of systems within the scope of this Code

10.5.3.4 Programming. Personnel programming a system shall be certified by the system manufacturer.

10.5.3.5 Evidence of Qualification. Evidence of qualifications shall be provided to the authority having jurisdiction upon request.

10.5.4 Supervising Station Operators. (SIG-SSS)

10.5.4.1 All operators in the supervising station shall demonstrate competence in all tasks required of them in Chapter 26 by one or more of the following:

(1) Certified by the manufacturer of the receiving system or equipment or the alarm-monitoring automation system
(2)*Certified by an organization acceptable to the authority having jurisdiction
(3) Licensed or certified by a state or local authority
(4) Other training or certification approved by the authority having jurisdiction

10.5.4.2 Evidence of qualifications and/or certification shall be provided when requested by the authority having jurisdiction. A license or qualification listing shall be current in accordance with the requirements of the issuing authority or organization.

10.5.4.3 Operator trainees shall be under the direct supervision of a qualified operator until qualified as required by 10.5.4.1.

10.6 Power Supplies.

10.6.1 Scope. The provisions of this section shall apply to power supplies used for protected premises fire alarm systems, supervising station alarm systems, public emergency alarm reporting systems, and emergency communications systems and equipment.

10.6.2 Code Conformance. All power supplies shall be installed in conformity with the requirements of *NFPA 70, National Electrical Code*, for such equipment and with the requirements indicated in this subsection.

10.6.3 Power Supply Sources.

10.6.3.1 Power shall be supplied in compliance with either 10.6.3.2 or 10.6.4.

10.6.3.2 Unless configured in compliance with 10.6.4, at least two independent and reliable power supplies shall be provided, one primary and one secondary.

10.6.3.3 Each power supply shall be of adequate capacity for the application.

10.6.3.4 Monitoring the integrity of power supplies shall be in accordance with 10.6.9.

10.6.4 Uninterruptible Power Supplies (UPS).

10.6.4.1 The UPS device shall be configured in compliance with NFPA 111, *Standard on Stored Electrical Energy Emergency and Standby Power Systems*, for a Type O, Class 24, Level 1 system.

10.6.4.2 The UPS device shall comply with the requirements of 10.6.5.

10.6.4.3 Failure of the UPS shall result in the initiation of a trouble signal in accordance with Section 10.15.

10.6.5 Primary Power Supply.

10.6.5.1 Branch Circuit. The branch circuit supplying the fire alarm equipment(s) or emergency communication system(s) shall supply no other loads and shall be supplied by one of the following:

(1) Commercial light and power
(2) An engine-driven generator or equivalent in accordance with 10.6.11.2, where a person specifically trained in its operation is on duty at all times
(3) An engine-driven generator or equivalent arranged for cogeneration with commercial light and power in accordance with 10.6.11.2, where a person specifically trained in its operation is on duty at all times

10.6.5.2 Circuit Identification and Accessibility.

10.6.5.2.1 The location of the branch circuit disconnecting means shall be permanently identified at the control unit.

10.6.5.2.2 System circuit disconnecting means shall be permanently identified as to its purpose in accordance with the following:

(1) "FIRE ALARM" for fire alarm systems
(2) "EMERGENCY COMMUNICATIONS" for emergency communications systems
(3) "FIRE ALARM/ECS" for combination fire alarm and emergency communications systems

10.6.5.2.3 For fire alarm and/or signaling systems, the circuit disconnecting means shall have a red marking.

10.6.5.2.4 The red marking shall not damage the overcurrent protective devices or obscure the manufacturer's markings.

10.6.5.2.5 The circuit disconnecting means shall be accessible only to authorized personnel.

10.6.5.3 Mechanical Protection. The branch circuit(s) and connections shall be protected against physical damage.

10.6.5.4 Circuit Breaker Lock. Where a circuit breaker is the disconnecting means, a listed breaker locking device shall be installed.

10.6.5.5 Overcurrent Protection. An overcurrent protective device of suitable current-carrying capacity that is capable of interrupting the maximum short-circuit current to which it can be subject shall be provided in each ungrounded conductor.

10.6.6* Continuity of Power Supplies.

10.6.6.1 The secondary power supply shall automatically provide power to the protected premises system within 10 seconds whenever the primary power supply fails to provide the minimum voltage required for proper operation.

10.6.6.2 The secondary power supply shall automatically provide power to the supervising station facility and equipment within 60 seconds whenever the primary power supply fails to provide the minimum voltage required for proper operation.

10.6.6.3 Required signals shall not be lost, interrupted, or delayed by more than 10 seconds as a result of the primary power failure.

10.6.6.3.1 Storage batteries dedicated to the system or UPS arranged in accordance with the provisions of NFPA 111, *Standard on Stored Electrical Energy Emergency and Standby Power Systems*, shall be permitted to supplement the secondary power supply to ensure required operation during the transfer period.

10.6.6.3.2 Where a UPS is employed in 10.6.6.3.1, a positive means for disconnecting the input and output of the UPS system while maintaining continuity of power supply to the load shall be provided.

10.6.7 Secondary Power Supply.

10.6.7.1 Secondary Power Operation.

10.6.7.1.1 Operation on secondary power shall not affect the required performance of a system or supervising station facility, including alarm, supervisory, and trouble signals and indications.

Exception: While operating on secondary power, audio amplifier monitoring shall be required only when an alarm is present.

10.6.7.2* Capacity. *horn strobe*

10.6.7.2.1 The secondary power supply shall have sufficient capacity to operate the system under quiescent load (system operating in a nonalarm condition) for a minimum of 24 hours and, at the end of that period, shall be capable of operating all alarm notification appliances used for evacuation or to direct aid to the location of an emergency for 5 minutes, unless otherwise permitted or required by the following:

(1) Battery calculations shall include a 20 percent safety margin to the calculated amp-hour rating.

(2) The secondary power supply for in-building fire emergency voice/alarm communications service shall be capable of operating the system under quiescent load for a minimum of 24 hours and then shall be capable of operating the system during a fire or other emergency condition for a period of 15 minutes at maximum connected load.

(3) The secondary power supply capacity for supervising station facilities and equipment shall be capable of supporting operations for a minimum of 24 hours.

(4) The secondary power supply for high-power speaker arrays used for wide-area mass notification systems shall be in accordance with 24.4.4.4.2.2.

(5) The secondary power supply for textual visible appliances shall be in accordance with 24.4.4.4.7.1.

(6) The secondary power supply capacity for emergency command centers of a wide-area mass notification systems shall be capable of supporting operations for a minimum of 24 hours.

(7) The secondary power supply for in-building mass notification systems shall be capable of operating the system under quiescent load for a minimum of 24 hours and then shall be capable of operating the system during emergency condition for a period of 15 minutes at maximum connected load.

(8) The secondary power supply for two-way radio communications enhancement systems shall be in accordance with 24.5.2.5.5.

10.6.7.2.2 The secondary power supply capacity required shall include all power supply loads that are not automatically disconnected upon the transfer to secondary power supply.

10.6.7.3* Secondary Power Supply for Protected Premises Fire Alarm Systems and Emergency Communications Systems.

10.6.7.3.1 The secondary power supply shall consist of one of the following:

(1) A storage battery dedicated to the system arranged in accordance with 10.6.10

(2) An automatic-starting, engine-driven generator serving the branch circuit specified in 10.6.5.1 and arranged in accordance with 10.6.11.3.1, and storage batteries dedicated to the system with 4 hours of capacity arranged in accordance with 10.6.10

10.6.7.3.2 Secondary circuits that provide power to the control unit and are not integral to the unit shall be protected against physical damage.

10.6.7.4 Secondary Power Supply for Supervising Station Facilities.

10.6.7.4.1 The secondary power supply shall consist of one of the following:

(1) Storage batteries dedicated to the supervising station equipment arranged in accordance with 10.6.10

(2) A branch circuit of an automatic-starting, engine-driven generator arranged in accordance with 10.6.11.3.2.1 and 10.6.11.3.2.2, and storage batteries dedicated to the supervising station equipment with 4 hours of capacity arranged in accordance with 10.6.10

(3) A branch circuit of multiple engine-driven generators, at least one of which is arranged for automatic starting in accordance with 10.6.11.3.2.1 and 10.6.11.3.2.2

10.6.7.4.2 Where a secondary power supply for supervising station facilities in accordance with 10.6.7.4.1(3) is used, the following shall apply:

(1) Each generator shall be capable of supplying the energy required.
(2) Generators that are started manually shall be arranged in accordance with 10.6.11.3.2.3 and 10.6.11.3.2.4.
(3) When manual-start generators are employed, a person trained in the procedure of starting the generator shall be on duty at all times.

10.6.8 Power Supply for Remotely Located Control Equipment.

10.6.8.1* Additional power supplies, where provided for control units, circuit interfaces, or other equipment essential to system operation, and located remotely from the main control unit, shall be comprised of a primary and secondary power supply that shall meet the same requirements as those of 10.6.1 through 10.6.6 and 10.6.9.

10.6.8.2 The location of any remotely located power supply shall be identified at the master control unit.

10.6.8.3 The master control unit display shall be permitted to satisfy the requirement of 10.6.8.2.

10.6.8.4 The location of any remotely located power supply shall be identified on the record drawings.

10.6.9 Monitoring Integrity of Power Supplies.

10.6.9.1 Unless otherwise permitted or required by 10.6.9.1.3 and 10.6.9.1.6, all primary and secondary power supplies shall be monitored for the presence of voltage at the point of connection to the system.

10.6.9.1.1 Failure of either supply shall result in a trouble signal in accordance with Section 10.15.

10.6.9.1.2 Where the digital alarm communicator transmitter (DACT) is powered from a protected premises fire alarm system control unit, power failure indication shall be in accordance with 10.6.9.1.

10.6.9.1.3 Monitoring shall not be required for a power supply for supplementary equipment.

10.6.9.1.4 Monitoring shall not be required for the neutral of a three-, four-, or five-wire alternating current (ac) or direct current (dc) supply source.

10.6.9.1.5 Monitoring shall not be required for the main power supply in a central station, provided that the fault condition is otherwise indicated so as to be obvious to the operator on duty.

10.6.9.1.6 Monitoring shall not be required for the output of an engine-driven generator that is part of the secondary power supply, provided that the generator is tested weekly in accordance with Chapter 14.

10.6.9.2* Power supply sources and electrical supervision for digital alarm communications systems shall be in accordance with Sections 10.6, 10.6.9, 10.19, and 12.6.

10.6.9.3* Unless prohibited by the authority having jurisdiction, supervising station alarm systems shall be arranged to delay transmission of primary power failure signals for a period ranging from 60 minutes to 180 minutes.

10.6.9.4 Power supervisory devices shall be arranged so as not to impair the receipt of fire alarm or supervisory signals.

10.6.10* Storage Batteries.

10.6.10.1 Marking.

10.6.10.1.1 Batteries shall be marked with the month and year of manufacture using the month/year format.

10.6.10.1.2 Where the battery is not marked with the month/year by the manufacturer, the installer shall obtain the date-code and mark the battery with the month/year of battery manufacture.

10.6.10.2 Location. Storage batteries shall be located so that the equipment, including overcurrent devices, are not adversely affected by battery gases and shall conform to the requirements of *NFPA 70, National Electrical Code*, Article 480.

10.6.10.2.1 Cells shall be suitably insulated against ground faults.

10.6.10.2.2 Cells shall be suitably insulated against crosses.

10.6.10.2.3 Cells shall be mounted in such a manner so as to be protected from physical damage.

10.6.10.2.4 Racks shall be suitably protected against deterioration.

10.6.10.2.5 If not located in or adjacent to the control unit, the batteries and their charger location shall be permanently identified at the control unit.

10.6.10.3 Battery Charging.

10.6.10.3.1 Adequate facilities shall be provided to automatically maintain the battery fully charged under all conditions of normal operation.

10.6.10.3.2 Adequate facilities shall be provided to recharge batteries within 48 hours after fully charged batteries have been subject to a single discharge cycle as specified in 10.6.7.2.

10.6.10.3.3 Upon attaining a fully charged condition, the charge rate shall not be so excessive as to result in battery damage.

10.6.10.3.4* Batteries shall be either trickle- or float-charged.

10.6.10.3.5 Supervising stations shall maintain spare parts or units available, which shall be used to restore failed charging capacity prior to the consumption of one-half of the capacity of the batteries for the supervising station equipment.

10.6.10.4 Overcurrent Protection.

10.6.10.4.1 The batteries shall be protected against excessive load current by overcurrent devices.

10.6.10.4.2 The batteries shall be protected from excessive charging current by overcurrent devices or by automatic current-limiting design of the charging source.

10.6.10.5 Metering. The charging equipment shall provide either integral meters or readily accessible terminal facilities for the connection of portable meters by which the battery voltage and charging current can be determined.

10.6.10.6 Monitoring Integrity of Battery Charger.

10.6.10.6.1 Means for monitoring integrity appropriate for the batteries and charger employed shall be provided to detect a battery charger failure.

10.6.10.6.2 Failure of the battery charger shall result in the initiation of a trouble signal in accordance with Section 10.15.

10.6.11 Engine-Driven Generators.

10.6.11.1 Application and Installation. The application and installation of engine-driven generators shall be as specified in 10.6.11.2 through 10.6.11.7.

10.6.11.2 Primary Power Supply.

10.6.11.2.1 Engine-driven generators arranged as the primary supply shall be designed in an approved manner.

10.6.11.2.2 Engine-driven generators arranged as the primary supply shall be installed in an approved manner.

10.6.11.3 Secondary Power Supplies.

10.6.11.3.1 Protected Premises.

10.6.11.3.1.1 Engine-driven generators used to provide secondary power for a protected premises fire alarm system or an emergency communications system shall comply with NFPA 110, *Standard for Emergency and Standby Power Systems*, Chapter 4, requirements for a Type 10, Class 24, Level 1 system.

10.6.11.3.1.2 Installation of engine-driven generators used to provide secondary power for a protected premises fire alarm system or an emergency communications system shall be in accordance with *NFPA 70, National Electrical Code*, Article 700.

10.6.11.3.1.3 Where survivability of circuits is required by another section of the Code, equal protection shall be provided for power supply circuits.

10.6.11.3.2 Supervising Station.

10.6.11.3.2.1 Automatic-starting, engine-driven generators used to provide secondary power for a supervising station shall comply with NFPA 110, *Standard for Emergency and Standby Power Systems*, Chapter 4, requirements for a Type 60, Class 24, Level 2 system.

10.6.11.3.2.2 Installation of automatic-starting, engine-driven generators used to provide secondary power for a supervising station shall be in accordance with *NFPA 70, National Electrical Code*, Article 701.

10.6.11.3.2.3 Manual-starting, engine-driven generators used to provide secondary power for a supervising station shall comply with NFPA 110, *Standard for Emergency and Standby Power Systems*, Chapter 10, requirements for a Type M, Class 24, Level 2 system.

10.6.11.3.2.4 Installation of manual-starting, engine-driven generators used to provide secondary power for a supervising station shall be in accordance with *NFPA 70, National Electrical Code*, Article 702.

10.6.11.4 Performance, Operation, Testing, and Maintenance. The requirements for performance, operation, testing, and maintenance of engine-driven generators shall conform to the applicable provisions of NFPA 110, *Standard for Emergency and Standby Power Systems*.

10.6.11.5 Capacity. The unit shall be of a capacity that is sufficient to operate the system under the maximum normal load conditions in addition to all other demands placed upon the unit.

10.6.11.6 Fuel. Unless otherwise required or permitted in 10.6.11.6.1 through 10.6.11.6.3, fuel shall be available in storage sufficient for 6 months of testing plus the capacity specified in 10.6.7.

10.6.11.6.1 For public emergency alarm reporting systems, the requirements of Chapter 27 shall apply.

10.6.11.6.2 If a reliable source of supply is available at any time on a 2-hour notice, it shall be permitted to have fuel in storage sufficient for 12 hours of operation at full load.

10.6.11.6.3 Fuel systems using natural or manufactured gas supplied through reliable utility mains shall not be required to have fuel storage tanks unless located in seismic risk zone 3 or greater as defined in ANSI A-58.1, *Building Code Requirements for Minimum Design Loads in Buildings and Other Structures*.

10.6.11.7 Battery and Charger. A separate storage battery and separate automatic charger shall be provided for starting the engine-driven generator and shall not be used for any other purpose.

10.7 Signal Priority. The priority of signals shall be in accordance with this section.

10.7.1 ECS priority signals when evaluated by stakeholders through a risk analysis in accordance with 24.3.11 shall be permitted to take precedence over all other signals.

10.7.2 Fire alarm signals shall take precedence over all other signals, except as permitted by 10.7.1 or 10.7.3.

10.7.3* Emergency mass notification signals and messages shall be permitted to have priority over fire alarm notification signals in accordance with the requirements of Chapter 24.

10.7.4 Emergency mass notification signals and messages shall have priority over supervisory and trouble signals in accordance with the requirements of Chapter 24.

10.7.5 Carbon monoxide signals shall be permitted to take precedence over supervisory and trouble signals.

10.7.6 Pre-alarm signals shall take precedence over supervisory and trouble signals.

10.7.7 Supervisory signals shall take precedence over trouble signals.

10.7.8 Hold-up alarms or other life-threatening signals shall be permitted to take precedence over supervisory and trouble signals where acceptable to the authority having jurisdiction.

10.7.9* Where separate systems are installed, they shall be permitted to achieve the priority of signals in accordance with Section 10.7.

10.8 Detection and Signaling of Conditions.

10.8.1 Abnormal Condition Detection. Where required by this Code, the system shall be provided with means to detect and signal abnormal conditions.

10.8.2 Alarm Condition Detection. Where required by this Code, the system shall be provided with means to detect and signal alarm conditions.

10.8.2.1 Pre-Alarm Condition Detection. Where required by this Code, the system shall be provided with means to detect and signal pre-alarm conditions.

10.8.2.2 Supervisory Condition Detection. Where required by this Code, the system shall be provided with means to detect and signal supervisory conditions.

10.8.2.3 Trouble Condition Detection. Where required by this Code, the system shall be provided with means to detect and signal trouble conditions.

10.8.2.4 Normal Condition Detection. Where required by this Code, the system shall generate a restoration signal when the device or signaling system returns to normal.

10.9 Responses.

10.9.1 Alarm. The response to an alarm signal shall be in accordance with this Code.

10.9.2 Pre-Alarm. The response to a pre-alarm signal shall be in accordance with this Code.

10.9.3 Supervisory. The response to a supervisory signal shall be in accordance with this Code.

10.9.4 Trouble. The response to trouble signal shall be in accordance with this Code.

10.10 Distinctive Signals.

10.10.1 Priority alarms, fire alarms, supervisory signals, pre-alarm signals, and trouble signals shall be distinctively and descriptively annunciated.

10.10.2 Audible alarm notification appliances for a fire alarm system shall produce signals that are distinctive from other similar appliances used for other purposes in the same area that are not part of the fire alarm or emergency communications system.

10.10.3 Audible alarm notification appliances for a carbon monoxide alarm system shall produce signals that are distinctive from other similar appliances used for other purposes in the same area that are not part of the carbon monoxide, fire alarm, or emergency communications system.

10.10.4* An audible notification appliance on a control unit, or on multiple control units that are interconnected to form a system, or at a remote location, shall be permitted to have the same audible characteristics for all alerting functions including, but not limited to, alarm, trouble, and supervisory, provided that the distinction between signals shall be by other appropriate means, such as visible annunciation.

10.10.5* Supervisory signals shall be distinctive in sound from other signals, and their sound shall not be used for any other purpose except as permitted in 10.10.4.

10.10.6 Trouble signals required to indicate at the protected premises shall be indicated by distinctive audible signals, which shall be distinctive from alarm signals except as permitted in 10.10.4.

10.10.7 Alarm evacuation signals shall be distinctive in sound from other signals, shall comply with the requirements of 18.4.2, and their sound shall not be used for any other purpose.

10.10.8 Pre-alarm signals shall be distinctive in sound from other signals, and their sound shall not be used for any other purpose except as permitted in 10.10.4.

10.11* ECS Priority Signals. Visible indication of priority signals shall be automatically indicated within 10 seconds at the fire alarm control unit or other designated location. (SIG-ECS)

10.12 Alarm Signals.

10.12.1 Actuation of alarm notification appliances or emergency voice communications, emergency control functions, and annunciation at the protected premises shall occur within 10 seconds after the activation of an initiating device.

10.12.2* A coded alarm signal shall consist of not less than three complete rounds of the number transmitted.

10.12.3 Each round of a coded alarm signal shall consist of not less than three impulses.

10.12.4* Resetting of alarm signals shall comply with the requirements of 23.8.2.2.

10.12.5 Unacknowledged alarm signals shall not be interrupted if a fault on an initiating device circuit or a signaling line circuit occurs while there is an alarm condition on that circuit unless the faulted circuit is used to interconnect control units.

10.12.6 An alarm signal that has been deactivated at the protected premises shall comply with 10.12.6.1 and 10.12.6.2.

10.12.6.1 The audible and visible alarm signal at the control unit only shall automatically reactivate every 24 hours or less until alarm signal conditions are restored to normal.

10.12.6.2 The audible and visible alarm signal shall operate until it is manually silenced or acknowledged.

10.13* Fire Alarm Notification Appliance Deactivation.

10.13.1 A means for turning off activated alarm notification appliance(s) shall be permitted.

10.13.2 When an occupant notification alarm signal deactivation means is actuated, both audible and visible notification appliances shall be simultaneously deactivated.

10.13.2.1* When voice instructions are in progress, visible appliances in same area where speakers are activated shall also be activated where required by the emergency response plan. (SIG-ECS)

10.13.3 The fire alarm notification deactivation means shall be key-operated or located within a locked cabinet, or arranged to provide equivalent protection against unauthorized use.

10.13.4 The means shall comply with the requirements of 10.18.1.

10.13.5 Subsequent Actuation of Initiating Devices.

10.13.5.1 Subsequent actuation of nonaddressable initiating devices on other initiating device circuits shall cause the notification appliances to reactivate.

10.13.5.2 Subsequent actuation of addressable initiating devices of a different type in the same room or addressable initiating devices in a different room on signaling line circuits shall cause the notification appliances to reactivate.

10.13.6 A fire alarm notification deactivation means that remains in the deactivated position when there is no alarm condition shall operate an audible trouble notification appliance until the means is restored to normal.

10.14 Supervisory Signals.

10.14.1 Self-Restoring Supervisory Signal Indication. Visible and audible indication of self-restoring supervisory signals and visible indication of their restoration to normal shall be automatically indicated within 90 seconds at the following locations:

(1) Fire alarm control unit for local fire alarm systems
(2) Building fire command center for in-building fire emergency voice/alarm communications systems
(3) Supervising station location for systems installed in compliance with Chapter 26

10.14.2 Latching Supervisory Signal Indication.

10.14.2.1 Visible and audible indication of latching supervisory signals shall be indicated within 90 seconds at the locations specified in 10.14.1.

10.14.2.2 Restoration of latching supervisory signals shall be indicated within 90 seconds at the locations specified in 10.14.1.

10.14.3 Coded Supervisory Signal.

10.14.3.1 A coded supervisory signal shall be permitted to consist of two rounds of the number transmitted to indicate a supervisory off-normal condition.

10.14.3.2 A coded supervisory signal shall be permitted to consist of one round of the number transmitted to indicate the restoration of the supervisory condition to normal.

10.14.4 Combined Coded Alarm and Supervisory Signal Circuits. Where both coded sprinkler supervisory signals and coded fire or waterflow alarm signals are transmitted over the same signaling line circuit, provision shall be made to obtain either alarm signal precedence or sufficient repetition of the alarm signal to prevent the loss of an alarm signal.

10.14.5 Supervisory Notification Appliance Location. The audible supervisory notification appliances shall be located in an area where they are likely to be heard.

10.14.6 Supervisory Signal Reactivation. A supervisory signal that has been deactivated at the protected premises shall comply with 10.14.6.1 and 10.14.6.2.

10.14.6.1 The audible and visible supervisory signal at the control unit only shall automatically reactivate every 24 hours or less until supervisory signal conditions are restored to normal.

10.14.6.2 The audible and visible supervisory signal shall operate until it is manually silenced or acknowledged.

10.14.7 Supervisory Notification Appliance Deactivation.

10.14.7.1 A means for deactivating supervisory notification appliances shall be permitted.

10.14.7.2 The means shall be key-operated or located within a locked cabinet, or arranged to provide equivalent protection against unauthorized use.

10.14.7.3 The means for deactivating supervisory notification appliances shall comply with the requirements of 10.18.2.

10.14.7.4 Subsequent actuation of supervisory initiating devices in other building zones shall cause supervisory notification appliances to actuate as required by the system input/output matrix.

10.14.7.5 A means for deactivating supervisory notification appliances that remains in the deactivated position when there is no supervisory condition shall operate an audible trouble notification appliance until the means is restored to normal.

10.15 Trouble Signals.

10.15.1 Trouble signals and their restoration to normal shall be indicated within 200 seconds at the locations identified in 10.15.7 and 10.15.8.

10.15.2 Indication of primary power failure trouble signals transmitted to a supervising station shall be in accordance with 10.6.9.3.

10.15.3 An audible trouble signal shall be permitted to be intermittent provided it sounds at least once every 10 seconds, with a minimum duration of ½ second.

10.15.4 A single audible trouble signal shall be permitted to annunciate multiple fault conditions.

10.15.5 The audible trouble notification appliances shall be located in an area where they are likely to be heard.

10.15.6 Actuated notification appliances at the protected premises shall continue to operate unless they are manually silenced as permitted by 10.15.10.1.

10.15.7 Visible and audible trouble signals and visible indication of their restoration to normal shall be indicated at the following locations:

(1) Fire alarm control unit for protected premises alarm systems
(2) Building fire command center for in-building fire emergency voice/alarm communications systems
(3) Central station or remote station location for systems installed in compliance with Chapter 26

10.15.8 Trouble signals and their restoration to normal shall be visibly and audibly indicated at the proprietary supervising station for systems installed in compliance with Chapter 26.

10.15.9* A trouble signal that has been deactivated at the protected premises shall comply with 10.15.9.1 and 10.15.9.2.

10.15.9.1 The audible and visible trouble signal shall automatically reactuate at the control unit every 24 hours or less until trouble signal conditions are restored to normal.

10.15.9.2 The audible and visible trouble signal associated with signaling the depletion or failure of the primary battery of a wireless system as required by 23.16.2(3) and (4) shall automatically resound every 4 hours or less until the depletion signal is restored to normal.

10.15.10 Trouble Notification Appliance Deactivation.

10.15.10.1 A means for deactivating trouble notification appliances shall be permitted.

10.15.10.2 The means shall be key-operated or located within a locked cabinet, or arranged to provide equivalent protection against unauthorized use.

10.15.10.3 The means for deactivating trouble notification appliances shall comply with the requirements of 10.18.2.

10.15.10.4 If an audible trouble notification appliance is also used to indicate a supervisory condition, as permitted by 10.10.4, a trouble notification appliance deactivation means shall not prevent subsequent actuation of supervisory notification appliances.

10.15.10.5 Subsequent trouble signals shall cause trouble notification appliances to activate as required by the system input/output matrix.

10.15.10.6 A means for deactivating trouble notification appliances that remains in the deactivated position when there is no trouble condition shall operate an audible trouble notification appliance until the means is restored to normal.

10.15.10.7* Unless otherwise permitted by the authority having jurisdiction, trouble notification appliances at the protected premises of a supervising station fire alarm system arranged in accordance with Chapter 26, that have been silenced at the protected premises shall automatically re-actuate every 24 hours or less until fault conditions are restored to normal.

10.16 Emergency Control Function Status Indicators.

10.16.1 All controls provided specifically for the purpose of manually overriding any automatic emergency control function shall provide visible indication of the status of the associated control circuits.

10.16.2* Where status indicators are provided for emergency equipment or control functions, they shall be arranged to reflect the actual status of the associated equipment or function.

10.17 Notification Appliance Circuits and Control Circuits.

10.17.1 An open, ground-fault, or short-circuit fault on the installation conductors of one alarm notification appliance circuit shall not affect the operation of any other alarm notification appliance circuit for more than 200 seconds regardless of whether the short-circuit fault is present during the normal or activated circuit state.

10.17.2* Notification appliance circuits that do not have notification appliances connected directly to the circuit shall be considered control circuits.

10.17.3 Control circuits shall not be required to comply with 10.17.1, provided that the circuit is monitored for integrity in accordance with Section 12.6 and a fault in installation conductors shall result in a trouble signal in accordance with Section 10.15.

10.18 Annunciation and Annunciation Zoning.

10.18.1 Alarm Annunciation.

10.18.1.1 Where required by other governing laws, codes, or standards, the location of an operated initiating device shall be annunciated by visible means.

10.18.1.1.1 Visible annunciation of the location of an operated initiating device shall be by an indicator lamp, alphanumeric display, printout, or other approved means.

10.18.1.1.2 The visible annunciation of the location of operated initiating devices shall not be canceled by the means used to deactivate alarm notification appliances.

10.18.2 Supervisory and Trouble Annunciation.

10.18.2.1 Where required by other governing laws, codes, or standards, supervisory and/or trouble conditions shall be annunciated by visible means.

10.18.2.1.1 Visible annunciation shall be by an indicator lamp, an alphanumeric display, a printout, or other means.

10.18.2.1.2 The visible annunciation of supervisory and/or trouble conditions shall not be canceled by the means used to deactivate supervisory or trouble notification appliances.

10.18.3* Annunciator Access and Location.

10.18.3.1 All required annunciation means shall be readily accessible to responding personnel.

10.18.3.2 All required annunciation means shall be located as required by the authority having jurisdiction to facilitate an efficient response to the situation.

10.18.4 Alarm Annunciation Display. Visible annunciators shall be capable of displaying all zones in alarm.

10.18.4.1 If all zones in alarm are not displayed simultaneously, the zone of origin shall be displayed.

10.18.4.2 If all zones in alarm are not displayed simultaneously, there shall be an indication that other zones are in alarm.

10.18.5* Annunciation Zoning.

10.18.5.1 For the purpose of alarm annunciation, each floor of the building shall be considered as a separate zone.

10.18.5.2 For the purposes of alarm annunciation, if a floor of the building is subdivided into multiple zones by fire or smoke barriers and the fire plan for the protected premises allows relocation of occupants from the zone of origin to another zone on the same floor, each zone on the floor shall be annunciated separately.

10.18.5.3 Where the system serves more than one building, each building shall be annunciated separately.

10.19 Monitoring Integrity of In-Building Fire Emergency Voice/Alarm Communications Systems.

10.19.1* Speaker Amplifier and Tone-Generating Equipment. If speakers are used to produce audible fire alarm signals, the required trouble signal for 10.19.1.1 through 10.19.1.3 shall be in accordance with Section 10.15.

10.19.1.1 When primary power is available, failure of any audio amplifier shall result in a trouble signal.

10.19.1.2 When an alarm is present and primary power is not available (i.e., system is operating from the secondary power source), failure of any audio amplifier shall result in a trouble signal.

10.19.1.3 Failure of any tone-generating equipment shall result in a trouble signal, unless the tone-generating and amplifying equipment are enclosed as integral parts and serve only a single, listed loudspeaker.

10.19.2 Two-Way Telephone Communications Circuits.

10.19.2.1 Two-way telephone communications circuit installation conductors shall be monitored for open circuit fault conditions that would cause the telephone communications circuit to become fully or partially inoperative.

10.19.2.2 Two-way telephone communications circuit installation conductors shall be monitored for short circuit fault conditions that would cause the telephone communications circuit to become fully or partially inoperative.

10.19.2.3 Two-way telephone communications circuit fault conditions shall result in a trouble signal in accordance with Section 10.15.

10.20 Documentation and Notification.

10.20.1 Documentation shall be in accordance with Chapter 7.

10.20.2 The authority having jurisdiction shall be notified prior to installation or alteration of equipment or wiring.

10.21* Impairments.

10.21.1 The system owner or their designated representative shall be notified when a system or part thereof is impaired. Impairments to systems shall include out-of-service events.

10.21.2 A record shall be maintained by the system owner or designated representative for a period of 1 year from the date the impairment is corrected.

10.21.3 The supervising station shall report to the authority having jurisdiction any fire alarm system for which required monitoring has been terminated.

10.21.4* The service provider shall report to the authority having jurisdiction any fire alarm system that is out of service more than 8 hours.

10.21.5* Where required, mitigating measures acceptable to the authority having jurisdiction shall be implemented for the period that the system is impaired.

10.21.6 The system owner or owner's designated representative shall be notified when an impairment period is completed or discontinued.

10.22* Unwanted Alarms. For the purpose of reporting, alarm signals that are not the result of hazardous conditions shall be classified as Unwanted and subclassified as one of the following:

(1) Malicious alarm
(2) Nuisance alarm
(3) Unintentional alarm
(4) Unknown alarm

Chapter 11 Reserved

Chapter 12 Circuits and Pathways

12.1 Application.

12.1.1 Pathways (interconnections) shall be designated based on the performance characteristics defined in this chapter.

12.1.2 The requirements of Chapter 14 shall apply.

12.2 General.

12.2.1* Performance and survivability characteristics of signaling pathways (interconnections) shall comply with the defined designations of this chapter.

12.2.2 A pathway (interconnection) class designation shall be dependent on the pathway (interconnection) capability to continue to operate during abnormal conditions.

12.2.3 The designation of the pathways shall be permitted to also include the performance of the pathway (interconnection) to survivability from attack by fire.

12.2.4 The installation of all pathway wiring, cable, and equipment shall be in accordance with *NFPA 70, National Electrical Code*, and the applicable requirements of 12.2.4.1 through 12.2.4.4. (SIG-FUN)

12.2.4.1 Optical fiber cables installed as part of the fire alarm system shall meet the requirements of *NFPA 70, National Electrical Code*, Article 770, and be protected against physical damage in accordance with *NFPA 70, National Electrical Code*, Article 760. (SIG-FUN)

12.2.4.2 All non-power-limited and power-limited signaling system circuits entering a building shall be provided with transient protection. (SIG-FUN)

12.2.4.3* Fire alarm system wiring and equipment, including all circuits controlled and powered by the fire alarm system, shall be installed in accordance with the requirements of this Code and of *NFPA 70, National Electrical Code*, Article 760. (SIG-FUN)

12.2.4.4* Wiring methods permitted by other sections of this Code to resist attack by fire shall be installed in accordance with manufacturer's published instructions and the requirements of *NFPA 70, National Electrical Code*, Article 760. (SIG-FUN)

12.2.5 Ground Connections.

12.2.5.1 All fire alarm systems shall test free of grounds.

Exception: Parts of circuits or equipment that are intentionally and permanently grounded to provide ground-fault detection, noise suppression, emergency ground signaling, and circuit protection grounding shall be permitted. (SIG-FUN)

12.2.5.2* On conductive pathways, operational capability shall be maintained during the application of a single ground connection. (SIG-FUN)

12.3* Pathway Class Designations. Pathways shall be designated as Class A, Class B, Class C, Class D, Class E, or Class X, depending on their performance.

12.3.1* Class A. A pathway shall be designated as Class A when it performs as follows:

(1) It includes a redundant path.
(2) Operational capability continues past a single open, and the single open fault shall result in the annunciation of a trouble signal.
(3) Conditions that affect the intended operation of the path are annunciated as a trouble signal.
(4) Operational capability is maintained during the application of a single ground fault.
(5) A single ground condition shall result in the annunciation of a trouble signal.

Exception: Requirements in 12.3.1(4) and (5) shall not apply to nonconductive pathways (e.g., wireless or fiber).

12.3.2* Class B. A pathway shall be designated as Class B when it performs as follows:

(1) It does not include a redundant path.
(2) Operational capability stops at a single open.
(3) Conditions that affect the intended operation of the path are annunciated as a trouble signal.
(4) Operational capability is maintained during the application of a single ground fault.
(5) A single ground condition shall result in the annunciation of a trouble signal.

Exception: Requirements in 12.3.2(4) and (5) shall not apply to nonconductive pathways (e.g., wireless or fiber).

12.3.3* Class C. A pathway shall be designated as Class C when it performs as follows:

(1) It includes one or more pathways where operational capability is verified via end-to-end communication, but the integrity of individual paths is not monitored.
(2) A loss of end-to-end communication is annunciated.

12.3.4* Class D. A pathway shall be designated as Class D when it has fail-safe operation, where no fault is annunciated, but the intended operation is performed in the event of a pathway failure.

12.3.5* Class E. A pathway shall be designated as Class E when it is not monitored for integrity.

12.3.6* Class X. A pathway shall be designated as Class X when it performs as follows:

(1) It includes a redundant path.
(2) Operational capability continues past a single open, and the single open fault shall result in the annunciation of a trouble signal.
(3) Operational capability continues past a single short-circuit, and the single short-circuit fault shall result in the annunciation of a trouble signal.
(4) Operational capability continues past a combination open fault and ground fault.
(5) Conditions that affect the intended operation of the path are annunciated as a trouble signal.
(6) Operational capability is maintained during the application of a single ground fault.
(7) A single ground condition shall result in the annunciation of a trouble signal.

Exception: Requirements in 12.3.6(3), (4), (6), and (7) shall not apply to nonconductive pathways (e.g., wireless or fiber).

12.3.7* Class A and Class X circuits using physical conductors (e.g., metallic, optical fiber) shall be installed such that the outgoing and return conductors, exiting from and returning to the control unit, respectively, are routed separately. The outgoing and return (redundant) circuit conductors shall be permitted in the same cable assembly (i.e., multi-conductor cable), enclosure, or raceway only under the following conditions:

(1) For a distance not to exceed 10 ft (3.0 m) where the outgoing and return conductors enter or exit the initiating device, notification appliance, or control unit enclosures
(2) For single raceway drops to individual devices or appliances
(3) For single raceway drops to multiple devices or appliances installed within a single room not exceeding 1000 ft² (93 m²) in area

12.4 Pathway Survivability. All pathways shall comply with *NFPA 70, National Electrical Code.*

12.4.1 Pathway Survivability Level 0. Level 0 pathways shall not be required to have any provisions for pathway survivability.

12.4.2 Pathway Survivability Level 1. Pathway survivability Level 1 shall consist of pathways in buildings that are fully protected by an automatic sprinkler system in accordance with NFPA 13, *Standard for the Installation of Sprinkler Systems*, with any interconnecting conductors, cables, or other physical pathways installed in metal raceways.

12.4.3 Pathway Survivability Level 2. Pathway survivability Level 2 shall consist of one or more of the following:

(1) 2-hour fire-rated circuit integrity (CI) cable
(2) 2-hour fire-rated cable system [electrical circuit protective system(s)]
(3) 2-hour fire-rated enclosure or protected area
(4) 2-hour performance alternatives approved by the authority having jurisdiction

12.4.4 Pathway Survivability Level 3. Pathway survivability Level 3 shall consist of pathways in buildings that are fully

protected by an automatic sprinkler system in accordance with NFPA 13, *Standard for the Installation of Sprinkler Systems*, and one or more of the following:

(1) 2-hour fire-rated circuit integrity (CI) cable
(2) 2-hour fire-rated cable system [electrical circuit protective system(s)]
(3) 2-hour fire-rated enclosure or protected area
(4) 2-hour performance alternatives approved by the authority having jurisdiction

12.5* Shared Pathway Designations. Shared pathways shall be designated as Level 0, Level 1, Level 2, or Level 3, depending on their performance.

12.5.1* Shared Pathway Level 0. Level 0 pathways shall not be required to segregate or prioritize life safety data from non–life safety data.

12.5.2* Shared Pathway Level 1. Level 1 pathways shall not be required to segregate life safety data from non–life safety data, but shall prioritize all life safety data over non–life safety data.

12.5.3* Shared Pathway Level 2. Level 2 pathways shall segregate all life safety data from non–life safety data.

12.5.4* Shared Pathway Level 3. Level 3 pathways shall use equipment that is dedicated to the life safety system.

12.6* Monitoring Integrity and Circuit Performance of Installation Conductors and Other Signaling Channels. (SIG-FUN)

12.6.1 Unless otherwise permitted or required by 12.6.3 through 12.6.14, all means of interconnecting equipment, devices, and appliances and wiring connections shall be monitored for the integrity of the interconnecting conductors or equivalent path so that the occurrence of a single open or a single ground-fault condition in the installation conductors or other signaling channels is automatically indicated within 200 seconds.

12.6.2 Unless otherwise permitted or required by 12.6.3 through 12.6.14, all means of interconnecting equipment, devices, and appliances and wiring connections shall be monitored for the integrity of the interconnecting conductors or equivalent path so that the restoration to normal of a single open or a single ground-fault condition in the installation conductors or other signaling channels is automatically indicated within 200 seconds. (SIG-FUN)

12.6.3 Shorts between conductors shall not be required to be monitored for integrity, unless required by 12.6.16, 12.6.17, and 10.19.2.

12.6.4 Monitoring for integrity shall not be required for a noninterfering shunt circuit, provided that a fault circuit condition on the shunt circuit wiring results only in the loss of the noninterfering feature of operation.

12.6.5 Monitoring for integrity shall not be required for connections to and between supplementary system components, provided that a single open, ground-fault, or short-circuit conditions of the supplementary equipment or interconnecting means, or both, do not affect the required operation of the fire alarm and/or signaling system.

12.6.6 Monitoring for integrity shall not be required for the circuit of an alarm notification appliance installed in the same room with the central control equipment, provided that the notification appliance circuit conductors are installed in conduit or are equivalently protected against mechanical injury.

12.6.7 Monitoring for integrity shall not be required for a trouble notification appliance circuit.

12.6.8* Monitoring for integrity shall not be required for the interconnection between listed equipment within a common enclosure.

12.6.9 Monitoring for integrity shall not be required for the interconnection between enclosures containing control equipment located within 20 ft (6 m) of each other where the conductors are installed in conduit or equivalently protected against mechanical injury.

12.6.10 Monitoring for integrity shall not be required for the conductors for ground-fault detection where a single ground-fault does not prevent the required normal operation of the system.

12.6.11 Monitoring for integrity shall not be required for central station circuits serving notification appliances within a central station.

12.6.12 Monitoring for integrity shall not be required for pneumatic rate-of-rise systems of the continuous line type in which the wiring terminals of such devices are connected in multiple across electrically supervised circuits.

12.6.13 Monitoring for integrity shall not be required for the interconnecting wiring of a stationary computer and the computer's keyboard, video monitor, mouse-type device, or touch screen, as long as the interconnecting wiring does not exceed 8 ft (2.4 m) in length; is a listed computer/data processing cable as permitted by *NFPA 70, National Electrical Code*; and failure of cable does not cause the failure of the required system functions not initiated from the keyboard, mouse, or touch screen.

12.6.14 Monitoring for integrity of the installation conductors for a ground-fault condition shall not be required for the communications and transmission channels extending from a supervising station to a subsidiary station(s) or protected premises, or both, that comply with the requirements of Chapter 26 and are electrically isolated from the fire alarm system (or circuits) by a transmitter(s), provided that a single ground-fault condition does not affect the required operation of the fire alarm system and/or signaling system.

12.6.15 Interconnection means shall be arranged so that a single break or single ground-fault does not cause an alarm signal.

12.6.16 A wire-to-wire short-circuit fault on any alarm notification appliance circuit shall result in a trouble signal in accordance with Section 10.15, except as permitted by 12.6.5, 12.6.6, or 12.6.11.

12.6.17 Where two or more systems are interconnected, the systems shall be connected using Class A, B, or X circuits as described in Section 12.3.

12.7 Nomenclature. To identify the properties of the system(s) interconnections and survivability requirements, the following identification nomenclature shall be used:

(1) System(s) interconnections
(2) Survivability levels (not required if Level 0)
(3) Shared pathway levels (not required if Level 0)

Chapter 13   Reserved

Chapter 14   Inspection, Testing, and Maintenance

14.1 Application.

14.1.1 The inspection, testing, and maintenance of systems, their initiating devices, and notification appliances shall comply with the requirements of this chapter.

14.1.2 The inspection, testing, and maintenance of single- and multiple-station smoke and heat alarms and household fire alarm systems shall comply with the requirements of this chapter.

14.1.3 Procedures that are required by other parties and that exceed the requirements of this chapter shall be permitted.

14.1.4 The requirements of this chapter shall apply to both new and existing systems.

14.1.5 The requirements of Chapter 7 shall apply where referenced in Chapter 14.

14.2 General.

14.2.1 Purpose.

14.2.1.1* The purpose for initial and reacceptance inspections is to ensure compliance with approved design documents and to ensure installation in accordance with this *Code* and other required installation standards.

14.2.1.2* The purpose for initial and reacceptance tests of fire alarm and signaling systems is to ensure system operation in accordance with the design documents.

14.2.1.3* The purpose for periodic inspections is to assure that obvious damages or changes that might affect the system operability are visually identified.

14.2.1.4* The purpose for periodic testing is to statistically assure operational reliability.

14.2.2 Performance.

14.2.2.1 Performance Verification. To ensure operational integrity, the system shall have an inspection, testing, and maintenance program.

14.2.2.1.1 Inspection, testing, and maintenance programs shall satisfy the requirements of this *Code* and conform to the equipment manufacturer's published instructions.

14.2.2.1.2 Inspection, testing, and maintenance programs shall verify correct operation of the system.

14.2.2.2 Impairments/Deficiencies.

14.2.2.2.1 The requirements of Section 10.21 shall be applicable when a system is impaired.

14.2.2.2.2 System deficiencies shall be corrected.

14.2.2.2.3 If a deficiency is not corrected at the conclusion of system inspection, testing, or maintenance, the system owner or the owner's designated representative shall be informed of the impairment in writing within 24 hours.

14.2.3 Responsibilities.

14.2.3.1* The property or building or system owner or the owner's designated representative shall be responsible for inspection, testing, and maintenance of the system and for alterations or additions to this system.

14.2.3.2 Where the property owner is not the occupant, the property owner shall be permitted to delegate the authority and responsibility for inspecting, testing, and maintaining the fire protection systems to the occupant, management firm, or managing individual through specific provisions in the lease, written use agreement, or management contract.

14.2.3.3 Inspection, testing, or maintenance shall be permitted to be done by the building or system owner or a person or organization other than the building or system owner if conducted under a written contract.

14.2.3.4 Where the building or system owner has delegated any responsibilities for inspection, testing, or maintenance, a copy of the written delegation required by 14.2.3.3 shall be provided to the authority having jurisdiction upon request.

14.2.3.5 Testing and maintenance of central station service systems shall be performed under the contractual arrangements specified in 26.3.3.

14.2.3.6* Service Personnel Qualifications and Experience. Service personnel shall be qualified and experienced in accordance with the requirements of 10.5.3.

14.2.4* Notification.

14.2.4.1 Before proceeding with any testing, all persons and facilities receiving alarm, supervisory, or trouble signals and all building occupants shall be notified of the testing to prevent unnecessary response.

14.2.4.2 At the conclusion of testing, those previously notified (and others, as necessary) shall be notified that testing has been concluded.

14.2.4.3 The owner or the owner's designated representative and service personnel shall coordinate system testing to prevent interruption of critical building systems or equipment.

14.2.5 System Documentation. Prior to system maintenance or testing, the record of completion and any information required by Chapter 7 regarding the system and system alterations, including specifications, wiring diagrams, and floor plans, shall be provided by the owner or a designated representative to the service personnel upon request.

14.2.5.1 The provided documentation shall include the current revisions of all fire alarm software and the revisions of software of any systems with which the fire alarm software interfaces.

14.2.5.2 The revisions of fire alarm software, and the revisions of the software in the systems with which the fire alarm software interfaces, shall be verified for compatibility in accordance with the requirements of 23.2.2.1.1.

14.2.6 Releasing Systems. Requirements pertinent to testing the fire alarm systems initiating fire suppression system releasing functions shall be covered by 14.2.6.1 through 14.2.6.6.

14.2.6.1 Testing personnel shall be qualified and experienced in the specific arrangement and operation of a suppression system(s) and a releasing function(s) and shall be cognizant of the hazards associated with inadvertent system discharge.

14.2.6.2 Occupant notification shall be required whenever a fire alarm system configured for releasing service is being serviced or tested.

14.2.6.3 Discharge testing of suppression systems shall not be required by this Code.

14.2.6.4 Suppression systems shall be secured from inadvertent actuation, including disconnection of releasing solenoids or electric actuators, closing of valves, other actions, or combinations thereof, for the specific system, for the duration of the fire alarm system testing.

14.2.6.5 Testing shall include verification that the releasing circuits and components energized or actuated by the fire alarm system are electrically monitored for integrity and operate as intended on alarm.

14.2.6.6 Suppression systems and releasing components shall be returned to their functional operating condition upon completion of system testing.

14.2.7 Interface Equipment and Emergency Control Functions.

14.2.7.1* Testing personnel shall be qualified and experienced in the arrangement and operation of interface equipment and emergency control functions.

14.2.7.2 Testing shall be accomplished in accordance with Table 14.4.3.2.

14.2.8 Automated Testing.

14.2.8.1 Automated testing arrangements that provide equivalent means of testing devices to those specified in Table 14.4.3.2 at a frequency at least equivalent to those specified in Table 14.4.3.2 shall be permitted to be used to comply with the requirements of this chapter.

14.2.8.2 Failure of a device on an automated test shall result in an audible and visual trouble signal.

14.2.9* Performance-Based Inspection and Testing. As an alternate means of compliance, subject to the authority having jurisdiction, components and systems shall be permitted to be inspected and tested under a performance-based program.

14.2.10* Test Plan.

14.2.10.1 A test plan shall be written to clearly establish the scope of the testing for the fire alarm or signaling system.

14.2.10.2 The test plan and results shall be documented with the testing records.

14.3 Inspection.

14.3.1* Unless otherwise permitted by 14.3.2, visual inspections shall be performed in accordance with the schedules in Table 14.3.1 or more often if required by the authority having jurisdiction.

> Table 14.3.1 column 2 heading was revised by a tentative interim amendment (TIA). See page 1.

Table 14.3.1 Visual Inspection

Component	Initial Acceptance	Periodic Frequency	Method	Reference
1. All equipment	X	Annual	Ensure there are no changes that affect equipment performance. Inspect for building modifications, occupancy changes, changes in environmental conditions, device location, physical obstructions, device orientation, physical damage, and degree of cleanliness.	14.3.4
2. Control equipment:				
(a) Fire alarm systems monitored for alarm, supervisory, and trouble signals			Verify a system normal condition.	
(1) Fuses	X	Annual		
(2) Interfaced equipment	X	Annual		
(3) Lamps and LEDs	X	Annual		
(4) Primary (main) power supply	X	Annual		
(5) Trouble signals	X	Semiannual		
(b) Fire alarm systems unmonitored for alarm, supervisory, and trouble signals			Verify a system normal condition.	
(1) Fuses	X	Weekly		
(2) Interfaced equipment	X	Weekly		
(3) Lamps and LEDs	X	Weekly		
(4) Primary (main) power supply	X	Weekly		
(5) Trouble signals	X	Weekly		
3. Reserved				
4. Supervising station alarm systems — transmitters			Verify location, physical condition, and a system normal condition.	
(a) Digital alarm communicator transmitter (DACT)	X	Annual		
(b) Digital alarm radio transmitter (DART)	X	Annual		
(c) McCulloh	X	Annual		
(d) Radio alarm transmitter (RAT)	X	Annual		
(e) All other types of communicators	X	Annual		
5. In-building fire emergency voice/alarm communications equipment	X	Semiannual	Verify location and condition.	
6. Reserved				
7. Reserved				
8. Reserved				
9. Batteries			Inspect for corrosion or leakage. Verify tightness of connections. Verify marking of the month/year of manufacture (all types).	10.6.10
(a) Lead-acid	X	Monthly	Visually inspect electrolyte level.	
(b) Nickel-cadmium	X	Semiannual		
(c) Primary (dry cell)	X	Monthly		
(d) Sealed lead-acid	X	Semiannual		
10. Reserved				

(continues)

Table 14.3.1 *Continued*

Component	Initial Acceptance	Periodic Frequency	Method	Reference
11. Remote annunciators	X	Semiannual	Verify location and condition.	
12. Notification appliance circuit power extenders	X	Annual	Verify proper fuse ratings, if any. Verify that lamps and LEDs indicate normal operating status of the equipment.	10.6
13. Remote power supplies	X	Annual	Verify proper fuse ratings, if any. Verify that lamps and LEDs indicate normal operating status of the equipment.	10.6
14. Transient suppressors	X	Semiannual	Verify location and condition.	
15. Reserved				
16. Fiber-optic cable connections	X	Annual	Verify location and condition.	
17. Initiating devices			Verify location and condition (all devices).	
(a) Air sampling				
(1) General	X	Semiannual	Verify that in-line filters, if any, are clean.	17.7.3.6
(2) Sampling system piping and sampling ports	X		Verify that sampling system piping and fittings are installed properly, appear airtight, and are permanently fixed. Confirm that sampling pipe is conspicuously identified. Verify that sample ports or points are not obstructed.	17.7.3.6
(b) Duct detectors				
(1) General	X	Semiannual	Verify that detector is rigidly mounted. Confirm that no penetrations in a return air duct exist in the vicinity of the detector. Confirm the detector is installed so as to sample the airstream at the proper location in the duct.	17.7.5.5
(2) Sampling tube	X		Verify proper orientation. Confirm the sampling tube protrudes into the duct in accordance with system design.	17.7.5.5
(c) Electromechanical releasing devices	X	Semiannual		
(d) Fire extinguishing system(s) or suppression system(s) switches	X	Semiannual		
(e) Manual fire alarm boxes	X	Semiannual		
(f) Heat detectors	X	Semiannual		
(g) Radiant energy fire detectors	X	Quarterly	Verify no point requiring detection is obstructed or outside the detector's field of view.	17.8
(h) Video image smoke and fire detectors	X	Quarterly	Verify no point requiring detection is obstructed or outside the detector's field of view.	17.7.7; 17.11.5
(i) Smoke detectors (excluding one- and two-family dwellings)	X	Semiannual		
(j) Projected beam smoke detectors	X	Semiannual	Verify beam path is unobstructed.	
(k) Supervisory signal devices	X	Quarterly		
(l) Waterflow devices	X	Quarterly		
18. Reserved				

Table 14.3.1 *Continued*

Component	Initial Acceptance	Periodic Frequency	Method	Reference
19. Combination systems			Verify location and condition (all types).	
(a) Fire extinguisher electronic monitoring device/systems	X	Semiannual		
(b) Carbon monoxide detectors/systems	X	Semiannual		
20. Fire alarm control interface and emergency control function interface	X	Semiannual	Verify location and condition.	
21. Guard's tour equipment	X	Semiannual	Verify location and condition.	
22. Notification appliances			Verify location and condition (all appliances).	
(a) Audible appliances	X	Semiannual		
(b) Audible textual notification appliances	X	Semiannual		
(c) Visible appliances				
(1) General	X	Semiannual		18.5.5
(2) Candela rating	X		Verify that the candela rating marking agrees with the approved drawings.	18.5.5
23. Exit marking audible notification appliances	X	Semiannual	Verify location and condition.	
24. Reserved				
25. Area of refuge two-way communication system	X	Annual	Verify location and condition.	
26. Reserved				
27. Supervising station alarm systems — receivers				
(a) Signal receipt	X	Daily	Verify receipt of signal.	
(b) Receivers	X	Annual	Verify location and normal condition.	
28. Public emergency alarm reporting system transmission equipment			Verify location and condition.	
(a) Publicly accessible alarm box	X	Semiannual		
(b) Auxiliary box	X	Annual		
(c) Master box				
(1) Manual operation	X	Semiannual		
(2) Auxiliary operation	X	Annual		
29. Reserved				
30. Mass notification system				
(a) Monitored for integrity			Verify a system normal condition.	
(1) Control equipment				
(i) Fuses	X	Annual		
(ii) Interfaces	X	Annual		
(iii) Lamps/LED	X	Annual		
(iv) Primary (main) power supply	X	Annual		
(2) Secondary power batteries	X	Annual		
(3) Initiating devices	X	Annual		
(4) Notification appliances	X	Annual		

(continues)

Table 14.3.1 *Continued*

Component	Initial Acceptance	Periodic Frequency	Method	Reference
30. Mass notification system *(continued)*				
(b) Not monitored for integrity; installed prior to adoption of the 2010 edition			Verify a system normal condition.	
(1) Control equipment				
(i) Fuses	X	Semiannual		
(ii) Interfaces	X	Semiannual		
(iii) Lamps/LED	X	Semiannual		
(iv) Primary (main) power supply	X	Semiannual		
(2) Secondary power batteries	X	Semiannual		
(3) Initiating devices	X	Semiannual		
(4) Notification appliances	X	Semiannual		
(c) Antenna	X	Annual	Verify location and condition.	
(d) Transceivers	X	Annual	Verify location and condition.	

14.3.2 Devices or equipment that is inaccessible for safety considerations (e.g., continuous process operations, energized electrical equipment, radiation, and excessive height) shall be permitted to be inspected during scheduled shutdowns if approved by the authority having jurisdiction.

14.3.3 Extended intervals shall not exceed 18 months.

14.3.4 The visual inspection shall be made to ensure that there are no changes that affect equipment performance.

14.4 Testing.

14.4.1 Initial Acceptance Testing.

14.4.1.1 All new systems shall be inspected and tested in accordance with the requirements of Chapter 14.

14.4.1.2 The authority having jurisdiction shall be notified prior to the initial acceptance test.

14.4.2* Reacceptance Testing.

14.4.2.1 When an initiating device, notification appliance, or control relay is added, it shall be functionally tested.

14.4.2.2 When an initiating device, notification appliance, or control relay is deleted, another device, appliance, or control relay on the circuit shall be operated.

14.4.2.3 When modifications or repairs to control equipment hardware are made, the control equipment shall be tested in accordance with Table 14.4.3.2, items 1(a) and 1(d).

14.4.2.4 When changes are made to site-specific software, the following shall apply:

(1) All functions known to be affected by the change, or identified by a means that indicates changes, shall be 100 percent tested.

(2) In addition, 10 percent of initiating devices that are not directly affected by the change, up to a maximum of 50 devices, also shall be tested and correct system operation shall be verified.

(3) A revised record of completion in accordance with 7.5.6 shall be prepared to reflect these changes.

14.4.2.5 Changes to the system executive software shall require a 10 percent functional test of the system, including a test of at least one device on each input and output circuit to verify critical system functions such as notification appliances, control functions, and off-premises reporting.

14.4.3* Test Methods.

14.4.3.1* At the request of the authority having jurisdiction, the central station facility installation shall be inspected for complete information regarding the central station system, including specifications, wiring diagrams, and floor plans that have been submitted for approval prior to installation of equipment and wiring.

14.4.3.2* Systems and associated equipment shall be tested according to Table 14.4.3.2.

> Table 14.4.3.2 was revised by tentative interim amendments (TIAs). See page 1.

Table 14.4.3.2 Testing

	Component	Initial Acceptance	Periodic Frequency	Method
1.	All equipment	X		See Table 14.3.1.
2.	Control equipment and transponder			
	(a) Functions	X	Annually	Verify correct receipt of alarm, supervisory, and trouble signals (inputs); operation of evacuation signals and auxiliary functions (outputs); circuit supervision, including detection of open circuits and ground faults; and power supply supervision for detection of loss of ac power and disconnection of secondary batteries.
	(b) Fuses	X	Annually	Verify rating and supervision.
	(c) Interfaced equipment	X	Annually	Verify integrity of single or multiple circuits providing interface between two or more control units. Test interfaced equipment connections by operating or simulating operation of the equipment being supervised. Verify signals required to be transmitted at the control unit.
	(d) Lamps and LEDs	X	Annually	Illuminate lamps and LEDs.
	(e) Primary (main) power supply	X	Annually	Disconnect and test all secondary (standby) power under maximum load, including all alarm appliances requiring simultaneous operation. Reconnect all secondary (standby) power at end of test. Test redundant power supplies separately.
3.	Fire alarm control unit trouble signals			
	(a) Audible and visual	X	Annually	Verify operation of control unit trouble signals. Verify ring-back feature for systems using a trouble-silencing switch that requires resetting.
	(b) Disconnect switches	X	Annually	If control unit has disconnect or isolating switches, verify performance of intended function of each switch. Verify receipt of trouble signal when a supervised function is disconnected.
	(c) Ground-fault monitoring circuit	X	Annually	If the system has a ground detection feature, verify the occurrence of ground-fault indication whenever any installation conductor is grounded.
	(d) Transmission of signals to off-premises location	X	Annually	Actuate an initiating device and verify receipt of alarm signal at the off-premises location. Create a trouble condition and verify receipt of a trouble signal at the off-premises location. Actuate a supervisory device and verify receipt of a supervisory signal at the off-premises location. If a transmission carrier is capable of operation under a single- or multiple-fault condition, activate an initiating device during such fault condition and verify receipt of an alarm signal and a trouble signal at the off-premises location.
4.	Supervising station alarm systems — transmission Equipment			
	(a) All equipment	X	Annually	[a]Test all system functions and features in accordance with the equipment manufacturer's published instructions for correct operation in conformance with the applicable sections of Chapter 26. Except for DACT, actuate initiating device and verify receipt of the correct initiating device signal at the supervising station within 90 seconds. Upon completion of the test, restore the system to its functional operating condition. If test jacks are used, conduct the first and last tests without the use of the test jack.
	(b) Digital alarm communicator transmitter (DACT)	X	Annually	Except for DACTs installed prior to adoption of the 2013 edition of NFPA 72 that are connected to a telephone line (number) that is also supervised for adverse conditions by a derived local channel, ensure connection of the DACT to two separate means of transmission. Test DACT for line seizure capability by initiating a signal while using the telephone line (primary line for DACTs using two telephone lines) for a telephone call. Ensure that the call is interrupted and that the communicator connects to the digital alarm receiver. Verify receipt of the correct signal at the supervising station. Verify each transmission attempt is completed within 90 seconds from going off-hook to on-hook.

(continues)

Table 14.4.3.2 *Continued*

Component	Initial Acceptance	Periodic Frequency	Method
4. Supervising station alarm systems — transmission Equipment			
(b) Digital alarm communicator transmitter (DACT) *(continued)*			Disconnect the telephone line (primary line for DACTs using two telephone lines) from the DACT.
			Verify indication of the DACT trouble signal occurs at the premises fire alarm control unit within 4 minutes of detection of the fault. Verify receipt of the telephone line trouble signal at the supervising station. Restore the telephone line (primary line for DACTs using two telephone lines), reset the fire alarm control unit, and verify that the telephone line fault trouble signal returns to normal. Verify that the supervising station receives the restoral signal from the DACT.
			Disconnect the secondary means of transmission from the DACT. Verify indication of the DACT trouble signal occurs at the premises fire alarm control unit within 4 minutes of detection of the fault. Verify receipt of the secondarey means trouble signal at the supervising station. Restore the secondary means of transmission, reset the fire alarm control unit, and verify that the trouble signal returns to normal. Verify that the supervising station receives the restoral signal from the secondary transmitter.
			Cause the DACT to transmit a signal to the DACR while a fault in the telephone line (number) (primary line for DACTs using two telephone lines) is simulated. Verify utilization of the secondary communication path by the DACT to complete the transmission to the DACR.
(c) Digital alarm radio transmitter (DART)	X	Annually	Disconnect the primary telephone line. Verify transmission of a trouble signal to the supervising station by the DART occurs within 4 minutes.
(d) McCulloh transmitter	X	Annually	Actuate initiating device. Verify production of not less than three complete rounds of not less than three signal impulses each by the McCulloh transmitter.
			If end-to-end metallic continuity is present and with a balanced circuit, cause each of the following four transmission channel fault conditions in turn, and verify receipt of correct signals at the supervising station:
			(1) Open
			(2) Ground
			(3) Wire-to-wire short
			(4) Open and ground
			If end-to-end metallic continuity is not present and with a properly balanced circuit, cause each of the following three transmission channel fault conditions in turn, and verify receipt of correct signals at the supervising station:
			(1) Open
			(2) Ground
			(3) Wire-to-wire short
(e) Radio alarm transmitter (RAT)	X	Annually	Cause a fault between elements of the transmitting equipment. Verify indication of the fault at the protected premises, or transmission of trouble signal to the supervising station.
(f) Performance-based technologies	X	Annually	Perform tests to ensure the monitoring of integrity of the transmission technology and technology path.
			Where a single communications path is used, disconnect the communication path. Manually initiate an alarm signal transmission or allow the check-in (handshake) signal to be transmitted automatically.[b] Verify the premises unit annunciates the failure within 200 seconds of the transmission failure. Restore the communication path.
			Where multiple communication paths are used, disconnect both communication paths. Manually initiate an alarm signal transmission. Verify the premises control unit annunciates the failure within 200 seconds of the transmission failure. Restore both communication paths.
5. Emergency communications equipment			
(a) Amplifier/tone generators	X	Annually	Verify correct switching and operation of backup equipment.
(b) Call-in signal silence	X	Annually	Operate/function and verify receipt of correct visual and audible signals at control unit.
(c) Off-hook indicator (ring down)	X	Annually	Install phone set or remove phone from hook and verify receipt of signal at control unit.
(d) Phone jacks	X	Annually	Visually inspect phone jack and initiate communications path through jack.

Table 14.4.3.2 *Continued*

Component	Initial Acceptance	Periodic Frequency	Method
(e) Phone set	X	Annually	Activate each phone set and verify correct operation.
(f) System performance	X	Annually	Operate the system with a minimum of any five handsets simultaneously. Verify voice quality and clarity.
6. Engine-driven generator	X	Monthly	If an engine-driven generator dedicated to the system is used as a required power source, verify operation of the generator in accordance with NFPA 110, *Standard for Emergency and Standby Power Systems,* by the building owner.
7. Secondary (standby) power supply[c]	X	Annually	Disconnect all primary (main) power supplies and verify the occurrence of required trouble indication for loss of primary power. Measure or verify the system's standby and alarm current demand and verify the ability of batteries to meet standby and alarm requirements using manufacturer's data. Operate general alarm systems a minimum of 5 minutes and emergency voice communications systems for a minimum of 15 minutes. Reconnect primary (main) power supply at end of test.
8. Uninterruptible power supply (UPS)	X	Annually	If a UPS system dedicated to the system is used as a required power source, verify by the building owner operation of the UPS system in accordance with NFPA 111, *Standard on Stored Electrical Energy Emergency and Standby Power Systems.*
9. Battery tests			Prior to conducting any battery testing, verify by the person conducting the test, that all system software stored in volatile memory is protected from loss.
(a) Lead-acid type			
(1) Battery replacement	X	Annually	Replace batteries in accordance with the recommendations of the alarm equipment manufacturer or when the recharged battery voltage or current falls below the manufacturer's recommendations.
(2) Charger test	X	Annually	With the batteries fully charged and connected to the charger, measure the voltage across the batteries with a voltmeter. Verify the voltage is 2.30 volts per cell ±0.02 volts at 77°F (25°C) or as specified by the equipment manufacturer.
(3) Discharge test	X	Annually	With the battery charger disconnected, load test the batteries following the manufacturer's recommendations. Verify the voltage level does not fall below the levels specified. Load testing can be by means of an artificial load equal to the full fire alarm load connected to the battery.
(4) Load voltage test	X	Semiannually	With the battery charger disconnected, load test the batteries following the manufacturer's recommendations. Verify the voltage level does not fall below the levels specified. Load testing can be by means of an artificial load equal to the full fire alarm load connected to the battery. Verify the battery does not fall below 2.05 volts per cell under load.
(5) Specific gravity	X	Semiannually	Measure as required the specific gravity of the liquid in the pilot cell or all of the cells. Verify the specific gravity is within the range specified by the manufacturer. Although the specified specific gravity varies from manufacturer to manufacturer, a range of 1.205–1.220 is typical for regular lead-acid batteries, while 1.240–1.260 is typical for high-performance batteries. Do not use a hydrometer that shows only a pass or fail condition of the battery and does not indicate the specific gravity, because such a reading does not give a true indication of the battery condition.
(b) Nickel-cadmium type			
(1) Battery replacement	X	Annually	Replace batteries in accordance with the recommendations of the alarm equipment manufacturer or when the recharged battery voltage or current falls below the manufacturer's recommendations.
(2) Charger test[d]	X	Annually	With the batteries fully charged and connected to the charger, place an ampere meter in series with the battery under charge. Verify the charging current is in accordance with the manufacturer's recommendations for the type of battery used. In the absence of specific information, use $\frac{1}{30}$ to $\frac{1}{25}$ of the battery rating.
(3) Discharge test	X	Annually	With the battery charger disconnected, load test the batteries following the manufacturer's recommendations. Verify the voltage level does not fall below the levels specified. Load testing can be by means of an artificial load equal to the full fire alarm load connected to the battery.
(4) Load voltage test	X	Semiannually	With the battery charger disconnected, load test the batteries following the manufacturer's recommendations. Verify the voltage level does not fall below the levels specified. Load testing can be by means of an artificial load equal to the full fire alarm load connected to the battery. Verify the float voltage for the entire battery is 1.42 volts per cell, nominal, under load. If possible, measure cells individually.

(continues)

Table 14.4.3.2 *Continued*

Component	Initial Acceptance	Periodic Frequency	Method
9. Battery tests *(continued)*			
(c) Sealed lead-acid type			
(1) Battery replacement	X	Annually	Replace batteries in accordance with the recommendations of the alarm equipment manufacturer or when the recharged battery voltage or current falls below the manufacturer's recommendations.
(2) Charger test	X	Annually	With the batteries fully charged and connected to the charger, measure the voltage across the batteries with a voltmeter. Verify the voltage is 2.30 volts per cell ±0.02 volts at 77°F (25°C) or as specified by the equipment manufacturer.
(3) Discharge test	X	Annually	With the battery charger disconnected, load test the batteries following the manufacturer's recommendations. Verify the voltage level does not fall below the levels specified. Load testing can be by means of an artificial load equal to the full fire alarm load connected to the battery.
(4) Load voltage test	X	Semiannually	Verify the battery performs under load, in accordance with the battery manufacturer's specifications.
10. Public emergency alarm reporting system — wired system	X	Daily	Manual tests of the power supply for public reporting circuits shall be made and recorded at least once during each 24-hour period. Such tests shall include the following: (1) Current strength of each circuit. Changes in current of any circuit exceeding 10 percent shall be investigated immediately. (2) Voltage across terminals of each circuit inside of terminals of protective devices. Changes in voltage of any circuit exceeding 10 percent shall be investigated immediately. (3)[e] Voltage between ground and circuits. If this test shows a reading in excess of 50 percent of that shown in the test specified in (2), the trouble shall be immediately located and cleared. Readings in excess of 25 percent shall be given early attention. These readings shall be taken with a calibrated voltmeter of not more than 100 ohms resistance per volt. Systems in which each circuit is supplied by an independent current source (Forms 3 and 4) require tests between ground and each side of each circuit. Common current source systems (Form 2) require voltage tests between ground and each terminal of each battery and other current source. (4) Ground current reading shall be permitted in lieu of (3). If this method of testing is used, all grounds showing a current reading in excess of 5 percent of the supplied line current shall be given immediate attention. (5) Voltage across terminals of common battery on switchboard side of fuses. (6) Voltage between common battery terminals and ground. Abnormal ground readings shall be investigated immediately. Tests specified in (5) and (6) shall apply only to those systems using a common battery. If more than one common battery is used, each common battery shall be tested.
11. Remote annunciators	X	Annually	Verify the correct operation and identification of annunciators. If provided, verify the correct operation of annunciator under a fault condition.
12. Reserved			
13. Reserved			
14. Reserved			
15. Conductors — metallic			
(a) Stray voltage	X	N/A	Test all installation conductors with a volt/ohmmeter to verify that there are no stray (unwanted) voltages between installation conductors or between installation conductors and ground. Verify the maximum allowable stray voltage does not exceed 1 volt ac/dc, unless a different threshold is specified in the published manufacturer's instructions for the installed equipment.
(b) Ground faults	X	N/A	Test all installation conductors, other than those intentionally and permanently grounded, for isolation from ground per the installed equipment manufacturer's published instructions.
(c) Short-circuit faults	X	N/A	Test all installation conductors, other than those intentionally connected together, for conductor-to-conductor isolation per the published manufacturer's instructions for the installed equipment. Also test these same circuits conductor-to-ground.

Table 14.4.3.2 *Continued*

Component	Initial Acceptance	Periodic Frequency	Method
(d) Loop resistance	X	N/A	With each initiating and indicating circuit installation conductor pair short-circuited at the far end, measure and record the resistance of each circuit. Verify that the loop resistance does not exceed the limits specified in the published manufacturer's instructions for the installed equipment.
(e) Circuit integrity	X	N/A	For initial and reacceptance testing, confirm the introduction of a fault in any circuit monitored for integrity results in a trouble indication at the fire alarm control unit. Open one connection at not less than 10 percent of the initiating devices, notification appliances and controlled devices on every initiating device circuit, notification appliance circuit, and signaling line circuit. Confirm all circuits perform as indicated in Sections 23.5, 23.6, and 23.7.
	N/A	Annually	For periodic testing, test each initiating device circuit, notification appliance circuit, and signaling line circuit for correct indication at the control unit. Confirm all circuits perform as indicated in Sections 23.5, 23.6, and 23.7.
16. Conductors — nonmetallic			
(a) Fiber optics	X	N/A	Test the fiber-optic transmission line by the use of an optical power meter or by an optical time domain reflectometer used to measure the relative power loss of the line. Test result data must meet or exceed ANSI/TIA 568-C.3, *Optical Fiber Cabling Components Standard*, related to fiber-optic lines and connection/splice losses and the control unit manufacturer's published specifications.
(b) Circuit integrity	X	N/A	For initial and reacceptance testing, confirm the introduction of a fault in any circuit monitored for integrity results in a trouble indication at the fire alarm control unit. Open one connection at not less than 10 percent of the initiating devices, notification appliances, and controlled devices on every initiating device circuit, notification appliance circuit, and signaling line circuit. Confirm all circuits perform as indicated in Sections 23.5, 23.6, and 23.7.
	N/A	Annually	For periodic testing, test each initiating device circuit, notification appliance circuit, and signaling line circuit for correct indication at the control unit. Confirm all circuits perform as indicated in Sections 23.5, 23.6, and 23.7.
17. Initiating devices[f]			
(a) Electromechanical releasing device			
(1) Nonrestorable-type link	X	Annually	Verify correct operation by removal of the fusible link and operation of the associated device. Lubricate any moving parts as necessary.
(2) Restorable-type link[g]	X	Annually	Verify correct operation by removal of the fusible link and operation of the associated device. Lubricate any moving parts as necessary.
(b) Fire extinguishing system(s) or suppression system(s) alarm switch	X	Annually	Operate the switch mechanically or electrically and verify receipt of signal by the fire alarm control unit.
(c) Fire–gas and other detectors	X	Annually	Test fire–gas detectors and other fire detectors as prescribed by the manufacturer and as necessary for the application.
(d) Heat detectors			
(1) Fixed-temperature, rate-of-rise, rate of compensation, restorable line, spot type (excluding pneumatic tube type)	X	Annually (see 14.4.4.5)	Perform heat test with a listed and labeled heat source or in accordance with the manufacturer's published instructions. Assure that the test method for the installed equipment does not damage the nonrestorable fixed-temperature element of a combination rate-of-rise/fixed-temperature element detector.
(2) Fixed-temperature, nonrestorable line type	X	Annually	Do not perform heat test. Test functionality mechanically and electrically. Measure and record loop resistance. Investigate changes from acceptance test.
(3) Fixed-temperature, nonrestorable spot type	X	See Method	After 15 years from initial installation, replace all devices or have 2 detectors per 100 laboratory tested. Replace the 2 detectors with new devices. If a failure occurs on any of the detectors removed, remove and test additional detectors to determine either a general problem involving faulty detectors or a localized problem involving 1 or 2 defective detectors. If detectors are tested instead of replaced, repeat tests at intervals of 5 years.
(4) Nonrestorable (general)	X	Annually	Do not perform heat tests. Test functionality mechanically and electrically.
(5) Restorable line type, pneumatic tube only	X	Annually	Perform heat tests (where test chambers are in circuit), with a listed and labeled heat source or in accordance with the manufacturer's published instructions of the detector or conduct a test with pressure pump.

(continues)

Table 14.4.3.2 *Continued*

Component	Initial Acceptance	Periodic Frequency	Method
17. Initiating devices[f]			
(d) Heat detectors *(continued)*			
(6) Single- and multiple-station heat alarms	X	Annually	Conduct functional tests according to manufacturer's published instructions. Do not test nonrestorable heat detectors with heat.
(e) Manual fire alarm boxes	X	Annually	Operate manual fire alarm boxes per the manufacturer's published instructions. Test both key-operated presignal and general alarm manual fire alarm boxes.
(f) Radiant energy fire detectors	X	Semiannually	Test flame detectors and spark/ember detectors in accordance with the manufacturer's published instructions to determine that each detector is operative. Determine flame detector and spark/ember detector sensitivity using any of the following: (1) Calibrated test method (2) Manufacturer's calibrated sensitivity test instrument (3) Listed control unit arranged for the purpose (4) Other approved calibrated sensitivity test method that is directly proportional to the input signal from a fire, consistent with the detector listing or approval If designed to be field adjustable, replace detectors found to be outside of the approved range of sensitivity or adjust to bring them into the approved range. Do not determine flame detector and spark/ember detector sensitivity using a light source that administers an unmeasured quantity of radiation at an undefined distance from the detector.
(g) Smoke detectors — functional test			
(1) In other than one- and two-family dwellings, system detectors	X	Annually	[h]Test smoke detectors in place to ensure smoke entry into the sensing chamber and an alarm response. Use smoke or a listed and labeled product acceptable to the manufacturer or in accordance with their published instructions. Other methods listed in the manufacturer's published instructions that ensure smoke entry from the protected area, through the vents, into the sensing chamber can be used.
(2) Single- and multiple-station smoke alarms connected to protected premises systems	X	Annually	Perform a functional test on all single- and multiple-station smoke alarms connected to a protected premises fire alarm system by putting the smoke alarm into an alarm condition and verifying that the protected premises system receives a supervisory signal and does not cause a fire alarm signal.
(3) System smoke detectors used in one- and two-family dwellings	X	Annually	Conduct functional tests according to manufacturer's published instructions.
(4) Air sampling	X	Annually	Test with smoke or a listed and labeled product acceptable to the manufacturer or in accordance with their published instructions. Test from the end sampling port or point on each pipe run. Verify airflow through all other ports or points.
(5) Duct type	X	Annually	In addition to the testing required in Table 14.4.3.2(g)(1) and Table 14.4.3.2(h), test duct smoke detectors that use sampling tubes to ensure that they will properly sample the airstream in the duct using a method acceptable to the manufacturer or in accordance with their published instructions.
(6) Projected beam type	X	Annually	Test the detector by introducing smoke, other aerosol, or an optical filter into the beam path.
(7) Smoke detector with built-in thermal element	X	Annually	Operate both portions of the detector independently as described for the respective devices.
(8) Smoke detectors with control output functions	X	Annually	Verify that the control capability remains operable even if all of the initiating devices connected to the same initiating device circuit or signaling line circuit are in an alarm state.
(h) Smoke detectors — sensitivity testing			
In other than one- and two-family dwellings, system detectors	N/A	See 14.4.4.3	[i]Perform any of the following tests to ensure that each smoke detector is within its listed and marked sensitivity range: (1) Calibrated test method (2) Manufacturer's calibrated sensitivity test instrument (3) Listed control equipment arranged for the purpose

Table 14.4.3.2 *Continued*

Component	Initial Acceptance	Periodic Frequency	Method
			(4) Smoke detector/control unit arrangement whereby the detector causes a signal at the control unit when its sensitivity is outside its listed sensitivity range
			(5) Other calibrated sensitivity test method approved by the authority having jurisdiction
(i) Carbon monoxide detectors/carbon monoxide alarms for the purposes of fire detection	X	Annually	Test the devices in place to ensure CO entry to the sensing chamber by introduction through the vents, to the sensing chamber of listed and labeled product acceptable to the manufacturer or in accordance with their published instructions.
(j) Initiating devices, supervisory			
(1) Control valve switch	X	Annually	Operate valve and verify signal receipt to be within the first two revolutions of the handwheel or within one-fifth of the travel distance, or per the manufacturer's published instructions.
(2) High- or low-air pressure switch	X	Annually	Operate switch and verify receipt of signal is obtained where the required pressure is increased or decreased a maximum 10 psi (70 kPa) from the required pressure level.
(3) Room temperature switch	X	Annually	Operate switch and verify receipt of signal to indicate the decrease in room temperature to 40°F (4.4°C) and its restoration to above 40°F (4.4°C).
(4) Water level switch	X	Annually	Operate switch and verify receipt of signal indicating the water level raised or lowered a maximum 3 in. (70 mm) from the required level within a pressure tank, or a maximum 12 in. (300 mm) from the required level of a nonpressure tank. Also verify its restoral to required level.
(5) Water temperature switch	X	Annually	Operate switch and verify receipt of signal to indicate the decrease in water temperature to 40°F (4.4°C) and its restoration to above 40°F (4.4°C).
(k) Mechanical, electrosonic, or pressure-type waterflow device	X	Semiannually	Water shall be flowed through an inspector's test connection indicating the flow of water equal to that from a single sprinkler of the smallest orifice size installed in the system for wet-pipe systems, or an alarm test bypass connection for dry-pipe, pre-action, or deluge systems in accordance with NFPA 25, *Standard for the Inspection, Testing, and Maintenance of Water-Based Fire Protection Systems.*
(l) Multi-sensor fire detector or multi-criteria fire detector or combination fire detector	X	Annually	Test each of the detection principles present within the detector (e.g., smoke/heat/CO, etc.) independently for the specific detection principle, regardless of the configuration status at the time of testing. Also test each detector in accordance with the published manufacturer's instructions.
			Test individual sensors together if the technology allows individual sensor responses to be verified.
			Perform tests as described for the respective devices by introduction of the physical phenomena to the sensing chamber of element, and an electronic check (magnets, analogue values, etc.) is not sufficient to comply with this requirement.
			Confirm the result of each sensor test through indication at the detector or control unit.
			Where individual sensors cannot be tested individually, test the primary sensor.[j]
			Record all tests and results.
18. Special hazard equipment			
(a) Abort switch (dead-man type)	X	Annually	Operate abort switch and verify correct sequence and operation.
(b) Abort switch (recycle type)	X	Annually	Operate abort switch and verify development of correct matrix with each sensor operated.
(c) Abort switch (special type)	X	Annually	Operate abort switch and verify correct sequence and operation in accordance with authority having jurisdiction. Observe sequencing as specified on as-built drawings or in system owner's manual.
(d) Cross-zone detection circuit	X	Annually	Operate one sensor or detector on each zone. Verify occurrence of correct sequence with operation of first zone and then with operation of second zone.
(e) Matrix-type circuit	X	Annually	Operate all sensors in system. Verify development of correct matrix with each sensor operated.
(f) Release solenoid circuit[k]	X	Annually	Verify operation of solenoid.
(g) Squibb release circuit	X	Annually	Use AGI flashbulb or other test light approved by the manufacturer. Verify operation of flashbulb or light.
(h) Verified, sequential, or counting zone circuit	X	Annually	Operate required sensors at a minimum of four locations in circuit. Verify correct sequence with both the first and second detector in alarm.
(i) All above devices or circuits or combinations thereof	X	Annually	Verify supervision of circuits by creating an open circuit.

(continues)

Table 14.4.3.2 *Continued*

Component	Initial Acceptance	Periodic Frequency	Method
19. Combination systems			
(a) Fire extinguisher electronic monitoring device/system	X	Annually	Test communication between the device connecting the fire extinguisher electronic monitoring device/system and the fire alarm control unit to ensure proper signals are received at the fire alarm control unit and remote annunciator(s) if applicable.
(b) Carbon monoxide[l] device/system	X	Annually	Test communication between the device connecting the carbon monoxide device/system and the fire alarm control unit to ensure proper signals are received at the fire alarm control unit and remote annunciator(s) if applicable.
20. Interface equipment[m]	X	See 14.4.4.4	Test interface equipment connections by operating or simulating the equipment being supervised. Verify signals required to be transmitted are received at the control unit. Test frequency for interface equipment is the same as the frequency required by the applicable NFPA standard(s) for the equipment being supervised.
21. Guard's tour equipment	X	Annually	Test the device in accordance with the manufacturer's published instructions.
22. Alarm notification appliances			
(a) Audible[n]	X	N/A	For initial and reacceptance testing, measure sound pressure levels for signals with a sound level meter meeting ANSI S1.4a, *Specifications for Sound Level Meters,* Type 2 requirements. Measure sound pressure levels throughout the protected area to confirm that they are in compliance with Chapter 18. Set the sound level meter in accordance with ANSI S3.41, *American National Standard Audible Evacuation Signal,* using the time-weighted characteristic F (FAST).
	N/A	Annually	[o]For periodic testing, verify the operation of the notification appliances.
(b) Audible textual notification appliances (speakers and other appliances to convey voice messages)	X	N/A	For initial and reacceptance testing, measure sound pressure levels for signals with a sound level meter meeting ANSI S1.4a, *Specifications for Sound Level Meters,* Type 2 requirements. Measure sound pressure levels throughout the protected area to confirm that they are in compliance with Chapter 18. Set the sound level meter in accordance with ANSI S3.41, *American National Standard Audible Evacuation Signal,* using the time-weighted characteristic F (FAST). Verify audible information to be distinguishable and understandable and in compliance with 14.4.11.
	N/A	Annually	[o]For periodic testing, verify the operation of the notification appliances.
(c) Visible	X	N/A	Perform initial and reacceptance testing in accordance with the manufacturer's published instructions. Verify appliance locations to be per approved layout and confirm that no floor plan changes affect the approved layout. Verify that the candela rating marking agrees with the approved drawing. Confirm that each appliance flashes.
	N/A	Annually	For periodic testing, verify that each appliance flashes.
23. Exit marking audible notification appliance	X	Annually	Perform tests in accordance with manufacturer's published instructions.
24. Emergency control functions[p]	X	Annually	For initial, reacceptance, and periodic testing, verify emergency control function interface device activation. Where an emergency control function interface device is disabled or disconnected during initiating device testing, verify that the disabled or disconnected emergency control function interface device has been properly restored. [
25. Area of refuge two-way communication system	X	Annually	At a minimum, test the two-way communication system to verify operation and receipt of visual and audible signals at the transmitting and receiving unit respectively. Operate systems with more than five stations with a minimum of five stations operating simultaneously. Verify voice quality and clarity.
26. Special procedures			
(a) Alarm verification	X	Annually	Verify time delay and alarm response for smoke detector circuits identified as having alarm verification.
(b) Multiplex systems	X	Annually	Verify communications between sending and receiving units under both primary and secondary power. Verify communications between sending and receiving units under open-circuit and short-circuit trouble conditions.

Table 14.4.3.2 *Continued*

Component	Initial Acceptance	Periodic Frequency	Method
			Verify communications between sending and receiving units in all directions where multiple communications pathways are provided. If redundant central control equipment is provided, verify switchover and all required functions and operations of secondary control equipment. Verify all system functions and features in accordance with manufacturer's published instructions.
27. Supervising station alarm systems — receiving equipment			
(a) All equipment	X	Monthly	Perform tests on all system functions and features in accordance with the equipment manufacturer's published instructions for correct operation in conformance with the applicable sections of Chapter 26. Actuate initiating device and verify receipt of the correct initiating device signal at the supervising station within 90 seconds. Upon completion of the test, restore the system to its functional operating condition. If test jacks are used, perform the first and last tests without the use of the test jack.
(b) Digital alarm communicator receiver (DACR)	X	Monthly	Disconnect each transmission means in turn from the DACR, and verify audible and visual annunciation of a trouble signal in the supervising station. Cause a signal to be transmitted on each individual incoming DACR line (path) at least once every 6 hours (24 hours for DACTs installed prior to adoption of the 2013 edition of *NFPA 72*). Verify receipt of these signals.
(c) Digital alarm radio receiver (DARR)	X	Monthly	Cause the following conditions of all DARRs on all subsidiary and repeater station receiving equipment. Verify receipt at the supervising station of correct signals for each of the following conditions: (1) AC power failure of the radio equipment (2) Receiver malfunction (3) Antenna and interconnecting cable failure (4) Indication of automatic switchover of the DARR (5) Data transmission line failure between the DARR and the supervising or subsidiary station
(d) McCulloh systems	X	Monthly	Test and record the current on each circuit at each supervising and subsidiary station under the following conditions: (1) During functional operation (2) On each side of the circuit with the receiving equipment conditioned for an open circuit Cause a single break or ground condition on each transmission channel. If such a fault prevents the functioning of the circuit, verify receipt of a trouble signal. Cause each of the following conditions at each of the supervising or subsidiary stations and all repeater station radio transmitting and receiving equipment; verify receipt of correct signals at the supervising station: (1) RF transmitter in use (radiating) (2) AC power failure supplying the radio equipment (3) RF receiver malfunction (4) Indication of automatic switchover
(e) Radio alarm supervising station receiver (RASSR) and radio alarm repeater station receiver (RARSR)	X	Monthly	Cause each of the following conditions at each of the supervising or subsidiary stations and all repeater station radio transmitting and receiving equipment; verify receipt of correct signals at the supervising station: (1) AC power failure supplying the radio equipment (2) RF receiver malfunction (3) Indication of automatic switchover, if applicable
(f) Private microwave radio systems	X	Monthly	Cause each of the following conditions at each of the supervising or subsidiary stations and all repeater station radio transmitting and receiving equipment; verify receipt of correct signals at the supervising station: (1) RF transmitter in use (radiating) (2) AC power failure supplying the radio equipment (3) RF receiver malfunction (4) Indication of automatic switchover

(continues)

Table 14.4.3.2　*Continued*

Component	Initial Acceptance	Periodic Frequency	Method
27. Supervising station alarm systems — receiving equipment *(continued)*			
(g) Performance-based technologies	X	Monthly	Perform tests to ensure the monitoring of integrity of the transmission technology and technology path. Where a single communications path is used, disconnect the communication path. Verify that failure of the path is annunciated at the supervising station within 60 minutes of the failure (within 5 minutes for communication equipment installed prior to adoption of the 2013 edition of *NFPA 72*). Restore the communication path. Where multiple communication paths are used, disconnect both communication paths and confirm that failure of the path is annunciated at the supervising station within not more than 6 hours of the failure (within 24 hours for communication equipment installed prior to adoption of the 2013 edition of *NFPA 72*). Restore both communication paths.
28. Public emergency alarm reporting system transmission equipment			
(a) Publicly accessible alarm box	X	Semiannually	Actuate publicly accessible initiating device(s) and verify receipt of not less than three complete rounds of signal impulses. Perform this test under normal circuit conditions. If the device is equipped for open circuit operation (ground return), test it in this condition as one of the semiannual tests.
(b) Auxiliary box	X	Annually	Test each initiating circuit of the auxiliary box by actuation of a protected premises initiating device connected to that circuit. Verify receipt of not less than three complete rounds of signal impulses.
(c) Master box			
(1) Manual operation	X	Semiannually	Perform the tests prescribed for 28(a).
(2) Auxiliary operation	X	Annually	Perform the tests prescribed for 28(b).
29. Low-power radio (wireless systems)	X	N/A	The following procedures describe additional acceptance and reacceptance test methods to verify wireless protection system operation: (1) Use the manufacturer's published instructions and the as-built drawings provided by the system supplier to verify correct operation after the initial testing phase has been performed by the supplier or by the supplier's designated representative. (2) Starting from the functional operating condition, initialize the system in accordance with the manufacturer's published instructions. Confirm the alternative communications path exists between the wireless control unit and peripheral devices used to establish initiation, indication, control, and annunciation. Test the system for both alarm and trouble conditions. (3) Check batteries for all components in the system monthly unless the control unit checks all batteries and all components daily.
30. Mass notification systems			
(a) Functions	X	Annually	At a minimum, test control equipment to verify correct receipt of alarm, supervisory, and trouble signals (inputs); operation of evacuation signals and auxiliary functions (outputs); circuit supervision, including detection of open circuits and ground faults; and power supply supervision for detection of loss of ac power and disconnection of secondary batteries.
(b) Fuses	X	Annually	Verify the rating and supervision.
(c) Interfaced equipment	X	Annually	Verify integrity of single or multiple circuits providing interface between two or more control units. Test interfaced equipment connections by operating or simulating operation of the equipment being supervised. Verify signals required to be transmitted at the control unit.
(d) Lamps and LEDs	X	Annually	Illuminate lamps and LEDs.
(e) Primary (main) power supply	X	Annually	Disconnect all secondary (standby) power and test under maximum load, including all alarm appliances requiring simultaneous operation. Reconnect all secondary (standby) power at end of test. For redundant power supplies, test each separately.
(f) Audible textual notification appliances (speakers and other appliances to convey voice messages)	X	Annually	Measure sound pressure level with a sound level meter meeting ANSI S1.4a, *Specifications for Sound Level Meters*, Type 2 requirements. Measure and record levels throughout protected area. Set the sound level meter in accordance with ANSI S3.41, *American National Standard Audible Evacuation Signal*, using the time-weighted characteristic F (FAST). Record the maximum output when the audible emergency evacuation signal is on. Verify audible information to be distinguishable and understandable.

Table 14.4.3.2 *Continued*

Component	Initial Acceptance	Periodic Frequency	Method
(g) Visible	X	Annually	Perform test in accordance with manufacturer's published instructions. Verify appliance locations to be per approved layout and confirm that no floor plan changes affect the approved layout. Verify that the candela rating marking agrees with the approved drawing. Confirm that each appliance flashes.
(h) Control unit functions and no diagnostic failures are indicated	X	Annually	Review event log file and verify that the correct events were logged. Review system diagnostic log file; correct deficiencies noted in file. Delete unneeded log files. Delete unneeded error files. Verify that sufficient free disk space is available. Verify unobstructed flow of cooling air is available. Change/clean filters, cooling fans, and intake vents.
(i) Control unit reset	X	Annually	Power down the central control unit computer and restart it.
(j) Control unit security	X	Annually	If remote control software is loaded onto the system, verify that it is disabled to prevent unauthorized system access.
(k) Audible/visible functional test	X	Annually	Send out an alert to a diverse set of predesignated receiving devices and confirm receipt. Include at least one of each type of receiving device.
(l) Software backup	X	Annually	Make full system software backup. Rotate backups based on accepted practice at site.
(m) Secondary power test	X	Annually	Disconnect ac power. Verify the ac power failure alarm status on central control equipment. With ac power disconnected, verify battery voltage under load.
(n) Wireless signals	X	Annually	Check forward/reflected radio power is within specifications.
(o) Antenna	X	Annually	Check forward/reflected radio power is within specifications. Verify solid electrical connections with no observable corrosion.
(p) Transceivers	X	Annually	Verify proper operation and mounting is not compromised.

[a]Some transmission equipment (such as but not limited to cable modems, fiber-optic interface nodes, and VoIP interfaces) are typically powered by the building's electrical system using a standby power supply that does not meet the requirements of this Code. This is intended to ensure that the testing authority verifies full standby power as required by Chapter 10. Additionally, refer to Table 14.4.3.2, Items 7 through 9 for secondary power supply testing.

[b]The automatic transmission of the check-in (handshake) signal can take up to 60 minutes to occur.

[c]See Table 14.4.3.2, Item 4(a) for the testing of transmission equipment.

[d]Example: 4000 mAh × $\frac{1}{25}$ = 160 mA charging current at 77°F (25°C).

[e]The voltmeter sensitivity has been changed from 1000 ohms per volt to 100 ohms per volt so that the false ground readings (caused by induced voltages) are minimized.

[f]Initiating devices such as smoke detectors used for elevator recall, closing dampers, or releasing doors held in the open position that are permitted by the Code (*see* NFPA *101, Life Safety Code, 9.6.3*) to initiate supervisory signals at the fire alarm control unit (FACU) should be tested at the same frequency (annual) as those devices when they are generating an alarm signal. They are not supervisory devices, but they initiate a supervisory signal at the FACU.

[g]Fusible thermal link detectors are commonly used to close fire doors and fire dampers. They are actuated by the presence of external heat, which causes a solder element in the link to fuse, or by an electric thermal device, which, when energized, generates heat within the body of the link, causing the link to fuse and separate.

[h]Note, it is customary for the manufacturer of the smoke detector to test a particular product from an aerosol provider to determine acceptability for use in smoke entry testing of their smoke detector/ smoke alarm. Magnets are not acceptable for smoke entry tests.

[i] There are some detectors that use magnets as a manufacturer's calibrated sensitivity test instrument.

[j]For example, it might not be possible to individually test the heat sensor in a thermally enhanced smoke detector.

[k]Manufacturer's instructions should be consulted to ensure a proper operational test. No suppression gas or agent is expected to be discharged during the test of the solenoid. See Test Plan of 14.2.10.

[l]Testing of CO device should be done to the requirements of NFPA 720, *Standard for the Installation of Carbon Monoxide (CO) Detection and Warning Equipment.*

[m]A monitor module installed on an interface device is not considered a supervisory device and therefore not subject to the quarterly testing frequency requirement. Test frequencies for interface devices should be in accordance with the applicable standard. For example, fire pump controller alarms such as phase reversal are required to be tested annually. If a monitor module is installed to identify phase reversal on the fire alarm control panel, it is not necessary to test for phase reversal four times a year.

[n]Chapter 18 would require 15 dB over average ambient sound for public mode spaces. Sometimes the ambient sound levels are different from what the design was based upon. Private operating mode would require 10 dB over average ambient at the location of the device.

[o]Where building, system, or occupancy changes have been observed, the owner should be notified of the changes. New devices might need to be installed and tested per the initial acceptance testing criteria.

[p]See A.14.4.3.2, and Table 14.4.3.2, Item 24.

14.4.3.3 Video image smoke and flame detectors shall be inspected, tested, and maintained in accordance with the manufacturer's published instructions.

> Paragraph 14.4.3.4 was added by a tentative interim amendment (TIA). See page 1.

14.4.3.4 Gas detectors shall be inspected, tested, and maintained in accordance with manufacturers' published instructions.

14.4.4* Testing Frequency. Unless otherwise permitted by other sections of this Code, testing shall be performed in accordance with the schedules in Table 14.4.3.2 or more often if required by the authority having jurisdiction.

14.4.4.1 Devices or equipment that are inaccessible for safety considerations (e.g., continuous process operations, energized electrical equipment, radiation, and excessive height) shall be permitted to be tested during scheduled shutdowns if approved by the authority having jurisdiction. Extended intervals shall not exceed 18 months.

14.4.4.2 If automatic testing is performed at least weekly by a remotely monitored fire alarm control unit specifically listed for the application, the manual testing frequency shall be permitted to be extended to annually. Table 14.4.3.2 shall apply.

14.4.4.3* In other than one- and two-family dwellings, sensitivity of smoke detectors shall be tested in accordance with 14.4.4.3.1 through 14.4.4.3.7.

14.4.4.3.1 Sensitivity shall be checked within 1 year after installation.

14.4.4.3.2 Sensitivity shall be checked every alternate year thereafter unless otherwise permitted by compliance with 14.4.4.3.3.

14.4.4.3.3 After the second required calibration test, if sensitivity tests indicate that the device has remained within its listed and marked sensitivity range (or 4 percent obscuration light gray smoke, if not marked), the length of time between calibration tests shall be permitted to be extended to a maximum of 5 years.

14.4.4.3.3.1 If the frequency is extended, records of nuisance alarms and subsequent trends of these alarms shall be maintained.

14.4.4.3.3.2 In zones or in areas where nuisance alarms show any increase over the previous year, calibration tests shall be performed.

14.4.4.3.4 To ensure that each smoke detector is within its listed and marked sensitivity range, it shall be tested using any of the following methods:

(1) Calibrated test method
(2) Manufacturer's calibrated sensitivity test instrument
(3) Listed control equipment arranged for the purpose
(4) Smoke detector/fire alarm control unit arrangement whereby the detector causes a signal at the fire alarm control unit where its sensitivity is outside its listed sensitivity range
(5) Other calibrated sensitivity test methods approved by the authority having jurisdiction

14.4.4.3.5 Unless otherwise permitted by 14.4.4.3.6, smoke detectors found to have a sensitivity outside the listed and marked sensitivity range shall be cleaned and recalibrated or be replaced.

14.4.4.3.6 Smoke detectors listed as field adjustable shall be permitted to either be adjusted within the listed and marked sensitivity range, cleaned, and recalibrated, or be replaced.

14.4.4.3.7 The detector sensitivity shall not be tested or measured using any device that administers an unmeasured concentration of smoke or other aerosol into the detector or smoke alarm.

14.4.4.4 Test frequency of interfaced equipment shall be the same as specified by the applicable NFPA standards for the equipment being supervised.

14.4.4.5 Restorable fixed-temperature, spot-type heat detectors shall be tested in accordance with 14.4.4.5.1 through 14.4.4.5.4.

14.4.4.5.1 Two or more detectors shall be tested on each initiating circuit annually.

14.4.4.5.2 Different detectors shall be tested each year.

14.4.4.5.3 Test records shall be kept by the building owner specifying which detectors have been tested.

14.4.4.5.4 Within 5 years, each detector shall have been tested.

14.4.4.6* Circuit and pathway testing of each monitored circuit or pathway shall be conducted with initial acceptance or reacceptance testing to verify signals are indicated at the control unit for each of the abnormal conditions specified in Sections 23.5 through 23.7.

> Paragraph 14.4.5 was revised by a tentative interim amendment. (TIA). See page 1.

14.4.5 Single- and Multiple-Station Smoke Alarms. Smoke alarms and all connected appliances shall be inspected and tested in accordance with the manufacturer's published instructions at least monthly. The responsibility for maintenance and testing shall be in accordance with 14.2.3. (SIG-HOU)

14.4.6 Household Fire Alarm Systems.

14.4.6.1 Testing. Household fire alarm systems shall be tested by a qualified service technician at least annually according to the methods of Table 14.4.3.2. The installing contractor shall be required to provide this information in writing to the customer upon completion of the system installation. To the extent that the fire alarm system is monitored offsite, the supervising station contractor shall provide notice of this requirement to the customer on a yearly basis. (SIG-HOU)

14.4.6.2 Maintenance. Maintenance of household fire alarm systems shall be conducted according to the manufacturer's published instructions. (SIG-HOU)

14.4.7 Replacement of Smoke Alarms in One- and Two-Family Dwellings.

14.4.7.1 Unless otherwise recommended by the manufacturer's published instructions, single- and multiple-station smoke alarms installed in one- and two-family dwellings shall be replaced when they fail to respond to operability tests but shall not remain in service longer than 10 years from the date of manufacture. (SIG-HOU)

14.4.7.2* Combination smoke/carbon monoxide alarms shall be replaced when the end-of-life signal activates or 10 years from the date of manufacture, whichever comes first. (SIG-HOU)

14.4.7.3 Where batteries are used as a source of energy for combination smoke/carbon monoxide alarms as well as single- and multiple-station smoke alarms, they shall be replaced in accordance with the alarm equipment manufacturer's published instructions. (SIG-HOU)

14.4.8 Circuits from Central Station. Tests of all circuits extending from the central station shall be made at intervals of not more than 24 hours.

14.4.9 Public Emergency Alarm Reporting Systems.

14.4.9.1 Emergency power sources other than batteries shall be tested at least weekly in accordance with 14.4.9.1.1 and 14.4.9.1.2.

14.4.9.1.1 Testing shall include operation of the power source to supply the system for a continuous period of 1 hour.

14.4.9.1.2 Testing shall require simulated failure of the normal power source.

14.4.9.2 Unless otherwise permitted by 14.4.9.3, testing facilities shall be installed at the communications center and each subsidiary communications center, if used.

14.4.9.3 Testing facilities for systems leased from a nonmunicipal organization shall be permitted to be installed at locations other than the communications center if approved by the authority having jurisdiction.

14.4.10* In-Building Emergency Radio Communication Systems. In-building emergency radio communication systems shall be inspected and operationally tested in accordance with the manufacturer's published requirements by the local fire department, the building owner, or a designated representative.

14.4.10.1 Signal Level Testing. Signal level testing shall be conducted to verify the signal strengths as required in 24.5.2.3 at the following times:

(1) Initial assessment of radio coverage in accordance with 24.5.2.2.1 and 24.5.2.2.2 for new or existing buildings
(2) After installation or modification of public safety radio enhancement system needed to ensure compliance with 24.5.2.2.3
(3) On an annual basis or other interval as specified by the authority having jurisdiction

14.4.10.2 System Commissioning Testing. System commissioning tests shall comply with the following:

(1) The building owner shall be responsible for ensuring that a commissioning test of the public safety radio enhancement system occurs prior to final acceptance testing with the authority having jurisdiction.
(2) The commissioning test shall ensure that two-way coverage on each floor of the building meets the minimum coverage requirements of 24.5.2.2.1 and 24.5.2.2.2.
(3) Tests shall be made using the frequencies assigned to the jurisdiction.
(4) Testing shall be coordinated with the authority having jurisdiction to ensure no undue interference to any public safety operations.
(5) All testing shall be done on frequencies authorized by the FCC.

14.4.10.3* Test Procedures. The test plan shall ensure testing throughout the building. Test procedures shall be as directed by the authority having jurisdiction.

14.4.10.4* Measurement Parameters. Signal levels shall be measured to ensure the system meets the criteria of 24.5.2.3 according to parameters as directed by the authority having jurisdiction.

14.4.10.5* Acceptance Test. An acceptance test of the public safety radio enhancement system shall be scheduled with the authority having jurisdiction. Acceptance test procedures and requirements shall be as directed by the authority having jurisdiction.

14.4.10.6* Annual Tests. Where a public safety radio enhancement system is required, it shall be the building owner's responsibility to have all live components of the system, such as signal boosters, newer supplies, and backup batteries tested at a minimum of once every 12 months. The authority having jurisdiction shall be notified in advance and shall direct annual test procedures and requirements.

14.4.11* Voice Intelligibility.

14.4.11.1 Voice communication using prerecorded messages and manual voice announcements shall be verified as being intelligible in accordance with the requirements of 18.4.10.

14.4.11.2 Intelligibility shall not be required to be determined through quantitative measurements.

14.4.11.3 Quantitative measurements as described in Annex D shall be permitted but shall not be required.

14.5 Maintenance.

14.5.1 System equipment shall be maintained in accordance with the manufacturer's published instructions.

14.5.2 The frequency of maintenance of system equipment shall depend on the type of equipment and the local ambient conditions.

14.5.3 The frequency of cleaning of system equipment shall depend on the type of equipment and the local ambient conditions.

14.5.4 All apparatus requiring rewinding or resetting to maintain normal operation shall be rewound or reset as promptly as possible after each test and alarm.

14.5.5 Unless otherwise permitted by 14.5.6, the retransmission means as defined in Section 26.3 shall be tested at intervals of not more than 12 hours.

14.5.6 When the retransmission means is the public-switched telephone network, testing shall be permitted at weekly intervals to confirm its operation to each communications center.

14.5.7 As a part of the testing required in 14.5.5, the retransmission signal and the time and date of the retransmission shall be recorded in the central station.

14.6 Records.

14.6.1* Permanent Records. After successful completion of acceptance tests approved by the authority having jurisdiction, the requirements in 14.6.1.1 through 14.6.1.3 shall apply.

14.6.1.1 A set of reproducible as-built installation drawings, operation and maintenance manuals, and a written sequence of operation shall be provided to the building owner or the owner's designated representative.

14.6.1.2* Site-Specific Software.

14.6.1.2.1 For software-based systems, a copy of the site-specific software shall be provided to the system owner or owner's designated representative.

14.6.1.2.2 A copy of the site-specific software shall be stored on-site in nonvolatile, nonerasable, nonrewritable memory.

14.6.1.3 The system owner shall be responsible for maintaining these records for the life of the system for examination by any authority having jurisdiction. Paper or electronic media shall be permitted.

14.6.2 Maintenance, Inspection, and Testing Records.

14.6.2.1 Records shall be retained until the next test and for 1 year thereafter.

14.6.2.2 For systems with restorable fixed-temperature, spot-type heat detectors tested over multiple years, records shall be retained for the 5 years of testing and for 1 year thereafter.

14.6.2.3 The records shall be on a medium that will survive the retention period. Paper or electronic media shall be permitted.

14.6.2.4* A record of all inspections, testing, and maintenance shall be provided in accordance with 7.8.2.

14.6.3 Supervising Station Records. For supervising station alarm systems, records pertaining to signals received at the supervising station that result from maintenance, inspection, and testing shall be maintained for not less than 12 months.

14.6.3.1 Records shall be permitted to be maintained on either paper or electronic media.

14.6.3.2 Upon request, a hard copy record shall be provided to the authority having jurisdiction.

14.6.4 Simulated Operation Note. If the operation of a device, circuit, fire alarm control unit function, or special hazard system interface is simulated, it shall be noted on the inspection/test form that the operation was simulated.

Chapter 15   Reserved

Chapter 16   Reserved

Chapter 17   Initiating Devices

17.1 Application.

17.1.1 The performance, selection, use, and location of automatic or manual initiating devices, including but not limited to fire detection devices, devices that detect the operation of fire suppression and extinguishing systems, waterflow detectors, pressure switches, manual fire alarm boxes, and other supervisory signal–initiating devices (including guard tour reporting) used to ensure timely warning for the purposes of life safety and the protection of a building, a space, a structure, an area, or an object shall comply with the minimum requirements of this chapter.

17.1.2* This chapter establishes the minimum installation criteria for initiating devices required by other governing laws, codes, standards, or section of this document. This chapter does not, by itself, require the installation of initiating devices.

17.1.3 The requirements of Chapters 7, 10, 12, 21, 23, and 24 shall also apply unless they are in conflict with this chapter.

17.1.4 The requirements of Chapter 14 shall apply.

17.1.5 The requirements of single- and multiple-station alarms and household fire alarm systems shall be determined in accordance with Chapter 29.

17.1.6 The material in this chapter shall be applied by persons knowledgeable in the application of fire detection and fire alarm systems and services.

17.1.7 The interconnection of initiating devices with control equipment configurations and power supplies, or with output systems responding to external actuation, shall be as detailed elsewhere in this Code or in other governing laws, codes, or standards.

17.2 Purpose. Automatic and manual initiating devices shall contribute to life safety, fire protection, and property conservation by providing a reliable means to signal other equipment arranged to monitor the initiating devices and to initiate a response to those signals.

17.3* Performance-Based Design.

17.3.1 Performance-based designs submitted to the authority having jurisdiction for review and approval shall include documentation, in an approved format, of each performance objective and applicable scenario, together with any calculations, modeling, or other technical substantiation used in establishing the proposed design's fire and life safety performance.

17.3.2 The authority having jurisdiction shall determine whether such identified performance objectives are appropriate and have been met.

17.3.3 The authority having jurisdiction shall approve modifications to or variations from the approved design or design basis in advance.

17.4 General Requirements.

17.4.1 The requirements of 17.4.2 through 17.4.9 shall apply to all initiating devices.

17.4.2 Where subject to mechanical damage, an initiating device shall be protected. A mechanical guard used to protect a smoke, heat, or radiant energy–sensing detector shall be listed for use with the detector.

17.4.3 Initiating devices shall be supported independently of their attachment to the circuit conductors.

17.4.4 Initiating devices shall be installed in a manner that provides accessibility for periodic inspection, testing, and maintenance.

17.4.5 Initiating devices shall be installed in all areas, compartments, or locations where required by other governing laws, codes, or standards.

17.4.6* Duplicate terminals, leads, or connectors that provide for the connection of installation wiring shall be provided on each initiating device for the express purpose of connecting into the fire alarm system to monitor the integrity of the signaling and power wiring.

Exception: Initiating devices connected to a system that provides the required monitoring.

17.4.7 Where smoke detectors are installed in concealed locations more than 10 ft (3.0 m) above the finished floor or in arrangements where the detector's alarm or supervisory indicator is not visible to responding personnel, the detectors shall be provided with remote alarm or supervisory indication in a location acceptable to the authority having jurisdiction.

Remote L.E.D

17.4.8* If a remote alarm indicator is provided for an automatic fire detector in a concealed location, the location of the detector and the area protected by the detector shall be prominently indicated at the remote alarm indicator by a permanently attached placard or by other approved means.

17.4.9 Where required by 17.4.7 and unless the specific detector alarm or supervisory signal is indicated at the control unit (and on the drawings with its specific location and functions), remote alarm or supervisory indicators shall be installed in an accessible location and shall be clearly labeled to indicate both their function and any device or equipment associated with each detector.

17.4.10* If the intent is to initiate action when smoke/fire threatens a specific object or space, the detector shall be permitted to be installed in close proximity to that object or space.

17.5 Requirements for Smoke and Heat Detectors.

17.5.1 Recessed Mounting. Unless tested and listed for recessed mounting, detectors shall not be recessed into the mounting surface.

17.5.2* Partitions. Where partitions extend to within 15 percent of the ceiling height, the spaces separated by the partitions shall be considered as separate rooms.

17.5.3* Detector Coverage.

17.5.3.1 Total (Complete) Coverage. Where required by other governing laws, codes, or standards, and unless otherwise modified by 17.5.3.1.1 through 17.5.3.1.5, total coverage shall include all rooms, halls, storage areas, basements, attics, lofts, spaces above suspended ceilings, and other subdivisions and accessible spaces, as well as the inside of all closets, elevator shafts, enclosed stairways, dumbwaiter shafts, and chutes.

17.5.3.1.1 Where inaccessible areas are constructed of or contain combustible material, unless otherwise specified in 17.5.3.1.2, they shall be made accessible and shall be protected by a detector(s).

17.5.3.1.2 Detectors shall not be required in combustible blind spaces if any of the following conditions exist:

(1) Where the ceiling is attached directly to the underside of the supporting beams of a combustible roof or floor deck
(2) Where the concealed space is entirely filled with a noncombustible insulation (In solid joist construction, the insulation shall be required to fill only the space from the ceiling to the bottom edge of the joist of the roof or floor deck.)
(3) Where there are small concealed spaces over rooms, provided that any space in question does not exceed 50 ft^2 (4.6 m^2) in area
(4) In spaces formed by sets of facing studs or solid joists in walls, floors, or ceilings, where the distance between the facing studs or solid joists is less than 6 in. (150 mm)

17.5.3.1.3 Detectors shall not be required below open grid ceilings if all of the following conditions exist:

(1) Openings of the grid are ¼ in. (6.4 mm) or larger in the least dimension.
(2) Thickness of the material does not exceed the least dimension.
(3) Openings constitute at least 70 percent of the area of the ceiling material.

17.5.3.1.4* Where concealed accessible spaces above suspended ceilings are used as a return air plenum meeting the requirements of NFPA 90A, *Standard for the Installation of Air-Conditioning and Ventilating Systems*, detection shall be provided in one of the following means:

(1) Smoke detection shall be provided in accordance with 17.7.4.2, or
(2) Smoke detection shall be provided at each connection from the return air plenum to the central air-handling system.

17.5.3.1.5 Detectors shall not be required underneath open loading docks or platforms and their covers and for accessible underfloor spaces if all of the following conditions exist:

(1) Space is not accessible for storage purposes or entrance of unauthorized persons and is protected against the accumulation of windborne debris.
(2) Space contains no equipment such as steam pipes, electric wiring, shafting, or conveyors.
(3) Floor over the space is tight.
(4) No flammable liquids are processed, handled, or stored on the floor above.

17.5.3.2* Partial or Selective Coverage. Where other governing laws, codes, or standards require the protection of selected areas only, the specified areas shall be protected in accordance with this Code.

17.5.3.3* Nonrequired Coverage.

17.5.3.3.1 Detection installed for reasons of achieving specific fire safety objectives, but not required by any laws, codes, or standards, shall meet all of the requirements of this Code, with the exception of the prescriptive spacing criteria of Chapter 17.

17.5.3.3.2 Where nonrequired detectors are installed for achieving specific fire safety objectives, additional detectors not necessary to achieve the objectives shall not be required.

17.6 Heat-Sensing Fire Detectors.

17.6.1 General.

17.6.1.1* The heat detection design documentation shall state the required performance objective of the system.

17.6.1.2 Designs not in accordance with 17.6.1.3 shall be deemed prescriptive designs and shall be designed in accordance with the prescriptive requirements of this chapter.

17.6.1.3* Performance-based designs shall be executed in accordance with Section 17.3.

17.6.1.4* Spot-type heat detectors shall include in their installation instructions, technical data, and listing documentation the operating temperature and response time index (RTI) as determined by the organization listing the device.

17.6.2 Temperature.

17.6.2.1 Classification. Heat-sensing fire detectors of the fixed-temperature or rate-compensated, spot type shall be classified as to the temperature of operation in accordance with Table 17.6.2.1.

17.6.2.2 Marking.

17.6.2.2.1 Color Coding.

17.6.2.2.1.1 Heat-sensing fire detectors of the fixed-temperature or rate-compensated, spot type shall be marked with a color code in accordance with Table 17.6.2.1.

Table 17.6.2.1 Temperature Classification and Color Code for Heat-Sensing Fire Detectors

Temperature Classification	Temperature Rating Range		Maximum Ceiling Temperature		Color Code
	°F	°C	°F	°C	
Low*	100–134	39–57	80	28	Uncolored
Ordinary	135–174	58–79	115	47	Uncolored
Intermediate	175–249	80–121	155	69	White
High	250–324	122–162	230	111	Blue
Extra high	325–399	163–204	305	152	Red
Very extra high	400–499	205–259	380	194	Green
Ultra high	500–575	260–302	480	249	Orange

*Intended only for installation in controlled ambient areas. Units shall be marked to indicate maximum ambient installation temperature.

17.6.2.2.1.2 If the overall color of a heat-sensing fire detector is the same as the color code marking required for that detector, one of the following arrangements, applied in a contrasting color and visible after installation, shall be employed:

(1) Ring on the surface of the detector
(2) Temperature rating in numerals at least ⅜ in. (9.5 mm) high

17.6.2.2.2 Operating Temperature.

17.6.2.2.2.1 Heat-sensing fire detectors shall be marked with their listed operating temperature.

17.6.2.2.2.2 Heat-sensing fire detectors where the alarm threshold is field adjustable shall be marked with the temperature range.

17.6.2.2.2.3 Spot-type heat detectors shall also be marked with their RTI.

17.6.2.3* Ambient Ceiling Temperature. Detectors having fixed-temperature or rate-compensated elements shall be selected in accordance with Table 17.6.2.1 for the maximum expected ambient ceiling temperature. The temperature rating of the detector shall be at least 20°F (11°C) above the maximum expected temperature at the ceiling.

17.6.3 Location and Spacing.

17.6.3.1 Smooth Ceiling.

17.6.3.1.1* Spacing. One of the following requirements shall apply:

(1) The distance between detectors shall not exceed their listed spacing, and there shall be detectors within a distance of one-half the listed spacing, measured at right angles from all walls or partitions extending upward to within the top 15 percent of the ceiling height.
(2) All points on the ceiling shall have a detector within a distance equal to or less than 0.7 times the listed spacing (0.7S).

17.6.3.1.2 Irregular Areas. For irregularly shaped areas, the spacing between detectors shall be permitted to be greater than the listed spacing, provided that the maximum spacing from a detector to the farthest point of a sidewall or corner within its zone of protection is not greater than 0.7 times the listed spacing.

17.6.3.1.3 Location.

17.6.3.1.3.1* Unless otherwise modified by 17.6.3.2.2, 17.6.3.3.2, or 17.6.3.7, spot-type heat-sensing fire detectors shall be located on the ceiling not less than 4 in. (100 mm) from the sidewall or on the sidewalls between 4 in. and 12 in. (100 mm and 300 mm) from the ceiling.

17.6.3.1.3.2 Unless otherwise modified by 17.6.3.2.2, 17.6.3.3.2, or 17.6.3.7, line-type heat detectors shall be located on the ceiling or on the sidewalls not more than 20 in. (510 mm) from the ceiling.

17.6.3.2* Solid Joist Construction.

17.6.3.2.1 Spacing. The design spacing of heat detectors, where measured at right angles to the solid joists, shall not exceed 50 percent of the listed spacing.

17.6.3.2.2 Location. Detectors shall be mounted at the bottom of the joists.

17.6.3.3* Beam Construction.

17.6.3.3.1 Spacing.

17.6.3.3.1.1 A ceiling shall be treated as a smooth ceiling if the beams project no more than 4 in. (100 mm) below the ceiling.

17.6.3.3.1.2 Where the beams project more than 4 in. (100 mm) below the ceiling, the spacing of spot-type heat detectors at right angles to the direction of beam travel shall be not more than two-thirds of the listed spacing.

17.6.3.3.1.3 Where the beams project more than 18 in. (460 mm) below the ceiling and are more than 8 ft (2.4 m) on center, each bay formed by the beams shall be treated as a separate area.

17.6.3.3.2 Location. Where beams are less than 12 in. (300 mm) in depth and less than 8 ft (2.4 m) on center, detectors shall be permitted to be installed on the bottom of beams.

17.6.3.4* Sloping Ceilings (Peaked and Shed).

17.6.3.4.1 Spacing.

17.6.3.4.1.1 Ceiling Slope Less Than 30 Degrees. For a ceiling slope of less than 30 degrees, all detectors shall be spaced using the height at the peak.

17.6.3.4.1.2 Ceiling Slopes of 30 Degrees or Greater. All detectors, other than those located in the peak, shall be spaced using the average slope height or the height of the peak.

17.6.3.4.1.3 Spacing shall be measured along a horizontal projection of the ceiling in accordance with the type of ceiling construction.

17.6.3.4.2 Location.

17.6.3.4.2.1 A row of detectors shall first be located at or within 36 in. (910 mm) of the peak of the ceiling.

17.6.3.4.2.2 Additional detectors shall be located as determined in 17.6.3.4.1.

17.6.3.5 High Ceilings.

17.6.3.5.1* On ceilings 10 ft to 30 ft (3.0 m to 9.1 m) high, heat detector spacing shall be reduced in accordance with Table 17.6.3.5.1 prior to any additional reductions for beams, joists, or slope, where applicable.

Exception: Table 17.6.3.5.1 shall not apply to the following detectors, which rely on the integration effect:

(1) Line-type electrical conductivity detectors (see 3.3.66.11)
(2) Pneumatic rate-of-rise tubing heat detectors (see 3.3.66.15)

In these cases, the manufacturer's published instructions shall be followed for appropriate alarm point and spacing.

Table 17.6.3.5.1 Heat Detector Spacing Reduction Based on Ceiling Height

Ceiling Height Greater than (>)		Up to and Including		Multiply Listed Spacing by
ft	m	ft	m	
0	0	10	3.0	1.00
10	3.0	12	3.7	0.91
12	3.7	14	4.3	0.84
14	4.3	16	4.9	0.77
16	4.9	18	5.5	0.71
18	5.5	20	6.1	0.64
20	6.1	22	6.7	0.58
22	6.7	24	7.3	0.52
24	7.3	26	7.9	0.46
26	7.9	28	8.5	0.40
28	8.5	30	9.1	0.34

17.6.3.5.2* Spacing Minimum. The minimum spacing of heat detectors shall not be required to be less than 0.4 times the height of the ceiling.

17.6.3.6* Integral Heat Sensors on Combination and Multi-Sensor Detectors. A heat-sensing detector integrally mounted on a smoke detector shall be listed for not less than 50 ft (15.2 m) spacing.

17.6.3.7 Other Applications. Where a detector is used in an application other than open area protection, the manufacturer's published instructions shall be followed.

17.6.3.8 Alternative Design Methods. Annex B shall be permitted to be used as one alternative design method for determining detector spacing.

17.7 Smoke-Sensing Fire Detectors.

17.7.1 General.

17.7.1.1* The smoke detection design documentation shall state the required performance objective of the system.

17.7.1.2* Designs not in accordance with 17.7.1.3 shall be deemed prescriptive designs and shall be designed in accordance with the prescriptive requirements of this chapter.

17.7.1.3* Performance-based designs shall be executed in accordance with Section 17.3.

17.7.1.4 The prescriptive requirements in this section shall be applied only where detectors are installed in ordinary indoor locations.

17.7.1.5 Where smoke detectors are being installed to control the spread of smoke, they shall be installed in accordance with the requirements of 17.7.5.

17.7.1.6 Smoke detectors shall be installed in all areas where required by other governing laws, codes, or standards or by other parts of this Code.

17.7.1.7 The selection and placement of smoke detectors shall take into account both the performance characteristics of the detector and the areas into which the detectors are to be installed to prevent nuisance and unintentional alarms or improper operation after installation.

17.7.1.8* Unless specifically designed and listed for the expected conditions, smoke detectors shall not be installed if any of the following ambient conditions exist:

(1) Temperature below 32°F (0°C)
(2) Temperature above 100°F (38°C)
(3) Relative humidity above 93 percent
(4) Air velocity greater than 300 ft/min (1.5 m/sec)

17.7.1.9* The location of smoke detectors shall be based on an evaluation of potential ambient sources of smoke, moisture, dust, or fumes, and electrical or mechanical influences, to minimize nuisance alarms.

17.7.1.10* The effect of stratification below the ceiling shall be taken into account. The guidelines in Annex B shall be permitted to be used.

17.7.1.11* Protection During Construction.

17.7.1.11.1 Where detectors are installed for signal initiation during construction, they shall be cleaned and verified to be operating in accordance with the listed sensitivity, or they shall be replaced prior to the final commissioning of the system.

17.7.1.11.2 Where detectors are installed but not operational during construction, they shall be protected from construction debris, dust, dirt, and damage in accordance with the manufacturer's recommendations and verified to be operating in accordance with the listed sensitivity, or they shall be replaced prior to the final commissioning of the system.

17.7.1.11.3 Where detection is not required during construction, detectors shall not be installed until after all other construction trades have completed cleanup.

17.7.2* Sensitivity.

17.7.2.1* Smoke detectors shall be marked with their nominal production sensitivity and tolerance (percent per foot obscuration), as required by the listing.

17.7.2.2 Smoke detectors that have provision for field adjustment of sensitivity shall have an adjustment range of not less than 0.6 percent per foot obscuration.

17.7.2.3 If the means of adjustment of sensitivity is on the detector, a method shall be provided to restore the detector to its factory calibration.

17.7.2.4 Detectors that have provision for program-controlled adjustment of sensitivity shall be permitted to be marked with their programmable sensitivity range only.

17.7.3 Location and Spacing.

17.7.3.1* General.

17.7.3.1.1 The location and spacing of smoke detectors shall be based upon the anticipated smoke flows due to the plume and ceiling jet produced by the anticipated fire, as well as any pre-existing ambient airflows that could exist in the protected compartment.

17.7.3.1.2 The design shall account for the contribution of the following factors in predicting detector response to the anticipated fires to which the system is intended to respond:

(1) Ceiling shape and surface
(2) Ceiling height
(3) Configuration of contents in the protected area
(4) Combustion characteristics and probable equivalence ratio of the anticipated fires involving the fuel loads within the protected area
(5) Compartment ventilation
(6) Ambient temperature, pressure, altitude, humidity, and atmosphere

17.7.3.1.3 If the intent is to protect against a specific hazard, the detector(s) shall be permitted to be installed closer to the hazard in a position where the detector can intercept the smoke.

17.7.3.2* Spot-Type Smoke Detectors.

17.7.3.2.1* Spot-type smoke detectors shall be located on the ceiling or, if on a sidewall, between the ceiling and 12 in. (300 mm) down from the ceiling to the top of the detector.

17.7.3.2.2* To minimize dust contamination, smoke detectors, where installed under raised floors, shall be mounted only in an orientation for which they have been listed.

17.7.3.2.3 On smooth ceilings, spacing for spot-type smoke detectors shall be in accordance with 17.7.3.2.3.1 through 17.7.3.2.3.4.

17.7.3.2.3.1* In the absence of specific performance-based design criteria, one of the following requirements shall apply:

(1) The distance between smoke detectors shall not exceed a nominal spacing of 30 ft (9.1 m) and there shall be detectors within a distance of one-half the nominal spacing, measured at right angles from all walls or partitions extending upward to within the top 15 percent of the ceiling height.
(2)*All points on the ceiling shall have a detector within a distance equal to or less than 0.7 times the nominal 30 ft (9.1 m) spacing (0.7S).

17.7.3.2.3.2 In all cases, the manufacturer's published instructions shall be followed.

17.7.3.2.3.3 Other spacing shall be permitted to be used depending on ceiling height, different conditions, or response requirements.

17.7.3.2.3.4 For the detection of flaming fires, the guidelines in Annex B shall be permitted to be used.

17.7.3.2.4* For solid joist and beam construction, spacing for spot-type smoke detectors shall be in accordance with 17.7.3.2.4.1 through 17.7.3.2.4.6.

17.7.3.2.4.1 Solid joists shall be considered equivalent to beams for smoke detector spacing guidelines.

17.7.3.2.4.2 For level ceilings, the following shall apply:

(1) For ceilings with beam depths of less than 10 percent of the ceiling height (0.1 H), smooth ceiling spacing shall be permitted. Spot-type smoke detectors shall be permitted to be located on ceilings or on the bottom of beams.
(2) For ceilings with beam depths equal to or greater than 10 percent of the ceiling height (0.1 H), the following shall apply:

(a) Where beam spacing is equal to or greater than 40 percent of the ceiling height (0.4 H), spot-type detectors shall be located on the ceiling in each beam pocket.
(b) Where beam spacing is less than 40 percent of the ceiling height (0.4 H), the following shall be permitted for spot detectors:
    i. Smooth ceiling spacing in the direction parallel to the beams and at one-half smooth ceiling spacing in the direction perpendicular to the beams
    ii. Location of detectors either on the ceiling or on the bottom of the beams

(3)*For beam pockets formed by intersecting beams, including waffle or pan-type ceilings, the following shall apply:
(a) For beam depths less than 10 percent of the ceiling height (0.1 H), spacing shall be in accordance with 17.7.3.2.4.2(1).
(b) For beam depths greater than or equal to 10 percent of the ceiling height (0.1 H), spacing shall be in accordance with 17.7.3.2.4.2(2).

(4)*For corridors 15 ft (4.6 m) in width or less having ceiling beams or solid joists perpendicular to the corridor length, the following shall apply:
(a) Smooth ceiling spacing shall be permitted.
(b) Location of spot-type smoke detectors on ceilings, sidewalls, or the bottom of beams or solid joists

(5) For rooms of 900 ft^2 (84 m^2) or less, the following shall be permitted:
(a) Use of smooth ceiling spacing
(b) Location of spot-type smoke detectors on ceilings or on the bottom of beams

17.7.3.2.4.3* For sloping ceilings with beams running parallel up slope, the following shall apply:

(1) Spot-type detector(s) shall be located on the ceiling within beam pocket(s).
(2) The ceiling height shall be taken as the average height over slope.
(3) Spacing shall be measured along a horizontal projection of the ceiling.
(4) Smooth ceiling spacing shall be permitted within beam pocket(s) parallel to the beams.
(5) For beam depths less than or equal to 10 percent of the ceiling height (0.1 H), spot-type detectors shall be located with smooth ceiling spacing perpendicular to the beams.
(6) For beam depths greater than 10 percent of the ceiling height (0.1 H), the following shall apply for spacing perpendicular to the beams:
(a) For beam spacing greater than or equal to 40 percent of the ceiling height (0.4 H), spot-type detectors shall be located in each beam pocket.
(b) For beam spacing less than 40 percent of the ceiling height (0.4 H), spot-type detectors shall not be required in every beam pocket but shall be spaced not greater than 50 percent of smooth ceiling spacing.

17.7.3.2.4.4* For sloping ceilings with beams running perpendicular across slope, the following shall apply:

(1) Spot-type detector(s) shall be located at the bottom of the beams.
(2) The ceiling height shall be taken as the average height over slope.
(3) Spacing shall be measured along a horizontal projection of the ceiling.

(4) Smooth ceiling spacing shall be permitted within beam pocket(s).

(5) For beam depths less than or equal to 10 percent of the ceiling height (0.1 *H*), spot-type detectors shall be located with smooth ceiling spacing.

(6) For beam depths greater than 10 percent of the ceiling height (0.1 *H*), spot-type detectors shall not be required to be located closer than (0.4 *H*) and shall not exceed 50 percent of smooth ceiling spacing.

17.7.3.2.4.5* For sloped ceilings with beam pockets formed by intersecting beams, the following shall apply:

(1) Spot-type detector(s) shall be located at the bottom of the beams.

(2) The ceiling height shall be taken as the average height over slope.

(3) Spacing shall be measured along a horizontal projection of the ceiling.

(4) For beam depths less than or equal to 10 percent of the ceiling height (0.1 *H*), spot-type detectors shall be spaced with not more than three beams between detectors and shall not exceed smooth ceiling spacing.

(5) For beam depths greater than 10 percent of the ceiling height (0.1 *H*), spot-type detectors shall be spaced with not more than two beams between detectors, but shall not be required to be spaced closer than (0.4 *H*), and shall not exceed 50 percent of smooth ceiling spacing.

17.7.3.2.4.6 For sloped ceilings with solid joists, the detectors shall be located on the bottom of the joist.

17.7.3.3* Peaked. Detectors shall first be spaced and located within 36 in. (910 mm) of the peak, measured horizontally. The number and spacing of additional detectors, if any, shall be based on the horizontal projection of the ceiling.

17.7.3.4* Shed. Detectors shall first be spaced and located within 36 in. (910 mm) of the high side of the ceiling, measured horizontally. The number and spacing of additional detectors, if any, shall be based on the horizontal projection of the ceiling.

17.7.3.5 Raised Floors and Suspended Ceilings. Spaces beneath raised floors and above suspended ceilings shall be treated as separate rooms for smoke detector spacing purposes. Detectors installed beneath raised floors or above suspended ceilings, or both, including raised floors and suspended ceilings used for environmental air, shall not be used in lieu of providing detection within the room.

17.7.3.5.1 For raised floors, the following shall apply:

(1) Detectors installed beneath raised floors shall be spaced in accordance with 17.7.3.1, 17.7.3.1.3, and 17.7.3.2.2.

(2) Where the area beneath the raised floor is also used for environmental air, detector spacing shall also conform to 17.7.4.1 and 17.7.4.2.

17.7.3.5.2 For suspended ceilings, the following shall apply:

(1) Detector spacing above suspended ceilings shall conform to the requirements of 17.7.3 for the ceiling configuration.

(2) Where detectors are installed in ceilings used for environmental air, detector spacing shall also conform to 17.7.4.1, 17.7.4.2, and 17.7.4.3.

17.7.3.6 Air Sampling–Type Smoke Detector.

17.7.3.6.1 Each sampling port of an air sampling–type smoke detector shall be treated as a spot-type detector for the purpose of location and spacing.

17.7.3.6.2 Maximum air sample transport time from the farthest sampling port to the detector shall not exceed 120 seconds.

17.7.3.6.3* Sampling pipe networks shall be designed on the basis of, and shall be supported by, sound fluid dynamic principles to ensure required performance.

17.7.3.6.4 Sampling pipe network design details shall include calculations showing the flow characteristics of the pipe network and each sample port.

17.7.3.6.5 Air-sampling detectors shall give a trouble signal if the airflow is outside the manufacturer's specified range.

17.7.3.6.6* The sampling ports and in-line filter, if used, shall be kept clear in accordance with the manufacturer's published instructions.

17.7.3.6.7 Air-sampling network piping and fittings shall be airtight and permanently fixed.

17.7.3.6.8 Sampling system piping shall be conspicuously identified as "SMOKE DETECTOR SAMPLING TUBE — DO NOT DISTURB," as follows:

(1) At changes in direction or branches of piping
(2) At each side of penetrations of walls, floors, or other barriers
(3) At intervals on piping that provide visibility within the space, but no greater than 20 ft (6.1 m)

17.7.3.7* Projected Beam–Type Smoke Detectors.

17.7.3.7.1 Projected beam–type smoke detectors shall be located in accordance with the manufacturer's published instructions.

17.7.3.7.2 The effects of stratification shall be evaluated when locating the detectors.

17.7.3.7.3 The beam length shall not exceed the maximum permitted by the equipment listing.

17.7.3.7.4 If mirrors are used with projected beams, the mirrors shall be installed in accordance with the manufacturer's published instructions.

17.7.3.7.5 A projected beam–type smoke detector shall be considered equivalent to a row of spot-type smoke detectors for level and sloping ceiling applications.

17.7.3.7.6 Projected beam–type detectors and mirrors shall be mounted on stable surfaces to prevent false or erratic operation due to movement.

17.7.3.7.7 The beam shall be designed so that small angular movements of the light source or receiver do not prevent operation due to smoke and do not cause nuisance or unintentional alarms.

17.7.3.7.8* The light path of projected beam–type detectors shall be kept clear of opaque obstacles at all times.

17.7.4 Heating, Ventilating, and Air-Conditioning (HVAC).

17.7.4.1* In spaces served by air-handling systems, detectors shall not be located where airflow prevents operation of the detectors.

17.7.4.2 In under-floor spaces and above-ceiling spaces that are used as HVAC plenums, detectors shall be listed for the anticipated environment as required by 17.7.1.8. Detector spacings and locations shall be selected on the basis of anticipated airflow patterns and fire type.

17.7.4.3* Detectors placed in environmental air ducts or plenums shall not be used as a substitute for open area detectors. Where detectors are used for the control of smoke spread, the requirements of 17.7.5 shall apply. Where open area protection is required, 17.7.3 shall apply.

17.7.4.4 Detectors placed in environmental air ducts or plenums shall be permitted to be either supervisory or alarm initiating devices.

17.7.5* Smoke Detectors for Control of Smoke Spread.

17.7.5.1* Classifications. Smoke detectors installed and used to prevent smoke spread by initiating control of fans, dampers, doors, and other equipment shall be classified in the following manner:

(1) Area detectors that are installed in the related smoke compartments
(2) Detectors that are installed in the air duct systems
(3) Video image smoke detection that is installed in related smoke compartments

17.7.5.2* Limitations.

17.7.5.2.1 Detectors that are installed in the air duct system in accordance with 17.7.5.1(2) shall not be used as a substitute for open area protection.

17.7.5.2.2 Where open area protection is required, 17.7.3 shall apply.

17.7.5.3* Purposes.

17.7.5.3.1 To prevent the recirculation of dangerous quantities of smoke, a detector approved for air duct use shall be installed on the supply side of air-handling systems as required by NFPA 90A, *Standard for the Installation of Air-Conditioning and Ventilating Systems*, and 17.7.5.4.2.1.

17.7.5.3.2 If smoke detectors are used to initiate selectively the operation of equipment to control smoke spread, the requirements of 17.7.5.4.2.2 shall apply.

17.7.5.3.3 If detectors are used to initiate the operation of smoke doors, the requirements of 17.7.5.6 shall apply.

17.7.5.3.4 If duct detectors are used to initiate the operation of smoke dampers within ducts, the requirements of 17.7.5.5 shall apply.

17.7.5.4 Application.

17.7.5.4.1 Area Smoke Detectors Within Smoke Compartments. Area smoke detectors within smoke compartments shall be permitted to be used to control the spread of smoke by initiating operation of doors, dampers, and other equipment.

17.7.5.4.2* Smoke Detection for Air Duct System.

17.7.5.4.2.1 Supply Air System. Where the detection of smoke in the supply air system is required by other NFPA standards, a detector(s) listed for the air velocity present and that is located in the supply air duct downstream of both the fan and the filters shall be installed.

Exception: Additional smoke detectors shall not be required to be installed in ducts where the air duct system passes through other smoke compartments not served by the duct.

17.7.5.4.2.2* Return Air System. Unless otherwise modified by 17.7.5.4.2.2(A) or 17.7.5.4.2.2(B), if the detection of smoke in the return air system is required by other NFPA standards, a detector(s) listed for the air velocity present shall be located where the air leaves each smoke compartment, or in the duct system before the air enters the return air system common to more than one smoke compartment.

(A) Additional smoke detectors shall not be required to be installed in ducts where the air duct system passes through other smoke compartments not served by the duct.

(B) Where total coverage smoke detection is installed in accordance with 17.5.3.1 in all areas of the smoke compartment served by the return air system, installation of additional detector(s) listed for the air velocity present where the air leaves each smoke compartment, or in the duct system before the air enters in the return air system shall not be required, provided that their function is accomplished by the design of the total coverage smoke detection system.

17.7.5.5 Location and Installation of Detectors in Air Duct Systems.

17.7.5.5.1 Detectors shall be listed for the purpose for which they are being used.

17.7.5.5.2* Air duct detectors shall be installed in such a way as to obtain a representative sample of the airstream. This installation shall be permitted to be achieved by any of the following methods:

(1) Rigid mounting within the duct
(2) Rigid mounting to the wall of the duct with the sensing element protruding into the duct
(3) Installation outside the duct with rigidly mounted sampling tubes protruding into the duct
(4) Installation through the duct with projected light beam

17.7.5.5.3 Detectors shall be mounted in accordance with the manufacturer's published instructions and shall be accessible for cleaning by providing access doors or control units in accordance with NFPA 90A, *Standard for the Installation of Air-Conditioning and Ventilating Systems*.

17.7.5.5.4 The location of all detectors in air duct systems shall be permanently and clearly identified and recorded.

17.7.5.5.5 Detectors mounted outside of a duct that employs sampling tubes for transporting smoke from inside the duct to the detector shall be designed and installed to allow verification of airflow from the duct to the detector.

17.7.5.5.6 Detectors shall be listed for operation over the complete range of air velocities, temperature, and humidity expected at the detector when the air-handling system is operating.

17.7.5.5.7 All penetrations of a return air duct in the vicinity of detectors installed on or in an air duct shall be sealed to prevent entrance of outside air and possible dilution or redirection of smoke within the duct.

17.7.5.6 Smoke Detectors for Door Release Service.

17.7.5.6.1 Smoke detectors that are part of an open area protection system covering the room, corridor, or enclosed space on each side of the smoke door and that are located and spaced as required by 17.7.3 shall be permitted to accomplish smoke door release service.

17.7.5.6.2 Smoke detectors that are used exclusively for smoke door release service shall be located and spaced as required by 17.7.5.6.

17.7.5.6.3 Where smoke door release is accomplished directly from the smoke detector(s), the detector(s) shall be listed for releasing service.

17.7.5.6.4 Smoke detectors shall be of the photoelectric, ionization, or other approved type.

17.7.5.6.5 The number of detectors required shall be determined in accordance with 17.7.5.6.5.1 through 17.7.5.6.5.4.

17.7.5.6.5.1 If doors are to be closed in response to smoke flowing in either direction, the requirements of 17.7.5.6.5.1(A) through 17.7.5.6.5.1(D) shall apply.

(A) If the depth of wall section above the door is 24 in. (610 mm) or less, one ceiling-mounted smoke detector shall be required on one side of the doorway only, or two wall-mounted detectors shall be required, one on each side of the doorway. Figure 17.7.5.6.5.1(A), part A or B, shall apply.

FIGURE 17.7.5.6.5.1(A) Detector Location Requirements for Wall Sections.

(B) If the depth of wall section above the door is greater than 24 in. (610 mm) on one side only, one ceiling-mounted smoke detector shall be required on the higher side of the doorway only, or one wall-mounted detector shall be required on both sides of the doorway. Figure 17.7.5.6.5.1(A), part D, shall apply.

(C)* If the depth of wall section above the door is greater than 24 in. (610 mm) on both sides, two ceiling-mounted or wall-mounted detectors shall be required, one on each side of the doorway. Figure 17.7.5.6.5.1(A), part F, shall apply.

(D) If a detector is specifically listed for door frame mounting, or if a listed combination or integral detector–door closer assembly is used, only one detector shall be required if installed in the manner recommended by the manufacturer's published instructions. Figure 17.7.5.6.5.1(A), parts A, C, and E, shall apply.

17.7.5.6.5.2 If door release is intended to prevent smoke transmission from one space to another in one direction only, detectors located in the space to which smoke is to be confined, regardless of the depth of wall section above the door, shall be in accordance with 17.7.5.6.6. Alternatively, a smoke detector conforming with 17.7.5.6.5.1(D) shall be permitted to be used.

17.7.5.6.5.3 If there are multiple doorways, additional ceiling-mounted detectors shall be required as specified in 17.7.5.6.5.3(A) through 17.7.5.6.5.3(C).

(A) If the separation between doorways exceeds 24 in. (610 mm), each doorway shall be treated separately. Figure 17.7.5.6.5.3(A), part E, shall apply.

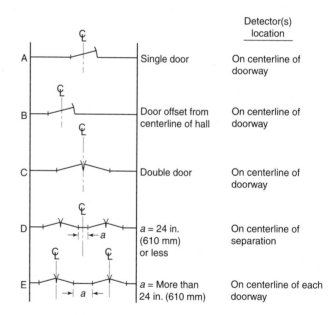

FIGURE 17.7.5.6.5.3(A) Detector Location Requirements for Single and Double Doors.

(B) Each group of three or more doorway openings shall be treated separately. Figure 17.7.5.6.5.3(B) shall apply.

(C) Each group of doorway openings that exceeds 20 ft (6.1 m) in width, measured at its overall extremes, shall be treated separately. Figure 17.7.5.6.5.3(C) shall apply.

17.7.5.6.5.4 If there are multiple doorways and listed door frame–mounted detectors, or if listed combination or integral detector–door closer assemblies are used, there shall be one detector for each single or double doorway.

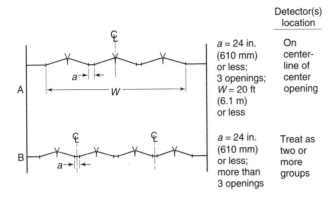

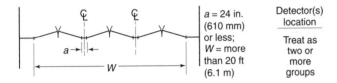

FIGURE 17.7.5.6.5.3(B) Detector Location Requirements for Group Doorways.

FIGURE 17.7.5.6.5.3(C) Detector Location Requirements for Group Doorways over 20 ft (6.1 m) in Width.

17.7.5.6.6 The locations of detectors shall be determined in accordance with 17.7.5.6.6.1 and 17.7.5.6.6.2.

17.7.5.6.6.1 If ceiling-mounted smoke detectors are to be installed on a smooth ceiling for a single or double doorway, they shall be located as follows [*Figure 17.7.5.6.5.3(A) shall apply*]:

(1) On the centerline of the doorway
(2) No more than 5 ft (1.5 m), measured along the ceiling and perpendicular to the doorway [*Figure 17.7.5.6.5.1(A) shall apply.*]
(3) No closer than shown in Figure 17.7.5.6.5.1(A), parts B, D, and F

17.7.5.6.6.2 If ceiling-mounted detectors are to be installed in conditions other than those outlined in 17.7.5.6.6.1, an engineering evaluation shall be made.

17.7.6 Special Considerations.

17.7.6.1 Spot-Type Detectors.

17.7.6.1.1 Combination and multi-sensor smoke detectors that have a fixed-temperature element as part of the unit shall be selected in accordance with Table 17.6.2.1 for the maximum ceiling temperature expected in service.

17.7.6.1.2* Holes in the back of a detector shall be covered by a gasket, sealant, or equivalent means, and the detector shall be mounted so that airflow from inside or around the housing does not prevent the entry of smoke during a fire or test condition.

17.7.6.2* High-Rack Storage. The location and spacing of smoke detectors for high-rack storage shall address the commodity, quantity, and configuration of the rack storage.

17.7.6.3 High Air Movement Areas.

17.7.6.3.1 General. The purpose and scope of 17.7.6.3 shall be to provide location and spacing guidance for smoke detectors intended for early warning of fire in high air movement areas.

Exception: Detectors provided for the control of smoke spread are covered by the requirements of 17.7.5.

17.7.6.3.2 Location. Smoke detectors shall not be located directly in the airstream of supply registers.

17.7.6.3.3* Spacing.

17.7.6.3.3.1 Smoke detector spacing shall be reduced where the airflow in a defined space exceeds 8 minutes per air change (total space volume) (equal to 7.5 air changes per hour).

17.7.6.3.3.2 Where spacing must be adjusted for airflow, spot-type smoke detector spacing shall be adjusted in accordance with Table 17.7.6.3.3.2 or Figure 17.7.6.3.3.2 before making any other spacing adjustments required by this Code.

Table 17.7.6.3.3.2 Smoke Detector Spacing Based on Air Movement (Not to Be Used for Under-Floor or Above-Ceiling Spaces)

Minutes per Air Change	Air Changes per Hour	Spacing per Detector	
		ft²	m²
1	60	125	12
2	30	250	23
3	20	375	35
4	15	500	46
5	12	625	58
6	10	750	70
7	8.6	875	81
8	7.5	900	84
9	6.7	900	84
10	6	900	84

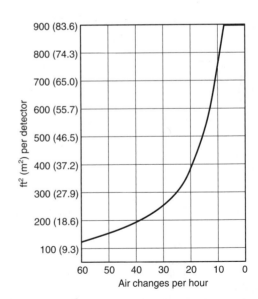

FIGURE 17.7.6.3.3.2 High Air Movement Areas (Not to Be Used for Under-Floor or Above-Ceiling Spaces).

17.7.6.3.3.3 Air-sampling or projected beam smoke detectors shall be installed in accordance with the manufacturer's published instructions.

17.7.6.3.4 HVAC Mechanical Rooms. Where HVAC mechanical rooms are used as an air plenum for return air, the spacings of smoke detectors shall not be required to be reduced based on the number of air changes.

17.7.7 Video Image Smoke Detection.

17.7.7.1 Video image smoke detection systems and all of the components thereof, including hardware and software, shall be listed for the purpose of smoke detection.

17.7.7.2 Video image smoke detection systems shall comply with all of the applicable requirements of Chapters 1, 10, 14, 17, and 23 of this Code.

17.7.7.2.1 Systems shall be designed in accordance with the performance-based design requirements of Section 17.3.

17.7.7.2.2 The location and spacing of video image smoke detectors shall comply with the requirements of 17.11.5.

17.7.7.3* Video signals generated by cameras that are components of video image smoke detection systems shall be permitted to be transmitted to other systems for other uses only through output connections provided specifically for that purpose by the video system manufacturer.

17.7.7.4* All component controls and software shall be protected from unauthorized changes. All changes to the software or component settings shall be tested in accordance with Chapter 14.

17.8 Radiant Energy–Sensing Fire Detectors.

17.8.1* General.

17.8.1.1 The radiant energy detection design documentation shall state the required performance objective of the system.

17.8.1.2 The purpose and scope of Section 17.8 shall be to provide requirements for the selection, location, and spacing of fire detectors that sense the radiant energy produced by burning substances. These detectors shall be categorized as flame detectors and spark/ember detectors.

17.8.2* Fire Characteristics and Detector Selection.

17.8.2.1* The type and quantity of radiant energy–sensing fire detectors shall be determined on the basis of the performance characteristics of the detector and an analysis of the hazard, including the burning characteristics of the fuel, the fire growth rate, the environment, the ambient conditions, and the capabilities of the extinguishing media and equipment.

17.8.2.2* The selection of the radiant energy–sensing detectors shall be based on the following:

(1) Matching of the spectral response of the detector to the spectral emissions of the fire or fires to be detected
(2) Minimizing the possibility of spurious nuisance alarms from non-fire sources inherent to the hazard area

17.8.3 Spacing Considerations.

17.8.3.1 General Rules.

17.8.3.1.1* Radiant energy–sensing fire detectors shall be employed consistent with the listing or approval and the inverse square law, which defines the fire size versus distance curve for the detector.

17.8.3.1.2 Detector quantity shall be based on the detectors being positioned so that no point requiring detection in the hazard area is obstructed or outside the field of view of at least one detector.

17.8.3.2 Spacing Considerations for Flame Detectors.

17.8.3.2.1* The location and spacing of detectors shall be the result of an engineering evaluation that includes the following:

(1) Size of the fire that is to be detected
(2) Fuel involved
(3) Sensitivity of the detector
(4) Field of view of the detector
(5) Distance between the fire and the detector
(6) Radiant energy absorption of the atmosphere
(7) Presence of extraneous sources of radiant emissions
(8) Purpose of the detection system
(9) Response time required

17.8.3.2.2 The system design shall specify the size of the flaming fire of given fuel that is to be detected.

17.8.3.2.3* In applications where the fire to be detected could occur in an area not on the optical axis of the detector, the distance shall be reduced or detectors shall be added to compensate for the angular displacement of the fire in accordance with the manufacturer's published instructions.

17.8.3.2.4* In applications in which the fire to be detected is of a fuel that differs from the test fuel used in the process of listing or approval, the distance between the detector and the fire shall be adjusted consistent with the fuel specificity of the detector as established by the manufacturer.

17.8.3.2.5 Because flame detectors are line-of-sight devices, their ability to respond to the required area of fire in the zone that is to be protected shall not be compromised by the presence of intervening structural members or other opaque objects or materials.

17.8.3.2.6* Provisions shall be made to sustain detector window clarity in applications where airborne particulates and aerosols coat the detector window between maintenance intervals and affect sensitivity.

17.8.3.3 Spacing Considerations for Spark/Ember Detectors.

17.8.3.3.1* The location and spacing of detectors shall be the result of an engineering evaluation that includes the following:

(1) Size of the spark or ember that is to be detected
(2) Fuel involved
(3) Sensitivity of the detector
(4) Field of view of the detector
(5) Distance between the fire and the detector
(6) Radiant energy absorption of the atmosphere
(7) Presence of extraneous sources of radiant emissions
(8) Purpose of the detection systems
(9) Response time required

17.8.3.3.2* The system design shall specify the size of the spark or ember of the given fuel that the detection system is to detect.

17.8.3.3.3 Spark detectors shall be positioned so that all points within the cross section of the conveyance duct, conveyor, or chute where the detectors are located are within the field of view *(as defined in 3.3.100)* of at least one detector.

17.8.3.3.4* The location and spacing of the detectors shall be adjusted using the inverse square law, modified for the atmospheric absorption and the absorption of nonburning fuel suspended in the air in accordance with the manufacturer's published instructions.

17.8.3.3.5* In applications where the sparks to be detected could occur in an area not on the optical axis of the detector, the distance shall be reduced or detectors shall be added to compensate for the angular displacement of the fire in accordance with the manufacturer's published instructions.

17.8.3.3.6* Provisions shall be made to sustain the detector window clarity in applications where airborne particulates and aerosols coat the detector window and affect sensitivity.

17.8.4 Other Considerations.

17.8.4.1 Radiant energy–sensing detectors shall be protected either by design or installation to ensure that optical performance is not compromised.

17.8.4.2 If necessary, radiant energy–sensing detectors shall be shielded or otherwise arranged to prevent action from unwanted radiant energy.

17.8.4.3 Where used in outdoor applications, radiant energy–sensing detectors shall be shielded or otherwise arranged in a fashion to prevent diminishing sensitivity by conditions such as rain or snow and yet allow a clear field of vision of the hazard area.

17.8.4.4 A radiant energy–sensing fire detector shall not be installed in a location where the ambient conditions are known to exceed the extremes for which the detector has been listed.

17.8.5 Video Image Flame Detection.

17.8.5.1 Video image flame detection systems and all of the components thereof, including hardware and software, shall be listed for the purpose of flame detection.

17.8.5.2 Video image flame detection systems shall comply with all of the applicable requirements of Chapters 1, 10, 14, 17, and 23 of this Code.

17.8.5.3* Video signals generated by cameras that are components of video image flame detection systems shall be permitted to be transmitted to other systems for other uses only through output connections provided specifically for that purpose by the video system manufacturer.

17.8.5.4* All component controls and software shall be protected from unauthorized changes. All changes to the software or component settings shall be tested in accordance with Chapter 14.

17.9 Combination, Multi-Criteria, and Multi-Sensor Detectors.

17.9.1 General. Section 17.9 provides requirements for the selection, location, and spacing of combination, multi-criteria, and multi-sensor detectors.

17.9.2 Combination Detectors.

17.9.2.1 A combination detector shall be listed for each sensor.

17.9.2.2 The device listings shall determine the locations and spacing criteria in accordance with Chapter 17.

17.9.3 Multi-Criteria Detectors.

17.9.3.1 A multi-criteria detector shall be listed for the primary function of the device.

17.9.3.2 Because of the device-specific, software-driven solution of multi-criteria detectors to reduce unwanted alarms and improve detector response to a nonspecific fire source, location and spacing criteria included with the detector installation instructions shall be followed.

17.9.4 Multi-Sensor Detectors.

17.9.4.1 A multi-sensor detector shall be listed for each sensor.

17.9.4.2 Because of the device-specific, software-driven solution of multi-sensor detectors to reduce unwanted alarms and improve detector response to a nonspecific fire source, location and spacing criteria included with the detector installation instructions shall be followed.

17.10 Gas Detection.

17.10.1 General. The purpose and scope of Section 17.10 shall be to provide requirements for the selection, installation, and operation of gas detectors.

17.10.2 Gas Characteristics and Detector Selection.

17.10.2.1 Gas detection equipment shall be listed for the specific gas or vapor it is intended to detect.

17.10.2.2 Any gas detection systems installed on a fire alarm system shall comply with all the applicable requirements of Chapters 1, 10, 14, 17, and 23 of this Code.

17.10.2.3 The requirements of this Code shall not apply to gas detection systems used solely for process control.

17.10.2.4* The selection and placement of the gas detectors shall be based on an engineering evaluation.

17.11 Other Fire Detectors.

17.11.1 Detectors that operate on principles different from those covered by Sections 17.6 through 17.8 shall be classified as "other fire detectors."

17.11.1.1 Such detectors shall be installed in all areas where they are required either by other NFPA codes and standards or by the authority having jurisdiction.

17.11.2* "Other fire detectors" shall operate where subjected to the abnormal concentration of combustion effects that occur during a fire.

17.11.3 Detection layout shall be based upon the size and intensity of fire to provide the necessary quantity of required products and related thermal lift, circulation, or diffusion for operation.

17.11.4 Room sizes and contours, airflow patterns, obstructions, and other characteristics of the protected hazard shall be taken into account.

17.11.5 Location and spacing of detectors shall comply with 17.11.5.1 through 17.11.5.3.

17.11.5.1 The location and spacing of detectors shall be based on the principle of operation and an engineering survey of the conditions anticipated in service.

17.11.5.1.1 The manufacturer's published instructions shall be consulted for recommended detector uses and locations.

17.11.5.2 Detectors shall not be spaced beyond their listed or approved maximums.

17.11.5.2.1 Closer spacing shall be used where the structural or other characteristics of the protected hazard warrant.

17.11.5.3 The location and sensitivity of the detectors shall be based on a documented engineering evaluation that includes the manufacturer's installation instructions and the following:

(1) Structural features, size, and shape of the rooms and bays
(2) Occupancy and uses of the area
(3) Ceiling height
(4) Ceiling shape, surface, and obstructions
(5) Ventilation
(6) Ambient environment
(7) Burning characteristics of the combustible materials present
(8) Configuration of the contents in the area to be protected

17.12 Sprinkler Waterflow Alarm-Initiating Devices.

17.12.1* The provisions of Section 17.12 shall apply to devices that initiate an alarm indicating a flow of water in a sprinkler system.

17.12.2* Activation of the initiating device shall occur within 90 seconds of waterflow at the alarm-initiating device when flow occurs that is equal to or greater than that from a single sprinkler of the smallest orifice size installed in the system.

17.12.3 Movement of water due to waste, surges, or variable pressure shall not initiate an alarm signal.

17.13* Detection of Operation of Other Automatic Extinguishing Systems. The operation of fire extinguishing systems or suppression systems shall initiate an alarm signal by alarm-initiating devices installed in accordance with their individual listings.

17.14 Manually Actuated Alarm-Initiating Devices. *← Pull station*

17.14.1 Manually actuated alarm-initiating devices for initiating signals other than for fire alarm shall be permitted if the devices are differentiated from manual for fire alarm boxes by a color other than red and labeling.

17.14.2 Combination manual fire alarm boxes and guard's signaling stations shall be permitted.

17.14.3 Manually actuated alarm-initiating devices shall be securely mounted.

17.14.4 Manually actuated alarm-initiating devices shall be mounted on a background of contrasting color.

17.14.5 The operable part of a manually actuated alarm-initiating device shall be not less than 42 in. (1.07 m) and not more than 48 in. (1.22 m) from the finished floor.

17.14.6 Manually actuated alarm-initiating devices shall be permitted to be single action or double action.

17.14.7* Listed protective covers shall be permitted to be installed over single- or double-action manually actuated alarm-initiating devices.

17.14.8 Manual fire alarm boxes shall comply with 17.14.8.1 through 17.14.8.6.

17.14.8.1 Manual fire alarm boxes shall be used only for fire alarm initiating purposes.

17.14.8.2 Manual fire alarm boxes shall be installed so that they are conspicuous, unobstructed, and accessible.

17.14.8.3* Unless installed in an environment that precludes the use of red paint or red plastic, manual fire alarm boxes shall be red in color.

17.14.8.4 Manual fire alarm boxes shall be located within 5 ft (1.5 m) of each exit doorway on each floor.

17.14.8.5* Additional manual fire alarm boxes shall be provided so that the travel distance to the nearest manual fire alarm box will not exceed 200 ft (61 m), measured horizontally on the same floor.

17.14.8.6 Manual fire alarm boxes shall be mounted on both sides of grouped openings over 40 ft (12.2 m) in width, and within 5 ft (1.5 m) of each side of the grouped opening.

17.15 Fire Extinguisher Electronic Monitoring Device. A fire extinguisher electronic monitoring device shall indicate those conditions for a specific fire extinguisher required by NFPA 10, *Standard for Portable Fire Extinguishers*, to a fire alarm control unit or other control unit.

17.16 Supervisory Signal–Initiating Devices. *Tamper switch*

17.16.1 Control Valve Supervisory Signal–Initiating Device.

17.16.1.1 Two separate and distinct signals shall be initiated: one indicating movement of the valve from its normal position (off-normal), and the other indicating restoration of the valve to its normal position.

17.16.1.2 The off-normal signal shall be initiated during the first two revolutions of the handwheel or during one-fifth of the travel distance of the valve control apparatus from its normal position.

17.16.1.3 The off-normal signal shall not be restored at any valve position except normal.

17.16.1.4 An initiating device for supervising the position of a control valve shall not interfere with the operation of the valve, obstruct the view of its indicator, or prevent access for valve maintenance.

17.16.2 Pressure Supervisory Signal–Initiating Device.

17.16.2.1 Two separate and distinct signals shall be initiated: one indicating that the required pressure has increased or decreased (off-normal), and the other indicating restoration of the pressure to its normal value.

17.16.2.2 The requirements in 17.16.2.2.1 through 17.16.2.2.4 shall apply to pressure supervisory signal–initiating devices.

17.16.2.2.1 Pressure Tank.

(A) A pressure tank supervisory signal–initiating device for a pressurized limited water supply, such as a pressure tank, shall indicate both high- and low-pressure conditions.

(B) The off-normal signal shall be initiated when the required pressure increases or decreases by 10 psi (70 kPa).

17.16.2.2.2 Dry Pipe Sprinkler System.

(A) A pressure supervisory signal–initiating device for a dry-pipe sprinkler system shall indicate both high- and low-pressure conditions.

(B) The off-normal signal shall be initiated when the pressure increases or decreases by 10 psi (70 kPa).

17.16.2.2.3 Steam Pressure.

(A) A steam pressure supervisory signal–initiating device shall indicate a low pressure condition.

(B) The off-normal signal shall be initiated prior to the pressure falling below 110 percent of the minimum operating pressure of the steam-operated equipment supplied.

17.16.2.2.4 Other Sources. An initiating device for supervising the pressure of sources other than those specified in 17.16.2.2.1 through 17.16.2.2.3 shall be provided as required by the authority having jurisdiction.

17.16.3 Water Level Supervisory Signal–Initiating Device.

17.16.3.1 Two separate and distinct signals shall be initiated: one indicating that the required water level has been lowered or raised (off-normal), and the other indicating restoration.

17.16.3.2 A pressure tank signal-initiating device shall indicate both high and low water level conditions.

17.16.3.2.1 The off-normal signal shall be initiated when the water level falls 3 in. (70 mm) or rises 3 in. (70 mm).

17.16.3.3 A supervisory signal–initiating device for other than pressure tanks shall initiate a low water level signal when the water level falls 12 in. (300 mm).

17.16.4 Water Temperature Supervisory Signal–Initiating Device.

17.16.4.1 A temperature supervisory device for a water storage container exposed to freezing conditions shall initiate two separate and distinctive signals, as specified in 17.16.4.2.

17.16.4.2 One signal shall indicate a decrease in water temperature to 40°F (4.4°C), and the other shall indicate its restoration to above 40°F (4.4°C).

17.16.5 Room Temperature Supervisory Signal–Initiating Device. A room temperature supervisory device shall indicate a decrease in room temperature to 40°F (4.4°C) and its restoration to above 40°F (4.4°C).

Chapter 18   Notification Appliances

18.1* Application.

18.1.1 The requirements of this chapter shall apply where required by the enforcing authority; governing laws, codes, or standards; or other parts of this Code.

18.1.2 The requirements of this chapter shall address the reception of a notification signal and not the signal's information content.

18.1.3 The performance, location, and mounting of notification appliances used to initiate or direct evacuation or relocation of the occupants, or for providing information to occupants or staff, shall comply with this chapter.

18.1.4 The performance, location, and mounting of annunciators, displays, and printers used to display or record information for use by occupants, staff, responding emergency personnel, or supervising station personnel shall comply with this chapter.

18.1.5* The requirements of this chapter shall apply to the areas, spaces, or system functions where required by the enforcing authority; governing laws, codes, or standards; or other parts of this Code requiring compliance with this chapter.

18.1.6 The requirements of Chapter 7 shall apply where referenced in Chapter 18.

18.1.7 The requirements of Chapters 10, 14, 23, and 24 shall apply to the interconnection of notification appliances, the control configurations, the power supplies, and the use of the information provided by notification appliances.

18.1.8 Notification appliances shall be permitted to be used within buildings or outdoors and to target the general building, area, or space, or only specific parts of a building, area, or space designated in specific zones and sub-zones.

18.2 Purpose. Notification appliances shall provide stimuli for initiating emergency action and provide information to users, emergency response personnel, and occupants.

18.3 General.

18.3.1 Listing. All notification appliances installed in conformity with Chapter 18 shall be listed for the purpose for which they are used.

18.3.2 Nameplates.

18.3.2.1 Notification appliances shall include on their nameplates reference to electrical requirements and rated audible or visible performance, or both, as defined by the listing authority.

18.3.2.2 Audible appliances shall include on their nameplates reference to their parameters or reference to installation documents (supplied with the appliance) that include the parameters in accordance with 18.4.3 or 18.4.4.

18.3.2.3 Visible appliances shall include on their nameplates reference to their parameters or reference to installation documents (supplied with the appliance) that include the parameters in accordance with 18.5.3.1 or Section 18.6.

18.3.3 Physical Construction.

18.3.3.1 Appliances intended for use in special environments, such as outdoors versus indoors, high or low temperatures, high humidity, dusty conditions, and hazardous locations, or where subject to tampering, shall be listed for the intended application.

18.3.3.2* Notification appliances used for signaling other than fire shall not have the word FIRE, or any fire symbol, in any form (i.e., stamped, imprinted, etc.) on the appliance visible to the public. Notification appliances with multiple visible elements shall be permitted to have fire markings only on those visible elements used for fire signaling.

18.3.4* Mechanical Protection.

18.3.4.1 Appliances subject to mechanical damage shall be suitably protected.

18.3.4.2 If guards, covers, or lenses are employed, they shall be listed for use with the appliance.

18.3.4.3 The effect of guards, covers, or lenses on the appliance's field performance shall be in accordance with the listing requirements.

18.3.5 Mounting.

18.3.5.1 Appliances shall be supported independently of their attachments to the circuit conductors.

18.3.5.2 Appliances shall be mounted in accordance with the manufacturer's published instructions.

18.3.6* Connections. Terminals, leads, or addressable communication, that provide for monitoring the integrity of the notification appliance connections shall be provided.

18.4 Audible Characteristics.

18.4.1 General Requirements.

18.4.1.1* An average ambient sound level greater than 105 dBA shall require the use of a visible notification appliance(s) in accordance with Section 18.5 where the application is public mode or Section 18.6 where the application is private mode.

18.4.1.2* The total sound pressure level produced by combining the ambient sound pressure level with all audible notification appliances operating shall not exceed 110 dBA at the minimum hearing distance.

18.4.1.3* Sound from normal or permanent sources, having a duration greater than 60 seconds, shall be included when measuring maximum ambient sound level. Sound from temporary or abnormal sources shall not be required to be included when measuring maximum ambient sound level.

18.4.1.4 Audible notification appliances for alert and evacuation signal tones shall meet the requirements of 18.4.3 (Public Mode Audible Requirements), 18.4.4 (Private Mode Audible Requirements), 18.4.5 (Sleeping Area Requirements), or 18.4.6 (Narrow Band Tone Signaling for Exceeding Masked Thresholds), as applicable.

18.4.1.4.1* The designer of the audible notification system shall identify the rooms and spaces that will have audible notification and those where audible notification will not be provided.

18.4.1.4.2* Unless otherwise required by other sections of this Code, the coverage area for audible occupant notification shall be as required by other governing laws, codes, or standards. Where the other governing laws, codes, or standards require audible occupant notification for all or part of an area or space, coverage shall only be required in occupiable areas as defined in 3.3.178.

18.4.1.4.3 The sound pressure levels that must be produced by the audible appliances in the coverage areas to meet the requirements of this Code shall be documented by the system designer during the planning and design of the notification system. The greater of the expected average ambient sound pressure level or expected maximum sound pressure level having a duration of at least 60 seconds shall also be documented for the coverage area by the system designer to ensure compliance with 18.4.3, 18.4.4, 18.4.5, or 18.4.6 for the coverage area.

18.4.1.4.4 The design sound pressure levels to be produced by the notification appliances for the various coverage areas shall be documented for use during acceptance testing of the system.

18.4.1.4.5 Where required by the authority having jurisdiction, documentation of the design sound pressure levels for the various coverage areas shall be submitted for review and approval.

18.4.1.5* Voice messages shall not be required to meet the audibility requirements of 18.4.3 (Public Mode Audible Requirements), 18.4.4 (Private Mode Audible Requirements), 18.4.5 (Sleeping Area Requirements), or 18.4.6 (Narrow Band Tone Signaling for Exceeding Masked Thresholds), but shall meet the intelligibility requirements of 18.4.10 where voice intelligibility is required.

18.4.1.6 Audible notification appliances used for exit marking shall not be required to meet the audibility requirements of 18.4.3 (Public Mode Audible Requirements), 18.4.4 (Private Mode Audible Requirements), 18.4.5 (Sleeping Area Requirements), or 18.4.6 (Narrow Band Tone Signaling for Exceeding Masked Thresholds), except as required by 18.4.7 (Exit Marking Audible Appliance Requirements).

18.4.2 Distinctive Evacuation Signal.

18.4.2.1* To meet the requirements of Section 10.10, the alarm audible signal pattern used to notify building occupants of the need to evacuate (leave the building) or relocate (from one area to another) shall be the standard alarm evacuation signal consisting of a three-pulse temporal pattern. The pattern shall be in accordance with Figure 18.4.2.1 and shall consist of the following in this order:

(1) "On" phase lasting 0.5 second ±10 percent
(2) "Off" phase lasting 0.5 second ±10 percent for three successive "on" periods
(3) "Off" phase lasting 1.5 seconds ±10 percent

Exception: Where approved by the authority having jurisdiction, continued use of the existing consistent evacuation signaling scheme shall be permitted.

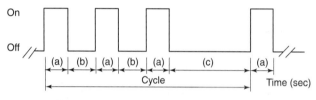

Key:
Phase (a) signal is on for 0.5 sec ±10%
Phase (b) signal is off for 0.5 sec ±10%
Phase (c) signal is off for 1.5 sec ±10% [(c) = (a) + 2(b)]
Total cycle lasts for 4 sec ±10%

FIGURE 18.4.2.1 Temporal Pattern Parameters.

18.4.2.2 A single-stroke bell or chime sounded at "on" intervals lasting 1 second ±10 percent, with a 2-second ±10 percent "off" interval after each third "on" stroke, shall be permitted.

18.4.2.3 The signal shall be repeated for a period appropriate for the purposes of evacuation of the building, but for not less than 180 seconds. The minimum repetition time shall be permitted to be manually interrupted.

18.4.2.4* The standard evacuation signal shall be synchronized within a notification zone.

18.4.3* Public Mode Audible Requirements.

18.4.3.1* To ensure that audible public mode signals are clearly heard, unless otherwise permitted by 18.4.3.2 through 18.4.3.5, they shall have a sound level at least 15 dB above the average ambient sound level or 5 dB above the maximum sound level having a duration of at least 60 seconds, whichever is greater, measured 5 ft (1.5 m) above the floor in the area required to be served by the system using the A-weighted scale (dBA).

18.4.3.2 Where approved by the authority having jurisdiction or other governing codes or standards, the requirements for audible signaling shall be permitted to be reduced or eliminated when visible signaling is provided in accordance with Section 18.5.

18.4.3.3 Audible alarm notification appliances installed in elevator cars shall be permitted to use the audibility criteria for private mode appliances detailed in 18.4.4.1.

18.4.3.4 If approved by the authority having jurisdiction, audible alarm notification appliances installed in restrooms shall be permitted to use the audibility criteria for private mode appliances detailed in 18.4.4.1.

18.4.3.5 A signaling system arranged to stop or reduce ambient noise shall comply with 18.4.3.5.1 through 18.4.3.5.3.

18.4.3.5.1 A signaling system arranged to stop or reduce ambient noise shall produce a sound level at least 15 dB above the reduced average ambient sound level or 5 dB above the maximum sound level having a duration of at least 60 seconds after reduction of the ambient noise level, whichever is greater, measured 5 ft (1.5 m) above the floor in the area required to be served by the system using the A-weighted scale (dBA).

18.4.3.5.2 Visible notification appliances shall be installed in the affected areas in accordance with Sections 18.5 or 18.6.

18.4.3.5.3 Relays, circuits, or interfaces necessary to stop or reduce ambient noise shall meet the requirements of Chapters 10, 12, 21, and 23.

18.4.4 Private Mode Audible Requirements.

18.4.4.1* To ensure that audible private mode signals are clearly heard, they shall have a sound level at least 10 dB above the average ambient sound level or 5 dB above the maximum sound level having a duration of at least 60 seconds, whichever is greater, measured 5 ft (1.5 m) above the floor in the area required to be served by the system using the A-weighted scale (dBA).

18.4.4.2* Where approved by the authority having jurisdiction or other governing codes or standards, the requirements for audible signaling shall be permitted to be reduced or eliminated when visible signaling is provided in accordance with Section 18.5.

18.4.4.3 A system arranged to stop or reduce ambient noise shall comply with 18.4.4.3.1 through 18.4.4.3.3.

18.4.4.3.1 A system arranged to stop or reduce ambient noise shall be permitted to produce a sound level at least 10 dB above the reduced average ambient sound level or 5 dB above the maximum sound level having a duration of at least 60 seconds after reduction of the ambient noise level, whichever is greater, measured 5 ft (1.5 m) above the floor, using the A-weighted scale (dBA).

18.4.4.3.2 Visible notification appliances shall be installed in the affected areas in accordance with Sections 18.5 or 18.6.

18.4.4.3.3 Relays, circuits, or interfaces necessary to stop or reduce ambient noise shall meet the requirements of Chapters 10, 12, 21, and 23.

18.4.5 Sleeping Area Requirements.

18.4.5.1* Where audible appliances are installed to provide signals for sleeping areas, they shall have a sound level of at least 15 dB above the average ambient sound level or 5 dB above the maximum sound level having a duration of at least 60 seconds or a sound level of at least 75 dBA, whichever is greater, measured at the pillow level in the area required to be served by the system using the A-weighted scale (dBA).

18.4.5.2 If any barrier, such as a door, curtain, or retractable partition, is located between the notification appliance and the pillow, the sound pressure level shall be measured with the barrier placed between the appliance and the pillow.

18.4.5.3* Effective January 1, 2014, audible appliances provided for the sleeping areas to awaken occupants shall produce a low frequency alarm signal that complies with the following:

(1) The alarm signal shall be a square wave or provide equivalent awakening ability.
(2) The wave shall have a fundamental frequency of 520 Hz ± 10 percent.

18.4.6* Narrow Band Tone Signaling for Exceeding Masked Thresholds.

18.4.6.1 Masked Threshold Allowance. Audible tone signaling shall be permitted to comply with the masked threshold requirements in this subsection in lieu of the A-weighted signaling requirements in 18.4.3 and 18.4.4.

18.4.6.2* Calculation Method. The effective masked threshold shall be calculated in accordance with ISO 7731, *Danger signals for work places — Auditory danger signals.*

18.4.6.3 Noise Data. Noise data for calculating the effective masked threshold shall be the peak value of noise lasting 60 seconds or more for each octave or one-third octave band.

18.4.6.4 Documentation. Analysis and design documentation shall be submitted to the authority having jurisdiction and shall contain the following information:

(1) Frequency data for the ambient noise, including the date, time, and location where measurements were taken for existing environments, or projected data for environments not yet constructed
(2) Frequency data of the audible notification appliance
(3) Calculations of the effective masked threshold for each set of noise data
(4) A statement of the sound pressure level that would be required by 18.4.3 or 18.4.4 if masked threshold signaling had not been done

18.4.6.5 Sound Pressure Level. For masked threshold signaling, the audible signal tone shall meet the requirements of either 18.4.6.5.1 or 18.4.6.5.2 but not for the reproduction of prerecorded, synthesized, or live messages.

18.4.6.5.1 The sound pressure level of the audible tone signal shall exceed the masked threshold in one or more octave bands by at least 10 dB in the octave band under consideration.

18.4.6.5.2 The sound pressure level of the audible tone signal shall exceed the masked threshold in one or more one-third octave bands by at least 13 dB in the one-third octave band under consideration.

18.4.7 Exit Marking Audible Notification Appliance Requirements.

18.4.7.1* Exit marking audible notification appliances shall meet or exceed the frequency and sound level settings and guidelines specified in the manufacturer's documented instructions.

18.4.7.2* In addition to 18.4.7.1, as a minimum, to ensure that exit marking audible notification appliance signals are clearly heard and produce the desired directional effects for 50 ft (15.24 m) within an unobstructed egress path, they shall meet the audibility requirements of 18.4.6 in at least one one-third octave band or one octave band within the effective frequency ranges of the interaural time difference (ITD), interaural level or intensity difference (ILD or IID), and anatomical transfer function or head-related transfer function (ATF or HRTF) localization cues. The signal shall penetrate both the ambient noise and the fire alarm signal.

18.4.7.3 Where required by the enforcing authority; governing laws, codes, or standards; or other parts of this Code, exit marking audible notification appliances shall be installed in accordance with the manufacturer's instructions.

18.4.7.4* Where required by the enforcing authority; governing laws, codes, or standards; or other parts of this Code, exit marking audible notification shall be located at the entrance to all building exits and areas of refuge as defined by the applicable building or fire code.

18.4.7.5 Where exit marking audible notification appliances are utilized to mark areas of refuge, they shall provide an audible signal distinct from that used for other exits that do not have areas of refuge.

18.4.8 Location of Audible Notification Appliances for Building or Structure.

18.4.8.1 If ceiling heights allow, and unless otherwise permitted by 18.4.8.2 through 18.4.8.5, wall-mounted appliances shall have their tops above the finished floors at heights of not less than 90 in. (2.29 m) and below the finished ceilings at distances of not less than 6 in. (150 mm).

18.4.8.2 Ceiling-mounted or recessed appliances shall be permitted.

18.4.8.3 If combination audible/visible appliances are installed, the location of the installed appliance shall be determined by the requirements of 18.5.5.

18.4.8.4 Appliances that are an integral part of a smoke detector, smoke alarm, or other initiating device shall be located in accordance with the requirements for that device.

18.4.8.5 Mounting heights other than required by 18.4.8.1 and 18.4.8.2 shall be permitted, provided that the sound pressure level requirements of 18.4.3 for public mode or 18.4.4 for private mode, or 18.4.5 for sleeping areas, based on the application, are met.

18.4.9 Location of Audible Notification Appliances for Wide-Area Signaling. Audible notification appliances for wide-area signaling shall be installed in accordance with the requirements of the authority having jurisdiction, approved design documents, and the manufacturer's installation instruction to achieve the required performance.

18.4.10* Voice Intelligibility. Within the acoustically distinguishable spaces (ADS) where voice intelligibility is required, voice communications systems shall reproduce prerecorded, synthesized, or live (e.g., microphone, telephone handset, and radio) messages with voice intelligibility.

18.4.10.1* ADSs shall be determined by the system designer during the planning and design of all emergency communications systems.

18.4.10.2 Each ADS shall be identified as requiring or not requiring voice intelligibility.

18.4.10.2.1* Unless specifically required by other governing laws, codes, or standards, or by other parts of this Code, intelligibility shall not be required in all ADSs.

18.4.10.3* Where required by the enforcing authority; governing laws, codes, or standards; or other parts of this Code, ADS assignments shall be submitted for review and approval.

18.4.10.4 Intelligibility shall not be required to be determined through quantitative measurements.

18.4.10.5 Quantitative measurements as described in D.2.4 shall be permitted but are not required.

18.5* Visible Characteristics — Public Mode.

18.5.1* Visible Signaling.

18.5.1.1 Public mode visible signaling shall meet the requirements of Section 18.5 using visible notification appliances.

18.5.1.2* The coverage area for visible occupant notification shall be as required by other governing laws, codes, or standards. Where the other governing laws, codes, or standards require visible occupant notification for all or part of an area or space, coverage shall only be required in occupiable areas as defined in 3.3.178.

18.5.2 Area of Coverage.

18.5.2.1 The designer of the visible notification system shall document the rooms and spaces that will have visible notification and those where visible notification will not be provided.

18.5.2.2* Unless otherwise specified or required by other sections of this Code, the required coverage area for visible occupant notification shall be as required by other governing laws, codes, or standards.

18.5.2.3 Where required by the authority having jurisdiction, documentation of the effective intensity (cd) of the visible appliances for the area of coverage shall be submitted for review and approval.

18.5.3 Light, Color, and Pulse Characteristics.

18.5.3.1 The flash rate shall not exceed two flashes per second (2 Hz) nor be less than one flash every second (1 Hz) throughout the listed voltage range of the appliance.

18.5.3.2 A maximum pulse duration shall be 0.2 second with a maximum duty cycle of 40 percent.

18.5.3.3 The pulse duration shall be defined as the time interval between initial and final points of 10 percent of maximum signal.

18.5.3.4* Lights used for fire alarm signaling only or to signal the intent for complete evacuation shall be clear or nominal white and shall not exceed 1000 cd (effective intensity).

18.5.3.5 Lights used to signal occupants to seek information or instructions shall be clear, nominal white, or other color as required by the emergency plan and the authority having jurisdiction for the area or building.

18.5.3.6* The strobe synchronization requirements of this chapter shall not apply where the visible notification appliances located inside the building are viewed from outside of the building.

18.5.4* Appliance Photometrics. The light output shall comply with the polar dispersion requirements of ANSI/UL 1971, *Standard for Signaling Devices for the Hearing Impaired*, or equivalent.

18.5.5 Appliance Location.

18.5.5.1* Wall-mounted appliances shall be mounted such that the entire lens is not less than 80 in. (2.03 m) and not greater than 96 in. (2.44 m) above the finished floor or at the mounting height specified using the performance-based alternative of 18.5.5.6.

18.5.5.2 Where low ceiling heights do not permit wall mounting at a minimum of 80 in. (2.03 m), wall mounted visible appliances shall be mounted within 6 in. (150 mm) of the ceiling. The room size covered by a strobe of a given value shall be reduced by twice the difference between the minimum mounting height of 80 in. (2.03 m) and the actual lower mounting height.

18.5.5.3* Visible appliances listed for mounting parallel to the floor shall be permitted to be located on the ceiling or suspended below the ceiling.

18.5.5.4* Spacing in Rooms.

18.5.5.4.1 Spacing shall be in accordance with either Table 18.5.5.4.1(a) and Figure 18.5.5.4.1 or Table 18.5.5.4.1(b).

Table 18.5.5.4.1(a) Room Spacing for Wall-Mounted Visible Appliances

Maximum Room Size		Minimum Required Light Output [Effective Intensity (cd)]	
ft	m	One Light per Room	Four Lights per Room (One Light per Wall)
20 × 20	6.10 × 6.10	15	NA
28 × 28	8.53 × 8.53	30	NA
30 × 30	9.14 × 9.14	34	NA
40 × 40	12.2 × 12.2	60	15
45 × 45	13.7 × 13.7	75	19
50 × 50	15.2 × 15.2	94	30
54 × 54	16.5 × 16.5	110	30
55 × 55	16.8 × 16.8	115	30
60 × 60	18.3 × 18.3	135	30
63 × 63	19.2 × 19.2	150	37
68 × 68	20.7 × 20.7	177	43
70 × 70	21.3 × 21.3	184	60
80 × 80	24.4 × 24.4	240	60
90 × 90	27.4 × 27.4	304	95
100 × 100	30.5 × 30.5	375	95
110 × 110	33.5 × 33.5	455	135
120 × 120	36.6 × 36.6	540	135
130 × 130	39.6 × 39.6	635	185

NA: Not allowable.

18.5.5.4.2 Visible notification appliances shall be installed in accordance with Table 18.5.5.4.1(a) or Table 18.5.5.4.1(b) using one of the following:

(1) A single visible notification appliance.
(2)* Two groups of visible notification appliances, where visual appliances of each group are synchronized, in the same room or adjacent space within the field of view. This shall include synchronization of strobes operated by separate systems.
(3) More than two visible notification appliances or groups of synchronized appliances in the same room or adjacent space within the field of view that flash in synchronization.

18.5.5.4.3 Room spacing in accordance with Table 18.5.5.4.1(a) and Figure 18.5.5.4.1 for wall-mounted appliances shall be based on locating the visible notification appliance at the halfway distance of the wall.

Table 18.5.5.4.1(b) Room Spacing for Ceiling-Mounted Visible Appliances

Maximum Room Size		Maximum Lens Height*		Minimum Required Light Output (Effective Intensity); One Light (cd)
ft	m	ft	m	
20 × 20	6.1 × 6.1	10	3.0	15
30 × 30	9.1 × 9.1	10	3.0	30
40 × 40	12.2 × 12.2	10	3.0	60
44 × 44	13.4 × 13.4	10	3.0	75
20 × 20	6.1 × 6.1	20	6.1	30
30 × 30	9.1 × 9.1	20	6.1	45
44 × 44	13.4 × 13.4	20	6.1	75
46 × 46	14.0 × 14.0	20	6.1	80
20 × 20	6.1 × 6.1	30	9.1	55
30 × 30	9.1 × 9.1	30	9.1	75
50 × 50	15.2 × 15.2	30	9.1	95
53 × 53	16.2 × 16.2	30	9.1	110
55 × 55	16.8 × 16.8	30	9.1	115
59 × 59	18.0 × 18.0	30	9.1	135
63 × 63	19.2 × 19.2	30	9.1	150
68 × 68	20.7 × 20.7	30	9.1	177
70 × 70	21.3 × 21.3	30	9.1	185

*This does not preclude mounting lens at lower heights.

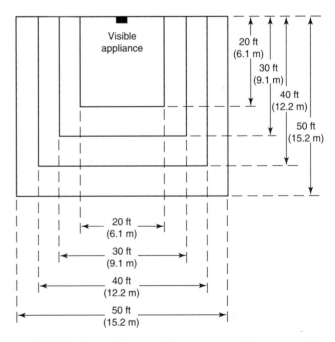

FIGURE 18.5.5.4.1 Room Spacing for Wall-Mounted Visible Appliances.

18.5.5.4.4 In square rooms with appliances not centered or in nonsquare rooms, the effective intensity (cd) from one visible wall-mounted notification appliance shall be determined by maximum room size dimensions obtained either by measuring the distance to the farthest wall or by doubling the distance to the farthest adjacent wall, whichever is greater, as required by Table 18.5.5.4.1(a) and Figure 18.5.5.4.1.

18.5.5.4.5 If a room configuration is not square, the square room size that allows the entire room to be encompassed or allows the room to be subdivided into multiple squares shall be used.

18.5.5.4.6* If ceiling heights exceed 30 ft (9.14 m), ceiling-mounted visible notification appliances shall be suspended at or below 30 ft (9.14 m) or at the mounting height determined using the performance-based alternative of 18.5.5.6, or wall-mounted visible notification appliances shall be installed in accordance with Table 18.5.5.4.1(a).

18.5.5.4.7 Table 18.5.5.4.1(b) shall be used if the ceiling-mounted visible notification appliance is at the center of the room. If the ceiling-mounted visible notification appliance is not located at the center of the room, the effective intensity (cd) shall be determined by doubling the distance from the appliance to the farthest wall to obtain the maximum room size.

18.5.5.5* Spacing in Corridors.

18.5.5.5.1 The installation of visible notification appliances in corridors 20 ft (6.1 m) or less in width shall be in accordance with the requirements of either 18.5.5.4 or 18.5.5.5.

18.5.5.5.2 Paragraph 18.5.5.5 shall apply to corridors not exceeding 20 ft (6.1 m) in width.

18.5.5.5.3 In a corridor application, visible appliances shall be rated not less than 15 cd.

18.5.5.5.4 Corridors greater than 20 ft (6.1 m) wide shall comply with the spacing requirements for rooms in accordance with 18.5.5.4.

18.5.5.5.5* Visible notification appliances shall be located not more than 15 ft (4.57 m) from the end of the corridor with a separation not greater than 100 ft (30.5 m) between appliances.

18.5.5.5.6 If there is an interruption of the concentrated viewing path, such as a fire door, an elevation change, or any other obstruction, the area shall be treated as a separate corridor.

18.5.5.5.7 In corridors where more than two visible notification appliances are in any field of view, they shall flash in synchronization.

18.5.5.5.8 Wall-mounted visible notification appliances in corridors shall be permitted to be mounted on either the end wall or the side wall of the corridor in accordance with spacing requirements of 18.5.5.5.5.

18.5.5.6* Performance-Based Alternative.

18.5.5.6.1 Any design that provides a minimum of 0.0375 lumens/ft^2 (0.4036 lumens/m^2) of illumination at any point within the covered area at all angles specified by the polar dispersion planes for wall- or ceiling-mounted visual appliances in ANSI/UL 1971, *Standard for Signaling Devices for the Hearing Impaired*, or equivalent, as calculated for the maximum distance from the nearest visual notification appliance, shall be permitted in lieu of the requirements of 18.5.5, excluding 18.5.5.7.

18.5.5.6.2 Documentation provided to the authority having jurisdiction shall include the following:

(1) Inverse Square Law calculations using each of the vertical and horizontal polar distribution angles in ANSI/UL 1971, *Standard for Signaling Devices for the Hearing Impaired*, or equivalent.
(2) The calculations shall account for the effects of polar distribution using one of the following:
  (a) The percentages from the applicable table(s) in ANSI/UL 1971, *Standard for Signaling Devices for the Hearing Impaired*, or equivalent
  (b) The actual results of laboratory tests of the specific appliance to be used as recorded by the listing organization

18.5.5.7 Sleeping Areas.

18.5.5.7.1 Combination smoke detectors and visible notification appliances or combination smoke alarms and visible notification appliances shall be installed in accordance with the applicable requirements of Chapters 17, 18, and 29.

18.5.5.7.2* Table 18.5.5.7.2 shall apply to sleeping areas.

Table 18.5.5.7.2 Effective Intensity Requirements for Sleeping Area Visible Notification Appliances

Distance from Ceiling to Top of Lens		Intensity (cd)
in.	mm	
≥24	≥610	110
<24	<610	177

18.5.5.7.3 For rooms with a linear dimension greater than 16 ft (4.87 m), the visible notification appliance shall be located within 16 ft (4.87 m) of the pillow.

18.5.6 Location of Visible Notification Appliances for Wide Area Signaling. Visible notification appliances for wide area signaling shall be installed in accordance with the requirements of the authority having jurisdiction, approved design documents, and the manufacturer's instructions to achieve the required performance.

18.6* Visible Characteristics — Private Mode. Visible notification appliances used in the private mode shall be of a sufficient quantity and intensity and located so as to meet the intent of the user and the authority having jurisdiction.

18.7 Supplementary Visible Signaling Method. A supplementary visible notification appliance shall be intended to augment an audible or visible signal.

18.7.1 A supplementary visible notification appliance shall comply with its marked rated performance.

18.7.2 Supplementary visible notification appliances shall be permitted to be located less than 80 in. (2.03 m) above the floor.

18.8 Textual Audible Appliances.

18.8.1 Speaker Appliances.

18.8.1.1 Speaker appliances shall comply with Section 18.4.

18.8.1.2* The sound pressure level, in dBA, of the tone produced by a signaling speaker shall comply with all the requirements in 18.4.3 (public), 18.4.4 (private), or 18.4.5 (sleeping) for the intended mode or shall comply with the requirements of 18.4.6 (narrow band tone signaling).

18.8.2 Telephone Appliances. Telephone appliances shall be in accordance with 24.5.1.

18.9* Textual and Graphical Visible Appliances.

18.9.1 Application.

18.9.1.1 Textual and graphical visible appliances shall be permitted to be used to signal information about fire or other emergency conditions or to direct intended responses to those conditions.

18.9.1.2 This section does not apply to means of egress signs, room identification signs, and other signage that could be required by other governing laws, codes, or standards.

18.9.1.3 Textual visible appliance messages shall be permitted to be static, flashing, or scrolling.

18.9.2 Location.

18.9.2.1 Private Mode. Unless otherwise permitted or required by other governing laws, codes, or standards, or by other parts of this Code or by the authority having jurisdiction, all textual and graphical visible notification appliances in the private mode shall be located in rooms that are accessible only to those persons directly concerned with the implementation and direction of emergency response in the areas protected by the system.

18.9.2.2 Public Mode. Textual and graphical visible notification appliances used in the public mode shall be located to ensure visibility to the occupants of the protected area or to the intended recipients.

18.9.2.3 Mounting. Desktop and surface-mounted textual and graphical appliances shall be permitted.

18.9.3 Performance. The information produced by textual and graphical visible appliances shall be clear and legible at the intended viewing distance.

18.9.4* Character and Symbol Requirements and Viewing Distance.

18.9.4.1 This section applies to visual characters and graphic elements and does not address raised characters or braille that could be required by other governing laws, codes, or standards.

18.9.4.2* Characters and symbols shall contrast with their background using either positive contrast (light on a dark background) or negative contrast (dark on a light background).

18.9.4.3 Characters and symbols and their background shall have a nonglare finish.

18.9.4.4* Characters shall be permitted to be uppercase or lowercase, or a combination of both.

18.9.4.5 Characters shall be conventional in form and not italic, oblique, script, highly decorative, or of other unusual form and shall use sans serif fonts.

18.9.4.6 Characters shall be selected from fonts where the width of the uppercase letter "O" is 55 percent minimum and 110 percent maximum of the height of the uppercase letter "I".

18.9.4.7* Character and symbol height for appliances other than desktop monitors or displays shall meet all of the following criteria:

(1) Minimum character height shall comply with Table 18.9.4.7.
(2) Viewing distance shall be measured as the horizontal distance between the character and an obstruction preventing further approach towards the appliance.
(3) Character height shall be based on the uppercase letter "I".

18.9.4.8* All characters and symbols displayed by textual and graphical visible notification appliances shall be a minimum of 40 in. (1.02 m) above the ground or finished floor.

18.9.4.9 Stroke thickness of the uppercase letter "I" shall be minimum 10 percent and maximum 30 percent of the height of the character.

18.9.4.10 Character spacing shall be measured between the two closest points of adjacent characters, excluding word spaces. Spacing between individual characters shall be minimum 10 percent and maximum 35 percent of character height.

18.9.4.11 Spacing between the baselines of separate lines of characters within a message shall be 135 percent minimum and 170 percent maximum of the character height.

18.10 Tactile Appliances.

18.10.1 Application. Tactile appliances shall be permitted if used in addition to audible or visible, or both, notification appliances.

18.10.2* Performance. Tactile appliances shall meet the performance requirements of ANSI/UL 1971, *Standard for Signaling Devices for the Hearing Impaired*, or equivalent.

18.11* Standard Emergency Service Interface. Where required by the enforcing authority; governing laws, codes, or standards; or other parts of this Code, annunciators, information display systems, and controls for portions of a system provided for use by emergency service personnel shall be designed, arranged, and located in accordance with the requirements of the organizations intended to use the equipment.

Chapter 19   Reserved

Chapter 20   Reserved

Chapter 21   Emergency Control Function Interfaces

21.1 Application. The provisions of Chapter 21 shall cover the minimum requirements and methods for emergency control function interfaces to fire alarm systems and emergency communications systems in accordance with this chapter.

21.1.1 The requirements of Chapters 7, 10, 17, 18, 23, 24, and 26 shall also apply, unless they are in conflict with this chapter.

21.1.2 The requirements of Chapter 14 shall apply.

21.1.3 The requirements of this chapter shall not apply to Chapter 29 unless otherwise noted.

Table 18.9.4.7 Visual Character and Graphic Symbol Heights Based on Height and Distance

Height of Character or Symbol Above Ground or Finished Floor		Horizontal Viewing Distance		Minimum Character or Symbol Height	
in.	m	ft	m	in.	mm
40 in. min. to ≤70 in.	1.02 m to 1.78 m	<6	1.83	⅝ in.	16 mm
		≥6	1.83	⅝ in., plus ⅛ in. per foot of horizontal viewing distance beyond 6 ft	16 mm plus 3 mm per 0.30 m of horizontal viewing distance beyond 1.83 m
>70 in. to ≤120 in.	1.78 m to 3.05 m	<15	4.57	2 in.	51 mm
		≥15	4.57	2 in. plus ⅛ in. per foot of horizontal viewing distance beyond 15 ft	51 mm plus 3 mm per 0.30 m of horizontal viewing distance beyond 4.57 m
>120 in.	3.05 m	<21	6.40	3 in.	75 mm
		≥21	6.40	3 in. plus ⅛ in. per foot of horizontal viewing distance beyond 21 ft	75 mm plus 3 mm per 0.30 m of horizontal viewing distance beyond 6.40 m

21.2 General.

21.2.1* Emergency control functions shall be permitted to be performed automatically.

21.2.2 The performance of automatic emergency control functions shall not interfere with power for lighting or for operating elevators.

21.2.3 The performance of automatic emergency control functions shall not preclude the combination of fire alarm services with other services requiring monitoring of operations.

21.2.4* Emergency control function interface devices shall be located within 3 ft (1 m) of the component controlling the emergency control function.

21.2.5 The emergency control function interface device shall function within the voltage and current limitations of the fire alarm control unit.

21.2.6 The installation wiring between the fire alarm control unit and the emergency control function interface device shall be Class A, Class B, Class D, or Class X in accordance with Chapter 12.

21.2.7 Emergency control functions shall not interfere with other operations of the fire alarm system.

21.2.8 The method(s) of interconnection between the fire alarm system and emergency control function interface device shall be monitored for integrity in accordance with Section 12.6.

21.2.9 The method(s) of interconnection between the emergency control function interface device and the component

controlling the emergency control function shall comply with the applicable provisions of *NFPA 70, National Electrical Code.*

21.2.10 The method(s) of interconnection between the emergency control function interface device and the component controlling the emergency control function shall be achieved by one of the following recognized means:

(1) Electrical contacts listed for the connected load
(2) Data communications over a signaling line circuit(s) dedicated to the fire alarm or shared with other premises operating systems
(3) Other listed methods

21.2.11 If a fire alarm system is a component of a life safety network and it communicates data to other systems providing life safety functions, or it receives data from such systems, the following shall apply:

(1) The path used for communicating data shall be monitored for integrity. This shall include monitoring the physical communication media and the ability to maintain intelligible communications.
(2) Data received from the network shall not affect the operation of the fire alarm system in any way other than to display the status of life safety network components.
(3) Where non-fire alarm systems are interconnected to the fire alarm system using a network or other digital communication technique, a signal (e.g., heartbeat, poll, ping, query) shall be generated between the fire alarm system and the non-fire alarm system. Failure of the fire alarm system to receive confirmation of the transmission shall cause a trouble signal to indicate within 200 seconds.

21.3* Elevator Recall for Fire Fighters' Service.

21.3.1 All initiating devices used to initiate fire fighters' service recall shall be connected to the building fire alarm system.

21.3.2* In facilities without a building fire alarm system, initiating devices used to initiate fire fighters' service recall shall be connected to a dedicated function fire alarm control unit that shall be designated as "elevator recall control and supervisory control unit," permanently identified on the dedicated function fire alarm control unit and on the record drawings.

21.3.3 Unless otherwise required by the authority having jurisdiction, only the elevator lobby, elevator hoistway, and elevator machine room smoke detectors, or other automatic fire detection as permitted by 21.3.9, shall be used to recall elevators for fire fighters' service.

Exception: A waterflow switch shall be permitted to initiate elevator recall upon activation of a sprinkler installed at the bottom of the elevator hoistway (the elevator pit), provided the waterflow switch and pit sprinkler are installed on a separately valved sprinkler line dedicated solely for protecting the elevator pit, and the waterflow switch is provided without time-delay capability.

21.3.4 Each initiating device used to initiate fire fighters' service recall shall be capable of initiating elevator recall when all other devices on the same initiating device circuit have been manually or automatically placed in the alarm condition.

21.3.5* A lobby smoke detector shall be located on the ceiling within 21 ft (6.4 m) of the centerline of each elevator door within the elevator bank under control of the detector.

Exception: For lobby ceiling configurations exceeding 15 ft (4.6 m) in height or that are other than flat and smooth, detector locations shall be determined in accordance with Chapter 17.

21.3.6 Smoke detectors shall not be installed in unsprinklered elevator hoistways unless they are installed to activate the elevator hoistway smoke relief equipment.

21.3.7* When sprinklers are installed in elevator pits, automatic fire detection shall be installed to initiate elevator recall in accordance with 2.27.3.2.1(c) of ANSI/ASME A.17.1/CSA B44, *Safety Code for Elevators and Escalators,* and the following shall apply:

(1) Where sprinklers are located above the lowest level of recall, the fire detection device shall be located at the top of the hoistway.
(2) Where sprinklers are located in the bottom of the hoistway (the pit), fire detection device(s) shall be installed in the pit in accordance with Chapter 17.
(3) Outputs to the elevator controller(s) shall comply with 21.3.14.

21.3.8* Smoke detectors shall not be installed in elevator pits to initiate elevator recall unless the smoke detector is listed for the environment.

21.3.9* If ambient conditions prohibit installation of automatic smoke detection, other automatic fire detection shall be permitted.

21.3.10 When actuated, any detector that has initiated fire fighters' recall shall also be annunciated at the building fire alarm control unit, or other fire alarm control unit as described in 21.3.2, and at required remote annunciators.

21.3.11 Actuation from the elevator hoistway, elevator machine room, elevator machinery space, elevator control space, or elevator control room smoke detectors, or other automatic fire detection as permitted by 21.3.9, shall cause separate and distinct visible annunciation at the building fire alarm control unit, or the fire alarm control unit described in 21.3.2, and at required annunciators to alert fire fighters and other emergency personnel that the elevators are no longer safe to use.

21.3.12 Where approved by the authority having jurisdiction, the detectors used to initiate elevator recall shall be permitted to initiate a supervisory signal in lieu of an alarm signal.

21.3.13 Where lobby detectors are used for other than initiating elevator recall, the signal initiated by the detector shall also initiate an alarm signal.

21.3.14* Separate outputs from the fire alarm systems to the elevator controller(s) shall be provided to implement elevator Phase I Emergency Recall Operation in accordance with Section 2.27 of ANSI/ASME A17.1/CSA B44, *Safety Code for Elevators and Escalators,* as required in 21.3.14.1 through 21.3.14.3.

21.3.14.1 Designated Level Recall. For each elevator or group of elevators, an output shall be provided to signal elevator recall to the designated level in response to the following:

(1) Activation of smoke detectors, or other automatic fire detection as permitted by 21.3.9, located at any elevator lobby served by the elevator(s) other than the lobby at the designated level
(2) Activation of smoke detectors, or other automatic fire detection as permitted by 21.3.9, located at any elevator machine room, elevator machinery space, elevator control space, or elevator control room serving the elevator(s), except where such rooms or spaces are located at the designated level
(3) Activation of smoke detectors, or other automatic fire detection as permitted by 21.3.9, located in the elevator hoistway serving the elevator where sprinklers are located in the hoistway, unless otherwise specified in 21.3.14.2(3)

21.3.14.2 Alternate Level Recall. For each elevator or group of elevators, an output shall be provided to signal elevator recall to the alternate level in response to the following:

(1) Activation of smoke detectors, or automatic fire detection as permitted by 21.3.9, located at the designated level lobby served by the elevator(s)
(2) Activation of smoke detectors, or other automatic fire detection as permitted by 21.3.9, located in the elevator machine room, elevator machinery space, elevator control space, or elevator control room serving the elevator(s) if such rooms or spaces are located at the designated level
(3)*Activation of the initiating devices identified in 21.3.14.1(3) if they are installed at or below the lowest level of recall in the elevator hoistway and the alternate level is located above the designated level

21.3.14.3* Visual Warning. For each elevator or group of elevators, an output(s) shall be provided for the elevator visual warning signal in response to the following:

(1) Activation of the elevator machine room, elevator machinery space, elevator control space, or elevator control room initiating devices identified in 21.3.14.1(2) or 21.3.14.2(2)
(2) Activation of the elevator hoistway initiating devices identified in 21.3.14.1(3) or 21.3.14.2(3)

21.4 Elevator Shutdown.

21.4.1* Where heat detectors are used to shut down elevator power prior to sprinkler operation, the detector shall have both a lower temperature rating and a higher sensitivity as compared to the sprinkler.

21.4.2* If heat detectors are used to shut down elevator power prior to sprinkler operation, they shall be placed within 24 in. (610 mm) of each sprinkler head and be installed in accordance with the requirements of Chapter 17. Alternatively, engineering methods, such as those specified in Annex B, shall be permitted to be used to select and place heat detectors to ensure response prior to any sprinkler head operation under a variety of fire growth rate scenarios.

21.4.3* If pressure or waterflow switches are used to shut down elevator power immediately upon, or prior to, the discharge of water from sprinklers, the use of devices with time-delay switches or time-delay capability shall not be permitted.

21.4.4* Control circuits to shut down elevator power shall be monitored for the presence of operating voltage. Loss of voltage to the control circuit for the disconnecting means shall cause a supervisory signal to be indicated at the control unit and required remote annunciators.

21.4.5 The initiating devices described in 21.4.2 and 21.4.3 shall be monitored for integrity by the fire alarm control unit required in 21.3.1 and 21.3.2.

21.5 Fire Service Access Elevators. Where one or more elevators are specifically designated and marked as fire service access elevators, the conditions specified in 21.5.1 for the elevators, associated lobbies, and machine rooms shall be continuously monitored and displayed during any such use.

21.5.1 The conditions monitored and displayed shall include, but are not limited to, the following:

(1) Availability of main and emergency power to operate the elevator(s), elevator controller(s), and machine room (if provided) ventilation
(2)*Status of the elevator(s), including location within the hoistway, direction of travel, and whether they are occupied
(3) Temperature and presence of smoke in associated lobbies and machine room (if provided)

21.5.2 The conditions shall be displayed on a standard emergency services interface complying with Section 18.11.

21.6 Occupant Evacuation Elevators.

21.6.1 Elevator Status. Where one or more elevators are specifically designated and marked for use by occupants for evacuation during fires, they shall comply with all of the provisions of Sections 21.5 and 21.6.

21.6.2 Elevator Occupant Evacuation Operation (OEO). Outputs from the fire alarm system to the elevator controller(s) shall be provided to implement elevator occupant evacuation operation in accordance with Section 2.27 of ASME A17.1/CSA B44 (2013), *Safety Code for Elevators and Escalators*, as required in 21.6.2.1 and 21.6.2.2.

21.6.2.1 Partial Evacuation. Where an elevator or group of elevators is designated for use by occupants for evacuation, the provisions of 21.6.2.1.1 through 21.6.2.1.4 shall apply for partial evacuation.

21.6.2.1.1 Initiation. Output signal(s) shall be provided to initiate elevator occupant evacuation operation upon automatic or manual detection of a fire on a specific floor or floors as a result of either or both of the following:

(1) Activation of any automatic fire alarm initiating device in the building, other than an initiating device used for elevator Phase I Emergency Recall Operation in accordance with 21.3.14
(2)*Activation of manual means at the fire command center by authorized or emergency personnel

21.6.2.1.2* Floor Identification.

(A) The output signal(s) shall identify each floor to be evacuated.

(B) The identified floors shall be a contiguous block of floors including the following:

(1) The floor with the first activated automatic initiating device.
(2) Floors with any subsequently activated automatic initiating device(s).
(3) Floors identified by manual means from the fire command center.
(4) Two floors above the highest floor identified by 21.6.2.1.2(B)(1) through 21.6.2.1.2(B)(3).
(5) Two floors below the lowest floor identified by 21.6.2.1.2(B)(1) through 21.6.2.1.2(B)(3).

(C) The identified floors shall be displayed on a standard emergency services interface along with the other elevator status information required by 21.6.1.

21.6.2.1.3 Manual Floor Selection.

(A) A means shall be provided at the fire command center to allow the manual selection of floors.

(B) The floors shall be selected on the basis of information from authorized or emergency personnel.

21.6.2.1.4* Occupant Notification. The in-building fire emergency voice/alarm communications system shall transmit coordinated messages throughout the building.

(A) Automatic voice evacuation messages shall be transmitted to the floors identified in 21.6.2.1.2 to indicate the need to evacuate and that elevator service is available.

(B) Automatic voice messages shall be transmitted to the floors not being evacuated to inform occupants of evacuation status and shall include an indication that elevator service is not available.

(C)* Automatic voice messages shall be transmitted to the floors identified in 21.6.2.1.2 to indicate that elevator service is not available when all elevators have been recalled on Phase I Emergency Recall Operation.

(D) All automatic voice messages shall be coordinated with the text displays provided separately by the elevator management system.

21.6.2.2 Total Evacuation. Where an elevator or group of elevators is designated for use by occupants for evacuation, the provisions of 21.6.2.2.1 through 21.6.2.2.3 shall apply for total evacuation.

21.6.2.2.1 Output(s) to signal elevator occupant evacuation operation for total evacuation shall be manually activated from the fire command center by a means labeled "ELEVATOR TOTAL BUILDING EVACUATION."

21.6.2.2.2 The output(s) shall identify that all floors are to be evacuated.

21.6.2.2.3 The in-building fire emergency voice/alarm communications system shall transmit an evacuation message throughout the building to indicate the need to evacuate.

21.7 Heating, Ventilating and Air-Conditioning (HVAC) Systems.

21.7.1 The provisions of Section 21.7 shall apply to the basic method by which a fire alarm system interfaces with the heating, ventilating, and air-conditioning (HVAC) systems.

21.7.2* If connected to the fire alarm system serving the protected premises, all detection devices used to cause the operation of HVAC systems smoke dampers, fire dampers, fan control, smoke doors, and fire doors shall be monitored for integrity in accordance with 10.6.9 and Section 12.6.

21.7.3* Connections between fire alarm systems and the HVAC system for the purpose of monitoring and control shall operate and be monitored in accordance with applicable NFPA standards.

21.7.4 Smoke detectors mounted in the air ducts of HVAC systems shall initiate a supervisory signal.

21.7.4.1 Smoke detectors mounted in the air ducts of HVAC systems in a fire alarm system without a constantly attended location or supervising station shall be permitted to initiate an alarm signal.

21.7.4.2 Smoke detectors mounted in the air ducts of HVAC systems shall be permitted to initiate an alarm signal where required by other governing laws, codes, or standards.

21.7.5 If the fire alarm control unit actuates the HVAC system for the purpose of smoke control, the automatic alarm-initiating zones shall be coordinated with the smoke control zones they actuate.

21.7.6 If carbon monoxide detection or a dedicated carbon monoxide system initiates a ventilation response, a smoke control response of the fire alarm system shall take precedence over the response of the carbon monoxide detectors during a fire alarm condition.

21.7.7 Where interconnected as a combination system, a fire fighter's smoke control station (FSCS) shall be provided to perform manual control over the automatic operation of the system's smoke control strategy.

21.7.8 Where interconnected as a combination system, the smoke control system programming shall be designed such that normal HVAC operation or changes do not prevent the intended performance of the smoke control strategy.

21.8 Door and Shutter Release.

21.8.1 The provisions of Section 21.8 shall apply to the methods of connection of door and shutter hold-open release devices and to integral door and shutter hold-open release, closer, and smoke detection devices.

21.8.2 All detection devices used for door and shutter hold-open release service shall be monitored for integrity in accordance with Section 12.6.

Exception: Smoke detectors used only for door and shutter release and not for open area protection.

21.8.3 All door and shutter hold-open release and integral door and shutter release and closure devices used for release service shall be monitored for integrity in accordance with Section 21.2.

21.8.4 Magnetic door and shutter holders that allow doors to close upon loss of operating power shall not be required to have a secondary power source.

21.9 Electrically Locked Doors.

21.9.1* Electrically locked doors in a required means of egress shall unlock in the direction of egress where required by other laws, codes, and governing standards.

21.9.2 For all means of egress doors connected in accordance with 21.9.1 where fire alarm control unit batteries are used, they shall comply with 10.6.7.

21.9.3* Fire alarm control unit batteries shall not be utilized to maintain means of egress doors in the locked condition unless the fire alarm control unit is arranged with circuitry and sufficient secondary power to ensure the means of egress doors will unlock within 10 minutes of loss of primary power.

21.9.4 Locks powered by independent power supplies dedicated to lock power and access control functions, and that unlock upon loss of power, shall not be required to comply with 21.9.2.

21.9.5 If means of egress doors are unlocked by the fire alarm system, the unlocking function shall occur prior to, or concurrent with, activation of any public-mode notification appliances in the area(s) served by the normally locked means of egress doors.

21.9.6 All doors that are required to be unlocked by the fire alarm system in accordance with 21.9.1 shall remain unlocked until the fire alarm condition is manually reset.

21.10* Exit Marking Audible Notification Systems.

21.10.1 Where required by other governing laws, codes, standards, or the authority having jurisdiction, exit marking audible notification appliances shall be activated by the building fire alarm system.

21.10.2 Exit marking systems shall meet the requirements of Chapter 18.

Chapter 22   Reserved

Chapter 23   Protected Premises Fire Alarm Systems

23.1 Application.

23.1.1* The application, installation, and performance of fire alarm systems within protected premises, including fire alarm and supervisory signals, shall comply with the requirements of this chapter.

23.1.2 The requirements of Chapters 7, 10, 12, 17, 18, 21, 24, and 26 shall also apply, unless they are in conflict with this chapter.

23.1.3 The requirements of Chapter 14 shall apply.

23.1.4 The requirements of this chapter shall not apply to Chapter 29 unless otherwise noted.

23.1.5 The requirements of 24.4.2 shall apply where in-building fire emergency voice/alarm communications systems are used.

23.2 General.

23.2.1* Purpose. The systems covered in Chapter 23 shall be for the protection of life or property, or both, by indicating the existence of heat, fire, smoke, or other emergencies impacting the protected premises.

23.2.2 Software and Firmware Control.

23.2.2.1 A record of installed software and firmware version numbers shall be maintained at the location of the fire alarm control unit.

23.2.2.1.1* Software and firmware within the fire alarm control system that interfaces to other required software or firmware shall be functionally compatible.

23.2.2.1.2* The compatible software or firmware versions shall be documented at the initial acceptance test and at any reacceptance tests.

23.2.2.2* All software and firmware shall be protected from unauthorized changes.

23.2.2.3 All changes shall be tested in accordance with 14.4.2.

23.3 System Features. The features required for a protected premises fire alarm system shall be documented as a part of the system design and shall be determined in accordance with 23.3.1 through 23.3.3.

23.3.1 Required Systems. Features for required systems shall be based on the requirements of other applicable codes or statutes that have been adopted by the enforcing jurisdiction.

23.3.2* Nonrequired (Voluntary) Systems and Components. The features for a nonrequired system shall be established by the system designer on the basis of the goals and objectives intended by the system owner.

23.3.2.1 Nonrequired protected premises systems and components shall meet the requirements of this Code.

23.3.2.2 Nonrequired systems and components shall be identified on the record drawings required in 7.2.1(12).

23.3.3 Required Features.

23.3.3.1* Building Fire Alarm Systems. Protected premises fire alarm systems that serve the general fire alarm needs of a building or buildings shall include one or more of the following systems or functions:

(1) Manual fire alarm signal initiation
(2) Automatic fire alarm and supervisory signal initiation
(3) Monitoring of abnormal conditions in fire suppression systems
(4) Activation of fire suppression systems
(5) Activation of emergency control functions
(6) Activation of fire alarm notification appliances
(7) In-building fire emergency voice/alarm communications
(8) Guard's tour supervisory service
(9) Process monitoring supervisory systems
(10) Activation of off-premises signals
(11) Combination systems

23.3.3.2* Dedicated Function Fire Alarm Systems.

23.3.3.2.1 In facilities without a building fire alarm system, a dedicated function fire alarm system shall be permitted and shall not be required to include other functions or features of a building fire alarm system.

23.3.3.2.2 Where a dedicated function fire alarm system exists and a building fire alarm system is subsequently installed, the systems shall be interconnected and comply with 23.8.2.

23.4 System Performance and Integrity.

23.4.1 Purpose. Section 23.4 provides information that shall be used in the design and installation of protected premises fire alarm systems for the protection of life and property.

23.4.2 Circuit Designations. Initiating device circuits, notification appliance circuits, and signaling line circuits shall be designated by class, depending on the circuit's capability to continue to operate during specified fault conditions as indicated in Sections 23.5 through 23.7.

23.4.2.1 Specified fault conditions shall result in the annunciation of a trouble signal at the protected premises within 200 seconds as required in Section 12.6.

23.4.2.2* Where the power to a device is supplied over a separate circuit from the signaling line circuit or initiating device circuit, the operation of the power circuit shall meet the performance requirements of the initiating device circuit or signaling line circuit, unless different performance requirements are established in accordance with the evaluation in 23.4.3 and approved by the authority having jurisdiction.

23.4.3 Pathway Classification.

23.4.3.1 The class of pathways shall be determined from an evaluation based on the path performance as required by governing laws, codes, standards, and a site-specific engineering analysis.

23.4.3.2 When determining the integrity and reliability of the interconnecting signaling paths (circuits) installed within the protected premises, the following influences shall be considered:

(1) Transmission media used
(2) Length of the circuit conductors
(3) Total building area covered by, and the quantity of initiating devices and notification appliances connected to, a single circuit
(4) Effect of a fault in the fire alarm system that would hinder the performance objectives of the system that protects the occupants, mission, and property of the protected premises
(5) Nature of hazards present within the protected premises
(6) Functional requirements of the system necessary to provide the level of protection required for the system
(7) Size and nature of the population of the protected premises

23.4.3.3 Results of the evaluation required by 23.4.3.1 shall be included with the documentation required by 7.3.9.

23.5 Performance of Initiating Device Circuits (IDCs). The assignment of class designations to initiating device circuits shall be based on their performance capabilities under abnormal (fault) conditions in accordance with the requirements for Class A or Class B pathways specified in Chapter 12.

23.6 Performance of Signaling Line Circuits (SLCs). The assignment of class designations to signaling line circuits shall be based on their performance capabilities under abnormal (fault) conditions in accordance with the requirements for Class A, Class B, or Class X pathways specified in Chapter 12.

23.6.1* A single fault on a pathway connected to the addressable devices shall not cause the loss of more than 50 addressable devices.

23.7 Performance of Notification Appliance Circuits (NACs). The assignment of class designations to notification appliance circuits shall be based on their performance capabilities under abnormal (fault) conditions in accordance with the requirements for Class A, Class B, or Class X pathways specified in Chapter 12.

23.8 System Requirements.

23.8.1 General.

23.8.1.1* Actuation Time. Actuation of alarm notification appliances or emergency voice communications, emergency control function interface devices, and annunciation at the protected premises shall occur within 10 seconds after the activation of an initiating device.

23.8.1.2* Presignal Feature.

23.8.1.2.1 Systems that have a presignal feature complying with 23.8.1.2 shall be permitted if approved by the authority having jurisdiction.

23.8.1.2.2 A presignal feature shall meet the following conditions:

(1) The initial fire alarm signals sound only in department offices, control rooms, fire brigade stations, or other constantly attended central locations.
(2) Where there is a connection to a remote location, the transmission of the fire alarm signal to the supervising station activates upon the initial alarm signal.
(3) Subsequent system operation is by either of the following means:
    (a) Human action that activates the general fire alarm
    (b) A feature that allows the control equipment to delay the general alarm by more than 1 minute after the start of the alarm processing

23.8.1.3 Positive Alarm Sequence.

23.8.1.3.1 Systems that have positive alarm features complying with 23.8.1.3 shall be permitted if approved by the authority having jurisdiction.

23.8.1.3.1.1 The positive alarm sequence operation shall comply with the following:

(1) To initiate the positive alarm sequence operation, the signal from an automatic fire detection device selected for positive alarm sequence operation shall be acknowledged at the fire alarm control unit by trained personnel within 15 seconds of annunciation.
(2) If the signal is not acknowledged within 15 seconds, notification signals in accordance with the building evacuation or relocation plan and remote signals shall be automatically and immediately activated.
(3) If the positive alarm sequence operation is initiated in accordance with 23.8.1.3.1.1(1), trained personnel shall have an alarm investigation phase of up to 180 seconds to evaluate the fire condition and reset the system.
(4) If the system is not reset during the alarm investigation phase, notification signals in accordance with the building evacuation or relocation plan and remote signals shall be automatically and immediately activated.
(5) If a second automatic fire detector selected for positive alarm sequence is actuated during the alarm investigation phase, notification signals in accordance with the building evacuation or relocation plan and remote signals shall be automatically and immediately activated.

(6)*If any other fire alarm initiating device is actuated, notification signals in accordance with the building evacuation or relocation plan and remote signals shall be automatically and immediately activated.

23.8.1.3.1.2* The system shall provide means for bypassing the positive alarm sequence.

23.8.2* Fire Alarm Control Units.

23.8.2.1 Fire alarm systems shall be permitted to combine all detection, notification, and auxiliary functions in a single system or be a combination of component subsystems.

23.8.2.2 Except as permitted in 23.8.2.3, the fire alarm systems components shall be permitted to share control equipment or shall be able to operate as stand-alone subsystems, but, in any case, they shall be arranged to function as a single system.

23.8.2.3 Where the building is not served by a building fire alarm system, independent dedicated function fire alarm systems and/or releasing fire alarm systems shall not be required to be interconnected to function as a single system.

23.8.2.4 All component subsystems shall be capable of simultaneous, full-load operation without degradation of the required overall system performance.

23.8.2.5 The method of interconnection of fire alarm control units shall meet the monitoring requirements of Section 12.6 and *NFPA 70, National Electrical Code,* Article 760, and shall be achieved by the following recognized means:

(1) Electrical contacts listed for the connected load
(2) Data communications over a signaling line circuit(s) dedicated to the fire alarm or shared with other premises operating systems
(3) Other listed methods

23.8.2.6 Where the signaling line circuit is shared by other premises operating systems, operation shall be in accordance with 23.8.4.

23.8.2.6.1 All signal control and transport equipment (such as routers and servers) located in a critical fire alarm or emergency control function interface device signaling path shall be listed for fire alarm service, unless the following conditions are met:

(1) The equipment meets the performance requirements of 10.3.5.
(2) The equipment is provided with primary and secondary power and monitored for integrity as required in Section 10.6, 10.6.9, Section 10.19, and Section 12.6.
(3) All programming and configuration ensure a fire alarm system actuation time as required in 23.8.1.1.
(4) System bandwidth is monitored to confirm that all communications between equipment that is critical to the operation of the fire alarm system or emergency control function interface devices take place within 10 seconds; failure shall be indicated within 200 seconds.
(5) Failure of any equipment that is critical to the operation of the fire alarm system or emergency control function interface devices is indicated at the master fire alarm control unit within 200 seconds.

23.8.2.6.2 A listed barrier gateway, integral with or attached to each control unit or group of control units, as appropriate, shall be provided to prevent the other systems from interfering with or controlling the fire alarm system.

23.8.2.7 Each interconnected fire alarm control unit shall be separately monitored for alarm, supervisory, and trouble conditions.

23.8.2.8 Interconnected fire alarm control unit alarm signals shall be permitted to be monitored by zone or by combined common signals.

23.8.2.9 Protected premises fire alarm control units shall be capable of being reset or silenced only from the fire alarm control unit at the protected premises, unless otherwise permitted by 23.8.2.10.

23.8.2.10 Remote resetting and silencing of a fire alarm control unit from other than the protected premises shall be permitted with the approval of the authority having jurisdiction.

23.8.3 Protected Premises Fire Alarm Systems Interconnected with Dwelling Unit Fire Warning Equipment.

23.8.3.1 A protected premises fire alarm system shall be permitted to be interconnected to a household fire alarm system(s) for the purpose of activating the notification appliances connected to the household fire alarm system(s).

23.8.3.2 The activation of dwelling unit smoke alarms shall only be permitted to be displayed at the protected premises control unit and annunciators as supervisory signals.

23.8.3.3 If interconnected, an alarm condition at the protected premises fire alarm system shall cause the fire alarm notification appliance(s) within the family living unit of the dwelling unit fire warning system to become energized. The notification appliances shall remain energized until the protected premises fire alarm system is silenced or reset.

23.8.3.4 The interconnection circuit or path from the protected premises fire alarm system to the dwelling unit fire warning system shall be monitored for integrity by the protected premises fire alarm system in accordance with Section 12.6.

23.8.3.5 An alarm condition occurring at the dwelling unit fire warning system or the operation of any test switches provided as part of the dwelling unit fire warning equipment shall not cause an alarm condition at the protected premises fire alarm system.

23.8.4 Combination Systems.

23.8.4.1* Fire alarm systems shall be permitted to share components, equipment, circuitry, and installation wiring with non–fire alarm systems.

23.8.4.2 Operation of a non–fire system function(s) originating within a connected non-fire system shall not interfere with the required operation of the fire alarm system, unless otherwise permitted by this Code.

23.8.4.3* For non–fire alarm equipment listed to the performance requirements specified in 10.3.5, the requirements of 23.8.4.3.1 through 23.8.4.3.3 shall apply.

23.8.4.3.1 The equipment shall be permitted to be attached to a fire alarm circuit, either among the fire alarm devices or as a branch or extension of the fire alarm pathways, when the following requirements are met:

(1) All the equipment and pathways shall meet the monitoring for integrity requirements of 10.6.9, Section 10.19, and Section 12.6.
(2) All the equipment and pathways shall be maintained by a single service organization.

(3) All the equipment and pathways shall be installed in accordance with the requirements of this Code.
(4) All the equipment shall be listed as compatible with the fire alarm equipment or the equipment shall have an interface listed as compatible with the fire alarm equipment.

23.8.4.3.2 If the equipment is attached to the fire alarm system via separate pathways, then short circuits or open circuits in this equipment, or between this equipment and the fire alarm system pathways, shall not impede or impair the monitoring for integrity of the fire alarm system or prevent alarm, supervisory, or fire safety control signal transmissions.

23.8.4.3.3 Grounds in this equipment, or between this equipment and the fire alarm system pathways, shall be reported, annunciated, and corrected in the same manner as grounds in the rest of the fire alarm system.

23.8.4.4 For non-fire equipment not listed to the performance requirements specified in 10.3.5, the requirements of 23.8.4.4.1 through 23.8.4.4.3 shall apply

23.8.4.4.1 Short circuits or open circuits in the equipment, or between the equipment and the fire alarm system pathways, shall not impede or impair the monitoring for integrity of the fire alarm system or prevent alarm, supervisory, or fire safety control signal transmissions.

23.8.4.4.2 Grounds in this equipment, or between this equipment and the fire alarm system pathways, shall be reported, annunciated, and corrected in the same manner as grounds in the rest of the fire alarm system.

23.8.4.4.3 Removal, replacement, failure, maintenance procedures, or ground on this hardware, software, or circuits shall not impair the required operation of the fire alarm system.

23.8.4.5 Speakers used as alarm notification appliances on fire alarm systems shall also be permitted to be used for emergency communications systems when installed in accordance with Chapter 24.

23.8.4.6* In combination systems, fire alarm signals shall be distinctive, clearly recognizable, and shall be indicated as follows in descending order of priority, except where otherwise required by other governing laws, codes or standards, or by other parts of this Code:

(1) Signals associated with life safety
(2) Signals associated with property protection
(3) Trouble signals associated with life and/or property protection
(4) All other signals

23.8.4.7 If the authority having jurisdiction determines that the information being displayed or annunciated on a combination system is excessive and is causing confusion and delayed response to a fire emergency, the authority having jurisdiction shall be permitted to require that the display or annunciation of information for the fire alarm system be separate from, and have priority in accordance with, 23.8.4.6, over information for the non–fire alarm systems.

23.8.4.8* Signals from carbon monoxide detectors and carbon monoxide detection systems transmitted to a fire alarm system shall be indicated as a carbon monoxide alarm signal.

Exception: When in accordance with the building's response plan, evacuation plan, fire safety plan, or similar documentation, signals from carbon monoxide detectors and carbon monoxide detection systems transmitted to a fire alarm system shall be permitted to be supervisory signals.

23.8.4.8.1 Signals from carbon monoxide detectors and carbon monoxide detection systems transmitted to a fire alarm system shall be indicated as "Carbon Monoxide Alarm" on the fire alarm system control unit or annunciator.

23.8.4.8.2* Fire alarm system processing for and occupant response to carbon monoxide alarm signals shall be in accordance with the building's response plan, evacuation plan, fire safety plan, or similar documentation.

23.8.4.9* Signals from a fire extinguisher electronic monitoring device or fire extinguisher monitoring system transmitted to a fire alarm system shall be permitted to be supervisory signals.

23.8.5 Fire Alarm System Inputs.

23.8.5.1 General.

23.8.5.1.1 All initiating devices shall be installed in accordance with Chapter 17 and tested in accordance with Chapter 14.

23.8.5.1.2* Where connected to a supervising station, fire alarm systems employing automatic fire detectors or waterflow detection devices shall include a manual fire alarm box to initiate a signal to the supervising station.

Exception: Fire alarm systems dedicated to elevator recall control and supervisory service as permitted in Section 21.3.

23.8.5.2 Fire Alarm Signal Initiation — Manual. Manual fire alarm signal initiation shall comply with the requirements of Section 17.14.

23.8.5.2.1 If signals from manual fire alarm boxes and other fire alarm initiating devices within a building are transmitted over the same signaling line circuit, there shall be no interference with manual fire alarm box signals when both types of initiating devices are operated at the same time.

23.8.5.2.2 Provision of the shunt noninterfering method of operation shall be permitted for this performance.

23.8.5.3 Fire Alarm Signal Initiation — Initiating Devices with Separate Power and Signaling Wiring.

23.8.5.3.1 Automatic fire alarm signal initiating devices that have integral trouble signal contacts shall be connected to the initiating device circuit so that a trouble condition within a device does not impair alarm transmission from any other initiating device.

Exception: Where the trouble condition is caused by electrical disconnection of the device or by removing the initiating device from its plug-in base.

23.8.5.3.2* Automatic fire alarm signal initiating devices that use a nonintegral device to monitor the integrity of the power supply wiring to the individual initiating devices shall have the nonintegral device connected to the initiating device circuit so that a fault on the power supply wiring does not impair alarm transmission from any operational initiating device.

23.8.5.4 Fire Alarm Signal Initiation — Detection Devices.

23.8.5.4.1* Systems equipped with alarm verification features shall be permitted under the following conditions:

(1) The alarm verification feature is not initially enabled, unless conditions or occupant activities that are expected to cause nuisance alarms are anticipated in the area that is protected by the smoke detectors. Enabling of the alarm verification feature shall be protected by password or limited access.

(2) A smoke detector that is continuously subjected to a smoke concentration above alarm threshold does not delay the system functions of Sections 10.7 through 10.16, 23.8.1.1, or 21.2.1 by more than 1 minute.

(3) Actuation of an alarm-initiating device other than a smoke detector causes the system functions of Sections 10.7 through 10.16, 23.8.1.1, or 21.2.1 without additional delay.

(4) The current status of the alarm verification feature is shown on the record of completion *[see Figure 7.8.2(a), item 4.3].*

23.8.5.4.2 If automatic drift compensation of sensitivity for a fire detector is provided, the fire alarm control unit shall identify the affected detector when the limit of compensation is reached.

23.8.5.4.3 Systems that require the operation of two automatic detectors to initiate the alarm response shall be permitted, provided that the following conditions are satisfied:

(1) The systems are not prohibited by the authority having jurisdiction.
(2) At least two automatic detectors are in each protected space.
(3) The alarm verification feature is not used.

23.8.5.4.4 For systems that require the operation of two automatic detectors to initiate emergency control functions or to actuate fire extinguishing or suppression systems, the detectors shall be installed at the spacing determined in accordance with Chapter 17.

23.8.5.4.5 For systems that require the operation of two automatic detectors to actuate public mode notification, the detectors shall be installed at a linear spacing not more than 0.7 times the linear spacing determined in accordance with Chapter 17.

23.8.5.4.6 Signal Initiation — Duct Smoke Detectors.

23.8.5.4.6.1 Where duct smoke detectors are required to be monitored and a building fire alarm system is installed, a duct detector activation signal shall meet the requirements of 21.7.4.

23.8.5.4.6.2 Where duct smoke detectors are connected to a protected premises fire alarm system, the operation of the power circuit shall meet the requirements of 23.4.2.2.

23.8.5.4.6.3* Where duct smoke detectors with separate power and signal wiring are installed and connected to a protected premises fire alarm system, they shall meet the requirements of 23.8.5.3.

23.8.5.4.6.4 Where duct smoke detectors are not resettable from the protected premises fire alarm system, a listed alarm/supervisory indicator with an integral reset switch shall be provided in an accessible location.

23.8.5.5* Fire Alarm Signal Initiation — Sprinkler Systems.

23.8.5.5.1 Where required by other governing laws, codes, or standards to be electronically monitored, waterflow alarm-initiating devices shall be connected to a dedicated function fire alarm control unit designated as "sprinkler waterflow and supervisory system" and permanently identified on the control unit and record drawings.

Exception: Where waterflow alarm-initiating devices are connected to a building fire alarm system, a dedicated function fire alarm control unit shall not be required.

23.8.5.5.2* The number of waterflow alarm-initiating devices permitted to be connected to a single initiating device circuit shall not exceed five.

23.8.5.5.3 If a valve is installed in the connection between a sprinkler system and an initiating device, the valve shall be supervised in accordance with 17.16.1.

23.8.5.6* Supervisory Signal Initiation — Sprinkler Systems.

23.8.5.6.1 Where required by other governing laws, codes, or standards to be electronically monitored, supervisory signal–initiating devices shall be connected to a dedicated function fire alarm control unit designated as "sprinkler waterflow and supervisory system" and permanently identified on the control unit and record drawings.

Exception: Where supervisory signal–initiating devices are connected to a building fire alarm system, a dedicated function fire alarm control unit shall not be required.

23.8.5.6.2* The number of supervisory signal–initiating devices permitted to be connected to a single initiating device circuit shall not exceed 20.

23.8.5.6.3 If a valve is installed in the connection between a sprinkler system and an initiating device, the valve shall be supervised in accordance with 17.16.1.

23.8.5.7 Alarm Signal Initiation — Fire Suppression Systems Other Than Sprinklers.

23.8.5.7.1 Where required by other governing laws, codes, or standards to be monitored and a building fire alarm system is installed, the actuation of a fire suppression system shall annunciate an alarm or supervisory condition at the building fire alarm control unit.

23.8.5.7.2 The integrity of each fire suppression system actuating device and its circuit shall comply with 12.6.1, 12.6.2, and other applicable NFPA standards.

23.8.5.7.3 If a valve is installed in the connection between a suppression system and an initiating device, the valve shall be supervised in accordance with 17.16.1.

23.8.5.8* Supervisory Signal Initiation — Fire Suppression Systems Other Than Sprinklers.

23.8.5.8.1 Where required to be monitored and a building fire alarm system is installed, an off-normal condition of a fire suppression system shall annunciate a supervisory condition at the building fire alarm control unit.

23.8.5.8.2 Supervisory signals that latch in the off-normal state and require manual reset of the system to restore them to normal shall be permitted.

23.8.5.8.3 If a valve is installed in the connection between a suppression system and an initiating device, the valve shall be supervised in accordance with 17.16.1.

23.8.5.9 Signal Initiation — Fire Pump.

23.8.5.9.1 Where fire pumps are required to be monitored and a building fire alarm system is installed, a pump running signal shall be permitted to be a supervisory or alarm signal.

23.8.5.9.2 Where fire pumps are required to be monitored and a building fire alarm system is installed, signals other than pump running shall be supervisory signals.

23.8.5.10 Fire Alarm and Supervisory Signal Initiation — Releasing Fire Alarm Systems.

23.8.5.10.1 Releasing service fire alarm control units shall be connected to the protected premises fire alarm system.

23.8.5.10.2 Fire alarm and supervisory signals generated at the releasing service fire alarm control unit shall be annunciated at a protected premises fire alarm unit.

23.8.5.10.3 Where required by other governing laws, codes, or standards, actuation of any suppression system connected to a releasing service fire alarm control unit shall be annunciated at the protected premises fire alarm control unit, even where the system actuation is by manual means or otherwise accomplished without actuation of the releasing service fire alarm control unit.

23.8.5.10.4 If a valve is installed in the connection between a suppression system and an initiating device, the valve shall be supervised in accordance with Chapter 17.

23.8.5.10.5 In facilities that are not required to install a protected premises fire alarm system, the alarm and supervisory devices shall be connected to the releasing service fire alarm control unit, and their actuation shall be annunciated at the releasing service control unit.

23.8.5.11 Trouble Signal Initiation.

23.8.5.11.1 Automatic fire suppression system alarm–initiating devices and supervisory signal-initiating devices and their circuits shall be designed and installed so that they cannot be subject to tampering, opening, or removal without initiating a signal. This provision shall include junction boxes installed outside of buildings to facilitate access to the initiating device circuit.

Exception No. 1: Covers of junction boxes inside of buildings.

Exception No. 2: Tamper–resistant screws or other approved mechanical means shall be permitted for preventing access to junction boxes and device covers installed outside of buildings.

23.8.5.11.2 The integrity of each fire suppression system actuating device and its circuit shall be supervised in accordance with 12.6.1 and 12.6.2 and with other applicable NFPA standards.

23.8.6 Fire Alarm System Notification Outputs.

23.8.6.1 Occupant Notification. Fire alarm systems provided for evacuation or relocation of occupants shall have one or more notification appliances listed for the purpose in each notification zone of the building and be so located that they have the characteristics described in Chapter 18 for public mode or private mode, as required.

23.8.6.2* Notification Appliances in Exit Stair Enclosures, Exit Passageways, and Elevator Cars. Notification appliances shall not be required in exit stair enclosures, exit passageways, and elevator cars in accordance with 23.8.6.2.1 through 23.8.6.2.4.

23.8.6.2.1 Visible signals shall not be required in exit stair enclosures and exit passageways.

23.8.6.2.2 Visible signals shall not be required in elevator cars.

23.8.6.2.3 The evacuation signal shall not be required to operate in exit stair enclosures and exit passageways.

23.8.6.2.4 The evacuation signal shall not be required to operate in elevator cars.

23.8.6.3 Notification Zones.

23.8.6.3.1 Notification zones shall be consistent with the emergency response or evacuation plan for the protected premises.

23.8.6.3.2 The boundaries of notification zones shall be coincident with building outer walls, building fire or smoke compartment boundaries, floor separations, or other fire safety subdivisions.

23.8.6.4 Circuits for Addressable Notification Appliances.

23.8.6.4.1 Circuit configuration for addressable notification appliances shall comply with the applicable performance requirements for notification zones.

23.8.6.4.2 Where there are addressable notification appliances on a signaling line circuit that serves different notification zones, a single open, short-circuit, or ground on that signaling line circuit shall not affect operation of more than one notification zone.

23.8.6.4.3 Riser conductors installed in accordance with 24.4.2.8.5.3 that are monitored for integrity shall not be required to operate in accordance with 23.8.6.4.2.

23.9 In-Building Fire Emergency Voice/Alarm Communications.

23.9.1 In-building fire emergency voice/alarm communications shall meet the requirements of Chapter 24.

23.9.2 All live voice communications systems shall meet the requirements of Chapter 24.

23.9.3 Two-Way Communication Service. Two-way communication service shall meet the requirements of Chapter 24.

23.10 Fire Alarm Systems Using Tone.

23.10.1 The requirements of Section 23.10 shall apply to tone and visible notification appliance circuits.

23.10.2* Fire alarm systems used for partial evacuation and relocation shall be designed and installed such that attack by fire within an evacuation signaling zone shall not impair control and operation of the notification appliances outside the evacuation signaling zone. Performance features provided to ensure survivability shall be described and technical justification provided in the documentation submitted to the authority having jurisdiction with the evaluation required in 23.4.3.1.

23.10.3 Speakers that transmit tone signals shall be permitted to be used as fire alarm notification appliances.

23.11 Suppression System Actuation.

23.11.1 Releasing service fire alarm control units used for automatic or manual activation of a fire suppression system shall be listed for releasing service.

23.11.2 Releasing devices for suppression systems shall be listed for use with releasing service control units.

23.11.3 Each releasing device (e.g., solenoid, relay) shall be monitored for integrity (supervised) in accordance with applicable NFPA standards.

23.11.4 The installation wiring shall be monitored for integrity in accordance with the requirements of Section 12.6.

23.11.5 Releasing service fire alarm systems used for fire suppression–releasing service shall be provided with a disconnect switch to allow the system to be tested without actuating the fire suppression systems.

23.11.5.1 Operation of a disconnect switch or a disable function shall cause a supervisory signal at the releasing service fire alarm control unit.

23.11.5.2 The disconnect shall be a physical switch and not be accomplished by using software.

23.11.5.3 Software disconnects, even if activated by dedicated buttons or key switches, shall not be permitted as a method to secure a suppression system from inadvertent discharge.

23.11.6 Sequence of operation shall be consistent with the applicable suppression system standards.

23.11.7* Each space protected by an automatic fire suppression system actuated by the fire alarm system shall contain one or more automatic fire detectors installed in accordance with Chapter 17.

23.11.8 Suppression systems or groups of systems shall be controlled by a single releasing service fire alarm control unit that monitors the associated initiating device(s), actuates the associated releasing device(s), and controls the associated agent release notification appliances.

23.11.9 If the configuration of multiple control units is listed for releasing device service, and if a trouble condition or manual disconnect on either control unit causes a trouble or supervisory signal, the initiating device on one control unit shall be permitted to actuate releasing devices on another control unit in lieu of 23.11.8.

23.11.10 If the releasing service fire alarm control unit is located in a protected premises having a separate fire alarm system, it shall be monitored for alarm, supervisory, and trouble signals, but shall not be dependent on or affected by the operation or failure of the protected premises fire alarm system.

23.11.11 Releasing fire alarm systems performing suppression system releasing functions shall be installed in such a manner that they are effectively protected from damage caused by activation of the suppression system(s) they control.

23.12 Off-Premises Signals.

23.12.1 Systems requiring transmission of signals to continuously attended locations providing supervising station service (e.g., central station, proprietary supervising station, remote supervising station) shall also comply with the applicable requirements of Chapter 26.

23.12.2 Relays or modules providing transmission of trouble signals to a supervising station shall be arranged to provide fail-safe operation.

23.12.3 Means provided to transmit trouble signals to supervising stations shall be arranged so as to transmit a trouble signal to the supervising station for any trouble condition received at the protected premises control unit, including loss of primary or secondary power.

23.12.4* It shall be permitted to provide supplementary transmission of real-time data from the fire system to off-premises equipment.

23.12.4.1 Transmission of real-time data off-premises shall not affect the operation or response of the fire alarm control unit.

23.12.4.2 Any data transmitted shall be consistent with the data generated by the system.

23.13 Guard's Tour Supervisory Service.

23.13.1 Guard's tour reporting stations shall be listed for the application.

23.13.2 The number of guard's tour reporting stations, their locations, and the route to be followed by the guard for operating the stations shall be approved for the particular installation in accordance with NFPA 601, *Standard for Security Services in Fire Loss Prevention.*

23.13.3 A permanent record indicating every time each signal-transmitting station is operated shall be made at a protected premises fire alarm control unit.

23.13.4 Where intermediate stations that do not transmit a signal are employed in conjunction with signal-transmitting stations, distinctive signals shall be transmitted at the beginning and end of each tour of a guard.

23.13.5 A signal-transmitting station shall be provided at intervals not exceeding 10 intermediate stations.

23.13.6 Intermediate stations that do not transmit a signal shall be capable of operation only in a fixed sequence.

23.14 Suppressed (Exception Reporting) Signal System.

23.14.1 The suppressed signal system shall comply with the provisions of 23.13.2.

23.14.2 The system shall transmit a start signal to the signal-receiving location.

23.14.3 The start signal shall be initiated by the guard at the start of continuous tour rounds.

23.14.4 The system shall automatically transmit a delinquency signal within 15 minutes after the predetermined actuation time if the guard fails to actuate a tour station as scheduled.

23.14.5 A finish signal shall be transmitted within a predetermined interval after the guard's completion of each tour of the premises.

23.14.6 For periods of over 24 hours during which tours are continuously conducted, a start signal shall be transmitted at least every 24 hours.

23.14.7 The start, delinquency, and finish signals shall be recorded at the signal-receiving location.

23.15 Protected Premises Emergency Control Functions.

23.15.1 Emergency Elevator Operations. Emergency elevator operations shall meet the requirements of Sections 21.3, 21.4, 21.5, and 21.6.

23.15.2 HVAC Systems. HVAC systems shall meet the requirements of Section 21.7.

23.15.3 Door Release Service. Door release service shall meet the requirements of Section 21.8.

23.15.4 Electrically Locked Doors. Door-unlocking devices shall meet the requirements of Section 21.9.

23.15.5 Exit Marking Audible Notification Systems. Exit marking audible notification systems shall meet the requirements of Section 21.10.

23.16* Special Requirements for Low-Power Radio (Wireless) Systems.

23.16.1* Listing Requirements. Compliance with Section 23.16 shall require the use of low-power radio equipment specifically listed for the purpose.

23.16.2 Power Supplies. A primary battery (dry cell) shall be permitted to be used as the sole power source of a low-power radio transmitter where all of the following conditions are met:

(1) Each transmitter shall serve only one device and shall be individually identified at the receiver/fire alarm control unit.
(2) The battery shall be capable of operating the low-power radio transmitter for not less than 1 year before the battery depletion threshold is reached.
(3) A battery depletion signal shall be transmitted before the battery has been depleted to a level below that required to support alarm transmission after 7 additional days of non-alarm operation. This signal shall be distinctive from alarm, supervisory, tamper, and trouble signals; shall visibly identify the affected low-power radio transmitter; and, when silenced, shall automatically re-sound at least once every 4 hours.
(4) Catastrophic (open or short) battery failure shall cause a trouble signal identifying the affected low-power radio transmitter at its receiver/fire alarm control unit. When silenced, the trouble signal shall automatically re-sound at least once every 4 hours.
(5) Any mode of failure of a primary battery in a low-power radio transmitter shall not affect any other low-power radio transmitter.

23.16.3 Alarm Signals.

23.16.3.1* When actuated, each low-power radio transmitter shall automatically transmit an alarm signal.

23.16.3.2 Each low-power radio transmitter shall automatically repeat alarm transmission at intervals not exceeding 60 seconds until the initiating device is returned to its non-alarm condition.

23.16.3.3 Fire alarm signals shall have priority over all other signals.

23.16.3.4 The maximum allowable response delay from activation of an initiating device to receipt and display by the receiver/fire alarm control unit shall be 10 seconds.

23.16.3.5* A fire alarm signal from a low-power radio transmitter shall latch at its receiver/fire alarm control unit until manually reset and shall identify the particular initiating device in alarm.

23.16.4 Monitoring for Integrity.

23.16.4.1 The low-power radio transmitter shall be specifically listed as using a transmission method that is highly resistant to misinterpretation of simultaneous transmissions and to interference (e.g., impulse noise and adjacent channel interference).

23.16.4.2 The occurrence of any single fault that disables transmission between any low-power radio transmitter and the receiver/fire alarm control unit shall cause a latching trouble signal within 200 seconds.

Exception: Until the expiration date for this exception of June 30, 2013, the time period for a low-power radio transmitter with only a single, connected alarm-initiating device shall be permitted to be increased to four times the minimum time interval permitted for a 1-second transmission up to the following:

(1) *4 hours maximum for a transmitter serving a single initiating device*
(2) *4 hours maximum for a retransmission device (repeater), where disabling of the repeater or its transmission does not prevent the receipt of signals at the receiver/fire alarm control unit from any initiating device transmitter.*

23.16.4.3 A single fault on the signaling channel shall not cause an alarm signal.

23.16.4.4 The periodic transmission required to comply with 23.16.4.2 from a low-power radio transmitter shall ensure successful alarm transmission capability.

23.16.4.5 Removal of a low-power radio transmitter from its installed location shall cause immediate transmission of a distinctive supervisory signal that indicates its removal and individually identifies the affected device.

23.16.4.6 Reception of any unwanted (interfering) transmission by a retransmission device (repeater) or by the main receiver/control unit, for a continuous period of 20 seconds or more, shall cause an audible and visible trouble indication at the main receiver/control unit. This indication shall identify the specific trouble condition as an interfering signal.

23.16.5 Output Signals from Receiver/Control. When the receiver/control is used to actuate remote appliances, such as notification appliances and relays, by wireless means, the remote appliances shall meet the following requirements:

(1) Power supplies shall comply with Chapter 10 or the requirements of 23.16.2.
(2) All monitoring for integrity requirements of Chapter 10, Chapter 12, Chapter 23, or 23.16.4 shall apply.
(3) The maximum allowable response delay from activation of an initiating device to activation of required alarm functions shall be 10 seconds.
(4) Each receiver/control shall automatically repeat alarm transmission at intervals not exceeding 60 seconds or until confirmation that the output appliance has received the alarm signal.
(5) The appliances shall continue to operate (latch-in) until manually reset at the receiver/control.

Chapter 24   Emergency Communications Systems (ECS)

24.1 Application.

24.1.1 The application, installation, and performance of emergency communications systems and their components shall comply with the requirements of this chapter.

24.1.2* The requirements of this chapter shall apply to emergency communications systems within buildings and outdoor areas.

24.1.3 The requirements of Chapters 7, 10, 12, 17, 18, 21, 23, 26, and 27 shall also apply unless they are in conflict with this chapter.

24.1.4 Inspection, testing, and maintenance shall be performed in accordance with testing frequencies and methods in Chapter 14.

24.1.5 The requirements of this chapter shall not apply to Chapter 29 unless specifically indicated.

24.2 Purpose.

24.2.1 The systems covered under Chapter 24 are for the protection of life by indicating the existence of an emergency situation and communicating information necessary to facilitate an appropriate response and action.

24.2.2 This chapter establishes minimum required levels of performance, reliability, and quality of installation for emergency communications systems but does not establish the only methods by which these requirements are to be achieved.

24.2.3 An emergency communications system is intended to communicate information about emergencies including, but not limited to, fire, human-caused events (accidental and intentional), other dangerous situations, accidents, and natural disasters.

24.3 General.

24.3.1* **Intelligible Voice Messages.** Emergency communications systems shall be capable of the reproduction of prerecorded, synthesized, or live (e.g., microphone, telephone handset, and radio) messages with voice intelligibility in accordance with Chapter 18.

24.3.2 Microphone Use.

24.3.2.1* All users of systems that have microphones for live voice announcements shall be provided with posted instructions for using the microphone.

24.3.3* **Required Emergency Communications Systems.** An emergency communications system shall be installed in occupancies where required by the authority having jurisdiction or by other applicable governing laws, codes, or standards.

24.3.4* **Nonrequired (Voluntary) Emergency Communications Systems.**

24.3.4.1 Nonrequired emergency communications systems and components shall meet the requirements of this chapter.

24.3.4.2 Nonrequired emergency communications systems and components shall be identified on the record drawings.

24.3.5 Ancillary Functions.

24.3.5.1 Ancillary functions shall not impair the required operation of the emergency communications system.

24.3.5.2* Loudspeakers used for emergency communications system functions also providing ancillary functions shall meet the conditions of either 24.3.5.2(1) or (2):

(1) The fire command center or the emergency command center as applicable shall be constantly attended by trained personnel, and selective paging is permitted by the authority having jurisdiction.
(2) All of the following conditions shall be met:
   (a) The loudspeakers and associated audio equipment are installed or located with safeguards to resist tampering or misadjustment of those components essential for intended emergency notification.
   (b) The monitoring integrity requirements of 10.6.9 and Sections 10.19 and 12.6 continue to be met while the system is used for non-emergency purposes.

24.3.5.3 Ancillary functions shall be inspected and tested annually to verify they will not impair the operation of the fire alarm system or the mass notification system.

24.3.6 Pathway Survivability.

24.3.6.1 Pathway survivability levels shall be as described in Section 12.4.

24.3.6.2 Other component survivability shall comply with the provisions of 24.4.2.8.5.6.

24.3.6.3* The pathway survivability requirements in 24.3.6.4 through 24.3.6.12 shall apply to notification and communications circuits and other circuits necessary to ensure the continued operation of the emergency communications system.

24.3.6.4 In-building fire emergency voice/alarm communications systems shall comply with 24.3.6.4.1 or 24.3.6.4.2.

24.3.6.4.1 For systems employing relocation or partial evacuation, a Level 2 or Level 3 pathway survivability shall be required.

24.3.6.4.2 For systems that do not employ relocation or partial evacuation, a Level 0, Level 1, Level 2, or Level 3 pathway survivability shall be required.

24.3.6.4.3 Refer to Annex F for previous nomenclature and cross reference.

24.3.6.5 Pathway survivability levels for in-building mass notification systems shall be determined by the risk analysis.

24.3.6.6 Pathway survivability levels for wide area mass notification systems shall be determined by the risk analysis.

24.3.6.7 Two-way in-building wired emergency communications systems shall have a pathway survivability of Level 2 or Level 3.

24.3.6.8 Two-way radio communications enhancement systems shall comply with 24.3.6.8.1 through 24.3.6.8.4.

24.3.6.8.1* Where a two-way radio communications enhancement system is used in lieu of a two-way in-building wired emergency communications system, it shall have a pathway survivability of Level 1, Level 2, or Level 3.

Exception: Where leaky feeder cable is utilized as the antenna, it shall not be required to be installed in metal raceway.

24.3.6.8.1.1 The feeder and riser coaxial cables shall be rated as plenum cables.

24.3.6.8.1.2 The feeder coaxial cables shall be connected to the riser coaxial cable using hybrid coupler devices of a value determined by the overall design.

24.3.6.8.2 Where a two-way radio communications enhancement system is used in lieu of a two-way in-building wired emergency communications system, the design of the system shall be approved by the authority having jurisdiction.

24.3.6.8.3* Riser coaxial cables shall be rated as riser cables and routed through a 2-hour-rated enclosure.

24.3.6.8.4 The connection between the riser and feeder coaxial cables shall be made within the 2-hour-rated enclosure, and passage of the feeder cable in and out of the 2-hour-rated enclosure shall be firestopped to 2-hour ratings.

24.3.6.9* Area of refuge (area of rescue assistance) emergency communications systems shall comply with 24.3.6.9.1 and 24.3.6.9.2.

24.3.6.9.1 Area of refuge emergency communications systems shall have a pathway survivability of Level 2 or Level 3.

24.3.6.9.2 Circuits intended to transmit off-premises shall have a pathway survivability of Level 0, Level 1, Level 2, or Level 3.

24.3.6.10 Elevator emergency communications systems shall have a pathway survivability of Level 0, Level 1, Level 2, or Level 3.

24.3.6.11 Central command station emergency communications systems shall have pathway survivability as determined by the risk analysis.

24.3.6.12 All other emergency communications system circuits shall have pathway survivability as determined by the risk analysis.

24.3.7* System Classification. Emergency communications systems (ECS) shall consist of two classifications of systems, one-way and two-way.

24.3.8* Mass Notification Layers. Emergency communications used for mass notification shall be categorized into layers and take into consideration type of audience and reach as follows:

(1) Layer 1 relates to means of notification of occupants by systems/equipment installed inside a building and controlled only by authorized users (in-building ECS)
(2) Layer 2 relates to means of notification of occupants on the exterior of a building and controlled only by authorized users (wide-area MNS)
(3) Layer 3 relates to means of notification of personnel through individual measures (distributed recipient MNS)
(4) Layer 4 relates to means of notification of personnel by public measures (broadcast radio, television, and so forth)

24.3.9* Design. Design documents in accordance with Section 7.3 shall be prepared prior to installation of any new system.

24.3.9.1 Systems that are altered shall have design documents prepared applicable to the portions of the system that are altered.

24.3.9.2 Documents shall be revised as necessary following installation to represent as-built conditions and include record drawings.

24.3.10 Listing. Control units installed as part of a mass notification system shall be in compliance with this Code and applicable standards such as ANSI/UL 864, *Standard for Control Units and Accessories for Fire Alarm Systems*, or ANSI/UL 2017, *Standard for General-Purpose Signaling Devices and Systems*, or ANSI/UL 2572, *Mass Notification Systems*.

24.3.11* Risk Analysis for Mass Notification Systems.

24.3.11.1* Each application of a mass notification system shall be specific to the nature and anticipated risks of each facility for which it is designed.

24.3.11.2 The designer shall consider both fire and non-fire emergencies when determining risk tolerances for survivability for the mass notification system.

24.3.11.3 Performance-based design and the risk analysis shall be applied in accordance with Section 24.7.

24.3.11.4 The risk analysis shall consider the number of persons, type of occupancy, and perceived peril to occupants.

24.3.11.5 The analysis shall be based on the maximum occupant load calculation for every occupiable room, building, area, space, campus, or region is expected to contain.

24.3.11.6 Occupancy characteristics shall comply with 24.3.11.6.1 and 24.3.11.6.2.

24.3.11.6.1 The risk analysis shall consider characteristics of the buildings, areas, spaces, campuses or regions, equipment, and operations that are not inherent in the design specifications.

24.3.11.6.2 Those elements that are not inherent in the design specifications, but that affect occupant behavior or the rate of hazard development, shall be explicitly identified and included in the risk analysis.

24.3.11.7 The risk analysis shall consider the following types of potential events, which are not all-inclusive but reflect the general categories that shall be considered in the risk analysis:

(1) Natural hazards — Geological events
(2) Natural hazards — Meteorological events
(3) Natural hazards — Biological events
(4) Human caused — Accidental events
(5) Human caused — Intentional events
(6) Technological — Caused events

24.3.11.8 The risk analysis shall include a review of the extent to which occupants and personnel are notified, based on the anticipated event (potential hazard).

24.3.11.9 The risk analysis shall be used as the basis for development of the ECS provisions of the facility emergency response plan.

24.3.12* Emergency Response Plan Elements. A well-defined emergency response plan shall be developed in accordance with *NFPA 1600, Standard on Disaster/Emergency Management and Business Continuity Programs,* and NFPA 1620, *Standard for Pre-Incident Planning,* as part of the design and implementation of a mass notification system.

24.4 One-Way Emergency Communications Systems.

24.4.1 General.

24.4.1.1* Messages shall be developed for each scenario developed in the emergency response plan.

24.4.1.2* A message template shall be developed for each message required in 24.4.1.1.

24.4.1.3 For an evacuation message, a tone in accordance with 18.4.2 shall be used with a minimum of two cycles preceding and following the voice message.

24.4.1.4 Test messages shall clearly state the phrase "This is a test."

24.4.2* In-Building Fire Emergency Voice/Alarm Communications Systems (EVACS). Subsection 24.4.2 shall be used in the design and application of in-building fire emergency voice/alarm communications for fire alarm systems.

24.4.2.1 Automatic Response. The in-building fire emergency voice/alarm communications system shall be used to provide an automatic response to the receipt of a signal indicative of a fire alarm or other emergency.

24.4.2.1.1 When the monitoring location is constantly attended by trained operators, and operator acknowledgment of receipt of a fire alarm or other emergency signal is received within 30 seconds, automatic response shall not be required.

24.4.2.1.2 If acceptable to the authority having jurisdiction, the system shall permit the application of an automatic evacuation signal to one or more evacuation signaling zones and, at the same time, shall permit manual voice paging to the other evacuation signaling zones selectively or in any combination.

24.4.2.2 Voice Evacuation Messages.

24.4.2.2.1 Unless otherwise permitted by 24.4.2.8, evacuation messages shall be preceded and followed by a minimum of two cycles of the emergency evacuation signal specified in 18.4.2.

24.4.2.2.2 Voice messages shall comply with the requirements of 24.3.1.

24.4.2.2.2.1 The following requirements shall be met for layout and design:

(1) The loudspeaker layout of the system shall be designed to ensure intelligibility and audibility.
(2) Intelligibility shall first be determined by ensuring that all areas in the building have the required level of audibility.

24.4.2.2.2.2* System design shall incorporate designation of acoustically distinguishable spaces (ADS) within the occupiable areas as required in Chapter 18.

24.4.2.2.2.3 Audibility shall be required in all areas in accordance with Chapter 18.

24.4.2.3 Positive Alarm Sequence. In-building fire emergency voice/alarm communications systems shall be permitted to use positive alarm sequence complying with 23.8.1.3.

24.4.2.4 Tones. The tone preceding any message shall comply with 24.4.2.4.1 through 24.4.2.4.4.

24.4.2.4.1 The tone preceding any message shall be permitted to be a part of the voice message or to be transmitted automatically from a separate tone generator.

24.4.2.4.2* Except as specified in 24.4.2.4.3, in occupancies where sleeping accommodations are provided and the voice message is intended to communicate information to those who could be asleep, a low-frequency tone that complies with 18.4.5 shall be used.

24.4.2.4.3* In areas where sleeping accommodation are provided, but the voice communication system is used to communicate to occupants who are awake, the low-frequency tone shall not be required.

24.4.2.4.4 Audible signal tones for alert or evacuation shall meet the audibility requirements of either 18.4.3 (public mode audible requirements), 18.4.4 (private mode audible requirements), 18.4.5.1 and 18.4.5.2 (sleeping area requirements), or 18.4.6 (narrow band tone signaling for exceeding masked thresholds), as applicable.

24.4.2.5 Controls.

24.4.2.5.1* Controls for the in-building fire emergency voice/alarm communications system shall be at a location approved by the authority having jurisdiction.

24.4.2.5.2 Controls shall be located or secured to allow access only by trained and authorized personnel.

24.4.2.5.3 Operating controls shall be clearly identified.

24.4.2.5.4 If there are multiple in-building fire emergency voice/alarm communications control locations, only one shall be in control at any given time.

24.4.2.5.5 The location having control of the system shall be identified by a visible indication at that location.

24.4.2.5.6 Manual controls shall be arranged to provide visible indication of the on/off status for their associated evacuation signaling zone.

24.4.2.5.7 If live voice instructions are provided, they shall perform as follows:

(1) Override previously initiated signals to the selected notification zone(s).
(2) Have priority over any subsequent automatically initiated signals to the selected notification zone(s).
(3) If a previously initiated recorded message is interrupted by live voice instructions, upon releasing of the microphone, the previously initiated recorded messages to the selected notification zones shall not resume playing automatically unless required by the emergency response plan.

24.4.2.6 Loudspeakers.

24.4.2.6.1* Loudspeakers and their enclosures shall be installed in accordance with Chapter 18.

24.4.2.6.2 Loudspeakers used as alarm notification appliances on fire alarm systems shall also be permitted to be used for mass notification.

24.4.2.7 Priority.

24.4.2.7.1* Notification appliances required to provide special suppression predischarge notification shall not be overridden by other systems.

24.4.2.7.2 Priority of mass notification messages over fire alarm evacuation shall be permitted when evaluated by the stakeholders through a risk analysis in accordance with 24.3.11.

24.4.2.7.3 When the fire alarm system has been activated, and mass notification has been given priority over the fire alarm system, a distinctive audible and visible indication shall be provided at the building fire alarm control unit to indicate MNS is active.

24.4.2.7.4 It shall not be required to transmit this condition to a supervising station.

24.4.2.7.5 The fire alarm system shall not automatically override emergency mass notification messages.

24.4.2.8* Relocation and Partial Evacuation.
The requirements of 24.4.2.8 shall apply only to systems used for relocation or partial evacuation during a fire condition.

24.4.2.8.1 New systems employing relocation or partial evacuation shall require documentation in accordance with Sections 7.3, 7.4, and 7.5 in addition to the minimum documentation requirements of Sections 7.2 and 24.8.

24.4.2.8.2 Systems shall be provided with manual voice transmission capabilities selectively to one or more zones or on an all-call basis.

24.4.2.8.3 Under a fire condition, where the system is used to transmit relocation instructions or other fire emergency non-evacuation messages, a 1-second to 3-second alert tone followed by a message (or messages where multi-channel capability is used) shall be provided.

24.4.2.8.3.1 The sequence [the alert tone followed by the message(s)] shall be repeated at least three times to inform and direct occupants in the evacuation signaling zone where the alarm initiation originated, as well as other evacuation signaling zones in accordance with the building fire safety plan.

24.4.2.8.3.2 Approved alternative fire alarm notification schemes shall be permitted so long as the occupants are effectively notified and are provided instructions in a timely and safe manner in accordance with the building fire safety plan.

24.4.2.8.4 Where provided, loudspeakers in each enclosed stairway, each exit passageway, and each group of elevator cars within a common hoistway shall be connected to separate notification zones for manual paging only.

24.4.2.8.4.1 The evacuation signal shall not operate in elevator cars, exit stair enclosures, and exit passageways.

24.4.2.8.4.2 Manually activated speakers shall be permitted in exit stair enclosures and exit passageways in buildings that have emergency voice/alarm communications systems in accordance with 24.4.2.

24.4.2.8.5 The requirements of 24.4.2.8.5 shall apply to both audible (tone and voice) and visible notification appliance circuits.

24.4.2.8.5.1* Fire alarm systems used for partial evacuation and relocation shall be designed and installed such that attack by fire within an evacuation signaling zone does not impair control and operation of the notification appliances outside the evacuation signaling zone.

24.4.2.8.5.2 Performance features provided to ensure operational reliability under adverse conditions shall be described and technical justification provided in the documentation submitted to the authority having jurisdiction with the analysis required in 23.4.3.1.

24.4.2.8.5.3* All circuits necessary for the operation of the notification appliances shall be protected until they enter the evacuation signaling zone that they serve by the protection provided by the pathway survivability level required in 24.3.6.4.1 or by performance alternatives approved by the authority having jurisdiction.

24.4.2.8.5.4 Where the separation of in-building fire emergency voice/alarm control equipment locations results in the portions of the system controlled by one location being dependent upon the control equipment in other locations, the circuits between the dependent controls shall be protected against attack by fire by the protection provided by the pathway survivability level required in 24.3.6.4.1 or by performance alternatives approved by the authority having jurisdiction.

24.4.2.8.5.5 Protection of circuits between redundant control equipment locations that are not mutually dependent shall not be required.

24.4.2.8.5.6 Where the separation of the in-building fire emergency voice/alarm control equipment occurs as in 24.4.2.8.5.4, and where the circuits are run through junction boxes, terminal cabinets or control equipment, such as system control units, power supplies and amplifiers, and where cable integrity is not maintained, these components shall, in addition to the pathway survivability required by 24.3.6.4.1, be protected by using one of the following methods:

(1) A 2-hour fire rated enclosure
(2) A 2-hour fire rated room

(3) Other equivalent means to provide a 2-hour fire resistance rating approved by the authority having jurisdiction

24.4.2.8.5.7 Paragraphs 24.4.2.8 through 24.4.2.8.5.6 shall not automatically apply when relocation or partial evacuation is of a non-fire emergency unless identified and required by a risk analysis.

24.4.2.9 Evacuation Signal Zoning.

24.4.2.9.1* Undivided fire or smoke areas shall not be divided into multiple evacuation signaling zones.

24.4.2.9.2 If multiple notification appliance circuits are provided within a single evacuation signaling zone, all of the notification appliances within the zone shall be arranged to activate or deactivate simultaneously, either automatically or by actuation of a common manual control.

24.4.2.9.3 Where there are different notification appliance circuits within an evacuation signaling zone that perform separate functions, such as presignal and general alarm signals, and pre-discharge and discharge signals, they shall not be required to activate or deactivate simultaneously.

24.4.3* In-Building Mass Notification Systems. The requirements of 24.4.3 shall apply to mass notification systems installed in buildings or structures for the purpose of notifying and instructing occupants in an emergency.

24.4.3.1* General Performance. The performance, selection, installation, operation, and use of a mass notification system shall comply with the requirements of 24.4.3.

24.4.3.1.1 Interconnection of protected premises emergency control functions with the mass notification systems shall comply with Chapter 21.

24.4.3.1.2 An in-building mass notification system shall include one or more of the following components:

(1) Autonomous control unit (ACU)
(2) Local operating console (LOC)
(3) Fire alarm control interface
(4) Notification appliance network
(5) Initiating devices
(6)*Interface to other systems and alerting sources

24.4.3.1.3 All mass notification system notification appliances that receive their power from a signaling line circuit of a mass notification system control unit shall be listed for use with the control unit.

24.4.3.1.4 Mass notification system components shall be installed, tested, and maintained in accordance with the manufacturer's published instructions and this Code.

24.4.3.1.5 In-building emergency mass notification operation shall be permitted to be initiated by manual or automatic means.

24.4.3.1.6 Mass notification system activation shall initiate recorded messages or live voice and visible notification.

24.4.3.1.7 The priority level of recorded messages shall be determined by the emergency response plan.

24.4.3.1.8 Only recorded messages determined by the emergency response plan to be of higher priority than fire alarm activation shall be permitted to override the fire alarm notification and initiate the mass notification priority indicator.

24.4.3.1.9 Activation of any other recorded message shall not interfere with the operation of fire alarm notification.

24.4.3.1.10 Initiation of live voice announcements from microphones on the fire alarm system at an ACU, and at an LOC, shall not automatically place the fire alarm system in a mass notification priority mode.

24.4.3.1.11 Combination of mass notification with fire alarm systems shall be permitted and shall meet the requirements of 23.8.4.

24.4.3.2 System Operation.

24.4.3.2.1* Authorized personnel shall be permitted to control message initiation over the mass notification system.

24.4.3.2.2* Where required by the emergency response plan, the mass notification system shall provide the capability for authorized personnel to remotely activate live and prerecorded emergency messages.

24.4.3.2.3* Operating controls shall be clearly identified.

24.4.3.2.4 If there are multiple control locations, only one shall be in control at any given time.

24.4.3.2.5* Any ACU shall provide a control status of all interconnected LOCs.

24.4.3.2.6 If there are multiple control locations, a visible indication shall be provided at all other control locations indicating that another control location is in use.

24.4.3.2.7 Manual controls shall be arranged to provide visible indication of the on/off status for their associated notification zone.

24.4.3.2.8 If live voice instructions are provided, they shall perform as follows:

(1) Override previously initiated signals to the selected notification zone(s).
(2) Have priority over any subsequent automatically initiated signals to the selected zone(s).

24.4.3.2.9 A manual means shall be provided at each mass notification system control location to permit the mass notification system to relinquish control of the fire alarm system.

24.4.3.2.10* During the period after the mass notification system has seized control of the audible and visible notification appliances, but before the mass notification system relinquishes control, the mass notification system shall activate the audible and visible notification appliances at least once every 30 seconds.

24.4.3.3 Coverage.

24.4.3.3.1* The mass notification system shall provide for live voice and prerecorded localized messaging within a protected individual building, areas surrounding the building, and other outdoor designated areas.

24.4.3.3.2 System design shall incorporate designation of acoustically distinguishable spaces (ADS) within any occupiable areas as required in Chapter 18.

24.4.3.3.3 Notification zones shall be established on the basis of a risk analysis.

24.4.3.3.4* If the mass notification system serves more than one building, it shall be capable of providing separate messages to one individual building or to multiple buildings at any given time.

24.4.3.4 Loudspeaker Circuits.

24.4.3.4.1* Loudspeaker circuits used for mass notification that are not fire alarm circuits shall be exempt from the monitoring requirements of this Code, provided that alternate methods of achieving comparable reliability are accepted by the authority having jurisdiction.

24.4.3.4.2 Survivability for loudspeaker circuits used for mass notification shall be determined by the risk analysis for the building.

24.4.3.5 Documentation. Mass notification systems shall require documentation in accordance with Sections 7.3, 7.4, and 7.5 in addition to the minimum documentation requirements of Sections 7.2 and 24.8.

24.4.3.5.1* Security. Security for mass notification systems documentation shall be determined by the stakeholders in accordance with 7.7.3.

24.4.3.5.2 Record of Completion.

24.4.3.5.2.1* A record of completion shall be required in accordance with Chapter 7 for documentation of the mass notification system.

24.4.3.5.2.2 All systems that are modified after the initial installation shall have the original, or latest overall system, record of completion revised or attached to show all changes from the original information and shall be identified with a revision date.

24.4.3.5.3 Required Documentation. Every system shall include the following documentation, which shall be delivered to the owner or the owner's representative upon final acceptance of the system:

(1) Owner's manual including a complete set of operations and maintenance manuals, manufacturer's published instructions, and product data sheets covering all system equipment
(2) Record and as-built drawings
(3) Written sequence of operation
(4) One current copy of the record of completion form, updated to reflect all system additions or modifications
(5) For software-based systems, a record copy of the system-specific software
(6) Copy of the site-specific software stored on-site in non-volatile, nonerasable, nonrewritable memory
(7) Emergency response plan, with operational management procedures defined for management and activation of the system
(8) Risk analysis, when provided

24.4.3.5.4 Risk Analysis Documentation. Document accessibility shall be in accordance with 7.7.2 and 24.4.3.5.4.

24.4.3.5.4.1 When a risk analysis is required to be prepared, such as for a mass notification system, findings of the risk assessment shall be documented.

24.4.3.5.4.2 When identified by the stakeholders, security and protection of the risk analysis shall be in accordance with 24.4.3.5.1.

24.4.3.5.5 Document Accessibility.

24.4.3.5.5.1 An as-built plans cabinet shall be provided to house the documentation required in 24.4.3.5.3.

24.4.3.5.5.2 The cabinet shall be sized so that it can neatly contain all necessary documentation, including future inspection and service reports.

24.4.3.5.5.3 Mass notification system and fire alarm system as-built plans and other related documentation shall be permitted to be maintained together, including the appearance of both systems on the same drawings.

24.4.3.6 Impairments. The requirements of Section 10.21 shall be applicable when a mass notification system is impaired.

24.4.3.7 Inspection, Testing, and Maintenance Requirements. Mass notification systems shall be inspected, tested, and maintained in accordance with the manufacturer's published instructions and the inspection, testing, and maintenance requirements of Chapter 14.

24.4.3.8* System Response Priorities. Priority levels shall be established on the basis of the risk analysis.

24.4.3.9 Initiation Indication. The source of system activation shall be visibly and audibly indicated at the emergency command center and at the building control unit, unless otherwise required by the emergency response plan.

24.4.3.10 Initiating Devices.

24.4.3.10.1 Devices connected to a mass notification system for the purpose of initiating an automatic response to an emergency shall be evaluated based on the emergency response plan.

24.4.3.10.2* All mass notification initiating devices shall be listed for their intended purpose.

24.4.3.10.3 Where no listed device exists for the detection required by the emergency response plan, nonlisted devices shall be permitted to be used if their failure will not impair the operation of the mass notification system.

24.4.3.10.4 Non-fire emergency manual actuating stations (boxes) shall be listed to ANSI/UL 2017, *Standard for General Purpose Signaling Devices and Systems.*

24.4.3.10.5 Non-fire emergency manual actuating boxes shall have tactile markings, be of a contrasting color to manual fire alarm boxes on the protected premises, and not be red.

24.4.3.10.6 Non-fire emergency manual actuating boxes shall be installed similarly to manual fire alarm boxes in accordance with the requirements of 17.14.3, 17.14.5, and 17.14.8.2.

24.4.3.11* Secure Access of Fire Alarm/Mass Notification System Interface. Access to, and physical protection of, the fire alarm/mass notification system interface shall be determined by the risk analysis and as defined in the emergency response plan.

24.4.3.12 Autonomous Control Unit (ACU).

24.4.3.12.1 Where provided, the building ACU shall monitor and control the notification appliance network.

24.4.3.12.2 Building occupants meeting the requirements of 24.4.3.2.1 shall be permitted to initiate communications from the ACU.

24.4.3.12.3 Unless otherwise identified in the emergency response plan, actions taken at the building ACU shall take precedence over actions taken at any remote location, including the LOC, or inputs from a wide-area mass notification system.

24.4.3.12.4 When there are multiple ACUs controlling the same notification appliance network, only one shall be in control at any given time.

24.4.3.12.5 When the ACU is integrated with the building fire alarm control unit to form one combined system that performs both functions, the system shall meet the standby power requirements of this chapter.

24.4.3.12.6 When a combined system is installed with an ACU and fire alarm control unit and placed in separate equipment enclosures, the ACU and fire alarm control unit shall be interfaced as required by this chapter.

24.4.3.12.7 When the ACU is part of a stand-alone mass notification system and no fire alarm system exists, the ACU shall meet the requirements of this chapter.

24.4.3.13 Local Operating Console (LOC).

24.4.3.13.1* Building occupants meeting the authorized personnel requirement of 24.4.3.2.1 shall be permitted to initiate communications from the LOC.

24.4.3.13.2 The use of lock wire seals or break-glass-type enclosures to house the operating consoles for the system, or equivalent protection against unauthorized use, shall be permitted.

24.4.3.13.3 Operating controls shall be clearly identified.

24.4.3.13.4 If there are multiple control locations, only one shall be in control at any given time.

24.4.3.13.5 The location having control of the system shall be identified by a visible indication at that location.

24.4.3.13.6 If live voice instructions are provided, they shall override previously initiated signals to the selected notification zone(s) and shall have priority over any subsequent automatically initiated signals to the selected zone(s).

24.4.3.13.7 Upon initiation of an emergency message, a visible indication shall be provided to the user that the LOC is connected to the audio network.

24.4.3.13.8 Manual controls shall be permitted to provide visible indication of the on/off status for their associated notification zone.

24.4.3.13.9 The emergency message shall be an all-call basis unless otherwise permitted by 24.4.3.13.10.

24.4.3.13.10 Selective notification zone paging shall be permitted only if the LOC has manual controls with visible indication of the on/off status for each associated notification zone.

24.4.3.14 Voice Message Priority.

24.4.3.14.1* The priority of mass notification messages shall be established using the emergency response plan.

24.4.3.14.2 The local building mass notification system shall have the ability to override the fire alarm system with live voice or manual activation of a higher priority message, but only where that message and operation are approved under the emergency response plan.

24.4.3.14.3 All other messages shall also be prioritized by using the emergency response plan.

24.4.3.14.4 When identified by the emergency response plan, messages from the mass notification system shall be permitted to take priority over fire alarm messages and signals.

24.4.3.14.5 If the fire alarm system is in the alarm mode and a recorded voice message is playing, or the audible signals are sounding, and then the mass notification system is actuated, it shall cause deactivation of all fire alarm–initiated audible and visible notification.

24.4.3.14.6 After the mass notification system relinquishes control, the following shall occur:

(1) Without an active fire alarm signal, the fire alarm system shall automatically restore to normal operation.
(2)*With an active fire alarm signal, the fire alarm system shall operate based on the emergency response plan.

24.4.3.14.7 Overriding of fire alarm audible and visible notification signals shall cause an audible and distinctive visible indication at each affected fire alarm control unit to indicate the MNS is active.

24.4.3.14.8 The fire alarm signal deactivation function shall be permitted to occur only when both the fire alarm system is in an alarm condition and notification is being given by the mass notification system.

24.4.3.14.9 When the fire alarm notification is overridden as permitted in 24.4.3.14.8, all other features of the fire alarm system shall remain unaffected.

24.4.3.15 Volume Control.

24.4.3.15.1 Local controls shall be permitted to adjust volume levels of ancillary functions.

24.4.3.15.2 Upon activation of an emergency signal, the system shall override any local volume setting to deliver at a preset volume setting that has been established through testing and acceptance of sound level and speech intelligibility as required by this Code.

24.4.3.16 Visible Notification.

24.4.3.16.1 Where audible notification is provided, mass notification systems shall also provide visible notification information to serve the hearing impaired and for high-noise areas.

24.4.3.16.2 The visible notification required by 24.4.3.16.1 shall be accomplished using strobes.

24.4.3.16.3 In addition to the strobes required by 24.4.3.16.1, textual, graphic, or video displays shall be permitted.

24.4.3.16.4 Transmission of visible notification and messages shall be simultaneous to audible notification and messages.

24.4.3.17 Visible Appliances.

24.4.3.17.1 Where strobes are used as visible appliances, they shall meet the requirements of 24.4.3.17.2 through 24.4.3.17.10.

24.4.3.17.2 Visible notification appliances shall be of a sufficient quantity and intensity and located so as to meet the intent of the design and be in compliance with Section 18.5.

24.4.3.17.3 Strobes used in combination systems where the same strobe is used for both mass notification and fire notification shall comply with the following:

(1) Be clear or nominal white, meeting the listing requirements of ANSI/UL 1971, *Standard for Signaling Devices for the Hearing Impaired*
(2) Have no marking or be marked with the word "ALERT" stamped or imprinted on the appliance
(3) Be visible to the public

24.4.3.17.4 In situations where existing notification appliances previously used exclusively for fire alarm applications, and are marked with the word "FIRE," and are to be used for other emergency notification purposes, field modification to the marking shall be permitted, provided that it is accomplished by one of the following methods:

(1) Replacement of the manufacturer's approved escutcheon or trim plate

(2) Covering of, or removal of, the word "FIRE" using a manufacturer's approved method

(3) Installation of a permanent sign directly adjacent or below the notification appliance indicating that it is multi-purpose and will operate for fire and other emergency conditions

24.4.3.17.5 Strobes with colored lenses shall be marked with the listed effective intensity using the lens color installed.

24.4.3.17.6 The spacing of colored strobes shall be in accordance with public mode spacing requirements of Section 18.5 using the effective intensity as the basis for spacing.

24.4.3.17.7 Where strobes are used solely for mass notification, the word "ALERT" shall be stamped or imprinted on the appliance and be visible to the public.

24.4.3.17.8 Where colored strobes are used solely for mass notification, they shall be listed to an applicable standard such as ANSI/UL 1638, *Visual Signaling Appliances — Private Mode Emergency and General Utility Signaling*.

24.4.3.17.9 Strobe appliances listed to ANSI/UL 1971, *Standard for Signaling Devices for the Hearing Impaired*, shall be considered as meeting the intent of this Code.

Exception: Color lens strobes shall meet the requirements of 24.4.3.17.8.

24.4.3.17.10 Strobes used for mass notification shall meet the synchronization requirements of Section 18.5.

24.4.3.18* Textual and Graphical Visible Appliances.

24.4.3.18.1 Textual and graphical visible notification appliances shall be permitted to be used for primary or supplemental notification.

24.4.3.18.2 Textual and graphical visible notification shall be considered to be primary notification where it is the only method used to convey emergency mass notification information to the general public or to specific individuals.

24.4.3.18.3 Primary and supplemental textual and graphical visible appliances shall meet the requirements of Chapter 18.

24.4.3.18.4 Textual and graphical visible appliances other than a main control unit shall be permitted to not have a dedicated primary circuit as required by Chapter 10, but shall meet all other requirements for the monitoring of primary power and all requirements for secondary power.

24.4.3.18.5 Textual and graphical visible appliances shall be permitted to be used for nonemergency purposes.

24.4.3.18.6 Emergency textual and graphical messages shall override nonemergency textual and graphical messages.

24.4.3.18.7 Supplemental textual and graphical visible appliances that are not monitored for integrity or loss of communication by a control unit shall be provided with visual status indicators, including loss of communication or loss of power, that are clearly visible on the appliance.

24.4.3.19 Tactile Notification Appliances. Where tactile notification appliances are provided for emergency notification, they shall meet the requirements of Section 18.10.

24.4.3.20* Video Alerting. Video display systems that provide alerts and messages to video appliances shall be permitted to be used to supplement mass notification.

24.4.3.21 Supplemental Notification. Supplemental notification shall be permitted to provide additional information or more detailed instructions than those transmitted by the primary notification means.

24.4.3.22 Interfaces. Any abnormal condition that would prevent reliable emergency operation of any interfaced system shall be annunciated both audibly and visibly as a trouble signal at the affected control location.

24.4.3.22.1 Fire Alarm Control Interface (FACI).

24.4.3.22.1.1 Where a fire alarm system is installed covering all or part of the same building or other area as the mass notification system, an interface shall be provided between the systems for operational coordination purposes.

24.4.3.22.1.2 A listed barrier gateway in accordance with 10.3.1, integral with, or attached to, each control unit or group of control units, as appropriate, shall be provided to prevent the other systems from interfering with or controlling the fire alarm system.

24.4.3.22.1.3* The fire alarm control interface shall coordinate signals to and from each system to accomplish the following:

(1) Indicate the failure at the system control unit that will be impaired

(2) Provide an audible and distinctive visible indication at the affected FACU(s) to indicate the MNS is active.

(3) Cause the fire alarm system to deactivate all audible and visible notification appliances whose operation could interfere with the intelligibility of the mass notification message or that will deliver conflicting information to occupants

(4) Not permit the fire alarm system to turn off audible and visible notification appliances for special suppression pre-discharge notification required by 24.4.2.7.1

(5) Where required by the emergency response plan or by other governing laws, codes, or standards, or by other parts of this Code, or by the authority having jurisdiction, provide for a supervisory signal to a supervising station with a response as directed by the emergency response plan that is indicative of the mass notification system overriding the fire alarm system notification appliances during simultaneous fire and mass notification events

24.4.3.22.1.4 If the fire alarm control interface is used to broadcast nonemergency messages, music, or other signals over the fire alarm notification appliance circuits, the operation shall meet the requirements of 24.4.3.15 and 23.8.4.

24.4.3.22.2 Interfaces to Emergency Control Functions. The mass notification system shall be permitted to provide emergency control functions in accordance with Chapter 21 as required by the emergency response plan and as permitted by the authority having jurisdiction.

24.4.3.22.2.1 When mass notifications systems are controlling building life safety systems, the mass notifications systems equipment shall be listed for ANSI/UL 864, *Control Units and Accessories for Fire Alarm Systems*.

24.4.3.22.3 Interfaces with Wide-Area Mass Notification Systems.

24.4.3.22.3.1* Individual building mass notification systems shall be permitted to interface with wide-area mass notification systems.

24.4.3.22.3.2 The in-building mass notification system shall not be activated or controlled by a wide-area mass notification system, unless the wide-area mass notification system also meets the design and performance requirements of this chapter or has been deemed to be acceptable by the risk analysis and the authority having jurisdiction.

24.4.3.23 Combination Emergency Communications Systems.

24.4.3.23.1* When the mass notification system is integrated with the building fire alarm control unit to form one combined system that performs both functions, the system shall comply with this chapter.

24.4.3.23.2 All components that affect the operation of the fire alarm system shall be listed for fire alarm use and shall be in compliance with applicable standards such as ANSI/UL 864, *Standard for Control Units and Accessories for Fire Alarm Systems.*

24.4.3.24 Public Address (PA) Systems Used for Emergency Communications.

24.4.3.24.1 The voice communications or public address system that is to be used for mass notification shall be evaluated by the emergency communications system designer, as defined in Chapter 10, to determine applicability and compliance.

24.4.3.24.2 Evaluation documentation in accordance with 7.3.9 shall be provided by the emergency communications system designer attesting to the fact that the public address system has been evaluated and meets the performance requirements of Chapter 24 and the emergency response plan.

24.4.3.25 Public Address (PA) System Interface with Facility Fire Alarm System.

24.4.3.25.1 When a public address system is used to deliver mass notification messages, the public address system shall provide (either internally as a design feature or with an approved or listed external controller) for a signal to control the facility's fire alarm system for the purpose of deactivating the fire alarm audible and visible notification appliances in accordance with 24.4.3.22.1.

24.4.3.25.2 All of the following features shall be provided in, or added to, the public address system:

(1) Emergency messages must have priority over non-emergency messages.
(2) All individual or zone speaker volume controls must default to the emergency sound level when used for an emergency mass notification message.
(3) When monitoring of circuit integrity is provided by the public address system, monitoring must continue, even if local loudspeaker volume controls are placed in the "off" position.
(4) The required visible notification appliance network (i.e., strobes and textual signs) must be provided where required.

24.4.4* Wide-Area Mass Notification Systems.

24.4.4.1 Voice Messages.

24.4.4.1.1 Voice messages shall comply with the requirements of 24.3.1.

24.4.4.1.2 Where required by the emergency response plan, multiple languages shall be permitted to be used.

24.4.4.1.3 Where required by the emergency response plan, specific warning tones shall be provided.

24.4.4.2* Password Protection. Wide-area mass notification systems shall have multiple levels of password protection access control, including levels for system administrators, system operators, maintainers, supervisors, and executives, or other means to limit access to system controls shall be provided based on the emergency response plan.

24.4.4.3* External Connections. Wide-area mass notification systems shall be permitted to connect to regional mass notification systems and public emergency alarm reporting systems as defined in this Code, and public reporting systems as defined in NFPA 1221, *Standard for the Installation, Maintenance, and Use of Emergency Services Communications Systems.*

24.4.4.4 Wide-Area Mass Notification System Components.

24.4.4.4.1 Emergency Command Center. Refer to Section 24.6 for requirements of an emergency command center.

24.4.4.4.2* High Power Speaker Array (HPSA). When required by the risk analysis, high power speaker arrays (HPSAs) shall be provided, installed, and maintained.

24.4.4.4.2.1 The HPSA shall be arranged in such a manner to provide intelligible voice and audible tone communications.

(A) When multiple HPSAs are used, they shall be arranged in physical or virtual notification zones so that each notification zone can be individually controlled by the emergency command center.

(B)* HPSAs shall be designed to maintain the intelligibility of voice signals within the notification zone in accordance with the requirements of Chapter 18.

24.4.4.4.2.2 Secondary power for HPSAs used for wide-area mass notification systems shall have sufficient capacity to operate the unit for a minimum of 7 days in standby, followed by 60 minutes of operation at full load.

24.4.4.4.2.3 An HPSA shall have the capability to provide voice communications and tones as determined by the emergency response plan.

24.4.4.4.2.4* An HPSA shall operate in the environment in which it is located, considering such factors as temperature, humidity, wind, dust, vibration, and other environmental factors.

24.4.4.4.3 High Power Speaker Array Enclosures.

24.4.4.4.3.1 Enclosures for HPSAs shall be of the NEMA 4 or 4X type.

24.4.4.4.3.2 HPSA enclosures shall have intrusion detection that signals the emergency command center.

(A) The signal shall be initiated whenever the door of the enclosure is in the open position.

(B) The transmitted signal shall be a latching supervisory signal.

24.4.4.4.4 High Power Speaker Array Mounting.

24.4.4.4.4.1 HPSAs shall be mounted at a minimum mounting height that is based on the rated output of the array.

24.4.4.4.4.2* HPSAs shall be installed at a height and orientation to prevent hearing damage to anyone in the immediate vicinity of the speakers.

24.4.4.4.4.3 All external conductors (conductors passing outside of the HPSA equipment cabinet) shall be provided with surge suppression to minimize potential equipment damage from lightning strikes.

24.4.4.4.5 High Power Speaker Array Noise Consideration. HPSA notification zones shall not be used to provide mass notification inside any structures.

24.4.4.4.6* High Power Speaker Array Structural Loads, Wind, and Seismic Design. HPSAs and their supporting structures shall meet the structural, wind, and seismic loads as identified in the risk analysis.

24.4.4.4.7 Textual Visible Appliances. Textual visible appliances shall meet the requirements of Section 18.9 and 24.4.3.18.

24.4.4.4.7.1 After loss of primary power, textual visible appliances shall have sufficient secondary power to operate for a minimum of 2 hours of continuous display time during an emergency event.

24.4.4.4.7.2 Scrolling message boards shall be provided with means to control the scrolling rate.

24.4.4.4.8 In-Building Mass Notification Systems. The in-building mass notification system shall meet the requirements of 24.4.3.

24.4.4.4.9 Interfaces with Wide-Area Mass Notification Systems. Interfaces between wide-area mass notification systems and in-building mass notification systems, other alert and notification systems, regional mass notification systems, and off-site interfaces shall have a standard interface method (such as an audio line-level output and multiple relay contacts) or supply the necessary communications protocols to provide interoperability and a secure communications link.

24.4.4.4.9.1 The interface shall be such that the primary function of both systems shall not be compromised.

24.4.4.4.9.2 The interface shall be monitored for integrity in accordance with 10.6.9 and Sections 10.19 and 12.6, so that an abnormal condition that could prevent reliable system operation is audibly and visibly annunciated as a trouble signal at both systems' control units.

24.4.4.4.10 Control Hierarchy. There shall be a predefined control hierarchy between the wide-area mass notification system, the in-building mass notification system, and the regional mass notification system for information flow from the remote control center, as well as information from specific locations.

24.4.4.4.11 Communications Links.

24.4.4.4.11.1 The wide-area mass notification system, including communications links, shall minimize the potential for interference from jamming, spoofing, hacking, eavesdropping, or other malicious acts.

24.4.4.4.11.2 The wide-area mass notification system shall have a primary and redundant communications link with minimal functional and spatial interconnection with each other.

24.4.4.4.11.3 Wide-area and in-building mass notification systems equipment and interface methods connecting to, or utilizing, public emergency alarm reporting systems and associated communications infrastructure shall be electrically and operationally compatible so as not to interfere with the public emergency alarm reporting systems.

24.4.5* Distributed Recipient Mass Notification Systems (DRMNSs).

24.4.5.1* Overview. Distributed recipient mass notification system (DRMNS) alerting shall not be used in lieu of required

audible and visible alerting mass notification systems but shall be integrated with mass notification systems whenever possible.

24.4.5.2* Targeted Recipients. The DRMNS shall be capable of sending alert messages to target recipients.

24.4.5.2.1* DRMNS shall provide means of populating and updating distributed recipients' data.

24.4.5.3* Network Security Compliance. DRMNSs shall be installed behind the appropriate internet system firewalls to protect the integrity of the network.

24.4.5.4 Network Architecture. The network shall be provided with net-centric architecture that fully supports local designated standards and security requirements.

24.4.5.5* Delivery Methods. The DRMNS shall be capable of sending alert messages to end-users (recipients) via multiple delivery methods.

24.4.5.6* Backup Distributed Recipient Mass Notification Systems. DRMNS used to send emergency messages shall be provided with a backup configuration to facilitate distribution of messages.

24.5 Two-Way, In-Building Emergency Communications Systems.

24.5.1* Two-Way, In-Building Wired Emergency Services Communications Systems.

24.5.1.1 Two-way telephone communications equipment shall be listed for two-way telephone communications service and installed in accordance with 24.5.1.

24.5.1.2 Two-way telephone communications service, if provided, shall be for use by the fire service and collocated with the in-building fire emergency voice/alarm communications equipment.

24.5.1.3 Monitoring of the integrity of two-way telephone communications circuits shall be in accordance with 10.19.2.

24.5.1.4 Additional uses shall be permitted to include signaling and communications for a building fire warden organization and signaling and communications for reporting a fire and other emergencies (e.g., voice call box service, signaling, and communications for guard's tour service).

24.5.1.5 Variation of equipment and system operation provided to facilitate additional use of the two-way telephone communications service shall not adversely affect performance when used by the fire service.

24.5.1.6* Two-way telephone communications service shall be capable of permitting the simultaneous operation of any five telephone stations in a common talk mode.

24.5.1.7 A notification signal at the control equipment, distinctive from any other alarm, supervisory, or trouble signal, shall indicate the off-hook condition of a calling telephone circuit. If a selective talk telephone communications service is supplied, a distinctive visible indicator shall be furnished for each selectable circuit, so that all circuits with telephones off-hook are continuously and visibly indicated.

24.5.1.8 A means for silencing the audible call-in signal sounding appliance shall be permitted, provided that it is key-operated or located in a locked cabinet, or provided with protection to prevent use by unauthorized persons. The means shall operate a visible indicator and sound a trouble signal whenever the means is in the silence position and no telephone circuits are in an off-hook condition.

24.5.1.9 If a selective talk system is used, means as specified in 24.5.1.8 shall be permitted, provided that subsequent telephone circuits going off-hook operate the distinctive off-hook signal.

24.5.1.10 Two-way telephone systems with common talk mode (i.e., a conference or party line circuit) shall be permitted.

24.5.1.11 In buildings provided with a two-way telephone communications system, at least one telephone station or jack shall be provided at the following locations:

(1) Each floor level
(2) Each notification zone
(3) Each elevator cab
(4) Elevator lobbies
(5) Elevator machine room(s)
(6) Emergency and standby power room(s)
(7) Fire pump room(s)
(8) Area(s) of refuge
(9) Each floor level inside an enclosed exit stair(s)
(10) Other room(s) or area(s) as required by the authority having jurisdiction

24.5.1.12 If the two-way telephone system is intended to be used by fire wardens in addition to the fire service, the minimum requirement shall be a selective talk system, where phones are selected from the control location.

24.5.1.13 Telephone circuits shall be selectable from the control location either individually or, if approved by the authority having jurisdiction, by floor or stairwell.

24.5.1.14 If the control equipment provided does not indicate the location of the caller (common talk systems), each telephone station or telephone jack shall be clearly and permanently labeled to allow the caller to identify his or her location to the control center by voice.

24.5.1.15 If telephone jacks are provided, two or more portable handsets, as determined by the authority having jurisdiction, shall be stored at each control center for use by emergency responders.

24.5.1.16 Telephone appliances shall be in accordance with EIA Tr 41.3, *Telephones*.

24.5.1.17 Wall-mounted telephone appliances or related jacks shall be not less than 36 in. (910 mm) and not more than 66 in. (1.68 m) above floor level with clear access to the appliance that is at least 30 in. (760 mm) wide.

24.5.1.18 If accessible to the general public, one telephone appliance per location shall be not more than 48 in. (1.22 m) above floor level.

24.5.1.19* All circuits necessary for the operation of two-way telephone communications systems shall be installed in accordance with the pathway survivability requirements in 24.3.6.7.

24.5.2* Two-Way Radio Communications Enhancement Systems.

24.5.2.1 General.

24.5.2.1.1 Non-Interference. No amplification system capable of operating on frequencies or causing interference on frequencies assigned to the jurisdiction by the FCC shall be installed without prior coordination and approval of the authority having jurisdiction. The building manager/owner shall suspend and correct other equipment installations that degrade the performance of the public safety radio system or public safety radio enhancement system.

24.5.2.1.2 Approval and Permit. Plans shall be submitted for approval prior to installation. At the conclusion of successful acceptance testing, a renewable permit shall be issued for the public safety radio enhancement system where required by the authority having jurisdiction.

24.5.2.2 Radio Coverage. Radio coverage shall be provided throughout the building as a percentage of floor area as specified in 24.5.2.2.1 through 24.5.2.2.3.

24.5.2.2.1 Critical Areas. Critical areas, such as the fire command center(s), the fire pump room(s), exit stairs, exit passageways, elevator lobbies, standpipe cabinets, sprinkler sectional valve locations, and other areas deemed critical by the authority having jurisdiction, shall be provided with 99 percent floor area radio coverage.

24.5.2.2.2 General Building Areas. General building areas shall be provided with 90 percent floor area radio coverage.

24.5.2.2.3 Amplification Components. Buildings and structures that cannot support the required level of radio coverage shall be equipped with a radiating cable system or a distributed antenna system (DAS) with FCC-certified signal boosters, or both, or with a system that is otherwise approved, in order to achieve the required adequate radio coverage.

24.5.2.3 Signal Strength.

24.5.2.3.1 Inbound. A minimum inbound signal strength of −95 dBm, or other signal strength as required by the authority having jurisdiction, shall be provided throughout the coverage area.

24.5.2.3.2 Outbound. A minimum outbound signal strength of −95 dBm at the donor site, or other signal strength as required by the authority having jurisdiction, shall be provided from the coverage area.

24.5.2.3.3 Isolation. If a donor antenna exists, isolation shall be maintained between the donor antenna and all inside antennas and shall be a minimum of 15 dB above the signal booster gain under all operating conditions.

24.5.2.4* System Radio Frequencies. The public safety radio enhancement system shall be capable of transmitting all public safety radio frequencies assigned to the jurisdiction and be capable of using any modulation technology.

24.5.2.4.1 List of Assigned Frequencies. The authority having jurisdiction shall maintain a list of all inbound/outbound frequency pairs for distribution to system designers.

24.5.2.4.2* Frequency Changes. Systems shall be capable of upgrade, to allow for instances where the jurisdiction changes or adds system frequencies, in order to maintain radio system coverage as originally designed.

24.5.2.5 System Components.

24.5.2.5.1 Component Approval. Components utilized in the installation of the public safety radio enhancement system, such as repeaters, transmitters, receivers, signal boosters, cabling, and fiber-distributed antenna systems, shall be approved and shall be compatible with the public safety radio system.

24.5.2.5.2 Component Enclosures. All repeater, transmitter, receiver, signal booster components, and battery system components shall be contained in a NEMA 4- or 4X-type enclosure(s).

24.5.2.5.3 External Filters. Permanent external filters and attachments shall not be permitted.

24.5.2.5.4 Signal Booster Components. If used, signal boosters shall meet the following requirements, as well as any other requirements determined by the authority having jurisdiction:

(1)*Signal boosters shall have FCC certification prior to installation.
(2) All signal boosters shall be compatible with both analog and digital communications simultaneously at the time of installation. The authority having jurisdiction shall provide the maximum acceptable propagation delay standard.

24.5.2.5.5 Power Supplies. At least two independent and reliable power supplies shall be provided for all repeater, transmitter, receiver, and signal booster components, one primary and one secondary.

24.5.2.5.5.1 Primary Power Source. The primary power source shall be supplied from a dedicated branch circuit and comply with 10.6.5.1.

24.5.2.5.5.2* Secondary Power Source. The secondary power source shall consist of one of the following:

(1) A storage battery dedicated to the system with at least 12 hours of 100 percent system operation capacity and arranged in accordance with 10.6.10.
(2) An automatic-starting, engine-driven generator serving the dedicated branch circuit or the system with at least 12 hours of 100 percent system operation capacity and storage batteries dedicated to the system with at least 2 hours of 100 percent system operation capacity and arranged in accordance with 10.6.11.3.

24.5.2.5.5.3 Monitoring Integrity of Power Supplies. Monitoring the integrity of power supplies shall be in accordance with 10.6.9.

24.5.2.6 System Monitoring.

24.5.2.6.1 Fire Alarm System. The public safety radio communications enhancement system shall include automatic supervisory and trouble signals for malfunctions of the signal booster(s) and power supply(ies) that are annunciated by the fire alarm system and comply with the following:

(1) The integrity of the circuit monitoring signal booster(s) and power supply(ies) shall comply with 10.6.9 and Section 12.6.
(2) System and signal booster supervisory signals shall include the following:
 (a) Antenna malfunction
 (b) Signal booster failure
 (c) Low-battery capacity indication when 70 percent of the 12-hour operating capacity has been depleted.
(3) Power supply signals shall include the following for each signal booster:
 (a) Loss of normal ac power
 (b) Failure of battery charger

24.5.2.6.2* Dedicated Panel. A dedicated monitoring panel shall be provided within the fire command center to annunciate the status of all signal booster locations. The monitoring panel shall provide visual and labeled indication of the following for each signal booster:

(1) Normal ac power
(2) Signal booster trouble
(3) Loss of normal ac power
(4) Failure of battery charger
(5) Low-battery capacity

24.5.2.7 Technical Criteria. The authority having jurisdiction shall maintain a document of technical information specific to its requirements, which shall contain, as a minimum, the following:

(1) Frequencies required
(2) Location and effective radiated power (ERP) of radio sites used by the public safety radio enhancement system
(3) Maximum propagation delay (in microseconds)
(4) List of specifically approved system components
(5) Other supporting technical information necessary to direct system design

24.5.3* Area of Refuge (Area of Rescue Assistance) Emergency Communications Systems.

24.5.3.1* Where required by the building code in force, an area of rescue assistance two-way emergency communications system shall be installed in accordance with 24.5.3.

24.5.3.2 The area of refuge (rescue assistance) emergency communications system shall be comprised of remotely located area of refuge stations and a central control point.

24.5.3.3 The remote area of refuge stations and the central control point shall communicate with each other.

24.5.3.4* If the central control point is not constantly attended, it shall have a timed automatic communications capability to connect with a constantly attended monitoring location acceptable to the authority having jurisdiction where responsible personnel can initiate the appropriate response.

24.5.3.5 The physical location of the central control point shall be as designated by the building code in force or the authority having jurisdiction.

24.5.3.6 The area of refuge station shall provide for hands-free, two-way communication, provide an audible and visible signal to indicate communication has occurred and indicate to the receiver the location sending the signal.

24.5.3.7 Instructions for the use of the two-way communications system, instructions for summoning assistance via the two-way communications system, and written identification, included in braille, of the location shall be posted adjacent to the two-way communications system.

24.5.4 Elevator Emergency Communications Systems.

24.5.4.1 Elevator two-way emergency communications systems shall be installed in accordance with the requirements of ANSI/ASME A17.1/CSA B44, *Safety Code for Elevators and Escalators.*

24.5.4.2 Communication shall be provided for the lobbies where the elevators are used for occupant-controlled evacuation.

24.6* Information, Command, and Control. The requirements of Section 24.6 shall apply to the communications methods and equipment used to receive and transmit information between premises sources or premises systems and the emergency command center(s).

24.6.1* Emergency Command Center for Emergency Communications Systems.

24.6.1.1* The location and accessibility of the emergency command center shall be determined by the risk analysis and approved by the emergency management coordinator.

24.6.1.2 The emergency command center shall contain the following:

(1) The in-building fire emergency voice/alarm communications system equipment including:
   (a) Fire alarm system controls
   (b) Fire alarm system annunciator
   (c) In-building fire emergency voice/alarm communications system controls
(2) Area of refuge (area of rescue assistance) emergency communications systems equipment
(3) Elevator emergency communications systems equipment
(4) Distributed recipient MNS control stations where provided
(5) Tables and chairs to accommodate emergency management staff
(6) Other equipment/information deemed necessary by the facility emergency response plan such as:
   (a) Displays indicating the location of the elevators and whether they are operational
   (b) Status indicators and controls for air-handling systems
   (c) Fire fighter's control panel for smoke control systems
   (d) Fire department communications unit
   (e) Controls for unlocking stairway doors simultaneously
   (f) Security systems
   (g) Emergency and standby power status indicators
   (h) Telephone for emergency use with controlled access to the public telephone system
   (i) Schematic building plans indicating the typical floor plan and detailing the building core, means of egress, fire protection systems, security systems, fire-fighting equipment, and fire department access
   (j) Generator supervision devices, manual start, and transfer features
   (k) Other monitoring, control, information display, and management systems associated with operation of the ECC

24.6.1.3 The level of security at the emergency command center shall be defined in the emergency response plan.

24.6.1.4* Staffing.

24.6.1.4.1 Emergency command center personnel requirements shall be defined in the documentation in the emergency response plan.

24.6.1.4.2* Individuals expected to operate an emergency communications system shall be properly trained in the purpose, functions, procedures, and anticipated actions of such systems.

24.6.1.5 The emergency command center shall be capable of receiving voice messages by telephone or radio and transmitting via equipment at the emergency command center.

24.6.1.6 The emergency command center operator shall have the ability to monitor inputs/sensors and control output devices automatically, manually, or automatically with operator override.

24.6.2 Emergency Communications Control Unit (ECCU).

24.6.2.1 An emergency communications control unit (ECCU), where identified by the risk analysis, and defined in the emergency response plan, shall be provided at each emergency command center.

24.6.2.2 The system operator shall be able to send live voice signals or activate prerecorded voice messages, tones, and other signals.

24.6.2.3 The signals shall be selectable to individual buildings; zones of buildings; individual outdoor speaker arrays; zones of outdoor speaker arrays; or a building, multiple buildings, outside areas, or a combination of these, in accordance with the emergency response plan established for the premises.

24.6.2.4 The central control emergency communications control unit shall automatically or manually assign priorities to all transmitted signals.

24.6.2.5 Multiple Emergency Communications Control Units.

24.6.2.5.1 In wide-area mass notification systems, the emergency command center shall have a primary emergency communications control unit.

24.6.2.5.2 Multiple emergency communications control units shall be permitted.

24.6.3* Signals. Where identified by the risk analysis and defined in the emergency response plan, the emergency communications control unit shall be permitted to automatically or manually send different messages or signals to different locations.

24.6.4 Power Supply.

24.6.4.1 All control units shall meet the requirements of Section 10.6.

24.6.4.2 The power supply for the emergency command center shall include an uninterrupted power source with capacity sufficient to support the emergency response plan established for the specific premises.

24.6.5 Transmission. Signals shall be capable of being automatically or manually transmitted to a regional or national emergency response center or to other nearby facilities that have a need to be alerted of the emergency.

24.6.6* Other Systems. The emergency command center shall be capable of interfacing with and controlling other notification systems, such as telephone dialers, tone alert systems, computer network alerting systems, pagers, facsimile machines, textual devices, and other visual control signs, as determined by the emergency response plan.

24.6.7 Inspection, Testing, and Maintenance. Inspection, testing, and maintenance shall be performed on a periodic basis, as described in Chapter 14, to verify and ensure proper system operation and readiness.

24.7* Performance-Based Design of Mass Notification Systems. The requirements of Section 24.7 shall apply to mass notification systems designed to recognize performance-based practices.

24.7.1 Goals and Objectives. The performance-based design shall meet the following goals and objectives:

(1) The risk analysis, design criteria, design brief, system performance, and testing criteria are developed in accordance with this section.
(2) The system disseminates information to the target audience in an accurate and timely manner.

(3) The design and performance criteria are specific to the nature and anticipated risks of each location.

(4) The system is capable of withstanding various scenarios and survives even if some damage has already occurred.

(5) Message initiation can be effected by all responding entities responsible for the safety and security of occupants.

24.7.2* Qualifications. The performance-based design and risk analysis shall be prepared by a design professional certified or approved by the authority having jurisdiction.

24.7.3 Independent Review. The authority having jurisdiction shall be permitted to require an approved, independent third party to review the proposed design brief and provide an evaluation of the design to the authority having jurisdiction.

24.7.4 Final Determination. The authority having jurisdiction shall make the final determination as to whether the performance objectives have been met.

24.7.5 Maintenance of Design Features. The design features required for the system to continue to meet the performance goals and objectives of this Code shall be maintained for the life of the building.

24.7.6 Performance Criteria.

24.7.6.1 General. All designs shall meet the goals and objectives specified in 24.7.1 and shall be considered equivalent, provided that the performance criterion in 24.7.6.2 is met, the design team concurs with the design, and the risk analysis considers the following factors:

(1) Number of persons to be notified
(2) Occupancy characteristics
(3) Anticipated threat
(4) Staff capabilities
(5) Coordination with the emergency response plan

24.7.6.2 Performance Criterion. The performance criterion shall include timely and accurate notification of all persons within the boundaries of the mass notification system in a medium to which they can respond when given directions by responding entities.

24.7.6.3* Design Team. The design team shall be comprised of the design professional, the owner or owner's representative, representatives of the authority having jurisdiction, and representatives of the responding entities.

24.7.6.4 Risk Analysis. The design of the mass notification system shall be based upon a risk analysis prepared in accordance with 24.3.11 specific to the nature and anticipated risks of each facility for which it is designed.

24.7.6.5 Operational Status and System Effectiveness. The performance of the system shall reflect the documented performance and reliability of the components of those systems or features, unless design specifications are incorporated to modify the expected performance.

24.7.6.5.1 The inclusion of trained employees as part of the mass notification system shall be identified and documented.

24.7.6.5.2 Emergency Response Personnel. The design shall consider the characteristics or other conditions related to the availability, speed of response, effectiveness, roles, and other characteristics of emergency response personnel.

24.7.6.6* Design Brief. The design of the mass notification system shall include the preparation of a design brief that is prepared utilizing recognized performance-based design practices.

24.7.6.6.1 Design specifications and briefs used in the performance-based design shall be clearly stated and shown to be realistic and sustainable.

24.7.6.6.2 Specific testing requirements that are necessary to maintain reliable performance shall be stated in the design brief.

24.8 Documentation.

24.8.1 New Systems. Documentation requirements for new emergency communications systems shall comply with Sections 7.3 through 7.8 in addition to the minimum requirements of Section 7.2.

24.8.2* Existing Systems The documentation that shall be provided for all additions or alterations to existing emergency communications systems shall be at the direction of the authority having jurisdiction.

24.8.3 Owner's Manual. For new emergency communications systems, an owner's manual shall be provided and shall contain the following documentation:

(1) Detailed narrative description of the system inputs, evacuation signaling, ancillary functions, annunciation, intended sequence of operations, expansion capability, application considerations, and limitations

(2) Written sequence of operation for the system including an operational input/output matrix

(3) Operator instructions for basic system operations, including alarm acknowledgment, system reset, interpretation of system output (LEDs, CRT display, and printout), operation of manual evacuation signaling and ancillary function controls, and change of printer paper

(4) Detailed description of routine maintenance and testing as required and recommended and as would be provided under a maintenance contract, including testing and maintenance instructions for each type of device installed, which includes the following:

    (a) Listing of the individual system components that require periodic testing and maintenance

    (b) Step-by-step instructions detailing the requisite testing and maintenance procedures, and the intervals at which these procedures shall be performed, for each type of device installed

    (c) Schedule that correlates the testing and maintenance procedures that are required by this section

(5) Service directory, including a list of names and telephone numbers of those who provide service for the system

Chapter 25   Reserved

Chapter 26   Supervising Station Alarm Systems

26.1* Application. The performance, installation, and operation of alarm systems at a continuously attended supervising station and between the protected premises and the continuously attended supervising station shall comply with the requirements of this chapter.

26.1.1* Where any system regulated by this Code sends signals to a supervising station, the entire system shall become a supervising station alarm system.

26.1.2 The requirements of Chapters 7, 10, 12, 14, and 23 shall also apply unless they are in conflict with this chapter.

26.1.3 The requirements of this chapter shall not apply to Chapter 29 unless otherwise noted.

26.2 General.

26.2.1* Alarm Signal Disposition. Except as permitted by 26.2.2 and 29.7.9.2, all fire alarm signals received by a supervising station shall be immediately retransmitted to the communications center.

26.2.2 Alarm Signal Preverification.

26.2.2.1 Where alarm signal verification is required by the responsible fire department, the supervising station shall immediately notify the communications center that a fire alarm signal has been received and verification is in process.

26.2.2.2 Verification shall meet the requirements of 26.2.3.

26.2.3 Alarm Signal Verification.

26.2.3.1 For applications other than those addressed under the scope of 29.7.9.2, supervising station personnel shall attempt to verify alarm signals prior to reporting them to the communication center where all the following conditions exist:

(1)*Alarm signal verification is required by the responsible fire department for a specific protected premises.
(2) Documentation of the requirement for alarm signal verification is provided by the responsible fire department to the supervising station and the protected premises.
(3) If the requirement for verification changes, the responsible fire department shall notify the supervising station and the protected premises.
(4)*The verification process does not take longer than 90 seconds from the time the alarm signal is received at the supervising station until the time that retransmission of the verified alarm signal is initiated.
(5) Verification of the alarm signal is received only from authorized personnel within the protected premises.
(6)*Verified alarm signals are immediately retransmitted to the communications center and include information that the signal was verified at the protected premises to be an emergency.
(7)*Alarm signals where verification is not conclusive are immediately retransmitted to the communications center.
(8) Alarm signals that are verified as nuisance alarms are not dispatched and are handled in accordance with 26.2.3.2.

26.2.3.2* Alarm signals not reported to the communications center shall be reported to the responsible fire department in a manner and at a frequency specified by the responsible fire department.

26.2.4 Alarm Signal Content. Where required by the enforcing authority, governing laws, codes, or standards, alarm signals transmitted to a supervising station shall be by addressable device or zone identification.

26.2.5 Restoral Signals.

26.2.5.1 All supervising station fire alarm systems shall be programmed to report restoral signals to the supervising station of all alarm, supervisory, and trouble signals upon restoration of the activation.

26.2.5.2* Effective January 1, 2014, any signal received by the supervising station that has not restored to normal condition within 24 hours of initial receipt shall be redisplayed to an operator as a nonrestored signal and shall be reported to the subscriber.

Exception: This provision shall not apply to scheduled impairments.

26.2.6 Multiple Buildings. For multiple building premises, the requirements of 10.18.5.3 shall apply to the alarm, supervisory, and trouble signals transmitted to the supervising station.

26.2.7* Change of Service.

26.2.7.1 Supervising station customers or clients and the authority having jurisdiction shall be notified in writing within 30 days of any scheduled change in service that results in signals from the client's property being handled by a different supervising station.

26.2.7.2 Where the supervising station provides the required testing and where service changes covered by 26.2.7.1 occur, the supervising station shall test all zones, points, and signals from each affected property in accordance with the requirements of Chapter 14.

26.2.7.3 Where the supervising station does not provide the required testing and where service changes covered by 26.2.7.1 occur, the supervising station shall notify the prime contractor of the need to test all zones, points, and signals from each affected property in accordance with the requirements of Chapter 14.

26.2.7.4 The supervising station shall notify the authority having jurisdiction prior to terminating service.

26.2.8 Supervising Station Signal Processing Equipment. Signal processing equipment located at the supervising station listed to ANSI/UL 60950, *Information Technology Equipment — Part 1: General Requirements*, and used for computer-aided alarm and supervisory signal processing shall not be required to comply with 10.3.5 provided it is installed and operated conforming to ANSI/UL 1981, *Central Station Automation Systems*, within an environment that is maintained at a level within the temperature, humidity, and voltage rating range of the equipment, and the equipment manufacturer's published instructions are available for examination.

26.2.9 Qualification of Supervising Station Operators. Supervising station operators shall be qualified in accordance with the requirements of 10.5.4.

26.3 Central Station Service Alarm Systems. Alarm systems used to provide central station service shall comply with the general requirements and the use requirements of Section 26.3.

26.3.1 System Scope. Alarm systems for central station service shall include the central station physical plant, exterior communications channels, subsidiary stations, and alarm and signaling equipment located at the protected premises.

26.3.2* Service Scope. Section 26.3 shall apply to central station service, which consists of the following elements:

(1) Installation of alarm transmitters
(2) Alarm, guard, supervisory, and trouble signal monitoring
(3) Retransmission
(4) Associated record keeping and reporting
(5) Testing and maintenance
(6) Runner service

26.3.3 Contract Requirements. The central station service elements shall be provided under contract to a subscriber by one of the following:

(1) A listed central station that provides all of the elements of central station service with its own facilities and personnel.

(2) A listed central station that provides, as a minimum, the signal monitoring, retransmission, and associated record keeping and reporting with its own facilities and personnel and shall be permitted to subcontract all or any part of the installation, testing, and maintenance and runner service.

(3) A listed alarm service–local company that provides the installation, testing, and maintenance with its own facilities and personnel and that subcontracts the monitoring, retransmission, and associated record keeping and reporting to a listed central station with the required runner service provided by the listed alarm service–local company with its own personnel or the listed central station with its own personnel.

(4) A listed central station that provides the installation, testing, and maintenance with its own facilities and personnel and that subcontracts the monitoring, retransmission, and associated record keeping and reporting to another listed central station with the required runner service provided by either central station.

26.3.4* Indication of Central Station Service. The prime contractor shall conspicuously indicate that the alarm system providing service at a protected premises complies with all the requirements of this Code through the use of a systematic follow-up program under the control of the organization that has listed the prime contractor.

26.3.4.1 Documentation indicating Code compliance of the alarm system shall be issued by the organization that has listed the prime contractor.

26.3.4.2 The documentation shall include, at a minimum, the following information:

(1) Name of the prime contractor involved with the ongoing Code compliance of the central station service
(2)*Full description of the alarm system as installed
(3) Issue and expiration dates of the documentation
(4) Name, address, and contact information of the organization issuing the document
(5) Identification of the authority(ies) having jurisdiction for the central station service installation

26.3.4.3 The documentation shall be physically posted within 3 ft (1 m) of the control unit, and copies of the documentation shall be made available to the authority(ies) having jurisdiction upon request.

26.3.4.4 A central repository of issued documentation, accessible to the authority having jurisdiction, shall be maintained by the organization that has listed the prime contractor.

26.3.4.5* Alarm system service that does not comply with all the requirements of Section 26.3 shall not be designated as central station service.

26.3.4.6* For the purpose of Section 26.3, the subscriber shall notify the prime contractor, in writing, of the identity of the authority(ies) having jurisdiction.

26.3.4.7 The authority(ies) having jurisdiction identified in 26.3.4.2(5) shall be notified of expiration or cancellation by the organization that has listed the prime contractor.

26.3.4.8 The subscriber shall surrender expired or canceled documentation to the prime contractor within 30 days of the termination date.

26.3.5 Facilities.

26.3.5.1 The central station building or that portion of a building occupied by a central station shall conform to the construction, fire protection, restricted access, emergency lighting, and power facilities requirements of the latest edition of ANSI/UL 827, *Standard for Central-Station Alarm Services.*

26.3.5.2 Subsidiary station buildings or those portions of buildings occupied by subsidiary stations shall conform to the construction, fire protection, restricted access, emergency lighting, and power facilities requirements of the latest edition of ANSI/UL 827, *Standard for Central-Station Alarm Services.*

26.3.5.2.1 All intrusion, fire, power, and environmental control systems for subsidiary station buildings shall be monitored by the central station in accordance with 26.3.5.

26.3.5.2.2 The subsidiary facility shall be inspected at least monthly by central station personnel for the purpose of verifying the operation of all supervised equipment, all telephones, all battery conditions, and all fluid levels of batteries and generators.

26.3.5.2.3 In the event of the failure of equipment at the subsidiary station or the communications channel to the central station, a backup shall be operational within 90 seconds.

26.3.5.2.4 With respect to 26.3.5.2.3, restoration of a failed unit shall be accomplished within 5 days.

26.3.5.2.5 Each communications channel shall be continuously supervised between the subsidiary station and the central station.

26.3.5.2.6 When the communications channel between the subsidiary station and the supervising station fails, the communications shall be switched to an alternate path. Public switched telephone network facilities shall be used only as an alternate path.

26.3.5.2.7 In the subsidiary station, there shall be a communications path, such as a cellular telephone, that is independent of the telephone cable between the subsidiary station and the serving wire center.

26.3.5.2.8 A plan of action to provide for restoration of services specified by this Code shall exist for each subsidiary station.

(A) This plan shall provide for restoration of services within 4 hours of any impairment that causes loss of signals from the subsidiary station to the central station.

(B) An exercise to demonstrate the adequacy of the plan shall be conducted at least annually.

26.3.6 Equipment.

26.3.6.1 The central station and all subsidiary stations shall be equipped so as to receive and record all signals in accordance with 26.6.4.

26.3.6.2 Circuit-adjusting means for emergency operation shall be permitted to be automatic or to be provided through manual operation upon receipt of a trouble signal.

26.3.6.3 Computer-aided alarm and supervisory signal–processing hardware and software shall be listed for the purpose.

26.3.6.4 Power supplies shall comply with the requirements of Chapter 10.

26.3.6.5 Transmission means shall comply with the requirements of Section 26.6.

26.3.6.6* Two independent means shall be provided to retransmit an alarm signal to the designated communications center.

26.3.6.6.1 The use of a universal emergency number, such as the 911 public safety answering point, shall not meet the intent of this Code for the principal means of retransmission.

26.3.6.6.2 If the principal means of retransmission is not equipped to allow the communications center to acknowledge receipt of each alarm report, both means shall be used to retransmit.

26.3.6.6.3 The retransmission means shall be tested in accordance with Chapter 14.

26.3.6.6.4 The retransmission signal and the time and date of retransmission shall be recorded at the central station.

26.3.7 Personnel.

26.3.7.1 The central station shall have not less than two qualified operators on duty at the central station at all times to ensure disposition of signals in accordance with the requirements of 26.3.8.

26.3.7.2 Operation and supervision shall be the primary functions of the operators, and no other interest or activity shall take precedence over the protective service.

26.3.8 Disposition of Signals.

26.3.8.1 Alarm Signals.

26.3.8.1.1 Alarm signals initiated by manual fire alarm boxes, automatic fire detectors, waterflow from the automatic sprinkler system, or actuation of other fire suppression system(s) or equipment shall be treated as fire alarms.

26.3.8.1.2 The central station shall perform the following actions:

(1)*Retransmit the alarm to the communications center in accordance with 26.2.1.
(2) Dispatch a runner or technician to the protected premises to arrive within 2 hours after receipt of a signal if equipment needs to be manually reset by the prime contractor. Except where prohibited by the authority having jurisdiction, the runner or technician shall be permitted to be recalled prior to arrival at the premises if a qualified representative of the subscriber at the premises can provide the necessary resetting of the equipment and is able to place the system back in operating condition.
(3) Immediately notify the subscriber.
(4) Provide notice to the subscriber or authority having jurisdiction, or both, if required.

Exception: If the alarm signal results from a prearranged test, the actions specified by 26.3.8.1.2(1) and (3) shall not be required.

26.3.8.2 Guard's Tour Supervisory Signal.

26.3.8.2.1 Upon failure to receive a guard's tour supervisory signal within a 15-minute maximum grace period, the central station shall perform the following actions:

(1) Communicate without unreasonable delay with personnel at the protected premises
(2) Dispatch a runner to the protected premises to arrive within 30 minutes of the delinquency if communications cannot be established

(3) Report all delinquencies to the subscriber or authority having jurisdiction, or both, if required

26.3.8.2.2 Failure of the guard to follow a prescribed route in transmitting signals shall be handled as a delinquency.

26.3.8.3* Supervisory Signals. Upon receipt of a supervisory signal from a sprinkler system, other fire suppression system(s), or other equipment, the central station shall perform the following actions:

(1)*Communicate immediately with the persons designated by the subscriber and notify the fire department or law enforcement agency, or both, when required by the authority having jurisdiction
(2) Dispatch a runner or maintenance person to arrive within 2 hours to investigate unless the supervisory signal is cleared in accordance with a scheduled procedure determined by 26.3.8.3(1)
(3) Notify the authority having jurisdiction when sprinkler systems or other fire suppression systems or equipment have been wholly or partially out of service for 8 hours
(4) When service has been restored, provide notice, if required, to the subscriber or the authority having jurisdiction, or both, as to the nature of the signal, the time of occurrence, and the restoration of service when equipment has been out of service for 8 hours or more

Exception: If the supervisory signal results from a prearranged test, the actions specified by 26.3.8.3(1), (3), and (4) shall not be required.

26.3.8.4 Trouble Signals. Upon receipt of trouble signals or other signals pertaining solely to matters of equipment maintenance of the alarm systems, the central station shall perform the following actions:

(1)*Communicate immediately with persons designated by the subscriber
(2) Dispatch personnel to arrive within 4 hours to initiate maintenance, if necessary
(3) When the interruption is more than 8 hours, provide notice to the subscriber and the fire department if so required by the authority having jurisdiction as to the nature of the interruption, the time of occurrence, and the restoration of service

26.3.8.5 Test Signals.

26.3.8.5.1 All test signals received shall be recorded to indicate date, time, and type.

26.3.8.5.2 Test signals initiated by the subscriber, including those for the benefit of an authority having jurisdiction, shall be acknowledged by central station personnel whenever the subscriber or authority inquires.

26.3.8.5.3* Any test signal not received by the central station shall be investigated immediately, and action shall be taken to reestablish system integrity.

26.3.8.5.4 The central station shall dispatch personnel to arrive within 2 hours if protected premises equipment needs to be manually reset after testing.

26.3.8.5.5 The prime contractor shall provide each of its representatives and each alarm system user with a unique personal identification code.

26.3.8.5.6 In order to authorize the placing of an alarm system into test status, a representative of the prime contractor or an alarm system user shall first provide the central station with his or her personal identification code.

26.3.9 Record Keeping and Reporting.

26.3.9.1 Complete records of all signals received shall be retained for at least 1 year.

26.3.9.2 Testing and maintenance records shall be retained as required by 14.6.3.

26.3.9.3 The central station shall make arrangements to furnish reports of signals received to the authority having jurisdiction in a manner approved by the authority having jurisdiction.

26.3.10 Testing and Maintenance. Testing and maintenance for central station service shall be performed in accordance with Chapter 14.

26.4 Proprietary Supervising Station Alarm Systems.

26.4.1 Application. Supervising facilities of proprietary alarm systems shall comply with the operating procedures of Section 26.4. The facilities, equipment, personnel, operation, testing, and maintenance of the proprietary supervising station shall also comply with Section 26.4.

26.4.2 General.

26.4.2.1 Proprietary supervising stations shall be operated by trained, competent personnel in constant attendance who are responsible to the owner of the protected property.

26.4.2.2 The protected property shall be either a contiguous property or noncontiguous properties under one ownership.

26.4.2.3 If a protected premises control unit is integral to or colocated with the supervising station equipment, the requirements of Section 26.6 shall not apply.

26.4.3 Facilities.

26.4.3.1* The proprietary supervising station shall be located in either of the following:

(1) Fire-resistive, detached building
(2) A fire-resistive room protected from the hazardous parts of the building

26.4.3.2 Access to the proprietary supervising station shall be restricted to those persons directly concerned with the implementation and direction of emergency action and procedure.

26.4.3.3 The proprietary supervising station, as well as remotely located power rooms for batteries or engine-driven generators, shall be provided with portable fire extinguishers that comply with the requirements of NFPA 10, *Standard for Portable Fire Extinguishers.*

26.4.3.4 The emergency lighting system shall comply with the requirements of 26.4.3.4.1 through 26.4.3.4.3.

26.4.3.4.1 The proprietary supervising station shall be provided with an automatic emergency lighting system.

26.4.3.4.2 The emergency source shall be independent of the primary lighting source.

26.4.3.4.3 In the event of a loss of the primary lighting for the supervising station, the emergency lighting system shall provide illumination for a period of not less than 26 hours to permit the operators to carry on operations and shall be tested in accordance with the requirements of Chapter 14.

26.4.3.5 If 25 or more protected buildings or premises are connected to a subsidiary station, both of the following shall be provided at the subsidiary station:

(1) Automatic means for receiving and recording signals under emergency staffing conditions
(2) A telephone

26.4.4 Equipment.

26.4.4.1 Signal-Receiving Equipment.

26.4.4.1.1 Signal-receiving equipment in a proprietary supervising station shall comply with 26.4.4.

26.4.4.1.2 Provision shall be made to designate the building in which a signal originates.

26.4.4.1.3 The floor, section, or other subdivision of the building in which a signal originates shall be designated at the proprietary supervising station or at the building that is protected.

Exception: Where the area, height, or special conditions of occupancy make detailed designation unessential as approved by the authority having jurisdiction.

26.4.4.1.4 Designation, as required by 26.4.4.1.2 and 26.4.4.1.3, shall use private-mode notification appliances approved by the authority having jurisdiction.

26.4.4.2 Signal-Alerting Equipment.

26.4.4.2.1 The proprietary supervising station shall have, in addition to a recording device, two different means for alerting the operator when each signal is received that indicates a change of state of any connected initiating device circuit.

26.4.4.2.1.1 One of these means shall be an audible signal, which shall persist until manually acknowledged.

26.4.4.2.1.2 Means shall include the receipt of alarm, supervisory, and trouble signals, including signals indicating restoration.

26.4.4.2.1.3 If means is provided in the proprietary supervising station to identify the type of signal received, a common audible indicating appliance shall be permitted to be used for alarm, supervisory, and trouble indication.

26.4.4.2.1.4 At a proprietary supervising station, an audible trouble signal shall be permitted to be silenced, provided that the act of silencing does not prevent the signal from operating immediately upon receipt of a subsequent trouble signal.

26.4.4.2.2 All signals required to be received by the proprietary supervising station that show a change in status shall be automatically and permanently recorded, including time and date of occurrence, in a form that expedites operator interpretation in accordance with any one of the means detailed in 26.4.4.2.2.1 through 26.4.4.2.2.4.

26.4.4.2.2.1 If a visual display is used that automatically provides change of status information for each required signal, including type and location of occurrence, any form of automatic permanent visual record shall be permitted.

(A) The recorded information shall include the content described in 26.4.4.2.2.

(B) The visual display shall show status information content at all times and be distinctly different after the operator has manually acknowledged each signal.

(C) Acknowledgment shall produce recorded information indicating the time and date of acknowledgment.

26.4.4.2.2.2 If a visual display is not provided, required signal content information shall be automatically recorded on duplicate, permanent visual recording instruments.

26.4.4.2.2.3 One recording instrument shall be used for recording all incoming signals, while the other shall be used for required alarm, supervisory, and trouble signals only.

(A) Failure to acknowledge a signal shall not prevent subsequent signals from recording.

(B) Restoration of the signal to its prior condition shall be recorded.

26.4.4.2.2.4 In the event that a system combines the use of a sequential visual display and recorded permanent visual presentation, the required signal content information shall be displayed and recorded.

(A) The visual information component shall be retained either on the display until manually acknowledged or repeated at intervals not greater than 5 seconds, for durations of 2 seconds each, until manually acknowledged.

(B) Each new displayed status change shall be accompanied by an audible indication that persists until manual acknowledgment of the signal is performed.

26.4.4.3* Redisplay of Status. A means shall be provided for the operator to redisplay the status of required signal-initiating inputs that have been acknowledged but not yet restored.

26.4.4.3.1 If the system retains the signal on the visual display until manually acknowledged, subsequent recorded presentations shall not be inhibited upon failure to acknowledge.

26.4.4.3.2 Alarm signals shall be segregated on a separate visual display in this configuration.

Exception: Alarm signals shall not be required to be segregated on a separate display if given priority status on the common visual display.

26.4.4.4 Display Rate. To facilitate the prompt receipt of alarm signals from systems handling other types of signals that are able to produce multiple simultaneous status changes, the requirements of either of the following shall be met:

(1) Record simultaneous status changes at a rate not slower than either a quantity of 50 or 10 percent of the total number of initiating device circuits connected, within 90 seconds, whichever number is smaller, without loss of any signal

(2) Display or record alarm signals at a rate not slower than one every 10 seconds, regardless of the rate or number of status changes occurring, without loss of any signals

26.4.4.5 Trouble Signals. Trouble signals and their restoration shall be automatically indicated and recorded at the proprietary supervising station.

26.4.4.5.1 The recorded information for the occurrence of any trouble condition of signaling line circuit, leg facility, or trunk facility that prevents receipt of alarm signals at the proprietary supervising station shall be such that the operator is able to determine the presence of the trouble condition.

26.4.4.5.2 Trouble conditions in a leg facility shall not affect or delay receipt of signals at the proprietary supervising station from other leg facilities on the same trunk facility.

26.4.5 Personnel.

26.4.5.1 The proprietary supervising station shall have at least two qualified operators on duty at all times. One of the two operators shall be permitted to be a runner.

Exception: If the means for transmitting alarms to the fire department is automatic, at least one operator shall be on duty at all times.

26.4.5.2 When the runner is not in attendance at the proprietary supervising station, the runner shall establish two-way communications with the station at intervals not exceeding 15 minutes, unless otherwise permitted by 26.4.5.3.

26.4.5.3 Where two or more operators are on duty in the supervising station, a runner physically in attendance at a noncontiguous protected premises and immediately available via telephone or other approved means of communication shall not be required to maintain two-way communications at 15-minute intervals if that runner is not responsible for another protected premises.

26.4.5.4 The primary duties of the operator(s) shall be to monitor signals, operate the system, and take such action as shall be required by the authority having jurisdiction.

26.4.5.5 The operator(s) shall not be assigned any additional duties that would take precedence over the primary duties.

26.4.6 Operations.

26.4.6.1 Communications and Transmission Channels.

26.4.6.1.1 All communications and transmission channels between the proprietary supervising station and the protected premises control unit shall be operated manually or automatically once every 24 hours to verify operation.

26.4.6.1.2 If a communications or transmission channel fails to operate, the operator shall immediately notify the person(s) identified by the owner or authority having jurisdiction.

26.4.6.2 Operator Controls.

26.4.6.2.1 All operator controls at the proprietary supervising station(s) designated by the authority having jurisdiction shall be operated at each change of shift.

26.4.6.2.2 If operator controls fail, the operator shall immediately notify the person(s) identified by the owner or authority having jurisdiction.

26.4.6.3 Retransmission. Indication of a fire shall be promptly retransmitted to the communications center or other locations accepted by the authority having jurisdiction, indicating the building or group of buildings from which the alarm has been received.

26.4.6.4* Retransmission Means. The means of retransmission shall be accepted by the authority having jurisdiction and shall be in accordance with 26.3.6.6, 26.5.4.4, or Chapter 27.

Exception: Secondary power supply capacity shall be as required in Chapter 10.

26.4.6.5* Coded Retransmission. Retransmission by coded signals shall be confirmed by two-way voice communications indicating the nature of the alarm.

26.4.6.6 Dispositions of Signals.

26.4.6.6.1 Alarms. Upon receipt of an alarm signal, the proprietary supervising station operator shall initiate action to perform the following:

(1) Notify the fire department, the emergency response team, and such other parties as the authority having jurisdiction requires in accordance with 26.2.1

(2) Dispatch a runner or technician to the alarm location to arrive within 2 hours after receipt of a signal

(3) Restore the system as soon as possible after disposition of the cause of the alarm signal

26.4.6.6.2 Guard's Tour Supervisory Signal. If a guard's tour supervisory signal is not received from a guard within a 15-minute maximum grace period, or if a guard fails to follow a prescribed route in transmitting the signals (where a prescribed route has been established), the proprietary supervising station operator shall initiate action to perform the following:

(1) Communicate at once with the protected areas or premises by telephone, radio, calling back over the system circuit, or other means accepted by the authority having jurisdiction

(2) Dispatch a runner to arrive within 30 minutes to investigate the delinquency if communications with the guard cannot be promptly established

26.4.6.6.3 Supervisory Signals. Upon receipt of sprinkler system and other supervisory signals, the proprietary supervising station operator shall initiate action to perform the following, if required:

(1) Communicate immediately with the designated person(s) to ascertain the reason for the signal

(2) Dispatch personnel to arrive within 2 hours to investigate, unless supervisory conditions are promptly restored

(3) Notify the fire department if required by the authority having jurisidiction

(4) Notify the authority having jurisdiction when sprinkler systems are wholly or partially out of service for 8 hours or more

(5) Provide written notice to the authority having jurisdiction as to the nature of the signal, time of occurrence, and restoration of service when equipment has been out of service for 8 hours or more

26.4.6.6.4 Trouble Signals. Upon receipt of trouble signals or other signals pertaining solely to matters of equipment maintenance of the alarm system, the proprietary supervising station operator shall initiate action to perform the following, if required:

(1) Communicate immediately with the designated person(s) to ascertain reason for the signal

(2) Dispatch personnel to arrive within 4 hours to initiate maintenance, if necessary

(3) Notify the fire department if required by the authority having jurisdiction

(4) Notify the authority having jurisdiction when interruption of service exists for 4 hours or more

(5) When equipment has been out of service for 8 hours or more, provide written notice to the authority having jurisdiction as to the nature of the signal, time of occurrence, and restoration of service

26.4.7 Record Keeping and Reporting.

26.4.7.1 Complete records of all signals received shall be retained for at least 1 year.

26.4.7.2 Testing and maintenance records shall be retained as required by 14.6.3.

26.4.7.3 The proprietary supervising station shall make arrangements to furnish reports of signals received to the authority having jurisdiction in a form the authority will accept.

26.4.8 Testing and Maintenance. Testing and maintenance of proprietary alarm systems shall be performed in accordance with Chapter 14.

26.5 Remote Supervising Station Alarm Systems.

26.5.1 Application and General.

26.5.1.1 Section 26.5 shall apply where central station service is neither required nor elected.

26.5.1.2 The installation, maintenance, testing, and use of a remote supervising station alarm system that serves properties under various ownership from a remote supervising station shall comply with the requirements of Section 26.5.

26.5.1.3 Remote supervising station physical facilities, equipment, operating personnel, response, retransmission, signals, reports, and testing shall comply with the minimum requirements of Section 26.5.

26.5.1.4 Remote supervising station alarm systems shall provide an automatic audible and visible indication of alarm, supervisory, and trouble conditions at a location remote from the protected premises.

26.5.1.5 Section 26.5 shall not require the use of audible or visible notification appliances other than those required at the remote supervising station. If it is desired to provide alarm evacuation signals in the protected premises, the alarm signals, circuits, and controls shall comply with the provisions of Chapters 18 and 23 in addition to the provisions of Section 26.5.

26.5.1.6 The loading capacities of the remote supervising station equipment for any approved method of transmission shall be as designated in Section 26.6.

26.5.2 Indication of Remote Station Service. Owners utilizing remote station alarm systems shall provide annual documentation to the authority having jurisdiction identifying the party responsible for the inspection, testing, and maintenance requirements of Chapter 14. This documentation shall take one of the following forms:

(1)*Affidavit attesting to the responsibilities and qualifications of the parties performing the inspection, testing, and maintenance and accepting responsibility of compliance with Chapter 14 and signed by a representative of the service provider

(2) Documentation indicating code compliance of the remote station alarm system issued by the organization that listed the service provider

(3) Other documentation acceptable to the authority having jurisdiction

26.5.3* Facilities.

26.5.3.1 Alarm systems utilizing remote supervising station connections shall transmit alarm and supervisory signals to a facility meeting the requirements of either 26.5.3.1.1, 26.5.3.1.2, or 26.5.3.1.3.

26.5.3.1.1 Alarm, supervisory, and trouble signals shall be permitted to be received at a communications center that complies with the requirements of NFPA 1221, *Standard for the Installation, Maintenance, and Use of Emergency Services Communications Systems.*

26.5.3.1.2 Alarm, supervisory, and trouble signals shall be permitted to be received at the fire station or at the governmental agency that has public responsibility for taking prescribed action to ensure response upon receipt of a alarm signal.

26.5.3.1.3* Where permitted by the authority having jurisdiction, alarm, supervisory, and trouble signals shall be permitted to be received at an alternate location approved by the authority having jurisdiction.

26.5.3.2* Trouble signals shall be permitted to be received at an approved location that has personnel on duty who are trained to recognize the type of signal received and to take prescribed action. The location shall be permitted to be other than that at which alarm and supervisory signals are received.

26.5.3.3 If locations other than the communications center are used for the receipt of signals, access to receiving equipment shall be restricted in accordance with the requirements of the authority having jurisdiction.

26.5.4 Equipment.

26.5.4.1 Signal-receiving equipment shall indicate receipt of each signal both audibly and visibly.

26.5.4.1.1 Audible signals shall meet the requirements of Chapter 18 for the private operating mode.

26.5.4.1.2 Means for silencing alarm, supervisory, and trouble signals shall be provided and shall be arranged so that subsequent signals shall re-sound.

26.5.4.1.3 A trouble signal shall be received when the system or any portion of the system at the protected premises is placed in a bypass or test mode.

26.5.4.1.4 An audible and visible indication shall be provided upon restoration of the system after receipt of any signal.

26.5.4.1.5 If visible means are provided in the remote supervising station to identify the type of signal received, a common audible notification appliance shall be permitted to be used.

26.5.4.2 Power supplies shall comply with the requirements of Chapter 10.

26.5.4.3 Transmission means shall comply with the requirements of Section 26.6.

26.5.4.4 Retransmission of an alarm signal, if required, shall be by one of the following methods, which appear in descending order of preference as follows:

(1) A dedicated circuit that is independent of any switched telephone network. This circuit shall be permitted to be used for voice or data communications.
(2) A one-way (outgoing only) telephone at the remote supervising station that utilizes the public-switched telephone network. This telephone shall be used primarily for voice transmission of alarms to a telephone at the communications center that cannot be used for outgoing calls.
(3) A private radio system using the fire department frequency, where permitted by the fire department.
(4) Other methods accepted by the authority having jurisdiction.

26.5.5 Personnel.

26.5.5.1 The remote supervising station shall have not less than two qualified operators on duty at the remote supervising station at all times to ensure disposition of signals in accordance with the requirements of 26.5.6.

26.5.5.2 Duties pertaining to other than operation of the remote supervising station receiving and transmitting equipment shall be permitted, subject to the approval of the authority having jurisdiction.

26.5.6 Operations.

26.5.6.1 If the remote supervising station is at a location other than the communications center, alarm signals shall be retransmitted to the communications center in accordance with 26.2.1.

26.5.6.2 Upon receipt of an alarm, supervisory, or trouble signal by the remote supervising station, the operator on duty shall be responsible for immediately notifying the owner or the owner's designated representative, and where required, the authority having jurisdiction.

26.5.6.3 All operator controls at the remote supervising station shall be operated at the beginning of each shift or change in personnel, and the status of all alarm, supervisory, and trouble signals shall be noted and recorded.

26.5.7 Record Keeping and Reporting.

26.5.7.1 A permanent record of the time, date, and location of all signals and restorations received and the action taken shall be maintained for at least 1 year and shall be able to be provided to the authority having jurisdiction.

26.5.7.2 Testing and maintenance records shall be retained as required in 14.6.3.

26.5.7.3 Records shall be permitted to be created by manual means.

26.5.8 Inspection, Testing, and Maintenance.

26.5.8.1 Inspection, testing, and maintenance for remote supervising stations shall be performed in accordance with Chapter 14.

26.5.8.2 Where required, inspection, testing, and maintenance reports shall be submitted to the authority having jurisdiction in a form acceptable to the authority having jurisdiction.

26.6 Communications Methods for Supervising Station Alarm Systems.

26.6.1* Application.

26.6.1.1 The methods of communications between the protected premises and the supervising station shall comply with the requirements in Section 26.6. These requirements shall include the following:

(1) Transmitter located at the protected premises
(2) Transmission channel between the protected premises and the supervising station or subsidiary station
(3) If used, any subsidiary station and its communications channel
(4) Signal receiving, processing, display, and recording equipment at the supervising station

Exception: Transmission channels owned by, and under the control of, the protected premises owner that are not facilities leased from a supplier of communications service capabilities, such as video cable, telephone, or other communications services that are also offered to other customers.

26.6.1.2 The minimum signaling requirement shall be an alarm signal, trouble signal, and supervisory signal, where used.

26.6.2 General.

26.6.2.1 Master Control Unit. If the protected premises master control unit is neither integral to nor colocated with the supervising station, the communications methods of Section 26.6 shall be used to connect the protected premises to either a subsidiary station, if used, or a supervising station for central station service in accordance with Section 26.3, proprietary station in accordance with Section 26.4, or remote station in accordance with Section 26.5.

26.6.2.2* Alternate Methods. Nothing in Chapter 26 shall be interpreted as prohibiting the use of listed equipment using alternate communications methods that provide a level of reliability and supervision consistent with the requirements of Chapter 10 and the intended level of protection.

26.6.2.3* Equipment.

26.6.2.3.1 Alarm system equipment and installations shall comply with Federal Communications Commission (FCC) rules and regulations, as applicable, concerning the following:

(1) Electromagnetic radiation
(2) Use of radio frequencies
(3) Connection to the public switched telephone network of telephone equipment, systems, and protection apparatus

26.6.2.3.2 Radio receiving equipment shall be installed in compliance with *NFPA 70, National Electrical Code*, Article 810.

26.6.2.3.3 The external antennas of all radio transmitting and receiving equipment shall be protected in order to minimize the possibility of damage by static discharge or lightning.

26.6.2.4 Dual Control.

26.6.2.4.1 Dual control, if required, shall provide for redundancy in the form of a standby circuit or other alternate means of transmitting signals over the primary trunk portion of a transmission channel.

26.6.2.4.2 The same method of signal transmission shall be permitted to be used over separate routes, or alternate methods of signal transmission shall be permitted to be used.

26.6.2.4.3 Public switched telephone network facilities shall be used only as an alternate method of transmitting signals.

26.6.2.4.4 If using facilities leased from a telephone company, that portion of the primary trunk facility between the supervising station and its serving wire center shall not be required to comply with the separate routing requirement of the primary trunk facility. Dual control, if used, shall require supervision as follows:

(1) Dedicated facilities that are able to be used on a full-time basis, and whose use is limited to signaling purposes as defined in this Code, shall be exercised at least once every hour.

> Paragraphs 26.6.2.4.4(2) and 26.6.3.2.2.2(F) were revised by a tentative interim amendment (TIA). See page 1.

(2) Public switched telephone network facilities shall be exercised at least once every 6 hours.

26.6.3 Communications Methods. The communications methods used to transmit signals to supervising stations shall meet the requirements of 26.6.3.1 for performance-based technologies, or 26.6.3.2 or 26.6.3.3 for prescriptive-based technologies.

26.6.3.1* Performance-Based Technologies.

26.6.3.1.1 Conformance. Communications methods operating on principles different from specific methods covered by this chapter shall be permitted to be installed if they conform to the performance requirements of this section and to all other applicable requirements of this Code.

26.6.3.1.2 Federal Communications Commission. Alarm system equipment and installations shall comply with the Federal Communications Commission (FCC) rules and regulations, as applicable, concerning electromagnetic radiation, use of radio frequencies, and connections to the public switched telephone network of telephone equipment, systems, and protection apparatus.

26.6.3.1.3 *NFPA 70, National Electrical Code.* Equipment shall be installed in compliance with *NFPA 70, National Electrical Code.*

26.6.3.1.4 Communications Integrity. Provision shall be made to monitor the integrity of the transmission technology and its communications path.

26.6.3.1.5 Single Communications Path. Unless prohibited by the enforcing authority, governing laws, codes, or standards, a single transmission path shall be permitted, and the path shall be supervised at an interval of not more than 60 minutes. A failure of the path shall be annunciated at the supervising station within not more than 60 minutes. The failure to complete a signal transmission shall be annunciated at the protected premises in accordance with Section 10.15.

26.6.3.1.6 Multiple Communications Paths. If multiple transmission paths are used, the following requirements shall be met:

(1) Each path shall be supervised within not more than 6 hours.
(2) The failure of any path of a multipath system shall be annunciated at the supervising station within not more than 6 hours.
(3) The failure to complete a signal transmission shall be annunciated at the protected premises in accordance with Section 10.15.

26.6.3.1.7* Single Technology. A single technology shall be permitted to be used to create the multiple paths provided the requirements of 26.6.3.1.6(1) through 26.6.3.1.6(3) are met.

26.6.3.1.8 Spare System Unit Equipment. An inventory of spare equipment shall be maintained at the supervising station such that any failed piece of equipment can be replaced and the systems unit restored to full operation within 30 minutes of failure.

26.6.3.1.9 Loading Capacity of System Unit.

26.6.3.1.9.1 The maximum number of independent fire alarm systems connected to a single system unit shall be limited to 512.

26.6.3.1.9.2 If duplicate spare system units are maintained at the supervising station and switchover can be achieved in 30 seconds, then the system capacity shall be permitted to be unlimited.

26.6.3.1.10 End-to-End Communication Time for Alarm. The maximum duration between the initiation of an alarm signal at the protected premises, transmission of the signal, and subsequent display and recording of the alarm signal at the supervising station shall not exceed 90 seconds.

26.6.3.1.11 Unique Identifier. If a transmitter shares a transmission or communications channel with other transmitters, it shall have a unique transmitter identifier.

26.6.3.1.12 Recording and Display Rate of Subsequent Alarms. Recording and display of alarms at the supervising station shall be at a rate no slower than one complete signal every 10 seconds.

26.6.3.1.13 Signal Error Detection and Correction.

26.6.3.1.13.1 Communication of alarm, supervisory, and trouble signals shall be in accordance with this section to prevent degradation of the signal in transit, which in turn would result in either of the following:

(1) Failure of the signal to be displayed and recorded at the supervising station
(2) Incorrect corrupted signal displayed and recorded at the supervising station

26.6.3.1.13.2 Reliability of the signal shall be achieved by any of the following:

(1) Signal repetition — multiple transmissions repeating the same signal
(2) Parity check — a mathematically check sum algorithm of a digital message that verifies correlation between transmitted and received message
(3) An equivalent means to 26.6.3.1.13.2(1) or 26.6.3.1.13.2(2) that provides a certainty of 99.99 percent that the received message is identical to the transmitted message

26.6.3.1.14* Sharing Communications Equipment On-Premises. If the fire alarm transmitter is sharing on-premises communications equipment, the shared equipment shall be listed as communications or information technology equipment.

26.6.3.1.15* Secondary Power.

26.6.3.1.15.1 Premises Equipment. Secondary power capacity for all equipment necessary for the transmission of alarm, supervisory, trouble, and other signals located at the protected premises shall be as follows:

(1) Fire alarm transmitters not requiring shared on-premises communications equipment shall comply with 10.6.7.
(2) If the fire alarm transmitter is sharing on-premises communications equipment, the shared equipment shall have a secondary power capacity of 24 hours.

Exception: Secondary power capacity for shared equipment shall be permitted to have a capacity of 8 hours where acceptable to the authority having jurisdiction and where a risk analysis is performed to ensure acceptable availability is provided.

26.6.3.1.15.2 Supervising Station. Secondary power capacity for all equipment necessary for reception of alarm, supervisory, trouble, and other signals located at the supervising station shall comply with 10.6.7.

26.6.3.1.16 Unique Flaws Not Covered by This Code. If a communications technology has a unique flaw that could result in the failure to communicate a signal, the implementation of that technology for alarm signaling shall compensate for that flaw so as to eliminate the risk of missing an alarm signal.

26.6.3.2 Digital Alarm Communicator Systems.

26.6.3.2.1 Digital Alarm Communicator Transmitter (DACT).

26.6.3.2.1.1* Public Switched Network. A DACT shall be connected to the public switched telephone network upstream of any private telephone system at the protected premises.

(A) The connections to the public switched telephone network shall be under the control of the subscriber for whom service is being provided by the supervising station alarm system.

(B) Special attention shall be required to ensure that this connection is made only to a loop start telephone circuit and not to a ground start telephone circuit.

26.6.3.2.1.2 Signal Verification. All information exchanged between the DACT at the protected premises and the digital alarm communicator receiver (DACR) at the supervising or subsidiary station shall be by digital code or some other approved means. Signal repetition, digital parity check, or some other approved means of signal verification shall be used.

26.6.3.2.1.3* Requirements for DACTs.

(A) A DACT shall be configured so that, when it is required to transmit a signal to the supervising station, it shall seize the telephone line (going off-hook) at the protected premises and disconnect an outgoing or incoming telephone call and prevent use of the telephone line for outgoing telephone calls until signal transmission has been completed. A DACT shall not be connected to a party line telephone facility.

(B) A DACT shall have the means to satisfactorily obtain a dial tone, dial the number(s) of the DACR, obtain verification that the DACR is able to receive signals, transmit the signal, and receive acknowledgment that the DACR has accepted that signal. In no event shall the time from going off-hook to on-hook exceed 90 seconds per attempt.

(C)* A DACT shall have means to reset and retry if the first attempt to complete a signal transmission sequence is unsuccessful. A failure to complete connection shall not prevent subsequent attempts to transmit an alarm where such alarm is generated from any other initiating device circuit or signaling line circuit, or both. Additional attempts shall be made until the signal transmission sequence has been completed, up to a minimum of 5 and a maximum of 10 attempts.

(D) If the maximum number of attempts to complete the sequence is reached, an indication of the failure shall be made at the premises.

26.6.3.2.1.4 Transmission Channels.

(A) A system employing a DACT shall employ one telephone line (number). In addition, one of the following transmission means shall be employed:

(1) One-way private radio alarm system
(2) Two-way RF multiplex system
(3) Transmission means complying with 26.6.3.1

Exception: Where access to two technologies in the preceding list is not available at the protected premises, with the approval of the authority having jurisdiction, a telephone line (number) shall be permitted to be used as the second transmission means. Each DACT shall be programmed to call a second DACR line (number) when the signal transmission sequence to the first called line (number) is unsuccessful. The DACT shall be capable of selecting the operable means of transmission in the event of failure of the other means. Where two telephone lines (numbers) are used, it shall be permitted to test each telephone line (number) at alternating 6-hour intervals.

(B) The following requirements shall apply to all combinations listed in 26.6.3.2.1.4(A):

(1) The means for supervising each channel shall be in a manner approved for the method means of transmission employed.
(2) The interval for testing each channel shall not exceed 6 hours.

(3) The failure of either channel shall send a trouble signal on the other channel within 4 minutes.

(4) When one transmission channel has failed, all status change signals shall be sent over the other channel.

(5) The primary channel shall be capable of delivering an indication to the DACT that the message has been received by the supervising station.

(6)*The first attempt to send a status change signal shall use the primary channel.

Exception: Where the primary channel is known to have failed.

(7) Simultaneous transmission over both channels shall be permitted.

(8) Failure of telephone lines (numbers) shall be annunciated locally.

26.6.3.2.1.5 DACT Transmission Means. The following requirements shall apply to all digital alarm communications transmitters:

(1) A DACT shall be connected to two separate means of transmission at the protected premises.

(2) The DACT shall be capable of selecting the operable means of transmission in the event of failure of the other means.

(3) The primary means of transmission shall be a telephone line (number) connected to the public switched network.

(4)*The first transmission attempt shall utilize the primary means of transmission.

(5) Each DACT shall be programmed to call a second receiver when the signal transmission sequence to the first called line (number) is unsuccessful.

(6) Each transmission means shall automatically initiate and complete a test signal transmission sequence to its associated receiver at least once every 6 hours. A successful signal transmission sequence of any other type, within the same 6-hour period, shall fulfill the requirement to verify the integrity of the reporting system, provided that signal processing is automated so that 6-hour delinquencies are individually acknowledged by supervising station personnel.

(7)*If a DACT is programmed to call a telephone line (number) that is call forwarded to the line (number) of the DACR, a means shall be implemented to verify the integrity of the call forwarding feature every 4 hours.

26.6.3.2.2 Digital Alarm Communicator Receiver (DACR).

26.6.3.2.2.1 Equipment.

(A) Spare DACRs shall be provided in the supervising or subsidiary station. The spare DACRs shall be on line or able to be switched into the place of a failed unit within 30 seconds after detection of failure.

(B) One spare DACR shall be permitted to serve as a backup for up to five DACRs in use.

(C) The number of incoming telephone lines to a DACR shall be limited to eight lines, unless the signal-receiving, processing, display, and recording equipment at the supervising or subsidiary station is duplicated and a switchover is able to be accomplished in less than 30 seconds with no loss of signal during this period, in which case the number of incoming lines to the unit shall be permitted to be unlimited.

26.6.3.2.2.2 Transmission Channels.

(A)* The DACR equipment at the supervising or subsidiary station shall be connected to a minimum of two separate incoming telephone lines (numbers). The lines (numbers) shall have the following characteristics:

(1) If the lines (numbers) are in a single hunt group, they shall be individually accessible; otherwise, separate hunt groups shall be required.

(2) The lines (numbers) shall be used for no other purpose than receiving signals from a DACT.

(3) The lines (numbers) shall be unlisted.

(B) The failure of any telephone line (number) connected to a DACR due to loss of line voltage shall be annunciated visually and audibly in the supervising station.

(C)* The loading capacity for a hunt group shall be in accordance with Table 26.6.3.2.2.2(C) or be capable of demonstrating a 90 percent probability of immediately answering an incoming call.

(1) Table 26.6.3.2.2.2(C) shall be based on an average distribution of calls and an average connected time of 30 seconds for a message.

(2) The loading figures in Table 26.6.3.2.2.2(C) shall presume that the lines are in a hunt group (i.e., DACT is able to access any line not in use).

(3) A single-line DACR shall not be allowed for any of the configurations shown in Table 26.6.3.2.2.2(C).

Table 26.6.3.2.2.2(C) Loading Capacities for Hunt Groups

System Loading at the Supervising Station	Number of Lines in Hunt Group				
	1	2	3	4	5–8
With DACR lines processed in parallel					
Number of initiating circuits	NA	5,000	10,000	20,000	20,000
Number of DACTs	NA	500	1,500	3,000	3,000
With DACR lines processed serially (put on hold, then answered one at a time)					
Number of initiating circuits	NA	3,000	5,000	6,000	6,000
Number of DACTs	NA	300	800	1,000	1,000

NA: Not allowed.

(D) Each supervised burglar alarm (open/close) or each suppressed guard's tour transmitter shall reduce the allowable DACTs as follows:

(1) Up to a four-line hunt group, by 10
(2) Up to a five-line hunt group, by 7
(3) Up to a six-line hunt group, by 6
(4) Up to a seven-line hunt group, by 5
(5) Up to an eight-line hunt group, by 4

(E) Each guard's tour transmitter shall reduce the allowable DACTs as follows:

(1) Up to a four-line hunt group, by 30
(2) Up to a five-line hunt group, by 21

(3) Up to a six-line hunt group, by 18

(4) Up to a seven-line hunt group, by 15

(5) Up to an eight-line hunt group, by 12

(F) A signal shall be received on each individual incoming DACR line at least once every 6 hours.

(G) The failure to receive a test signal from the protected premises shall be treated as a trouble signal.

26.6.3.3 Radio Systems.

26.6.3.3.1 Two-Way Radio Frequency (RF) Multiplex Systems.

26.6.3.3.1.1 Maximum Operating Time. The maximum end-to-end operating time parameters allowed for a two-way RF multiplex system shall be as follows:

(1) The maximum allowable time lapse from the initiation of a single alarm signal until it is recorded at the supervising station shall not exceed 90 seconds. When any number of subsequent alarm signals occur at any rate, they shall be recorded at a rate no slower than one every additional 10 seconds.

(2) The maximum allowable time lapse from the occurrence of an adverse condition in any transmission channel until recording of the adverse condition is started shall not exceed 200 seconds for Type 4 and Type 5 systems. The requirements of 26.6.3.3.1.4 shall apply.

(3) In addition to the maximum operating time allowed for alarm signals, the requirements of one of the following shall be met:

    (a) A system unit that has more than 500 initiating device circuits shall be able to record not less than 50 simultaneous status changes within 90 seconds.

    (b) A system unit that has fewer than 500 initiating device circuits shall be able to record not less than 10 percent of the total number of simultaneous status changes within 90 seconds.

26.6.3.3.1.2 Supervisory and Control Functions. Facilities shall be provided at the supervising station for the following supervisory and control functions of the supervising or subsidiary station and the repeater station radio transmitting and receiving equipment, which shall be accomplished via a supervised circuit where the radio equipment is remotely located from the system unit:

(1) RF transmitter in use (radiating)

(2) Failure of ac power supplying the radio equipment

(3) RF receiver malfunction

(4) Indication of automatic switchover

(5) Independent deactivation of either RF transmitter controlled from the supervising station

26.6.3.3.1.3 Transmission Channel.

(A) The RF multiplex transmission channel shall terminate in an RF transmitter/receiver at the protected premises and in a system unit at the supervising or subsidiary station.

(B) Operation of the transmission channel shall conform to the requirements of this Code whether channels are private facilities, such as microwave, or leased facilities furnished by a communications utility company. If private signal transmission facilities are used, the equipment necessary to transmit signals shall also comply with requirements for duplicate equipment or replacement of critical components, as described in 26.6.4.2.

26.6.3.3.1.4* Categories. Two-way RF multiplex systems shall be divided into Type 4 or Type 5 classifications based on their ability to perform under adverse conditions.

(A) A Type 4 system shall have two or more control sites configured as follows:

(1) Each site shall have an RF receiver interconnected to the supervising or subsidiary station by a separate channel.

(2) The RF transmitter/receiver located at the protected premises shall be within transmission range of at least two RF receiving sites.

(3) The system shall contain two RF transmitters that are one of the following:

    (a) Located at one site with the capability of interrogating all of the RF transmitters/receivers on the premises

    (b) Dispersed with all of the RF transmitters/receivers on the premises having the capability to be interrogated by two different RF transmitters

(4) Each RF transmitter shall maintain a status that allows immediate use at all times. Facilities shall be provided in the supervising or subsidiary station to operate any off-line RF transmitter at least once every 8 hours.

(5) Any failure of one of the RF receivers shall in no way interfere with the operation of the system from the other RF receiver. Failure of any receiver shall be annunciated at the supervising station.

(6) A physically separate channel shall be required between each RF transmitter or RF receiver site, or both, and the system unit.

(B) A Type 5 system shall have a single control site configured as follows:

(1) A minimum of one RF receiving site

(2) A minimum of one RF transmitting site

26.6.3.3.1.5 Loading Capacities.

(A) The loading capacities of two-way RF multiplex systems shall be based on the overall reliability of the signal receiving, processing, display, and recording equipment at the supervising or subsidiary station and the capability to transmit signals during adverse conditions of the transmission channels.

(B) Allowable loading capacities shall comply with Table 26.6.3.3.1.5(B).

(C) The capacity of a system unit shall be permitted to be unlimited if the signal-receiving, processing, display, and recording equipment are duplicated at the supervising station and a switchover is able to be accomplished in not more than 30 seconds, with no loss of signals during this period.

26.6.3.3.1.6 Adverse Conditions.

(A) The occurrence of an adverse condition on the transmission channel between a protected premises and the supervising station that prevents the transmission of any status change signal shall be automatically indicated and recorded at the supervising station. This indication and record shall identify the affected portions of the system so that the supervising station operator will be able to determine the location of the adverse condition by trunk or leg facility, or both.

(B) For two-way RF multiplex systems that are part of a central station alarm system, restoration of service to the affected portions of the system shall be automatically recorded. When service is restored, the first status change of any initiating device circuit, any initiating device directly connected to a signal-

Table 26.6.3.3.1.5(B) Loading Capacities for Two-Way RF Multiplex Systems

Trunks	System Type	
	Type 4	Type 5
Maximum number of alarm service initiating device circuits per primary trunk facility	5,120	1,280
Maximum number of leg facilities for alarm service per primary trunk facility	512	128
Maximum number of leg facilities for all types of alarm service per secondary trunk facility*	128	128
Maximum number of all types of initiating device circuits per primary trunk facility in any combination	10,240	2,560
Maximum number of leg facilities for types of alarm service per primary trunk facility in any combination*	1,024	256
System Units at the Supervising Station		
Maximum number of all types of initiating device circuits per system unit*	10,240	10,240
Maximum number of protected buildings and premises per system unit	512	512
Maximum number of alarm service initiating device circuits per system	5,120	5,120
Systems Emitting from Subsidiary Station†	—	—

*Includes every initiating device circuit (e.g., waterflow, alarm, supervisory, guard, burglary, hold-up).
†Same as system units at the supervising station.

ing line circuit, or any combination thereof that occurred at any of the affected premises during the service interruption also shall be recorded.

26.6.3.3.2* One-Way Private Radio Alarm Systems.

26.6.3.3.2.1 Independent Receivers.

(A) The requirements of 26.6.3.3.2 for a radio alarm repeater station receiver (RARSR) shall be satisfied if the signals from each radio alarm transmitter (RAT) are received and supervised, in accordance with Chapter 26, by at least two independently powered, independently operating, and separately located RARSRs or radio alarm supervising station receivers (RASSRs), or by one of each.

(B) At least two separate paths shall be provided from a RAT to the ultimate RASSR.

(C) Only one path to the RASSR shall be required to be utilized in the event alarms can be transmitted from a RAT to the RASSR and the RAT has the ability to receive a positive acknowledgment that the RASSR has received the signal.

26.6.3.3.2.2* Maximum Operating Time. The end-to-end operating time parameters allowed for a one-way radio alarm system shall be as follows:

(1) There shall be a 90 percent probability that the time between the initiation of a single alarm signal until it is recorded at the supervising station will not exceed 90 seconds.
(2) There shall be a 99 percent probability that the time between the initiation of a single alarm signal until it is recorded at the supervising station will not exceed 180 seconds.
(3) There shall be a 99.999 percent probability that the time between the initiation of a single alarm signal until it is recorded at the supervising station will not exceed 7.5 minutes (450 seconds), at which time the RAT shall cease transmitting. When any number of subsequent alarm signals occurs at any rate, they shall be recorded at an average rate no slower than one every additional 10 seconds.
(4) In addition to the maximum operating time allowed for alarm signals, the system shall be able to record not less than 12 simultaneous status changes within 90 seconds at the supervising station.
(5) The system shall be supervised to ensure that at least two independent RARSRs or one RARSR and one independent RASSR are receiving signals for each RAT during each 24-hour period.

26.6.3.3.2.3 Supervision. Equipment shall be provided at the supervising station for the supervisory and control functions of the supervising or subsidiary station and for the repeater station radio transmitting and receiving equipment. This shall be accomplished via a supervised circuit where the radio equipment is remotely located from the system unit and the conditions of 26.6.3.3.2.3(A) through 26.6.3.3.2.3(D) are met.

(A) The following conditions shall be supervised at the supervising station:

(1) Failure of ac power supplying the radio equipment
(2) Malfunction of RF receiver
(3) Indication of automatic switchover, if applicable

(B) Interconnections between elements of transmitting equipment, including any antennas, shall be supervised either to cause an indication of failure at the protected premises or to transmit a trouble signal to the supervising station.

(C) If elements of transmitting equipment are physically separated, the wiring or cabling between them shall be protected by conduit.

(D) Personnel shall be dispatched to arrive within 12 hours to initiate maintenance after detection of primary power failure.

26.6.3.3.2.4 Transmission Channels. Transmission channels shall comply with 26.6.3.3.2.4(A) through 26.6.3.3.2.4(F).

(A) The one-way RF transmission channel shall originate with a RAT at the protected premises and shall terminate at the RF receiving system of an RARSR or RASSR capable of receiving transmissions from such transmitting devices.

(B) A receiving network transmission channel shall terminate at an RARSR at one end and with either another RARSR or an RASSR at the other end.

(C) Operation of receiving network transmission channels shall conform to the requirements of this Code whether channels are private facilities, such as microwave, or leased facilities furnished by a communications utility company.

(D) If private signal transmission facilities are used, the equipment necessary to transmit signals shall also comply with requirements for duplicate equipment or replacement of critical components as described in 26.6.4.2.

(E) The system shall provide information that indicates the quality of the received signal for each RARSR supervising each RAT in accordance with 26.6.3.3.2 and shall provide information at the supervising station when such signal quality falls below the minimum signal quality levels set forth in 26.6.3.3.2.

(F) Each RAT shall be installed in such a manner so as to provide a signal quality over at least two independent one-way RF transmission channels, of the minimum quality level specified, that satisfies the performance requirements in 26.6.2.3 and 26.6.4.

26.6.3.3.2.5 System Categories. One-way radio alarm systems shall be divided into two categories on the basis of the following number of RASSRs present in the system:

(1) A Type 6 system shall have one RASSR and at least two RARSRs.
(2) A Type 7 system shall have more than one RASSR and at least two RARSRs.
(3) In a Type 7 system, when more than one RARSR is out of service and, as a result, any RATs are no longer being supervised, the affected supervising station shall be notified.
(4) In a Type 6 system, when any RARSR is out of service, a trouble signal shall be annunciated at the supervising station.

26.6.3.3.2.6 Loading Capacities. The loading capacities of one-way radio alarm systems shall be based on the overall reliability of the signal-receiving, processing, display, and recording equipment at the supervising or subsidiary station and the capability to transmit signals during adverse conditions of the transmission channels. Loading capacities shall comply with 26.6.3.3.2.6(A) and 26.6.3.3.2.6(B).

(A) Allowable loading capacities shall be in accordance with Table 26.6.3.3.2.6(A), except as modified by the following:

(1) Each guard's tour transmitter shall reduce the allowable RATs by 15.
(2) Each two-way protected premises radio transmitter shall reduce the allowable RATs by two.
(3) Each supervised burglar alarm (open/close) or each suppressed guard's tour transmitter shall reduce the allowable RATs by five.

(B) If the signal-receiving, processing, display, and recording equipment is duplicated at the supervising station and a switchover is able to be accomplished in not more than 30 seconds, with no loss of signals during this period, the capacity of a system unit shall be permitted to be unlimited.

26.6.3.3.2.7 Adverse Conditions. The system shall be supervised to ensure that at least two independent radio alarm repeater station receivers (RARSRs) are receiving signals for each radio alarm transmitter (RAT) during each 24-hour period.

(A) The occurrence of a failure to receive a signal by either RARSR shall be automatically indicated and recorded at the supervising station.

(B) The indication shall identify which RARSR failed to receive such supervisory signals.

Table 26.6.3.3.2.6(A) Loading Capacities of One-Way Radio Alarm Systems

Radio Alarm Repeater Station Receiver (RARSR)	System Type	
	Type 6	Type 7
Maximum number of fire alarm service initiating device circuits per RARSR	5,120	5,120
Maximum number of RATs for fire	512	512
Maximum number of all types of initiating device circuits per RARSR in any combination*	10,240	10,240
Maximum number of RATs for all types of fire alarm service per RARSR in any combination*	1,024	1,024
System Units at the Supervising Station		
Maximum number of all types of initiating device circuits per system unit*	10,240	10,240
Maximum number of fire-protected buildings and premises per system unit	512	512
Maximum number of fire alarm service initiating device circuits per system unit	5,120	5,120

*Includes every initiating device circuit (e.g., waterflow, fire alarm, supervisory, guard, burglary, hold-up).

(C) Received test signals shall not be required to be indicated at the supervising station.

26.6.4 Display and Recording Requirements for All Transmission Technologies.

26.6.4.1* Any status changes, including the initiation or restoration to normal of a trouble condition, that occur in an initiating device or in any interconnecting circuits or equipment, including the local protected premises controls from the location of the initiating device(s) to the supervising station, shall be presented in a form to expedite prompt operator interpretation. Status change signals shall provide the following information:

(1) Identification of the type of signal to show whether it is an alarm, supervisory, delinquency, or trouble signal
(2) Identification of the signal to differentiate between an initiation of an alarm, a supervisory, a delinquency, or a trouble signal and a clearing from one or more of these conditions
(3) Identification of the site of origin of each status change signal
(4)*Identification of specific types of signals that dictate a different response

26.6.4.2* If duplicate equipment for signal receiving, processing, display, and recording is not provided, the installed equipment shall be designed so that any critical assembly is able to be replaced from on-premises spares and the system is able to be restored to service within 30 minutes. A critical assembly shall be an assembly in which a malfunction prevents the receipt and interpretation of signals by the supervising station operator.

Exception: Proprietary station systems.

26.6.4.3* Any method of recording and display or indication of change of status signals shall be permitted, provided that all of the following conditions are met:

(1) Each change of status signal requiring action to be taken by the operator shall result in an audible signal and not less than two independent methods of identifying the type, condition, and location of the status change.
(2) Each change of status signal shall be automatically recorded. The record shall provide the type of signal, condition, and location, as required by 26.6.4.1, in addition to the time and date the signal was received.
(3) Failure of an operator to acknowledge or act upon a change of status signal shall not prevent subsequent alarm signals from being received, indicated or displayed, and recorded.
(4) Change of status signals requiring action to be taken by the operator shall be displayed or indicated in a manner that clearly differentiates them from those that have been acted upon and acknowledged.
(5) Each incoming signal to a DACR shall cause an audible signal that persists until manually acknowledged.

Exception: Test signals required by 26.6.3.2.1.5(6) received at a DACR.

26.6.5 Testing and Maintenance Requirements for All Transmission Technologies. Testing and maintenance of communications methods shall be in accordance with the requirements of Chapter 14.

Chapter 27   Public Emergency Alarm Reporting Systems

27.1 Application.

27.1.1 The provisions of this chapter apply to the proper configuration, performance, installation, and operation of public emergency alarm reporting systems and auxiliary alarm systems. Public emergency alarm reporting systems shall consist of alarm boxes and alarm processing equipment that communicate on a wired or wireless network(s), one-way or two-way, meeting the requirements of this chapter. This shall include systems that use a communications infrastructure that is publicly owned, operated, and controlled or where public emergency alarm reporting systems and equipment are used in other applications.

27.1.2 The installation and use of public emergency alarm reporting systems and auxiliary alarm systems shall comply with the requirements of this chapter.

27.1.3 The requirements of this chapter shall apply to systems and equipment for the transmission and reception of alarm and other emergency signals, including those from auxiliary alarm systems, connected to the public emergency alarm reporting system.

27.1.4 The requirements of Chapters 10 and 14 shall also apply unless they are in conflict with this chapter.

27.1.5 Only those requirements from Chapter 7 that are required by Chapter 14 shall apply.

27.1.6 The requirements of this chapter shall not apply to Chapter 29 unless otherwise noted.

27.1.7 The application of public emergency alarm reporting systems and auxiliary alarm systems to provide defined reporting functions from or within private premises shall be permitted where approved by the authority having jurisdiction.

27.1.8* Where a protected premises fire alarm system or other emergency system at the protected premises has its signals sent to a communications center via public emergency alarm reporting system, the protected premises system shall become an auxiliary alarm system.

27.2 General Fundamentals.

27.2.1* Public emergency alarm reporting systems shall be designed, installed, operated, and maintained in accordance with this chapter to provide reliable transmission and receipt of alarms in a manner acceptable to the authority having jurisdiction.

27.2.2 A public emergency alarm reporting system, as described herein, shall be permitted to be used for the transmission of other signals or calls of a public emergency nature, provided that such transmission does not interfere with the transmission and receipt of fire alarms.

27.2.3* All devices shall be designed to function satisfactorily under the climatic and environmental conditions to which they could be exposed.

27.2.3.1 All devices shall be identified as suitable for the location and conditions for which they are installed.

27.2.4 All circuits, paths, and equipment necessary for the receipt of signals from a protected premises shall be monitored for integrity.

27.3 Management and Maintenance.

27.3.1 All systems shall be under the control of a designated jurisdictional employee.

27.3.2 Maintenance by an organization or person other than from the jurisdiction or an employee of the jurisdiction shall be by written contract, guaranteeing performance acceptable to the authority having jurisdiction.

27.3.3 Where maintenance is provided by an organization or person(s) other than the jurisdiction or its employees, complete written records of the installation, maintenance, test, and extension of the system shall be forwarded to the designated employee in a time period and manner approved by the authority having jurisdiction.

27.3.4 All equipment shall be installed in locations accessible to the authority having jurisdiction for the purpose of maintenance and inspection.

27.3.5 Records of wired public emergency alarm reporting system circuits shall include all of the following:

(1) Outline plans showing terminals and box sequence
(2) Diagrams of applicable office wiring
(3) List of materials used, including trade name, manufacturer, and year of purchase or installation

27.3.6 Public emergency alarm reporting systems as defined in this chapter shall, in their entirety, be subject to a complete operational acceptance test upon completion of system installation.

27.3.6.1 The test(s) required by 27.3.6 shall be made in accordance with the requirements of the authority having jurisdiction; however, in no case shall the operational functions tested be less than those stipulated in Chapter 14.

27.3.6.2 Operational acceptance tests shall be performed on any alarm-reporting devices, as covered in this chapter, that are installed or modified subsequent to the test required by 27.3.6.

27.3.7 Personnel Qualification.

27.3.7.1 System Designer.

27.3.7.1.1 Public emergency alarm reporting system plans and specifications shall be developed in accordance with this Code by persons who are qualified in the proper design, application, installation, and testing of public emergency alarm reporting systems.

27.3.7.1.2 The system design documents shall include the name and contact information of the system designer.

27.3.7.2 System Installer. Installation personnel shall be qualified in the installation, inspection, and testing of public emergency alarm reporting systems.

27.3.7.3 Service Personnel. Service personnel shall be qualified in the service, inspection, maintenance, and testing of public emergency alarm reporting systems.

27.3.7.4 Qualification.

27.3.7.4.1 Personnel shall demonstrate qualification by being trained and certified in public emergency alarm reporting system design, installation, or service (as appropriate) by one or more of the following:

(1) Certified by the manufacturer of the system or equipment
(2)*Certified by an organization acceptable to the authority having jurisdiction
(3) Licensed or certified by a state or local authority

27.3.7.4.2 Evidence of qualifications and/or certification shall be provided when requested by the authority having jurisdiction. A license or qualification listing shall be current in accordance with the requirements of the issuing authority or organization.

27.4 Communications Methods.

27.4.1 Application.

27.4.1.1 A public emergency alarm reporting system shall include wired or wireless network(s), for one-way signaling or two-way command and control communications between alarm boxes, alarm processing equipment, and the communications center.

27.4.1.2 A public emergency alarm reporting system shall be permitted to be used with emergency communications systems covered under Chapter 24.

27.4.2 Wired Network(s). The terms *wired network* and *public cable plant* shall be considered the same and interchangeable throughout this chapter.

27.4.2.1 All wired networks or public cable plants shall meet the requirements of Section 27.7.

27.4.2.1.1 Fiber-optic cabling shall be considered an acceptable transmission medium, provided that the cabling and installation comply with the requirements of Section 27.7 and the conversion equipment used to interface to the fiber-optic signal complies with all applicable requirements of Chapter 27.

27.4.2.2 Alarm processing equipment at the communications center shall meet the requirements of 27.5.2 and 27.5.4.

27.4.2.3 Alarm processing equipment at a remote communications center shall meet the requirements of 27.4.2.2 and 27.5.3.

27.4.2.4 Alarm boxes shall meet one of the following requirements:

(1) Publicly accessible boxes shall meet the requirements of 27.6.1 through 27.6.2 and 27.6.5.
(2) Auxiliary boxes shall meet the requirements of 27.6.1, 27.6.3, and 27.6.5.
(3) Master boxes shall meet the requirements of 27.6.1 through 27.6.3 and 27.6.5.

27.4.3 Wireless Network(s). The terms *wireless network* and *radio system* shall be considered the same and interchangeable throughout this chapter.

27.4.3.1 All wireless networks shall meet the requirements of 27.4.3.2 through 27.4.3.5.

27.4.3.2 In addition to the requirements of this Code, all wireless equipment shall be designed and operated in compliance with all applicable rules and regulations of the Federal Communications Commission (FCC) or, where required, the National Telecommunications and Information Administration (NTIA).

27.4.3.3* Unlicensed radio frequencies shall not be permitted.

27.4.3.4 Fire alarm signals, other emergency alarm signals, and monitoring for integrity signals shall be permitted on the same radio frequency, dedicated for that purpose.

27.4.3.5 The wireless network capacity for the number of alarm boxes permitted on a single radio frequency shall comply with one of the following:

(1) For networks that use one-way transmission in which the individual alarm box automatically initiates the required message *(see 27.5.5.3.3)* using circuitry integral to the alarm box, not more than 500 alarm boxes are permitted on a single radio frequency.
(2) For networks that use a two-way concept in which interrogation signals *(see 27.5.5.3.3)* are transmitted to the individual alarm boxes from the communications center on the same radio frequency used for receipt of alarms, not more than 250 alarm boxes are permitted on a single radio frequency.
(3) For networks that use a two-way concept where interrogation signals are transmitted on a radio frequency that differs from that used for receipt of alarms, not more than 500 alarm boxes are permitted on a single radio frequency.

27.4.3.6 Alarm processing equipment at the communications center shall meet the requirements of 27.5.2 and 27.5.5.

27.4.3.7 Alarm processing equipment at a remote communications center shall meet the requirements of 27.4.3.6 and 27.5.3.

27.4.3.8 Alarm boxes shall meet one of the following requirements:

(1) Publicly accessible boxes shall meet the requirements of 27.6.1 through 27.6.2 and 27.6.6.

(2) Auxiliary boxes shall meet the requirements of 27.6.1, 27.6.3, and 27.6.6.

(3) Master boxes shall meet the requirements of 27.6.1 through 27.6.3 and 27.6.6.

27.5 Alarm Processing Equipment. The alarm processing equipment required to receive and control the public emergency alarm reporting system shall be installed in the communications center or remote communications center used by emergency response agencies as defined in NFPA 1221, *Standard for the Installation, Maintenance, and Use of Emergency Services Communications Systems.*

27.5.1 General. The requirements of 27.5.2 shall apply to all processing equipment, wired or wireless, for a public emergency alarm reporting network.

27.5.2 Alarm Processing Equipment at Communications Center.

27.5.2.1 Type A and Type B Systems.

27.5.2.1.1 Alarm systems shall be Type A or Type B.

27.5.2.1.2 A Type A system shall be provided where the number of all alarms required to be retransmitted exceeds 2500 per year.

27.5.2.1.3 Where a Type A system is required, the automatic electronic retransmission of incoming alarms shall be permitted, provided that both of the following conditions are met:

(1) Approved facilities are provided for the automatic receipt, storage, retrieval, and retransmission of alarms in the order received.

(2) The operator(s) of the dispatch facility has the capability to immediately override the automatic retransmission and revert to manual retransmission.

27.5.2.2 Visual Recording Devices.

27.5.2.2.1 Alarms from alarm boxes shall be automatically received and recorded at the communications center.

27.5.2.2.2 A device for producing a permanent graphic recording of all alarm, supervisory, trouble, and test signals received or retransmitted, or both, shall be provided at each communications center for each alarm circuit and tie circuit.

27.5.2.2.3 Reserve recording devices shall be provided in accordance with 27.5.2.2.3.1 and 27.5.2.2.3.2.

27.5.2.2.3.1 Where each circuit is served by a dedicated recording device, the number of reserve recording devices required on-site shall be equal to at least 5 percent of the circuits in service and in no case less than one device.

27.5.2.2.3.2 Where two or more circuits are served by a common recording device, a reserve recording device shall be provided on-site for each circuit connected to a common recorder.

27.5.2.2.4 In a Type B wired system, one such recording device shall be installed in each emergency response facility, and at least one shall be installed in the communications center.

27.5.2.2.5 A permanent visual record and an audible signal shall be required to indicate the receipt of an alarm. The permanent record shall indicate the exact location from which the alarm is being transmitted.

27.5.2.2.6 The audible signal device shall be permitted to be common to two or more box circuits and arranged so that the emergency alarm operator is able to manually silence the signal temporarily by a self-restoring switch.

27.5.2.2.7 Facilities shall be provided that automatically record the date and time of receipt of each alarm.

Exception: Only the time shall be required to be automatically recorded for voice recordings.

27.5.2.3 System Integrity.

27.5.2.3.1 Wired circuits upon which transmission and receipt of alarms depend shall be constantly monitored for integrity to provide prompt warning of conditions adversely affecting reliability.

27.5.2.3.2 The power supplied to all required circuits and devices of the system shall be constantly monitored for integrity.

27.5.2.4 Trouble Signals.

27.5.2.4.1 Trouble signals shall be indicated where there is a trained and competent person on duty at all times.

27.5.2.4.2 Trouble signals shall be distinct from alarm signals and shall be indicated by a visual and audible signal.

27.5.2.4.3 The audible signal shall be permitted to be common to more than one circuit that is monitored for integrity.

27.5.2.4.4 A switch for silencing the audible trouble signal shall be permitted, provided that the visual signal remains operating until the silencing switch is restored to its normal position.

27.5.2.4.5 The audible signal shall be responsive to faults on any other circuits that occur prior to restoration of the silencing switch to its normal position.

27.5.2.5 Power Supply.

27.5.2.5.1 Each box circuit or wireless receiving system shall be powered by one of the following:

(1)*Form 4A, which is an inverter, powered from a common rectifier, receiving power by a single source of alternating current with a floating storage battery having a 24-hour standby capacity

(2)*Form 4B, which is an inverter, powered from a common rectifier, receiving power from two sources of alternating current with a floating storage battery having a 4-hour standby capacity

(3)*Form 4C, which is a rectifier, converter, or motor generator receiving power from two sources of alternating current with transfer facilities to apply power from the secondary source to the system within 30 seconds

27.5.2.5.2 Form 4A and Form 4B shall be permitted to distribute the system load between two or more common rectifiers and batteries.

27.5.2.5.3 The capacity of batteries, motor generators, rectifiers, or other permitted power supplies shall exceed the calculated load of all connected circuits, so that circuits developing grounds or crosses with other circuits each shall be able to be supplied by an independent source to the extent required by 27.5.2.5.1.

27.5.2.5.4 Provision shall be made to connect any circuit to any battery, generator, or rectifier, or other permitted power supply.

27.5.2.5.5 Individual circuits supplied from common leads shall be protected by the installation of enclosed fuses located at the point where the circuit conductors receive their supply.

27.5.2.5.6 Local circuits at communications centers shall be supplied in accordance with 27.5.2.5.6.1 and 27.5.2.5.6.2.

27.5.2.5.6.1 The source of power for local circuits required to operate the essential features of the system shall be monitored for integrity.

27.5.2.5.6.2 Local circuits at communications centers shall be permitted to be connected to the same power source as box circuits, wireless receiving system circuits, or a separate power source.

27.5.2.5.7 Visual and audible means to indicate a 15 percent or greater reduction of normal power supply (rated voltage) shall be provided.

27.5.2.5.8 Where the electrical service/capacity of the equipment required under Section 4.7 of NFPA 1221, *Standard for the Installation, Maintenance, and Use of Emergency Services Communications Systems,* satisfies the needs of equipment in this chapter, such equipment shall not be required to be duplicated.

27.5.2.6 Rectifiers, Converters, Inverters, and Motor Generators.

27.5.2.6.1 Rectifiers shall be supplied from the secondary of an isolating transformer.

27.5.2.6.1.1 The primary of the isolating transformer shall be connected to a circuit not exceeding 250 volts.

27.5.2.6.2 Complete spare units or spare parts shall be in reserve.

27.5.2.6.3 One spare rectifier shall be provided for every 10 operating rectifiers on a system. No system shall have less than one spare.

27.5.2.6.4 Leads from rectifiers or motor generators, with a float-charged battery, shall be protected by fuses rated at a minimum of 1 ampere and a maximum of 200 percent of connected load at nominal circuit voltage. Where not provided with a float-charged battery, the fuses shall be rated at a minimum of 3 amperes.

27.5.2.7 Engine-Driven Generators. The installation of engine-driven generator sets shall conform to the provisions of NFPA 37, *Standard for the Installation and Use of Stationary Combustion Engines and Gas Turbines;* NFPA 110, *Standard for Emergency and Standby Power Systems;* and NFPA 1221, *Standard for the Installation, Maintenance, and Use of Emergency Services Communications Systems.*

27.5.2.8 Float-Charged Batteries.

27.5.2.8.1 Float-charged batteries shall be of the storage type. Primary batteries (dry cells) shall not be used. Lead-acid batteries shall be in jars of glass or other identified or approved transparent materials; other types of batteries shall be in containers identified or approved for the purpose.

27.5.2.8.2 Float-charged batteries shall be above building grade level.

27.5.2.8.3 Float-charged batteries shall be located on the same floor of the building as the operating equipment.

27.5.2.8.4 Float-charged batteries shall be accessible for maintenance and inspection.

27.5.2.8.5 Float-charged batteries shall be installed in accordance with Article 480 of *NFPA 70, National Electrical Code.*

27.5.2.8.6 Batteries shall be mounted to provide effective insulation from the ground or working platform and from other batteries. Mounting equipment shall be listed and identified for the location. It shall be permissible for the authority having jurisdiction to waive this requirement to allow the use of alternative mounting equipment where it is assured that equivalent objectives can be achieved.

27.5.2.8.7 Battery mounting shall be protected against deterioration and shall provide stability, especially in geographic areas subject to seismic disturbance.

27.5.2.9 Equipment Fire Protection. Where applicable, electronic computer/data processing equipment shall be protected in accordance with NFPA 75, *Standard for the Fire Protection of Information Technology Equipment.*

27.5.3 Alarm Processing Equipment at a Remote Communications Center. Where the alarm-receiving equipment is located at a location other than where the box circuit protection, controls, and power supplies are located, the requirements of 27.5.3.1 through 27.5.3.8, in addition to all of the requirements of Section 27.5, shall apply.

27.5.3.1 All equipment used to provide the primary and remote receiving facilities shall be listed for its intended use and shall be installed in accordance with *NFPA 70, National Electrical Code.*

27.5.3.2 The monitoring for integrity of all box circuits shall be provided with a visual and audible means to indicate a 20 percent or greater reduction or increase in the normal current in any box alarm circuit. The visual means shall identify the exact circuit affected.

27.5.3.3 Monitoring for integrity of all power supplies shall be provided with visual and audible means to indicate a loss of primary or standby power supplies at both the communications center and remote communications center.

27.5.3.4 A minimum of two separate means of interconnection shall be provided between the communications center and remote communications center receiving equipment. This interconnection shall be dedicated and shall not be used for any other purpose.

27.5.3.5 Where data transmission or multiplexing equipment is used that is not an integral part of the alarm-receiving equipment, a visual and audible means shall be provided to monitor the integrity of the external equipment. This shall include monitoring all primary and standby power supplies as well as the transmission of data.

27.5.3.6 Power shall be provided in accordance with 27.5.2.5.

27.5.3.7 The use of an uninterruptible power supply (UPS) to comply with standby power requirements shall not be permitted.

27.5.3.8 Tie circuits shall be provided in accordance with 27.5.3.8.1 through 27.5.3.8.3.

27.5.3.8.1 A separate tie circuit shall be provided from the communications center to each subsidiary communications center.

27.5.3.8.2 The tie circuit between the communications center and the subsidiary communications center shall not be used for any other purpose.

27.5.3.8.3 In a Type B wired system, where all boxes in the system are of the succession type, it shall be permitted to use the tie circuit as a dispatch circuit to the extent permitted by NFPA 1221, *Standard for the Installation, Maintenance, and Use of Emergency Services Communications Systems.*

27.5.4 Wired Network Systems.

27.5.4.1 System Arrangement and Operation.

27.5.4.1.1 For a Type B system, the effectiveness of noninterference and succession functions between box circuits shall be no less than between boxes in any one circuit.

27.5.4.1.2 A metallic box open circuit condition shall cause a warning signal in all other circuits, and, thereafter, the circuit(s) not in the open circuit condition shall be automatically restored to operative condition.

27.5.4.1.3 Box circuits shall be sufficient in number and laid out so that the areas that would be left without box protection in case of disruption of a circuit do not exceed those covered by 20 properly spaced boxes where all or any part of the circuit is of aerial open-wire, or by 30 properly spaced boxes where the circuit is entirely in underground or messenger-supported cable.

27.5.4.1.4 Where all boxes on any individual circuit and associated equipment are designed and installed to provide for receipt of alarms through the ground in the event of a break in the circuit, the circuit shall be permitted to serve twice the number of aerial open-wire and cable circuits, respectively, as are specified in 27.5.4.1.3.

27.5.4.1.5 The installation of additional boxes in an area served by the number of boxes spaced as indicated in 27.5.4.1.1 through 27.5.4.1.4 shall not constitute geographical overloading of a circuit.

27.5.4.1.6 Sounding devices for signals shall be provided for box circuits.

27.5.4.1.6.1 A common sounding device for more than one circuit shall be permitted to be used in a Type A system and shall be installed at the communications center.

27.5.4.1.6.2 In a Type B system, a sounding device shall be installed in each emergency response facility at the same location as the recording device for that circuit, unless installed at the communications center, where a common sounding device shall be permitted.

27.5.4.2 Constant-Current (100 milliampere) Systems.
Constant-current systems shall comply with the requirements of 27.5.4.2.1 through 27.5.4.2.6.

27.5.4.2.1 Means shall be provided for manually regulating the current in box circuits so that the operating current is maintained within 10 percent of normal throughout changes in external circuit resistance from 20 percent above normal to 50 percent below normal.

27.5.4.2.2 The voltage supplied to maintain normal line current on box circuits shall not exceed 150 volts, measured under no-load conditions, and shall be such that the line current cannot be reduced below the approved operating value by the simultaneous operation of four boxes.

27.5.4.2.3 Visual and audible means to indicate a 20 percent or greater reduction in the normal current in any alarm circuit shall be provided.

27.5.4.2.4 All devices connected in series with any alarm circuit shall function when the alarm circuit current is reduced to 70 percent of normal.

27.5.4.2.5 Meters shall be provided to indicate the current in any box circuit and the voltage of any power source. Meters used in common for two or more circuits shall be provided with cut-in devices designed to reduce the probability of cross-connecting circuits.

27.5.4.2.6 Necessary switches, testing, and signal transmitting and receiving devices shall be provided to allow the isolation, control, and test of each circuit up to at least 10 percent of the total number of box and dispatch circuits, but never less than two circuits.

27.5.4.3 Grounded Common-Current Systems. Where common-current source systems are grounded, the requirements of 27.5.4.3.1 and 27.5.4.3.2 shall apply.

27.5.4.3.1 Where common-current source systems are grounded, the resistance of the ground shall not exceed 10 percent of resistance of any connected circuit and shall be located at one side of the battery.

27.5.4.3.2 Visual and audible indicating devices shall be provided for each box and dispatch circuit to give immediate warning of ground leakage current that will have a detrimental effect on circuit operation.

27.5.4.4 Telephone (Series) Reporting Systems.

27.5.4.4.1 A permanent visual recording device installed in the communications center shall be provided to record all incoming box signals.

27.5.4.4.2 A spare recording device shall be provided for five or more box circuits.

27.5.4.4.3 A second visual means of identifying the calling box shall be provided.

27.5.4.4.4 Audible signals shall indicate all incoming calls from box circuits.

27.5.4.4.5 All voice transmissions from boxes for emergencies shall be recorded with the capability of instant playback.

27.5.4.4.6 A voice-recording facility shall be provided for each operator handling incoming alarms to eliminate the possibility of interference.

27.5.4.4.7 Box circuits shall be sufficient in number and laid out so that the areas that would be left without box protection in case of disruption of a circuit do not exceed those covered by 20 properly spaced boxes where all or any part of the circuit is of aerial open-wire, or 30 properly spaced boxes where the circuit is entirely in underground or messenger-supported cable.

27.5.4.4.8 Where all boxes on any individual circuit and associated equipment are designed and installed to provide for receipt of alarms through the ground in the event of a break in the circuit, the circuit shall be permitted to serve twice the number of aerial open-wire and cable circuits, respectively, as is specified in 27.5.4.4.7.

27.5.4.4.9 The installation of additional boxes in an area served by the number of boxes spaced as indicated in 27.5.4.4.7 shall not constitute geographical overloading of a circuit.

27.5.5 Wireless Network.

27.5.5.1 System Arrangement and Operation.

27.5.5.1.1 Type A systems shall comply with 27.5.5.1.1.1 through 27.5.5.1.1.6.

27.5.5.1.1.1* Two separate receiving networks shall be required for each frequency. Each network shall include the following:

(1) Antenna
(2) RF receiver
(3) Signaling processing equipment
(4) Time/date alarm printer
(5) Audible alerting device
(6) Power supply

27.5.5.1.1.2 Both receiving networks shall be installed at the communications center.

27.5.5.1.1.3 The failure of one receiving network shall not interfere with the other receiving network's ability to receive messages from boxes.

27.5.5.1.1.4 Where the system configuration is such that a polling device is incorporated into the receiving network to allow remote or selective initiation of box tests, a separate device shall be included in each of the two required receiving networks.

27.5.5.1.1.5 The polling devices shall be configured for automatic cycle initiation in their primary operating mode, shall be capable of continuous self-monitoring, and shall be integrated into the network(s) to provide automatic switchover and operational continuity in the event of failure of either device.

27.5.5.1.1.6 Test signals from boxes shall not be required to include the date as part of their permanent recording, provided that the date is automatically printed on the recording tape at the beginning of each calendar day.

27.5.5.1.2 Type B systems shall comply with 27.5.5.1.2.1 and 27.5.5.1.2.2.

27.5.5.1.2.1 For each frequency used, a single, complete receiving network shall be permitted in each emergency response facility, provided that the communications center conforms to 27.5.5.1.1.1 through 27.5.5.1.1.3. Where the jurisdiction maintains two or more alarm reception points in operation, one receiving network shall be permitted to be at each alarm reception point.

27.5.5.1.2.2 Where alarm signals are transmitted to an emergency response facility from the communications center using the wireless-type receiving equipment in the emergency response facility to receive and record the alarm message, a second receiving network conforming to 27.5.5.1.2.1 shall be provided at each emergency response facility, and that receiving network shall employ a frequency other than that used for the receipt of box messages.

27.5.5.1.3 A device for producing a permanent graphic recording of all alarm, supervisory, trouble, and test signals received or retransmitted, or both, shall be provided at the communications center.

27.5.5.1.4* Where box message signals to the communications center or acknowledgment of message receipt signals from the communications center to the box are repeated, associated repeating facilities shall conform to the requirements of 27.5.5.1.1.1(1), (2), (3), and (6) and include two separate transmitters.

27.5.5.2 Power. Power shall be provided in accordance with 27.5.2.5.

27.5.5.3 Monitoring for Integrity.

27.5.5.3.1 All wireless box systems shall provide constant monitoring of each radio frequency in use. Both an audible and a visual indication of any sustained signal in excess of a 15-second duration shall be provided for each receiving system at the communications center.

27.5.5.3.2 The power supplied to all required circuits and devices of the system shall be monitored for integrity.

27.5.5.3.3* Each wireless box shall automatically transmit a test message at least once in each 24-hour period.

27.5.5.3.4 Receiving equipment associated with wireless-type systems, including any related repeater(s), shall be tested at least hourly. The receipt of test messages that do not exceed 60-minute intervals shall meet this requirement.

27.5.5.3.5 Radio repeaters upon which receipt of alarms depend shall be provided with dual receivers, transmitters, and power supplies. Failure of the primary receiver, transmitter, or power supply shall cause an automatic switchover to the secondary receiver, transmitter, or power supply.

Exception: Manual switchover shall be permitted, provided that it is completed within 30 seconds.

27.5.5.3.6 Trouble signals shall actuate a sounding device located where there is always a trained, competent person on duty.

27.5.5.3.7 Trouble signals shall be distinct from alarm signals and shall be indicated by a visual and audible signal.

27.5.5.3.7.1 The audible signal shall be permitted to be common to two or more monitored circuits.

27.5.5.3.7.2 A switch for silencing the audible trouble signal shall be permitted where the visual signal remains operating until the silencing switch is restored to its normal position.

27.5.5.3.8 The audible signal shall be responsive to subsequent faults in other monitored functions prior to restoration of the silencing switch.

27.5.5.4 Physical Protection of Transmission Line. The antenna transmission line between the transmitter and the antenna shall be installed in rigid metal, intermediate metal conduit, or electrical metallic tubing in accordance with *NFPA 70, National Electrical Code.*

27.6 Alarm Boxes.

27.6.1* General. The requirements of 27.6.1.1 through 27.6.1.6 shall apply to all alarm boxes.

27.6.1.1 Concurrent operation of at least four boxes shall not result in the loss of an alarm.

27.6.1.2 Boxes and associated equipment, when in an abnormal condition, shall not disable the public emergency alarm reporting system circuit.

27.6.1.3 Boxes shall be designed so that recycling does not occur when a box-actuating device is held in the actuating position and shall be ready to accept a new signal as soon as the actuating device is released.

27.6.1.4* Boxes, when actuated, shall give a visible or audible indication to the user that the box is operating or that the signal has been transmitted to the communications center.

27.6.1.5 Box cases and parts that are accessible to the public shall be permitted to be of nonconductive material.

27.6.1.6 Box cases and parts that are accessible to the public and that are constructed of conductive materials shall be installed in accordance with the requirements of *NFPA 70, National Electrical Code*, Articles 250 and 760.

27.6.2* Publicly Accessible Alarm Boxes.

27.6.2.1 Fundamental Requirements. The requirements of 27.6.2.1.1 through 27.6.2.1.11 shall apply to all publicly accessible alarm boxes.

27.6.2.1.1 Means for actuation of alarms by the public shall be located where they are visible, unobstructed, and readily accessible.

27.6.2.1.2 The box housing shall protect the internal components and shall be identified for the location installed.

27.6.2.1.3 Doors on boxes shall remain operable under adverse climatic conditions, including icing and salt spray.

27.6.2.1.4 Boxes shall be recognizable as such and shall have instructions for use plainly marked on their exterior surfaces.

27.6.2.1.5 Boxes shall be securely mounted on poles, pedestals, or structural surfaces as directed by the authority having jurisdiction.

27.6.2.1.6* The location of publicly accessible boxes shall be designated by the authority having jurisdiction.

27.6.2.1.7 Schools, hospitals, nursing homes, and places of public assembly shall have a box located at the main entrance, as directed by the authority having jurisdiction.

27.6.2.1.8 Boxes shall be conspicuously visible and be highlighted with a distinctive color.

27.6.2.1.9 All publicly accessible boxes mounted on support poles shall be identified by a wide band of distinctive colors or signs placed 8 ft (2.44 m) above the ground and visible from all directions wherever possible.

27.6.2.1.10* Location-designating lights of distinctive color, visible for at least 1500 ft (460 m) in all directions, shall be installed over boxes. The street light nearest the box, where equipped with a distinctively colored light, shall meet this requirement.

27.6.2.1.11 Where boxes are installed inside a structure, the installation shall comply with 27.6.2.1.11.1 and 27.6.2.1.11.2.

27.6.2.1.11.1 The box shall be placed as close as is practicable to the point of entrance of the circuit.

27.6.2.1.11.2 The exterior wire shall be installed in rigid metal conduit or intermediate metal conduit in accordance with Chapter 3 of *NFPA 70, National Electrical Code*.

Exception: Schedule 80 rigid nonmetallic conduit shall be permitted for underground installations, provided that all elbows used are rigid or intermediate metal conduit.

27.6.3 Auxiliary Alarm Box.

27.6.3.1 Fundamental Requirements. The requirements of 27.6.3.1.1 through 27.6.3.1.6 shall apply to all auxiliary alarm boxes.

27.6.3.1.1 The authority having jurisdiction shall designate the location of the auxiliary box.

27.6.3.1.2 All exterior wire and cable shall be installed in rigid metal conduit or intermediate metal conduit in accordance with Chapter 3 of *NFPA 70, National Electrical Code*.

Exception: Schedule 80 rigid nonmetallic conduit shall be permitted for underground installations, provided that all elbows used are rigid or intermediate metal conduit.

27.6.3.1.3* Wiring between the auxiliary alarm system and the auxiliary alarm box or master alarm box shall meet the requirements of pathway survivability Level 2 *(see 12.4.3)*.

27.6.3.1.4 Where installed outside a structure, the requirements of 27.6.2.1.2 and 27.6.2.1.5 shall apply.

27.6.3.1.5 Where the auxiliary box is a wired box, the requirements of Section 27.7 shall apply.

27.6.3.1.6 Where the auxiliary box is a wireless box, the requirements of 27.6.6 shall apply.

27.6.3.2 Auxiliary Alarm Systems.

27.6.3.2.1 Application. The equipment and circuits necessary to connect a protected premises to a public emergency alarm reporting system shall comply with the requirements of 27.6.3.2.

27.6.3.2.1.1 The requirements of Chapter 10, in addition to those of Chapters 14 and 17, shall apply to auxiliary alarm systems unless they conflict with the requirements of 27.6.3.2.

27.6.3.2.1.2 Where permitted by the authority having jurisdiction, the use of systems described in Chapter 27 shall be permitted to provide defined reporting functions from or within private premises.

27.6.3.2.1.3 The requirements of Section 27.7 shall also apply to wired auxiliary alarm systems.

27.6.3.2.2 Types of Systems.

27.6.3.2.2.1 Auxiliary alarm systems shall be one of the following types:

(1)*Local energy type
  (a) Local energy systems shall be permitted to be of the coded or noncoded type.
  (b) Power supply sources for local energy systems shall conform to Chapter 10.
  (c) Transmitter trouble signals shall be indicated at the control unit and the building fire command center in accordance with 10.15.7.

(2)*Shunt type
  (a) Shunt systems shall be noncoded with respect to any remote electrical tripping or actuating devices.
  (b) All conductors of the shunt circuit shall be installed in accordance with *NFPA 70, National Electrical Code*, Article 344, for rigid metal conduit, or Article 358, for electrical metallic tubing.
  (c) Both sides of the shunt circuit shall be in the same conduit.
  (d) Where a shunt loop is used, it shall not exceed a length of 750 ft (230 m) and shall be in conduit.
  (e) Conductors of the shunt circuits shall not be smaller than 14 AWG and shall be insulated as prescribed in *NFPA 70, National Electrical Code*, Article 310.

(f) The power for shunt-type systems shall be provided by the public emergency alarm reporting system.

(g)*A local system made to an auxiliary alarm system by the addition of a relay whose coil is energized by a local power supply and whose normally closed contacts trip a shunt-type master box shall not be permitted.

27.6.3.2.2.2 The interface of the two types of auxiliary alarm systems with the three types of public emergency alarm reporting systems shall be in accordance with Table 27.6.3.2.2.2.

Table 27.6.3.2.2.2 Application of Public Emergency Alarm Reporting Systems with Auxiliary Alarm Systems

Reporting Systems	Local Energy Type	Shunt Type
Wired	Yes	Yes
Wireless	Yes	No
Telephone series	Yes	No

27.6.3.2.2.3 The application of the two types of auxiliary alarm systems shall be limited to the initiating devices specified in Table 27.6.3.2.2.3.

Table 27.6.3.2.2.3 Application of Initiating Devices with Auxiliary Alarm Systems

Initiating Devices	Local Energy Type	Shunt Type
Manually actuated alarm-initiating device	Yes	Yes
Waterflow or actuation of the fire extinguishing system(s) or suppression system(s)	Yes	Yes
Automatic detection devices	Yes	No

27.6.3.2.3 System Arrangement and Operation.

27.6.3.2.3.1 Shunt-type auxiliary alarm systems shall be arranged so that one auxiliary transmitter does not serve more than 100,000 ft² (9290 m²) total area.

Exception: Where otherwise permitted by the authority having jurisdiction.

27.6.3.2.3.2 A separate auxiliary transmitter shall be provided for each building, or where permitted by the authority having jurisdiction, for each group of buildings of single ownership or occupancy.

27.6.3.2.3.3 The same box shall be permitted to be used as a public emergency alarm reporting system box and as a transmitting device for an auxiliary alarm system where permitted by the authority having jurisdiction, provided that the box is located at the outside of the entrance to the protected property.

27.6.3.2.3.4 Where 27.6.3.2.3.3 is applied, the authority having jurisdiction shall be permitted to require the box to be equipped with a signal light to differentiate between automatic and manual operation, unless local outside alarms at the protected property serve the same purpose.

27.6.3.2.3.5 The transmitting device shall be located as required by the authority having jurisdiction.

27.6.3.2.3.6 The system shall be designed and arranged so that a single fault on the auxiliary alarm system shall not jeopardize operation of the public emergency alarm reporting system and shall not, in case of a single fault on either the auxiliary or public emergency alarm reporting system, transmit a false alarm on either system.

Exception: Shunt systems complying with 27.6.3.2.2.1(2).

27.6.3.2.3.7 A means that is available only to the agency responsible for maintaining the public emergency alarm reporting system shall be provided for disconnecting the auxiliary loop to the connected property.

27.6.3.2.3.8 Notification shall be given to the designated representative of the property when the auxiliary box is not in service.

27.6.3.2.3.9 An auxiliary alarm system shall be used only in connection with a public emergency alarm reporting system that is approved for the service. A system approved by the authority having jurisdiction shall meet this requirement.

27.6.3.2.3.10 Permission for the connection of an auxiliary alarm system to a public emergency alarm reporting system, and acceptance of the type of auxiliary transmitter and its actuating mechanism, circuits, and components connected thereto, shall be obtained from the authority having jurisdiction.

27.6.3.2.3.11 Paragraph 27.6.3.2 shall not require the use of audible alarm signals other than those necessary to operate the auxiliary alarm system. Where it is desired to provide evacuation signals in the protected property, the notification appliances, circuits, and controls shall comply with the provisions of Chapter 23 in addition to the provisions of 27.6.3.2.

27.6.3.2.3.12 Where an auxiliary alarm system is in an alarm condition that has been acknowledged, deactivated, or bypassed, subsequent actuation of initiating devices on other initiating device circuits or subsequent actuation of addressable initiating devices on signaling line circuits shall cause an alarm signal to be transmitted to the communications center.

27.6.3.2.3.13 Where an auxiliary transmitter is located within a private premises, it shall be installed in accordance with 27.6.2.1.11 and 27.7.2.

27.6.3.2.3.14 Where data communications between a microprocessor-based control unit and an auxiliary alarm system are utilized, they shall comply with all of the requirements in 27.6.3.2.3.14(A) through 27.6.3.2.3.14(C):

(A) The monitoring for integrity shall include communications test messages transmitted between the control unit and the auxiliary alarm system.

(B) The communications test message shall be initiated by either the control unit or the auxiliary alarm system and shall require a response from the corresponding unit, and the following shall apply:

(1) An invalid response or no response from the control unit or the auxiliary alarm system shall be recognized as a communications failure.

(2) A communications failure shall initiate a specific communications failure trouble message, which shall be transmitted from the auxiliary alarm system and shall be automatically indicated within 200 seconds at the communications center.

(3) A trouble condition in 27.6.3.2.3.14(B)(2) shall activate an audible and distinctive visual signal at the auxiliary box indicating a communications failure.

(4) A trouble condition shall be indicated at the control unit and the building fire command center in accordance with 10.15.7.

(C) Where a separate device is required to interface the control unit to the auxiliary alarm system, all communication paths shall be monitored for integrity and shall comply with 27.6.3.2.3.14.

27.6.4 Master Alarm Boxes. Master alarm boxes shall comply with the requirements of 27.6.2 and 27.6.3.

27.6.5 Wired Network Boxes. The requirements of Section 27.7 shall apply to wired network boxes.

27.6.5.1 Telephone Boxes. The requirements of Section 27.7 shall also apply to telephone boxes.

27.6.5.1.1 Where a handset is used, the caps on the transmitter and receiver shall be secured to reduce the probability of the telephone box being disabled due to vandalism.

27.6.5.1.2 Telephone boxes shall be designed to allow the communications center operator to determine whether or not the telephone box has been restored to normal condition after use.

27.6.6 Wireless Network Boxes.

27.6.6.1 In addition to the requirements of this Code, wireless boxes shall be designed and operated in compliance with all applicable rules and regulations of the Federal Communications Commission (FCC) or, where required by other governing laws, the National Telecommunications and Information Administration (NTIA).

27.6.6.2* Each wireless box shall automatically transmit a test message at least once in each 24-hour period.

27.6.6.3 Wireless network boxes shall be capable of transmitting no less than three specific signals to the communications center, in addition to the box number, with priority as follows:

(1) Alarm
(2) Tamper
(3) Test

27.6.6.4 Wireless boxes shall transmit to the communications center with priority as follows:

(1) No less than two repetitions for "alarm"
(2) No less than one repetition for "tamper"
(3) No less than one repetition for "test"

27.6.6.5 Where wireless network boxes transmit more than one alarm signal, in addition to those in 27.6.6.3, each such signal shall be individually identifiable.

27.6.6.6 Where wireless network boxes transmit more than one alarm signal, they shall be designed to prevent the loss of supplemental or concurrently actuated signals.

27.6.6.7* Where wireless network boxes transmit more than one alarm signal, the priority of each alarm shall be as assigned by the authority having jurisdiction.

27.6.6.8 An actuating device held or locked in the activating position shall not prevent the activation and transmission of other signals.

27.6.6.9 The primary power source for wireless boxes shall be permitted to be from one or more of the following, as approved by the authority having jurisdiction:

(1) Utility distribution system
(2) Solar photovoltaic power system
(3) User power
(4) Self-powered, using either an integral battery or other stored energy source

27.6.6.10 Boxes powered by a utility distribution system shall comply with 27.6.6.10.1 through 27.6.6.10.6.

27.6.6.10.1 Boxes shall have an integral standby, sealed, rechargeable battery that is capable of powering box functions for at least 60 hours in the event of primary power failure. Transfer to standby battery power shall be automatic and without interruption to box operation.

27.6.6.10.2 A local trouble indication shall activate upon primary power failure.

27.6.6.10.3 Boxes operating from primary power shall be capable of operation with a dead or disconnected battery.

27.6.6.10.4 A battery charger shall be provided in compliance with 10.6.10.3, except as modified in 27.6.6.10.

27.6.6.10.5 When the primary power has failed, boxes shall transmit a power failure message to the communications center as part of subsequent test messages until primary power is restored.

27.6.6.10.6 A low-battery message shall be transmitted to the communications center where the remaining battery standby time is less than 54 hours.

27.6.6.11 Boxes powered by a solar photovoltaic system shall comply with 27.6.6.11.1 through 27.6.6.11.5.

27.6.6.11.1 Solar photovoltaic power systems shall provide box operation for not less than 6 months.

27.6.6.11.2 Solar photovoltaic power systems shall be monitored for integrity.

27.6.6.11.3 The battery shall have power to sustain operation for a minimum period of 15 days without recharging.

27.6.6.11.4 The box shall transmit a trouble message to the communications center when the charger has failed for more than 24 hours. This message shall be part of all subsequent transmissions.

27.6.6.11.5 Where the remaining battery standby duration is less than 10 days, a low-battery message shall be transmitted to the communications center.

27.6.6.12 User-powered boxes shall have an automatic self-test feature.

27.6.6.13 Self-powered boxes shall comply with 27.6.6.13.1 through 27.6.6.13.3.

27.6.6.13.1 Self-powered boxes shall operate for a period of not less than 6 months.

27.6.6.13.2 Self-powered boxes shall transmit a low-power warning message to the communications center for at least 15 days prior to the time the power source will fail to operate the box. This message shall be part of all subsequent transmissions.

27.6.6.13.3 Use of a charger to extend the life of a self-powered box shall be permitted where the charger does not interfere with box operation. The box shall be capable of operation for not less than 6 months with the charger disconnected.

27.7 Public Cable Plant. Metallic and fiber-optic cabling systems and interconnections between alarm transmission equipment and alarm-receiving equipment shall comply with the requirements of Section 27.7.

27.7.1 Requirements for Metallic and Fiber-Optic Systems — Metallic and Fiber-Optic Interconnections.

27.7.1.1 Circuit Conductors and Fiber-Optic Strands.

27.7.1.1.1 Exterior metallic, fiber-optic cable and wire shall conform to International Municipal Signal Association (IMSA) specifications or an approved equivalent.

Exception: Where circuit conductors or fiber-optic strands are provided by a public utility on a lease basis, IMSA specifications shall not apply.

27.7.1.1.2 Where a public box is installed inside a building, the circuit from the point of entrance to the public box shall be installed in rigid metal conduit, intermediate metal conduit, or electrical metallic tubing in accordance with *NFPA 70, National Electrical Code.*

Exception: This requirement shall not apply to wireless box systems.

27.7.1.1.3 Wires and fiber-optic strands shall be terminated so as to prevent breaking from vibration or stress.

27.7.1.1.4 Circuit conductors and fiber-optic cables on terminal racks shall be identified and isolated from conductors of other systems wherever possible and shall be protected from mechanical injury.

27.7.1.2 Cables. The requirements of 27.7.1.2 shall apply to 27.7.1.3 through 27.7.1.6.

27.7.1.2.1 Exterior metallic and fiber-optic cable and wire shall conform to IMSA specifications or an approved equivalent.

27.7.1.2.2 Overhead, underground, or direct burial cables shall be specifically approved for the purpose.

27.7.1.2.3 Metallic and fiber-optic cables used in interior installations shall comply with *NFPA 70, National Electrical Code*, and shall be installed in accordance with the manufacturer's installation instructions and practices.

27.7.1.2.4 Conductors and/or fiber-optic strands used to transmit signals of other systems that are under the control of a governmental agency shall be permitted to be contained within the same multi-conductor cable as conductors and/or fiber-optic strands used to transmit signals of public emergency alarm reporting systems.

27.7.1.2.5 By special permission as defined in *NFPA 70*, cables not under the control of a governmental agency shall be permitted to contain conductors and/or fiber-optic strands used to transmit signals of a public emergency alarm reporting System.

27.7.1.2.6 Signaling wire and fiber-optic cables containing metallic protection or strength members shall comply with 27.7.1.2.6.1 and 27.7.1.2.6.2.

27.7.1.2.6.1 Signaling wires supplied by a power source having a voltage and/or current rating sufficient to introduce a hazard shall be installed in accordance with *NFPA 70, National Electrical Code*, Article 760, Part II.

27.7.1.2.6.2 Fiber-optic cables containing metallic protection or strength members shall be grounded and protected in accordance with *NFPA 70, National Electrical Code.*

27.7.1.2.7 All metallic cables, with all taps and splices made, shall be tested for insulation resistance when installed but before connection to terminals. Such tests shall indicate an insulation resistance of at least 200 megohms per mile between any one conductor and all other conductors, the sheath, and the ground.

27.7.1.3 Underground Cables.

27.7.1.3.1 Underground metallic and fiber-optic cables in duct or direct burial shall be permitted to be brought aboveground only at locations approved by the authority having jurisdiction.

27.7.1.3.1.1 Protection from physical damage or heat incidental to fires in adjacent buildings shall be provided.

27.7.1.3.2 Only fiber-optic and power-limited cables and conductors shall be permitted to be located in duct systems and manholes that contain power-limited public emergency alarm reporting system conductors.

27.7.1.3.3 Where located in duct systems or manholes that contain power circuit conductors over 250 volts to ground, metallic and fiber-optic emergency alarm cables shall be located as far as possible from such power cables and shall be separated from them by a noncombustible barrier or other means approved by the authority having jurisdiction to protect the emergency alarm cables from physical damage.

27.7.1.3.4 All cables installed in manholes shall be racked and marked for identification.

27.7.1.3.5 Raceways or ducts entering buildings from underground duct systems shall be effectively sealed with an identified sealing compound or other means acceptable to the authority having jurisdiction to prevent the entrance of moisture or gases from the underground duct system.

27.7.1.3.6 All cable joints shall be located in manholes, emergency response facilities, or other accessible locations acceptable to the authority having jurisdiction where equivalent protection is provided to minimize physical damage to the cable.

27.7.1.3.6.1 Cable joints shall be made to provide and maintain conductivity, optical continuity for fiber-optic cable, insulation, and protection at least equal to that afforded by the cables that are joined.

27.7.1.3.6.2 Open cable ends shall be sealed against moisture.

27.7.1.3.7 Direct-burial cable, without enclosure in ducts, shall be laid in grass plots, under sidewalks, or in other places where the ground is not likely to be opened for other underground construction.

27.7.1.3.7.1 Where splices are made, such splices shall be accessible for inspection and tests.

27.7.1.3.7.2 Such cables shall be buried at least 18 in. (500 mm) deep and, where crossing streets or other areas likely to be opened for other underground construction, shall be in duct or conduit.

27.7.1.4 Aerial Construction.

27.7.1.4.1 Cables containing conductors and/or fiber-optic strands used to transmit signals of public emergency alarm reporting systems shall be located below all other cables and conductors, except those used for communications purposes.

27.7.1.4.1.1 Precautions shall be provided where passing through trees, under bridges, over railroads, and at other places where subject to physical damage.

27.7.1.4.1.2 Conductors and cables for public emergency alarm reporting system use shall not be attached to a crossarm that carries electric light and power conductors.

Exception: Power conductors for public emergency alarm reporting system use, operating at 250 volts or less, shall be permitted to share the crossarm with the conductors and cables and shall be tagged.

27.7.1.4.2 Aerial cable shall be supported by messenger wire of approved tensile strength or shall conform to one of the following:

(1) IMSA specifications as a self-supporting cable assembly or an approved equivalent
(2) Fiber-optic cable with integral supporting means or all-dielectric self-supporting (ADSS) type

27.7.1.4.3 Single wire shall meet IMSA specifications and shall not be smaller than No. 10 Roebling gauge if of galvanized iron or steel; 10 AWG if of hard-drawn copper; 12 AWG if of approved copper-covered steel; or 6 AWG if of aluminum. Span lengths shall not exceed the manufacturer's recommendations.

27.7.1.4.4 Wires to buildings shall contact only intended supports and shall enter through an approved weatherhead or sleeves slanting upward and inward. Drip loops shall be formed on wires outside of buildings.

27.7.1.5 Leads Down Poles.

27.7.1.5.1 Leads down poles shall be protected from physical damage. Any metallic covering shall form a continuous conducting path to ground. Installation, in all cases, shall prevent water from entering the conduit or box.

27.7.1.5.2 Leads to boxes shall have 600-volt insulation listed or approved for wet locations, as defined in *NFPA 70, National Electrical Code.*

27.7.1.6 Wiring Inside Buildings.

27.7.1.6.1 At the communications center, all conductors, cables, and fiber-optic cables shall extend as directly as possible to the operations center in conduits, ducts, shafts, raceways, or overhead racks and troughs listed or identified as suitable to provide protection against physical damage.

27.7.1.6.2* Where installed in buildings, conductors and fiber-optic cables shall be installed in any of the following wiring methods:

(1) Electrical metallic tubing
(2) Intermediate metal conduit
(3) Rigid metal conduit

Exception: Rigid nonmetallic conduit shall be permitted where approved by the authority having jurisdiction.

27.7.1.6.3 Conductors and fiber-optic cables shall have an approved insulation. The insulation or other outer covering shall be flame-retardant and moisture resistant.

27.7.1.6.4 Conductors and fiber-optic cables shall be installed as far as possible without splices or joints. Splices or

joints shall be permitted only in listed junction or terminal boxes.

27.7.1.6.4.1 Enclosures containing public emergency alarm reporting system circuits shall be provided with red covers or doors. The words "public emergency alarm reporting system circuit" shall be clearly marked on all terminal and junction locations to prevent unintentional interference.

27.7.1.6.4.2 Wire and fiber-optic terminals, terminal boxes, splices, and joints shall conform to *NFPA 70, National Electrical Code.*

27.7.1.6.5 Metallic and fiber-optic cables and wiring exposed to a hazard shall be protected in an approved manner.

27.7.1.6.6 Metallic and fiber-optic cable terminals and cross-connecting facilities shall be located in or adjacent to the operations room.

27.7.1.6.7 Where signal conductors, non-dielectric fiber-optic cables, and electric light and power wires are run in the same shaft, they shall be separated by at least 2 in. (51 mm), or either system shall be encased in a noncombustible enclosure.

27.7.2 Signal Transmission and Receiving Circuits. Signal transmission and receiving circuits shall comply with the requirements of 27.7.2.1 and 27.7.2.2.

27.7.2.1 General.

27.7.2.1.1 ANSI/IEEE C2, *National Electrical Safety Code,* shall be used as a guide for the installation of outdoor circuitry.

27.7.2.1.2 Installation shall provide for the following:

(1) Continuity of service
(2) Protection from mechanical damage
(3) Disablement from heat that is incidental to fire
(4) Damage by floods, corrosive vapors, or other causes

27.7.2.1.3 Open local circuits within single buildings shall be permitted in accordance with Chapter 23.

27.7.2.1.4 All circuits shall be routed so as to allow tracing of circuits for trouble.

27.7.2.1.5 Circuits shall not pass over, under, through, or be attached to buildings or property not owned by or under the control of the authority having jurisdiction or the agency responsible for maintaining the system.

Exception: Where the circuit is terminated at a public emergency alarm reporting system initiating device on the premises and where a means, approved by the authority having jurisdiction, is provided to disconnect the circuit from the building or property.

27.7.2.2 Interior Box Circuits.

27.7.2.2.1 A means accessible only to the authority having jurisdiction or the agency responsible for maintaining the public emergency alarm reporting systems shall be provided to disconnect all circuit conductors inside a building or other structure.

27.7.2.2.2 Definite notification shall be given to the designated building representative when the interior box(es) is out of service.

27.7.3* Circuit Protection.

27.7.3.1 The protective devices shall be located close to or be combined with the cable terminals.

27.7.3.2 Surge arresters designed and approved for the purpose shall be installed at a location accessible to qualified persons and shall be marked with the name of the manufacturer and model designation.

27.7.3.3 All surge arresters shall be connected to a ground in accordance with *NFPA 70, National Electrical Code.*

27.7.3.4 All fuses, fuseholders, and adapters shall be plainly marked with their ampere rating. All fuses rated over 2 amperes shall be of the enclosed type.

27.7.3.5 Circuit protection required at the communications center shall be provided in every building that houses communications center equipment.

27.7.3.6 Each metallic conductor entering an emergency response facility from partially or entirely aerial lines shall be protected by a lightning arrester.

27.7.3.7 All metallic conductors entering the communications center shall be protected by the following devices, in the order named, starting from the exterior circuit:

(1) Fuse rated at 3 amperes minimum to 7 amperes maximum and not less than 2000 volts
(2) Surge arrester(s)
(3) Fuse or circuit breaker rated at ½ ampere

27.7.3.8 In regard to 27.7.3.7, the ½-ampere protection on the tie circuits shall be omitted at subsidiary communications centers.

27.7.3.9 At junction points of open aerial metallic conductors and metallic cable, each conductor shall be protected by a surge arrester(s) of the weatherproof type. A connection shall also be between the surge arrester ground, any metallic sheath, and the messenger wire.

27.7.3.10 Aerial open-wire and nonmessenger-supported, two-conductor cable circuits shall be protected by a surge arrester(s) at intervals not to exceed 2000 ft (610 m).

27.7.3.11 Where used for aerial construction, surge arresters, other than of the air-gap or self-restoring type, shall not be installed in public emergency alarm reporting circuits.

27.7.3.12 All protective devices used for aerial construction shall be accessible for maintenance and inspection.

27.8 Emergency Communications Systems (ECS).

27.8.1* ECS shall be permitted to be connected to public emergency alarm reporting systems.

27.8.2 ECS equipment and interface methods connecting to or utilizing public emergency alarm reporting systems shall be electrically and operationally compatible so as not to interfere with the public emergency alarm reporting systems.

Chapter 28   Reserved

Chapter 29   Single- and Multiple-Station Alarms and Household Fire Alarm Systems

29.1 Application.

29.1.1* The performance, selection, installation, operation, and use of single- and multiple-station alarms and household fire alarm systems shall comply with the requirements of this chapter.

29.1.2* Smoke and heat alarms shall be installed in all occupancies where required by other governing laws, codes, or standards.

29.1.3 The requirements of Chapters 10, 12, 14, 17, 18, 21, 23, 24, 26, and 27 shall not apply unless otherwise noted.

29.1.4* The requirements of this chapter shall not apply to installations in manufactured homes.

29.1.5 This chapter shall apply to the life safety of occupants and not to the protection of property.

29.2* Purpose. Fire-warning equipment for residential occupancies shall provide a reliable means to notify the occupants of the presence of a threatening fire and the need to escape to a place of safety before such escape might be impeded by untenable conditions in the normal path of egress.

29.3 Basic Requirements.

29.3.1 All devices, combinations of devices, and equipment to be installed in conformity with this chapter shall be approved or listed for the purposes for which they are intended.

29.3.2 Fire-warning equipment shall be installed in accordance with the listing and manufacturer's published instructions.

29.3.3* The installation of smoke alarms or fire alarm systems, or combinations of these, shall comply with the requirements of this chapter and shall satisfy the minimum requirements for number and location of smoke alarms or smoke detectors by one of the following arrangements:

(1) The required minimum number and location of smoke detection devices shall be satisfied (independently) through the installation of smoke alarms. The installation of additional smoke alarms shall be permitted. The installation of additional system-based smoke detectors, including partial or complete duplication of the smoke alarms satisfying the required minimum, shall be permitted.
(2) The required minimum number and location of smoke detection devices shall be satisfied (independently) through the installation of system smoke detectors. The installation of additional smoke detectors shall be permitted. The installation of additional smoke alarms, including partial or complete duplication of the smoke detectors satisfying the required minimum, shall be permitted.

29.3.4 Supplementary functions, including the extension of an alarm beyond the residential occupancy, shall be permitted and shall not interfere with the performance requirements of this chapter.

29.3.5* Fire-warning equipment to be installed in residential occupancies shall produce the audible emergency evacuation signal described in ANSI S3.41, *American National Standard Emergency Evacuation Signal,* whenever the intended response is to evacuate the building.

29.3.5.1 The audible emergency evacuation signal shall be permitted to be used for other devices as long as the desired response is immediate evacuation.

29.3.5.2* Fire-warning equipment producing the audible emergency evacuation signal shall be permitted to incorporate voice notification under either or both of the following conditions:

(1) Where the voice message is contained completely within the 1.5-second pause period of the audible emergency evacuation signal

(2) Where the voice message complies with 29.3.5.2(2)(a) and (b) as follows:

    (a) The voice message is first preceded by a minimum of eight cycles of the audible emergency evacuation signal.

    (b) The voice message periodically interrupts the signal for no longer than 10 seconds, followed by a minimum of two cycles of the audible emergency evacuation signal between each voice message. The initial eight-cycle period shall not be required to be repeated.

29.3.6 All audible fire alarm signals installed shall meet the performance requirements of 18.4.3, 18.4.5.1, 18.4.5.2, and 29.3.8.

29.3.7* When visible appliances are provided, they shall meet the requirements of Section 18.5. Since hearing deficits are often not apparent, the responsibility for advising the appropriate person(s) of the existence of this deficit shall be that of the party with hearing loss.

29.3.8 Notification appliances provided in sleeping rooms and guest rooms for those with hearing loss shall comply with 29.3.8.1 and 29.3.8.2, as applicable.

29.3.8.1* Mild to Severe Hearing Loss. Notification appliances provided for those with mild to severe hearing loss shall comply with the following:

(1) An audible notification appliance producing a low frequency alarm signal shall be installed in the following situations:

    (a) Where required by governing laws, codes, or standards for people with hearing loss

    (b) Where provided voluntarily for those with hearing loss

(2)*The low frequency alarm signal output shall comply with the following:

    (a) The waveform shall have a fundamental frequency of 520 Hz ±10 percent.

    (b) The minimum sound level at the pillow shall be 75 dBA, or 15 dB above the average ambient sound level, or 5 dB above the maximum sound level having a duration of at least 60 seconds, whichever is greater.

29.3.8.2* Moderately Severe to Profound Hearing Loss. Visible notification appliances in accordance with the requirements of 18.5.5.7 and tactile notification appliances in accordance with the requirements of Section 18.10 shall be required for those with moderately severe to profound hearing loss in the following situations:

(1)*Where required by governing laws, codes, or standards for people with hearing loss

(2) Where provided voluntarily for those with hearing loss

29.3.9 Signals from notification appliances shall not be required to be synchronized.

29.4 Assumptions.

29.4.1* Occupants. The requirements of this chapter shall assume that occupants are not intimate with the ignition and are capable of self-rescue.

29.4.2* Escape Route.

29.4.2.1 The requirements of this chapter shall assume that the occupants have an escape plan.

29.4.2.2 An escape route shall be assumed to be available to occupants and to be unobstructed prior to the event of the fire.

29.4.2.3* The escape route shall be along the normal path of egress for the occupancy.

29.4.3* Equipment. The performance of fire-warning equipment discussed in this chapter shall depend on such equipment being properly selected, installed, operated, tested, and maintained in accordance with the provisions of this Code and with the manufacturer's published instructions provided with the equipment.

29.5 Detection and Notification. The use of fire alarm system smoke detectors and notification appliances shall be permitted to meet the fire-warning requirements for smoke alarms specified in 29.5.1.

29.5.1* Required Detection.

29.5.1.1* Where required by other governing laws, codes, or standards for a specific type of occupancy, approved single- and multiple-station smoke alarms shall be installed as follows:

(1)*In all sleeping rooms and guest rooms

(2)*Outside of each separate dwelling unit sleeping area, within 21 ft (6.4 m) of any door to a sleeping room, with the distance measured along a path of travel

(3) On every level of a dwelling unit, including basements

(4) On every level of a residential board and care occupancy (small facility), including basements and excluding crawl spaces and unfinished attics

(5)*In the living area(s) of a guest suite

(6) In the living area(s) of a residential board and care occupancy (small facility)

29.5.1.2 Where the area addressed in 29.5.1.1(2) is separated from the adjacent living areas by a door, a smoke alarm shall be installed in the area between the door and the sleeping rooms, and additional alarms shall be installed on the living area side of the door as specified by 29.5.1.1 and 29.5.1.3.

29.5.1.3 In addition to the requirements of 29.5.1.1(1) through (3), where the interior floor area for a given level of a dwelling unit, excluding garage areas, is greater than 1000 ft^2 (93 m^2), smoke alarms shall be installed per 29.5.1.3.1 and 29.5.1.3.2.

29.5.1.3.1* All points on the ceiling shall have a smoke alarm within a distance of 30 ft (9.1 m) travel distance or shall have an equivalent of one smoke alarm per 500 ft^2 (46 m^2) of floor area. One smoke alarm per 500 ft^2 (46 m^2) is evaluated by dividing the total interior square footage of floor area per level by 500 ft^2 (46 m^2).

29.5.1.3.2 Where dwelling units include great rooms or vaulted/cathedral ceilings extending over multiple floors, smoke alarms located on the upper floor that are intended to protect the aforementioned area shall be permitted to be considered as part of the lower floor(s) protection scheme used to meet the requirements of 29.5.1.3.1.

29.5.2 Required Occupant Notification.

29.5.2.1 Fire-warning equipment used to provide required or optional detection shall produce audible fire alarm signals that comply with 29.5.2.1.1 or 29.5.2.1.2.

29.5.2.1.1* Smoke and Heat Alarms. Unless exempted by applicable laws, codes, or standards, smoke or heat alarms used to provide a fire-warning function, and when two or more alarms are installed within a dwelling unit, suite of rooms, or similar area, shall be arranged so that the operation of any smoke or heat alarm causes all alarms within these locations to sound.

Exception: The arrangement for all alarms to sound shall not be required for mechanically powered single-station heat alarms.

29.5.2.1.2 Household Fire Alarm System. Where a household fire alarm system is used to provide a fire-warning function, notification appliances shall be installed to meet the performance requirements of 29.3.6.

29.5.2.2* Unless otherwise permitted by the authority having jurisdiction, audible fire alarm signals shall sound only in an individual dwelling unit, suite of rooms, or similar area and shall not be arranged to operate fire-warning equipment or fire alarm systems outside these locations. Remote annunciation shall be permitted.

29.6 Power Supplies.

29.6.1 Smoke and Heat Alarms. Smoke and heat alarms shall be powered by one of the following means:

(1) A commercial light and power source along with a secondary power source that is capable of operating the device for at least 7 days in the normal condition, followed by 4 minutes of alarm
(2) If a commercial light and power source is not normally available, a noncommercial ac power source along with a secondary power source that is capable of operating the device for at least 7 days in the normal condition, followed by 4 minutes of alarm
(3) A nonrechargeable, nonreplaceable primary battery that is capable of operating the device for at least 10 years in the normal condition, followed by 4 minutes of alarm, followed by 7 days of trouble
(4) If a battery primary power supply is specifically permitted, a battery meeting the requirements of 29.6.6 (nonrechargeable primary battery) or the requirements of 29.6.7 (rechargeable primary battery)
(5) A suitable spring-wound mechanism for the nonelectrical portion of a listed single-station alarm with a visible indication to show that sufficient operating power is not available

29.6.2 Household Fire Alarm Systems. Power for household fire alarm systems shall comply with the following requirements:

(1) Household fire alarm systems shall have two independent power sources consisting of a primary source that uses commercial light and power and a secondary source that consists of a rechargeable battery.
(2) The secondary source shall be capable of operating the system for at least 24 hours in the normal condition, followed by 4 minutes of alarm.
(3) The secondary power source shall be supervised and shall cause a distinctive audible and visible trouble signal upon removal or disconnection of a battery or a low-battery condition.
(4) A rechargeable battery used as a secondary power source shall meet the following criteria:
  (a) Be automatically recharged by an ac circuit of the commercial light and power source
  (b) Be recharged within 48 hours
  (c) Provide a distinctive audible trouble signal before the battery is incapable of operating the device(s) for alarm purposes

(5) Low-power wireless systems shall comply with the performance criteria of Section 23.16.

29.6.3 AC Primary Power Source. The ac power source shall comply with the following conditions:

(1) A visible "power on" indicator shall be provided.
(2) All electrical systems designed to be installed by other than a qualified electrician shall be powered from a source not in excess of 30 volts that meets the requirements for power-limited fire alarm circuits as defined in *NFPA 70, National Electrical Code,* Article 760.
(3) A restraining means shall be used at the plug-in of any cord-connected installation.
(4) AC primary (main) power shall be supplied either from a dedicated branch circuit or the unswitched portion of a branch circuit also used for power and lighting.
(5) Operation of a switch (other than a circuit breaker) shall not cause loss of primary (main) power. Operation of a ground-fault circuit-interrupter (GFCI) receptacle shall not cause loss of primary (main) power. Smoke alarms powered by branch circuits protected by arc-fault circuit-interrupters (AFCI) or GFCI circuit breakers shall have a secondary power source.
(6) Neither loss nor restoration of primary (main) power shall cause an alarm signal.

Exception: An alarm signal shall be permitted but shall not exceed 2 seconds.

(7) Where a secondary (standby) battery is provided, the primary (main) power supply shall be of sufficient capacity to operate the system under all conditions of loading with any secondary (standby) battery disconnected or fully discharged.

29.6.4 Secondary (Standby) Power Source. Where alarms include a battery that is used as a secondary power source, the following conditions shall be met:

(1) The secondary power source shall be supervised and shall cause a distinctive audible or visible trouble signal upon removal or disconnection of a battery or a low-battery condition.
(2) Acceptable replacement batteries shall be clearly identified by the manufacturer's name and model number on the unit near the battery compartment.
(3) A rechargeable battery used as a secondary power source shall meet the following criteria:
  (a) Be automatically recharged by the primary power source
  (b) Be recharged within 4 hours where power is provided from a circuit that can be switched on or off by means other than a circuit breaker, or within 48 hours where power is provided from a circuit that cannot be switched on or off by means other than a circuit breaker
  (c) Provide a distinctive audible trouble signal before the battery is incapable of operating the device(s) for alarm purposes
  (d) At the battery condition at which a trouble signal is obtained, be capable of producing an alarm signal for at least 4 minutes, followed by not less than 7 days of trouble signal operation
  (e) Produce an audible trouble signal at least once every minute for 7 consecutive days

29.6.5 Notification Appliance (with Smoke or Heat Alarm). If a visible notification appliance is used in conjunction with a smoke or heat alarm application for compliance with 29.3.7, the notification appliance shall not be required to be supplied with a secondary power source.

29.6.6 Primary Power Source (Nonrechargeable Battery). If smoke alarms are powered by a primary battery, the battery shall be monitored to ensure the following conditions are met:

(1) All power requirements are met for at least 1 year of battery life, including weekly testing.
(2) A distinctive audible trouble signal before the battery is incapable of operating (from causes such as aging or terminal corrosion) the device(s) for alarm purposes.
(3) For a unit employing a lock-in alarm feature, automatic transfer is provided from alarm to a trouble condition.
(4) At the battery voltage at which a trouble signal is obtained, the unit is capable of producing an alarm signal for at least 4 minutes, followed by not less than 7 days of trouble signal operation.
(5) The audible trouble signal is produced at least once every minute for 7 consecutive days.
(6) Acceptable replacement batteries are clearly identified by the manufacturer's name and model number on the unit near the battery compartment.
(7) A noticeable, visible indication is displayed when a primary battery is removed from the unit.

29.6.7 Primary Power Source (Rechargeable Battery). If smoke alarms are powered by a rechargeable battery, the following conditions shall be met:

(1) The battery shall, with proper charging, be able to power the alarm for a life of 1 year.
(2) The battery shall be automatically recharged by an circuit of the commercial light and power source.
(3) The battery shall be recharged within 4 hours where power is provided from a circuit that can be switched on or off by means other than a circuit breaker, or within 48 hours where power is provided from a circuit that cannot be switched on or off by means other than a circuit breaker.
(4) A distinctive audible trouble signal shall sound before the battery is incapable of operating the device(s) for alarm purposes.
(5) For a unit employing a lock-in alarm feature, automatic transfer shall be provided from alarm to a trouble condition.
(6) At the battery condition at which a trouble signal is obtained, the unit shall be capable of producing an alarm signal for at least 4 minutes, followed by not less than 7 days of trouble signal operation.
(7) The audible trouble signal shall be produced at least once every minute for 7 consecutive days.

29.6.8 Secondary (Standby) Non-Battery Power Source. Where alarms include a secondary power source (non-battery), the following conditions shall be met:

(1) The secondary power source shall be supervised and shall cause a distinctive audible or visible trouble signal upon depletion or failure.
(2) A distinctive audible trouble signal shall be provided before the power source is incapable of operating the device(s) for alarm purposes.

(3) At a power source condition at which a trouble signal is obtained, the power source shall be capable of producing an alarm signal for at least 4 minutes, followed by not less than 7 days of trouble signal operation.
(4) The audible trouble signal shall be produced at least once every minute for 7 consecutive days.
(5) A rechargeable secondary power source shall meet the following criteria:
   (a) Be automatically recharged.
   (b) Be recharged within 4 hours where power is provided from a circuit that can be switched on or off by means other than a circuit breaker, or within 48 hours where power is provided from a circuit that cannot be switched on or off by means other than a circuit breaker.

29.7 Equipment Performance.

29.7.1 Self-Diagnostic. Any failure of any nonreliable or short-life component that renders the detector inoperable shall result in a trouble signal or otherwise be apparent to the occupant of the living unit without the need for test.

29.7.2* Smoke Alarms, System Smoke Detectors, and Other Non-Heat Fire Detectors. Each device shall detect abnormal quantities of smoke or applicable fire signature, shall operate in the normal environmental conditions, and shall be in compliance with applicable standards such as ANSI/UL 268, *Standard for Smoke Detectors for Fire Alarm Systems*, or ANSI/UL 217, *Standard for Single and Multiple Station Smoke Alarms*.

29.7.3 Resistance to Nuisance Source. Effective January 1, 2019, smoke alarms and smoke detectors used in household fire alarm systems shall be listed for resistance to common nuisance sources.

29.7.4* Heat Detectors and Heat Alarms.

29.7.4.1 Each heat detector and heat alarm, including a heat detector or heat alarm integrally mounted on a smoke detector or smoke alarm, shall detect abnormally high temperature or rate-of-temperature rise, and all such detectors shall be listed for not less than 50 ft (15 m) spacing.

29.7.4.2* Fixed-temperature detectors or alarms shall have a temperature rating at least 25°F (14°C) above the normal ambient temperature and shall not be rated 50°F (28°C) higher than the maximum anticipated ambient temperature in the room or space where installed.

29.7.5 Operability. Single- and multiple-station alarms, including heat alarms, shall be provided with a convenient means for testing its operability by the occupant, system owner, or other responsible parties.

29.7.6 System Control Equipment.

29.7.6.1 The system control equipment shall be automatically restoring upon restoration of electrical power.

29.7.6.2 The system control equipment shall be of a type that "locks in" on an alarm condition. Smoke detection circuits shall not be required to lock in.

29.7.6.3 If a reset switch is provided, it shall be of a self-restoring (momentary operation) type.

29.7.6.4 A means for silencing the trouble notification appliance(s) shall be permitted only if the following conditions are satisfied:

(1) The means is key-operated or located within a locked enclosure, or arranged to provide equivalent protection against unauthorized use.

(2) The means transfers the trouble indication to an identified lamp or other acceptable visible indicator, and the visible indication persists until the trouble condition has been corrected.

29.7.6.5 A means for turning off activated alarm notification appliances shall be permitted only if the following conditions are satisfied:

(1) The means is key-operated or located within a locked cabinet, or arranged to provide equivalent protection against unauthorized use.
(2) The means includes the provision of a visible alarm silence indication.

29.7.6.6 Household fire alarm system smoke detectors, initiating devices, and notification appliances shall be monitored for integrity so that the occurrence of a single open or single ground fault in the interconnection, which prevents normal operation of the interconnected devices, is indicated by a distinctive trouble signal.

29.7.6.7 System control equipment shall be in compliance with applicable standards such as ANSI/UL 985, *Standard for Household Fire Warning System Units*; ANSI/UL 1730, *Standard for Smoke Detector Monitors and Accessories for Individual Living Units of Multifamily Residences and Hotel/Motel Rooms*; or ANSI/UL 864, *Standard for Control Units and Accessories for Fire Alarm Systems*.

29.7.7 Combination System.

29.7.7.1 If designed and installed to perform additional functions, fire-warning equipment shall operate reliably and without compromise to its primary functions.

29.7.7.2 Fire signals shall take precedence over any other signal or functions, even if a non-fire signal is activated first.

29.7.7.3 Signals shall be distinctive so that a fire signal can be distinguished from signals that require different actions by the occupants.

29.7.7.4 Faults in other systems or components shall not affect the operation of the fire alarm system.

29.7.7.5 Where common wiring is employed for a combination system, the equipment for other than the fire alarm system shall be connected to the common wiring of the system so that short circuits, open circuits, grounds, or any fault in this equipment or interconnection between this equipment and the fire alarm system wiring does not interfere with the supervision of the fire alarm system or prevent alarm or trouble signal operation.

29.7.7.6 In a fire/burglar system, the operation shall be as follows:

(1) A fire alarm signal shall take precedence or be clearly recognizable over any other signal, even when the non-fire alarm signal is initiated first.
(2) Distinctive alarm signals shall be used so that fire alarms can be distinguished from other functions, such as burglar alarms. The use of a common-sounding appliance for fire and burglar alarms shall be permitted where distinctive signals are used.

29.7.7.7* Installations that include the connection of single- or multiple-station alarms with other input or output devices shall be permitted. An open, ground fault or short circuit of the wiring connecting input or output devices to the single- or multiple-station alarms shall not prevent operation of each individual alarm.

29.7.7.7.1 Single- or multiple-station smoke alarms shall be permitted to be connected to system control equipment located within the dwelling unit.

29.7.7.7.2 When connected, the actuation of a single- or multiple-station smoke alarm shall initiate an alarm signal at the system control equipment located within the dwelling unit.

29.7.7.7.3 A sprinkler waterflow alarm initiating device shall be permitted to be connected to the multiple-station alarms or household fire alarm system to activate an alarm signal.

29.7.8 Wireless Devices.

29.7.8.1 Wireless Systems. Household fire alarm systems utilizing low-power wireless transmission of signals within the protected dwelling unit shall comply with the requirements of Section 23.16.

29.7.8.2 Nonsupervised Wireless Interconnected Alarms.

29.7.8.2.1* To ensure adequate transmission and reception capability, nonsupervised, low-power wireless alarms shall be capable of reliably communicating at a distance of 100 ft (30.5 m) indoors as tested to an equivalent open area test distance, D_{EOAT} between two devices in accordance with the following equations:

$$D_{EOAT} = 30.5 \times \left(10^{\frac{L_b}{40}} \right)$$

where L_b is the building attenuation factor, a value dependent on the frequency of the wireless transmission. The building attenuation factor, L_b, represents the maximum attenuation value of typical floors and walls within a majority of structures. The factor L_b shall assume four walls and two floors and be calculated as follows:

$$L_b = 4 \times L_w + 2 \times L_f$$

where:
L_w = attenuation value of a wall
　　= $2 \times L_1 + L_2$
L_f = attenuation value of a floor
　　= $L_1 + L_2 + L_3 + L_4$
L_1 = frequency-dependent attenuation value for ½ in. (13 mm) drywall
L_2 = frequency-dependent attenuation value for 1½ in. (38 mm) structural lumber
L_3 = frequency-dependent attenuation value for ¾ in. (19 mm) plywood
L_4 = frequency-dependent attenuation value for ½ in. (13 mm) glass/tile floor

29.7.8.2.2 Fire alarm signals shall have priority over all other signals.

29.7.8.2.3 The maximum allowable response delay from activation of an initiating device to receipt and alarm/display by the receiver/control unit shall be 20 seconds.

29.7.8.2.4* Wireless interconnected smoke alarms (in receive mode) shall remain in alarm as long as the originating unit (transmitter) remains in alarm.

29.7.8.2.5 The occurrence of any single fault that disables a transceiver shall not prevent other transceivers in the system from operating.

29.7.9 Supervising Stations.

29.7.9.1 Means to transmit alarm signals to a constantly attended, remote monitoring location shall be processed by a household fire alarm system and shall perform as described in Chapter 26, except as modified by 29.7.9.1.1 through 29.7.9.1.6.

29.7.9.1.1 Where a digital alarm communicator transmitter (DACT) is used, the DACT serving the protected premises shall only require a single telephone line and shall only require a call to a single digital alarm communicator receiver (DACR) number.

29.7.9.1.2 Where a DACT is used, the DACT test signals shall be transmitted at least monthly.

29.7.9.1.3 Where a communication or transmission means other than DACT is used, only a single communication technology and path is required to serve the protected premises.

29.7.9.1.4 Failure of the communication path referenced in 29.7.9.1.3 shall be annunciated at the constantly attended remote monitoring location and at the protected premises within not more than 7 days of the failure.

29.7.9.1.5 Supervising station systems shall not be required to comply with requirements for indication of central station service in 26.3.4.

29.7.9.1.6 A dedicated cellular telephone connection shall be permitted to be used as a single means to transmit alarms to a constantly attended remote monitoring location.

29.7.9.2* Remote monitoring stations shall be permitted to verify alarm signals prior to reporting them to the fire service, provided that the verification process does not delay the reporting by more than 90 seconds.

29.7.9.3 Household fire alarm systems shall be programed by the manufacturer to generate at least a monthly test of the communication or transmission means.

29.7.9.4 The activation of a keypad fire alarm signal shall require a manual operation of two simultaneous or sequential operations.

29.8 Installation.

29.8.1 General.

29.8.1.1 All equipment shall be installed in accordance with the manufacturer's published instructions and applicable electrical standards.

29.8.1.2 All devices shall be so located and mounted that accidental operation is not caused by jarring or vibration.

29.8.1.3 All fire-warning equipment shall be mounted so as to be supported independently of its attachment to wires.

29.8.1.4 The supplier or installing contractor shall provide the system owner or other responsible parties with the following:

(1) An instruction booklet illustrating typical installation layouts
(2) Instruction charts describing the operation, method, and frequency of testing and maintenance of fire-warning equipment
(3) Printed information for establishing an emergency evacuation plan

(4) Printed information to inform system owners where they can obtain repair or replacement service, and where and how parts requiring regular replacement, such as batteries or bulbs, can be obtained within 2 weeks
(5) Information noting both of the following:
   (a) Unless otherwise recommended by the manufacturer's published instructions, smoke alarms shall be replaced when they fail to respond to tests.
   (b) Smoke alarms installed in one- and two-family dwellings shall not remain in service longer than 10 years from the date of manufacture.

29.8.2 Interconnection of Detectors or Multiple-Station Alarms.

29.8.2.1 Smoke detectors shall be connected to central controls for power, signal processing, and activation of notification appliances.

29.8.2.2* The interconnection of smoke or heat alarms shall comply with the following:

(1) Smoke or heat alarms shall not be interconnected in numbers that exceed the manufacturer's published instructions.
(2) In no case shall more than 18 initiating devices be interconnected (of which 12 can be smoke alarms) where the interconnecting means is not supervised.
(3) In no case shall more than 64 initiating devices be interconnected (of which 42 can be smoke alarms) where the interconnecting means is supervised.
(4) Smoke or heat alarms shall not be interconnected with alarms from other manufacturers unless listed as being compatible with the specific model.
(5) When alarms of different types are interconnected, all interconnected alarms shall produce the appropriate audible response for the phenomena being detected or remain silent.

29.8.2.3 A single fault on the interconnecting means between multiple-station alarms shall not prevent single-station operation of any of the interconnected alarms.

29.8.2.4 Remote notification appliance circuits of multiple-station alarms shall be capable of being tested for integrity by activation of the test feature on any interconnected alarm. Activation of the test feature shall result in the operation of all interconnected notification appliances.

29.8.3* Smoke Alarms and Smoke Detectors. Smoke alarms, smoke detectors, devices, combination of devices, and equipment shall be installed in accordance with the manufacturer's listing and published instructions, and, unless specifically listed for the application, shall comply with requirements in 29.8.3.1 through 29.8.3.4.

29.8.3.1* Peaked Ceilings. Smoke alarms or smoke detectors mounted on a peaked ceiling shall be located within 36 in. (910 mm) horizontally of the peak, but not closer than 4 in. (100 mm) vertically to the peak.

29.8.3.2* Sloped Ceilings. Smoke alarms or smoke detectors mounted on a sloped ceiling having a rise greater than 1 ft in 8 ft (1 m in 8 m) horizontally shall be located within 36 in. (910 mm) of the high side of the ceiling, but not closer than 4 in. (100 mm) from the adjoining wall surface.

29.8.3.3* Wall Mounting. Smoke alarms or smoke detectors mounted on walls shall be located not farther than 12 in. (300 mm) from the adjoining ceiling surface.

29.8.3.4 Specific Location Requirements. The installation of smoke alarms and smoke detectors shall comply with the following requirements:

(1) Smoke alarms and smoke detectors shall not be located where ambient conditions, including humidity and temperature, are outside the limits specified by the manufacturer's published instructions.

(2) Smoke alarms and smoke detectors shall not be located within unfinished attics or garages or in other spaces where temperatures can fall below 40°F (4°C) or exceed 100°F (38°C).

(3)*Where the mounting surface could become considerably warmer or cooler than the room, such as a poorly insulated ceiling below an unfinished attic or an exterior wall, smoke alarms and smoke detectors shall be mounted on an inside wall.

(4)*Smoke alarms and smoke detectors shall not be installed within an area of exclusion determined by a 10 ft (3.0 m) radial distance along a horizontal flow path from a stationary or fixed cooking appliance, unless listed for installation in close proximity to cooking appliances. Smoke alarms and smoke detectors installed between 10 ft (3.0 m) and 20 ft (6.1 m) along a horizontal flow path from a stationary or fixed cooking appliance shall be equipped with an alarm-silencing means or use photoelectric detection.

Exception: Smoke alarms or smoke detectors that use photoelectric detection shall be permitted for installation at a radial distance greater than 6 ft (1.8 m) from any stationary or fixed cooking appliance when the following conditions are met:

(a) *The kitchen or cooking area and adjacent spaces have no clear interior partitions or headers and*

(b) *The 10 ft (3.0 m) area of exclusion would prohibit the placement of a smoke alarm or smoke detector required by other sections of this code.*

(5) Effective January 1, 2016, smoke alarms and smoke detectors used in household fire alarm systems installed between 6 ft (1.8 m) and 20 ft (6.1 m) along a horizontal flow path from a stationary or fixed cooking appliance shall be listed for resistance to common nuisance sources from cooking.

(6)*Smoke alarms and smoke detectors shall not be installed within a 36 in. (910 mm) horizontal path from a door to a bathroom containing a shower or tub unless listed for installation in close proximity to such locations.

(7) Smoke alarms and smoke detectors shall not be installed within a 36 in. (910 mm) horizontal path from the supply registers of a forced air heating or cooling system and shall be installed outside of the direct airflow from those registers.

(8) Smoke alarms and smoke detectors shall not be installed within a 36 in. (910 mm) horizontal path from the tip of the blade of a ceiling-suspended (paddle) fan.

(9) Where stairs lead to other occupiable levels, a smoke alarm or smoke detector shall be located so that smoke rising in the stairway cannot be prevented from reaching the smoke alarm or smoke detector by an intervening door or obstruction.

(10) For stairways leading up from a basement, smoke alarms or smoke detectors shall be located on the basement ceiling near the entry to the stairs.

(11)*For tray-shaped ceilings (coffered ceilings), smoke alarms and smoke detectors shall be installed on the highest portion of the ceiling or on the sloped portion of the ceiling within 12 in. (300 mm) vertically down from the highest point.

(12) Smoke alarms and detectors installed in rooms with joists or beams shall comply with the requirements of 17.7.3.2.4.

(13) Heat alarms and detectors installed in rooms with joists or beams shall comply with the requirements of 17.6.3.

29.8.4* Heat Detectors and Heat Alarms.

29.8.4.1* On smooth ceilings, heat detectors and heat alarms shall be installed within the strict limitations of their listed spacing.

29.8.4.2* For sloped ceilings having a rise greater than 1 ft in 8 ft (1 m in 8 m) horizontally, the detector or alarm shall be located within 36 in. (910 mm) of the peak. The spacing of additional detectors or alarms, if any, shall be based on a horizontal distance measurement, not on a measurement along the slope of the ceiling.

29.8.4.3* Heat detectors or alarms shall be mounted on the ceiling at least 4 in. (100 mm) from a wall or on a wall with the top of the detector or alarm not less than 4 in. (100 mm), nor more than 12 in. (300 mm), below the ceiling.

Exception: Where the mounting surface could become considerably warmer or cooler than the room, such as a poorly insulated ceiling below an unfinished attic or an exterior wall, the detectors or alarms shall be mounted on an inside wall.

29.8.4.4 In rooms with open joists or beams, all ceiling-mounted detectors or alarms shall be located on the bottom of such joists or beams.

29.8.4.5* Detectors or alarms installed on an open-joisted ceiling shall have their smooth ceiling spacing reduced where this spacing is measured at right angles to solid joists; in the case of heat detectors or heat alarms, this spacing shall not exceed one-half of the listed spacing.

29.8.5 Wiring and Equipment. The installation of wiring and equipment shall be in accordance with the requirements of *NFPA 70, National Electrical Code,* Article 760.

29.9 Optional Functions. The following optional functions of fire-warning equipment shall be permitted:

(1) Notification of the fire department, either directly or through an alarm monitoring service

(2) Monitoring of other safety systems, such as fire sprinklers for alarm or proper operating conditions

(3) Notification of occupants or others of potentially dangerous conditions, such as the presence of fuel gases or toxic gases such as carbon monoxide

(4) Notification of occupants or others of the activation of intrusion (burglar alarm) sensors

(5) Any other function, safety related or not, that could share components or wiring

---

Section 29.10 final content is the result of a tentative interim amendment (TIA). See page 1.

29.10 Maintenance and Tests. Fire-warning equipment shall be maintained and tested in accordance with the manufacturer's published instructions and per the requirements of Chapter 14.

29.11 Markings and Instructions.

29.11.1 Alarms. All alarms shall be plainly marked with the following information on the unit:

(1) Manufacturer's or listee's name, address, and model number
(2) A mark or certification that the unit has been approved or listed by a testing laboratory
(3) Electrical rating (where applicable)
(4) Manufacturer's published operating and maintenance instructions
(5) Test instructions
(6) Replacement and service instructions
(7) Identification of lights, switches, meters, and similar devices regarding their function, unless their function is obvious
(8) Distinction between alarm and trouble signals on units employing both
(9) The sensitivity setting for an alarm having a fixed setting (For an alarm that is intended to be adjusted in the field, the range of sensitivity shall be indicated. The marked sensitivity shall be indicated as a percent per foot obscuration level. The marking shall include a nominal value plus tolerance.)
(10) Reference to an installation diagram and system owner's manual
(11) Date of manufacture in the format YEAR (in four digits), MONTH (in letters), and DAY (in two digits) located on the outside of the alarm

Exception: Where space limitations prohibit inclusion of 29.11.1(4) and (6), it is not prohibited for this information to be in the installation instructions instead.

29.11.2 Fire Alarm Control Unit. All household fire-warning equipment or systems shall be plainly marked with the following information on the unit:

(1) Manufacturer's or listee's name, address, and model number
(2) A mark or certification that the unit has been approved or listed by a testing laboratory
(3) Electrical rating (where applicable)
(4) Identification of all user interface components and their functions (such as, but not limited to, lights, switches, and meters) located adjacent to the component
(5) Manufacturer's published operating and maintenance instructions
(6) Test instructions
(7) Replacement and service instructions
(8) Reference to an installation wiring diagram and homeowner's manual, if not attached to control unit, by drawing number and issue number and/or date

Exception: Where space limitations prohibit inclusion of 29.11.2(5) and (7), it is not prohibited for this information to be in the installation instructions instead.

Annex A   Explanatory Material

Annex A is not a part of the requirements of this NFPA document but is included for informational purposes only. This annex contains explanatory material, numbered to correspond with the applicable text paragraphs.

A.1.2 Fire alarm systems intended for life safety should be designed, installed, and maintained to provide indication and warning of abnormal fire conditions. The system should alert building occupants and summon appropriate aid in adequate time to allow for occupants to travel to a safe place and for rescue operations to occur. The fire alarm system should be part of a life safety plan that also includes a combination of prevention, protection, egress, and other features particular to that occupancy.

A.1.2.4 The intent of this paragraph is to make it clear that the protection requirements are derived from the applicable building or fire code, not from *NFPA 72*.

A.1.6.5 Where dimensions are expressed in inches, it is intended that the precision of the measurement be 1 in., thus plus or minus ½ in. The conversion and presentation of dimensions in millimeters would then have a precision of 25 mm, thus plus or minus 13 mm.

A.3.2.1 Approved. The National Fire Protection Association does not approve, inspect, or certify any installations, procedures, equipment, or materials; nor does it approve or evaluate testing laboratories. In determining the acceptability of installations, procedures, equipment, or materials, the authority having jurisdiction may base acceptance on compliance with NFPA or other appropriate standards. In the absence of such standards, said authority may require evidence of proper installation, procedure, or use. The authority having jurisdiction may also refer to the listings or labeling practices of an organization that is concerned with product evaluations and is thus in a position to determine compliance with appropriate standards for the current production of listed items.

A.3.2.2 Authority Having Jurisdiction (AHJ). The phrase "authority having jurisdiction," or its acronym AHJ, is used in NFPA documents in a broad manner, since jurisdictions and approval agencies vary, as do their responsibilities. Where public safety is primary, the authority having jurisdiction may be a federal, state, local, or other regional department or individual such as a fire chief; fire marshal; chief of a fire prevention bureau, labor department, or health department; building official; electrical inspector; or others having statutory authority. For insurance purposes, an insurance inspection department, rating bureau, or other insurance company representative may be the authority having jurisdiction. In many circumstances, the property owner or his or her designated agent assumes the role of the authority having jurisdiction; at government installations, the commanding officer or departmental official may be the authority having jurisdiction.

A.3.2.3 Code. The decision to designate a standard as a "code" is based on such factors as the size and scope of the document, its intended use and form of adoption, and whether it contains substantial enforcement and administrative provisions.

A.3.2.5 Listed. The means for identifying listed equipment may vary for each organization concerned with product evaluation; some organizations do not recognize equipment as listed unless it is also labeled. The authority having jurisdiction should utilize the system employed by the listing organization to identify a listed product.

A.3.3.6 Acoustically Distinguishable Space (ADS). All parts of a building or area intended to have occupant notification are subdivided into ADSs as defined. Some ADSs might be designated to have voice communication capability and require that those communications be intelligible. Other spaces might not require voice intelligibility or might not be capable of reliable voice intelligibility. An ADS might have acoustical design features that are conducive for voice intelligibility, or it might be a space where voice intelligibility could be difficult or impossible to achieve. Each is still referred to as an ADS.

In smaller areas, such as those under 400 ft² (40 m²), walls alone will define the ADS. In larger areas, other factors might have to be considered. In spaces that might be subdivided by temporary or movable partitions, such as ballrooms and meeting rooms, each individual configuration should be considered a separate ADS. Physical characteristics, such as a change in ceiling height of more than 20 percent, or a change in acoustical finish, such as carpet in one area and tile in another, would require those areas to be treated as separate ADSs. In larger areas, there might be noise sources that require a section to be treated as a separate ADS. Any significant change in ambient noise level or frequency might necessitate an area be considered a separate ADS.

In areas of 85 dBA or greater ambient sound pressure level, meeting the pass/fail criteria for intelligibility might not be possible, and other means of communication might be necessary. So, for example, the space immediately surrounding a printing press or other high-noise machine might be designated as a separate ADS, and the design might call for some form of effective notification but not necessarily require the ability to have intelligible voice communication. The aisles or operator's control stations might be separate ADSs where intelligible voice communication might be desired.

Significant differences in furnishings, for example, an area with tables, desks, or low dividers, adjacent to an area with high shelving, would require separate consideration. The entire desk area could be a single acoustic zone, whereas each area between shelving could be a unique zone. Essentially, any noteworthy change in the acoustical environment within an area will mandate consideration of that portion of the area to be treated as an acoustic zone. Hallways and stairwells will typically be considered as individual acoustic zones.

Spaces confined by walls with carpeting and acoustical ceilings can be deemed to be one ADS. An ADS should be an area of consistent size and material. A change of materials from carpet to hard tile, the existence of sound sources, such as decorative waterfalls, large expanses of glass, and changes in ceiling height, are all factors that might separate one ADS from another.

Each ADS might require different components and design features to achieve intelligible voice communication. For example, two ADSs with similar acoustical treatments and noise levels might have different ceiling heights. The ADS with the lower ceiling height might require more ceiling-mounted speakers to ensure that all listeners are in a direct sound field

(see Figure A.3.3.6). Other ADSs might benefit from the use of alternate speaker technologies, such as line arrays, to achieve intelligibility.

An ADS that differs from another because of the frequency and level of ambient noise might require the use of speakers and system components that have a wider frequency bandwidth than conventional emergency communications equipment. However, designers should not use higher bandwidth speakers in all locations, unless needed to overcome certain acoustic and ambient conditions. This is because the higher bandwidth appliance will require more energy to perform properly. This increases amplifier and wire size and power supply requirements.

In some spaces, it might be impractical to achieve intelligibility, and, in such a case, alternatives to voice evacuation might be required within such areas.

There might be some areas of a facility where there are several spaces of the same approximate size and the same acoustic properties. For example, there might be an office space with multiple individual offices, each with one speaker. If one or two are satisfactorily tested, there is no need to test all of them for speech intelligibility.

A.3.3.29 Average Ambient Sound Level. The term *average ambient sound level* is also called the equivalent A-weighted sound level measured over t hours, where t is the time period over which the measurement is made. The standard industry symbol is $L_{A.eq.t}$. Where a measurement is taken over a 24-hour time period, the designation would be $L_{A.eq.24}$.

A.3.3.35.3 Sloping Peaked-Type Ceiling. Refer to Figure A.17.6.3.4(a) for an illustration of smoke or heat detector spacing on peaked-type sloped ceilings.

A.3.3.35.4 Sloping Shed-Type Ceiling. Refer to Figure A.17.6.3.4(b) for an illustration of smoke or heat detector spacing on shed-type sloped ceilings.

A.3.3.37.3 Smooth Ceiling. Open truss constructions are not considered to impede the flow of fire products unless the upper member, in continuous contact with the ceiling, projects below the ceiling more than 4 in. (100 mm).

A.3.3.43.3 Radio Channel. The width of the channel depends on the type of transmissions and the tolerance for the frequency of emission. Channels normally are allocated for radio transmission in a specified type for service by a specified transmitter.

A.3.3.47 Coded. Notification signal examples are numbered strokes of an impact-type appliance and numbered flashes of a visible appliance.

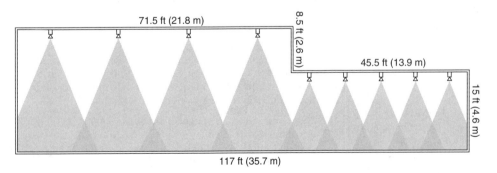

FIGURE A.3.3.6 Illustration Demonstrating the Effect of Ceiling Height. *(Source: R. P. Schifiliti Associates, Inc.)*

A.3.3.53 Communications Center. Examples of functions of a communications center are as follows:

(1) Communications between the public and the communications center
(2) Communications between the communications centers, the emergency response agency (ERA), and emergency response facilities (ERFs)
(3) Communications within the ERA and between different ERAs
[**1221:** A.3.3.17]
(4) Communications with the public emergency alarm reporting system

The central operating part of the public emergency alarm reporting system is usually located at the communications center.

A.3.3.57 Condition. See Figure A.3.3.57 that describes the Condition — Signal — Response model used in this Code. There are varying degrees of conditions that require varying degrees of response that are initiated by various types of signals. A condition could be present without being detected (either because detection of the condition was not required or was not feasible), in which case, there is no signal or response. A condition could be detected, resulting in a signal, but there could be no required response. A signal could be generated erroneously in the absence of a condition (due to malfunction or other causes) resulting in an unwarranted response. The condition is normal when no abnormal conditions are present.

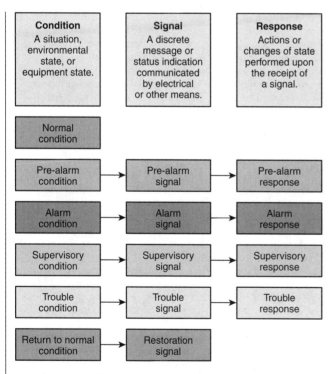

FIGURE A.3.3.57 Condition-Signal-Response Model.

A.3.3.57.1.1 Alarm Condition. When an alarm condition is present, damage to life or property has begun or will begin. Detection, signaling, and response, effected quickly, can limit or prevent damage. The extent of damage is often reduced with inverse proportion to the time required for detection, signaling, and response. The amount of time available for de-

tection, signaling, and response is generally not a known quantity and damage might not be preventable. Alarm conditions can result due to the presence of fire, chemicals, freezing temperatures, or other circumstances.

A.3.3.57.1.2 Pre-Alarm Condition. Some examples of pre-alarm conditions include the following: the presence of a very small amount of visible smoke (at levels below listed initiating device alarm thresholds), the presence of a smoke-like odor, a somewhat elevated temperature, and a gradually increasing temperature. Any abnormal condition that typically precedes an alarm condition can be termed a *pre-alarm condition.*

The amount of time available for investigating the cause of a pre-alarm condition is not a known quantity. If conditions deteriorate to the point of alarm, time is no longer available for investigation. Pre-alarm conditions might or might not progress to alarm conditions.

The detection of pre-alarm conditions may be desirable in some occupancies, particularly if environmental conditions are ordinarily well controlled (e.g., integrated circuit fabrication facility) and personnel are trained to respond appropriately. In other occupancies, the detection of pre-alarm conditions may not be desirable or necessary.

The term *pre-alarm condition* is different from the terms *positive alarm sequence, alarm verification,* and *pre-signal.*

A.3.3.57.1.3 Supervisory Condition. A supervisory condition occurs when one system supervises another system, process, or equipment for failure or impairment, and a functional failure or impairment to operation of the supervised system, process or equipment has occurred. A supervisory condition might be a regularly occurring and expected event such as a valve closed on a sprinkler system. A closed valve is an abnormal condition for the sprinkler system, but it does not constitute a trouble condition in the fire alarm or signaling system.

In some cases, a fault in one system, causing a trouble condition in that system, results in a supervisory condition in another system because the other system is supervising some function of the faulted system, and the supervised function has been impaired. In those cases, both supervisory and trouble conditions exist at the same time.

Some examples of supervisory conditions can include the following:

(1) An event causing the activation of a supervisory initiating device used to monitor an environmental parameter, system element, component, or function, whose failure poses a risk to life, property, or mission (e.g., sprinkler valve closed, water tank low water level, low building temperature, ECS impairment, and so forth).
(2) The failure of a guard to remain within established constraints while on tour, usually indicated by the absence of a guard's tour supervisory signal within prescribed timing requirements, or the presence of a guard's tour supervisory signal outside of prescribed sequencing requirements, or the presence of a delinquency signal.
(3) Public safety radio communications enhancement system antenna malfunction, signal booster failure, or battery depletion.
(4) In some cases, the presence of smoke in an HVAC duct or in other places as defined by the authority having jurisdiction.

A.3.3.57.1.4 Trouble Condition. A trouble condition is a fault in the fire alarm or signaling system. The system or some aspect of it is somehow broken. This is different from a supervisory condition that is an abnormal condition in a system that is supervised by the fire alarm or signaling system. Abnormal conditions, such as a closed valve in a sprinkler system, not caused by a fault are not considered trouble conditions.

In some cases, a fault in one system, causing a trouble condition in that system, results in a supervisory condition because another system is supervising some function of the faulted system, and the supervised function has been impaired by the fault *(see A.3.3.57.1.3, Supervisory Condition)*. In those cases, both supervisory and trouble conditions exist at the same time.

A.3.3.59.1 Autonomous Control Unit (ACU). Although an ACU might incorporate provisions for messages or signals from external sources, the ACU is fully capable of building controls without the need for sources outside the building. An ACU is allowed to be located within a primary building and supply circuits to immediately adjacent support buildings such as detached storage buildings. Larger buildings will generally have their own ACUs to allow individual control within each building.

A.3.3.66.4 Combination Detector. These detectors do not utilize a mathematical evaluation principle of signal processing more than a simple "or" function. Normally, these detectors provide a single response resulting from either sensing method, each of which operates independent of the other. These detectors can provide a separate and distinct response resulting from either sensing method, each of which is processed independent of the other.

A.3.3.66.7 Fixed-Temperature Detector. The difference between the operating temperature of a fixed-temperature device and the surrounding air temperature is proportional to the rate at which the temperature is rising. The rate is commonly referred to as *thermal lag*. The air temperature is always higher than the operating temperature of the device.

Typical examples of fixed-temperature sensing elements are as follows:

(1) *Bimetallic.* A sensing element comprised of two metals that have different coefficients of thermal expansion arranged so that the effect is deflection in one direction when heated and in the opposite direction when cooled.
(2) *Electrical Conductivity.* A line-type or spot-type sensing element in which resistance varies as a function of temperature.
(3) *Fusible Alloy.* A sensing element of a special composition metal (eutectic) that melts rapidly at the rated temperature.
(4) *Heat-Sensitive Cable.* A line-type device in which the sensing element comprises, in one type, two current-carrying wires separated by heat-sensitive insulation that softens at the rated temperature, thus allowing the wires to make electrical contact. In another type, a single wire is centered in a metallic tube, and the intervening space is filled with a substance that becomes conductive at a critical temperature, thus establishing electrical contact between the tube and the wire.
(5) *Liquid Expansion.* A sensing element comprising a liquid that is capable of marked expansion in volume in response to an increase in temperature.

A.3.3.66.8 Flame Detector. Flame detectors are categorized as ultraviolet, single wavelength infrared, ultraviolet infrared, or multiple wavelength infrared.

A.3.3.66.12 Multi-Criteria Detector. A multi-criteria detector is a detector that contains multiple sensing methods that respond to fire signature phenomena and utilizes mathematical evalua-

tion principles to determine the collective status of the device and generates a single output. Typical examples of multi-criteria detectors are a combination of a heat detector with a smoke detector, or a combination rate-of-rise and fixed-temperature heat detector that evaluates both signals using an algorithm to generate an output such as pre-alarm or alarm. The evaluation can be performed either at the detector or at the control unit. Other examples are detectors that include sensor combinations that respond in a predictable manner to any combination of heat, smoke, carbon monoxide, or carbon dioxide.

A.3.3.66.13 Multi-Sensor Detector. Typical examples of multi-sensor detectors are a combination of a heat detector with a smoke detector, or a combination rate-of-rise and fixed-temperature heat detector that evaluates both signals using an algorithm to generate an output such as pre-alarm or alarm. The evaluation can be performed either at the detector or at the control unit. Other examples are detectors that include sensor combinations that respond in a predictable manner to any combination of heat, smoke, carbon monoxide, or carbon dioxide.

A.3.3.66.18 Rate Compensation Detector. A typical example of a rate compensation detector is a spot-type detector with a tubular casing of a metal that tends to expand lengthwise as it is heated and an associated contact mechanism that closes at a certain point in the elongation. A second metallic element inside the tube exerts an opposing force on the contacts, tending to hold them open. The forces are balanced in such a way that, on a slow rate-of-temperature rise, there is more time for heat to penetrate to the inner element, which inhibits contact closure until the total device has been heated to its rated temperature level. However, on a fast rate-of-temperature rise, there is not as much time for heat to penetrate to the inner element, which exerts less of an inhibiting effect so that contact closure is achieved when the total device has been heated to a lower temperature. This, in effect, compensates for thermal lag.

A.3.3.66.19 Rate-of-Rise Detector. Typical examples of rate-of-rise detectors are as follows:

(1) *Pneumatic Rate-of-Rise Tubing.* A line-type detector comprising small-diameter tubing, usually copper, that is installed on the ceiling or high on the walls throughout the protected area. The tubing is terminated in a detector unit that contains diaphragms and associated contacts set to actuate at a predetermined pressure. The system is sealed except for calibrated vents that compensate for normal changes in temperature.
(2) *Spot-Type Pneumatic Rate-of-Rise Detector.* A device consisting of an air chamber, a diaphragm, contacts, and a compensating vent in a single enclosure. The principle of operation is the same as that described for pneumatic rate-of-rise tubing.
(3) *Electrical Conductivity–Type Rate-of-Rise Detector.* A line-type or spot-type sensing element in which resistance changes due to a change in temperature. The rate of change of resistance is monitored by associated control equipment, and an alarm is initiated when the rate of temperature increase exceeds a preset value.

A.3.3.78 Double Doorway. Refer to Figure 17.7.5.6.5.3(A) for an illustration of detector location requirements for double doors.

A.3.3.84 Ember. Class A and Class D combustibles burn as embers under conditions where the flame typically associated with fire does not necessarily exist. This glowing combustion yields radiant emissions in parts of the radiant energy spectrum that are radically different from those parts affected by flaming combustion. Specialized detectors that are specifically designed to detect those emissions should be used in applications where this type of combustion is expected. In general, flame detectors are not intended for the detection of embers.

A.3.3.89 Emergency Communications System — Emergency Command Center. An emergency command center can also include the mass notification system control.

A.3.3.90 Emergency Control Function Interface Device. The emergency control function interface device is a listed relay or other listed appliance that is part of the fire alarm system. An example of an emergency control function interface device is the fire alarm control relay that removes power to a fan control unit.

A.3.3.91 Emergency Control Functions. Emergency control functions are meant to be observed functions, not equipment or devices. Examples of emergency control functions are fan control (operation or shutdown), smoke damper operation, elevator recall, elevator power shutdown, door holder release, shutter release, door unlocking, activation of exit marking devices, and so forth. Fans, elevators, smoke dampers, door holders, shutters, locked doors, or exit marking devices themselves are not emergency control functions.

A.3.3.92 Emergency Response Facility (ERF). Examples of ERFs include a fire station, a police station, an ambulance station, a rescue station, a ranger station, and similar facilities. [**1221:** A.3.3.36]

A.3.3.94 Evacuation. Evacuation does not include the relocation of occupants within a building.

A.3.3.102 Fire Alarm Control Unit (FACU). In addition to the functions identified in the definition, a fire alarm control unit might have an integral operator interface, supply power to detection devices, notification appliances, transponder(s), or off-premises transmitter(s) or any combination of these. The control unit might also provide transfer of condition to relay or devices connected to the control unit. There can be multiple fire alarm control units in a fire alarm system.

A.3.3.102.2.1 Dedicated Function Fire Alarm Control Unit. Examples of a dedicated function fire alarm control unit include an automatic sprinkler alarm and supervisory control unit or an elevator recall control and supervisory control unit.

A.3.3.105.1 Combination System. Examples of non-fire systems are security, card access control, closed circuit television, sound reinforcement, background music, paging, sound masking, building automation, time, and attendance.

A.3.3.105.4 Protected Premises (Local) Fire Alarm System. A protected premises fire alarm system is any fire alarm system located at the protected premises. It can include any of the functions identified in Section 23.3. Where signals are transmitted to a communication center or supervising station, the protected premises fire alarm system also falls under the definition of one of the following systems: central station service alarm system, remote supervising station alarm system, proprietary supervising station alarm system, or auxiliary alarm system. The requirements that pertain to these systems apply in addition to the requirements for the protected premises fire alarm systems.

A.3.3.106 Fire Command Center. The fire command center should contain the following features as applicable to the specific facility:

(1) Emergency voice/alarm communication system unit
(2) Fire department communications unit
(3) Fire detection and alarm system annunciator unit
(4) Annunciator unit visually indicating the location of the elevators and whether they are operational
(5) Status indicators and controls for air-handling systems
(6) The required fire-fighter's control panel for smoke control systems installed in the building
(7) Controls for unlocking stairway doors simultaneously
(8) Sprinkler valve and waterflow detector display panels
(9) Emergency and standby power status indicators
(10) Telephone for fire department use with controlled access to the public telephone system
(11) Fire pump status indicators
(12) Schematic building plans indicating the typical floor plan and detailing the building core, means of egress, fire protection systems, fire-fighting equipment, and fire department access
(13) Worktable
(14) Generator supervision devices, manual start, and transfer features
(15) Public address system
(16) Other emergency systems identified in emergency response plan

A.3.3.122 Hearing Loss. The severity of hearing loss is measured by the degree of loudness, as measured in decibels, a sound must attain before being detected by an individual. Hearing loss can be ranked as mild, moderate, severe, or profound. It is quite common for someone to have more than one degree of hearing loss (e.g., mild sloping to severe). The following list shows the rankings and their corresponding decibel ranges:

(1) Mild:
   (a) For adults: between 25 and 40 dB
   (b) For children: between 15 and 40 dB
(2) Moderate: between 41 and 55 dB
(3) Moderately severe: between 56 and 70 dB
(4) Severe: between 71 and 90 dB
(5) Profound: 90 dB or greater

NIOSH defines material hearing impairment as an average of the hearing threshold levels for both ears that exceeds 25 dB at 1000, 2000, 3000, and 4000 Hz.

The American Medical Association indicates that a person has suffered material impairment when testing reveals a 25 dB average hearing loss from audiometric zero at 500, 1000, 2000, and 3000 Hz. OSHA has recognized that this is the lowest level of hearing loss that constitutes any material hearing impairment.

A.3.3.129 Identified (as Applied to Equipment). Some examples of ways to determine suitability of equipment for a specific purpose, environment, or application include investigations by a qualified testing laboratory (listing and labeling), an inspection agency, or other organizations concerned with product evaluation. [**70:**100, Informational Note]

A.3.3.130 Impairment. An impairment is a system component or function that is not working properly. This might be due to an intentional act, such as closing a valve or disabling an initiating device. Or, the impairment might be caused by a deficiency in a piece of equipment or subsystem.

Temporarily shutting down a system as part of performing the routine inspection, testing, and maintenance on that system while under constant attendance by qualified personnel, and where the system can be restored to service quickly, should not be considered an impairment. Good judgment should be considered for the hazards presented.

A.3.3.130.1 Emergency Impairment. Examples of emergency impairment include things such as physical damage to a control unit or wiring.

A.3.3.130.2 Planned Impairment. Examples of a planned impairment include things such as the addition of new devices or appliances or reprogramming of system software.

A.3.3.136 Intelligible. The term *intelligible* is intended to address only the communications channel and the acoustic environment as shown in Figure A.3.3.136. Intelligibility assumes that the talker or recorded voice message is in a language and using words known to the listener. It also assumes that the listener has normal hearing.

A.3.3.137.1.2 Emergency Control Function Interface. See Figure A.3.3.137.1.2.

A.3.3.137.2 Fire Alarm Control Interface. Some mass notification systems' autonomous control units (ACUs) might not be listed to UL 864 for fire alarm service. Any component that is connected to the fire alarm system must be connected through a listed interface that will protect the functions of other systems should one system experience a failure. This can be through isolation modules, control relays, or other approved means that are listed for the intended use. As an example, failure of a stand-alone ACU should not affect any function of the FACU.

A.3.3.146 Local Operating Console (LOC). An LOC allows users within a building to activate prerecorded messages, deliver live voice messages, observe current status of the main autonomous control unit (ACU), or have similar such ACU operator functions at various locations within the building. An LOC serves a similar function as a remote fire alarm annunciator. However, there can be multiple LOC locations within a building, such as on each floor, at each main entry point, at the switchboard or receptionist's console, or as determined by a risk analysis.

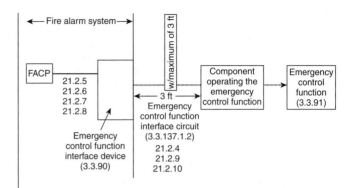

FIGURE A.3.3.137.1.2 Emergency Control Function Interface.

A.3.3.152 Managed Facilities-Based Voice Network (MFVN). Managed facilities-based voice network service is functionally equivalent to traditional PSTN-based services provided by authorized common carriers (public utility telephone companies) with respect to dialing, dial plan, call completion, carriage of signals and protocols, and loop voltage treatment and provides all of the following features:

(1) A loop start telephone circuit service interface.
(2) Pathway reliability that is assured by proactive management, operation, and maintenance by the MFVN provider.
(3) 8 hours of standby power supply capacity for MFVN communications equipment either located at the protected premises or field deployed. Industry standards followed by the authorized common carriers (public utility telephone companies), and the other communications service providers that operate MFVNs, specifically engineer the selection of the size of the batteries, or other permanently located standby power source, in order to provide 8 hours of standby power with a reasonable degree of accuracy. Of course, over time, abnormal ambient conditions and battery aging can always have a potentially adverse effect on battery capacity. The MFVN field-deployed equipment typically monitors the condition of the standby battery and signals potential battery failure to permit the communications service provider to take appropriate action.
(4) 24 hours of standby power supply capacity for MFVN communications equipment located at the communication service provider's central office.

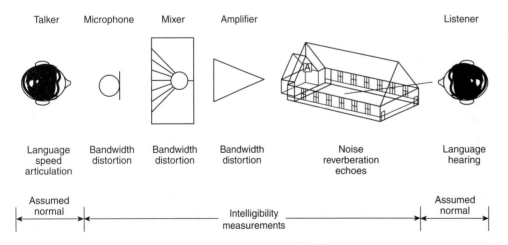

FIGURE A.3.3.136 Voice Signal Path. *(Source: K. Jacob, Bose® Professional Systems)*

(5) Installation of network equipment at the protected premises with safeguards to prevent unauthorized access to the equipment and its connections.

When providing telephone service to a new customer, MFVN providers give notice to the telephone service subscriber of the need to have any connected alarm system tested by authorized fire alarm service personnel in accordance with Chapter 14 to make certain that all signal transmission features have remained operational. These features include the proper functioning of line seizure and the successful transmission of signals to the supervising station. In this way, the MFVN providers assist their new customers in complying with a testing procedure similar to that outlined in 26.2.7 for changes to providers of supervising station service.

The evolution of the deployment of telephone service has moved beyond the sole use of metallic conductors connecting a telephone subscriber's premises with the nearest telephone service provider's control and routing point (wire center). In the last 25 years, telephone service providers have introduced a variety of technologies to transport multiple, simultaneous telephone calls over shared communication's pathways. In order to facilitate the further development of the modernization of the telephone network, the authorized common carriers (public utility telephone companies) have transitioned their equipment into a managed facilities-based voice network (MFVN) capable of providing a variety of communications services in addition to the provision of traditional telephone service.

Similarly, the evolution of digital communications technology has permitted entities other than the authorized common carriers (public utility telephone companies) to deploy robust communications networks and offer a variety of communications services, including telephone service.

These alternate service providers fall into two broad categories. The first category includes those entities that have emulated the MFVN provided by the authorized common carriers. The second category includes those entities that offer telephone service using means that do not offer the rigorous quality assurance, operational stability, and consistent features provided by an MFVN.

The Code intends to only recognize the use of the telephone network transmission of alarm, supervisory, trouble, and other emergency signals by means of MFVNs.

For example, the Code intends to permit an MFVN to provide facilities-based telephone (voice) service that interfaces with the premises fire alarm or emergency signal control unit through a digital alarm communicator transmitter (DACT) using a loop start telephone circuit and signaling protocols fully compatible with and equivalent to those used in public switched telephone networks. The loop start telephone circuit and associated signaling can be provided through traditional copper wire telephone service (POTS — "plain old telephone service") or by means of equipment that emulates the loop start telephone circuit and associated signaling and then transmits the signals over a pathway using packet switched (IP) networks or other communications methods that are part of an MFVN.

Providers of MFVNs have disaster recovery plans to address both individual customer outages and widespread events such as tornados, ice storms, or other natural disasters, which include specific network power restoration procedures equivalent to those of traditional landline telephone services.

A.3.3.154 Manufacturer's Published Instructions. Manufacturer's applicable documentation can be subject to revision.

A.3.3.155 Mass Notification Priority Mode. Nonemergency mass notification activations are not intended to initiate this mode of operation.

A.3.3.156 Mass Notification System. A mass notification system can use intelligible voice communications, visible signals, text, graphics, tactile, or other communications methods. The system can be used to initiate evacuation or relocation or to provide information to occupants. The system can be intended for fire emergencies, weather emergencies, terrorist events, biological, chemical or nuclear emergencies, or any combination of these. The system can be automatic, manual, or both. Access to and control of the system can be from a single, on-site location or can include multiple command locations, including some remote from the area served. Systems can be wired, wireless, or some combination of the two.

A.3.3.171 Nonrequired. There are situations where the applicable building or fire code does not require the installation of a fire alarm system or specific fire alarm system components, but the building owner wants to install a fire alarm system or component to meet site-specific needs or objectives. A building owner always has the option of installing protection that is above the minimum requirements of the Code. It is the intent of the Code that any fire alarm system, or fire alarm system components installed voluntarily by a building owner, meet the requirements of the applicable portions of the Code. However, it is not the intent of the Code that the installation of a nonrequired fire alarm system, or fire alarm system components, trigger requirements for the installation of additional fire alarm system components or features. For example, the installation of a fire alarm control unit and fire detectors to service a specific area, such as a computer room or flammable liquid storage room, does not trigger a requirement for audible or visible notification appliances, manual fire alarm boxes, or other fire alarm system features in other parts of the building.

A.3.3.173.1.2 Textual Audible Notification Appliance. An example of a textual audible notification appliance is a speaker that reproduces a voice message.

A.3.3.177 Occupiable. The term *occupiable* is used in this Code and in other governing laws, codes, or standards to determine areas that require certain features of a system. It is important for designers to understand that unless otherwise required, spaces that are not occupiable might not require or need coverage by initiating devices or occupant notification appliances. For example, most closets would not be considered to be occupiable. However, a space of the same size used as a file room would be considered occupiable.

A.3.3.179 Octave Band. Frequencies are generally reported based on a standard, preferred center frequency, f_c. The bandwidth of a particular octave band has a lower frequency, f_n, and an upper frequency, f_{n+1}. The relationships are as follows:

$$f_{n+1}/f_n = 2^k$$

where:

$k = 1$ for octave bands

$k = \frac{1}{3}$ for one-third octave bands

and

$$f_c = f_n\, 2^{1/2}$$

For example, the 500 Hz octave band (center frequency) has a lower limit of 354 and an upper limit of 707 Hz. The octave band with a center frequency of 1000 Hz has a lower frequency of 707 Hz and an upper frequency of 1414 Hz.

A.3.3.187 Ownership. Inspection, testing, and maintenance is the responsibility of the property or building owner, or it can be transferred by contract. Systems installed, owned, or leased by a tenant are the responsibility of the tenant. The installing company should provide written notice of these responsibilities to the system user.

A.3.3.215.1 Auxiliary Alarm System. Alarms from an auxiliary alarm system are received at the communications center on the same equipment and by the same methods as alarms transmitted from public alarm boxes.

A.3.3.222 Qualified. *Qualified* might also mean that the person has knowledge of the installation, construction, or operation of apparatus and the hazards involved.

A.3.3.229 Radio Frequency. The present practicable limits of radio frequency (RF) are roughly 10 kHz to 100,000 MHz. Within this frequency range, electromagnetic waves can be detected and amplified as an electric current at the wave frequency. *Radio frequency* usually refers to the *RF* of the assigned channel. [**1221**: A.3.3.65]

A.3.3.244 Response. Responses can be effected manually or automatically. One response to a signal might be to actuate notification appliances or transmitters, which in turn generate additional signals. See A.3.3.57.

A.3.3.244.1 Alarm Response. Examples include the actuation of alarm notification appliances, elevator recall, smoke control measures, emergency responder dispatch, deployment of resources in accordance with a risk analysis and emergency action plan, and so forth.

A.3.3.244.2 Pre-Alarm Response. Examples include the actuation of appropriate notification appliances, dispatch of personnel, investigation of circumstances and problem resolution in accordance with a risk analysis and action plan, preparation for a potential alarm response, and so forth.

A.3.3.244.3 Supervisory Response. Examples include the actuation of supervisory notification appliances, the shutdown of machines, fan shutdown or activation, dispatch of personnel, investigation of circumstances and problem resolution in accordance with a risk analysis and action plan, and so forth.

A.3.3.244.4 Trouble Response. Examples include the activation of trouble notification appliances, dispatch of service personnel, deployment of resources in accordance with an action plan, and so forth.

A.3.3.257 Signal. See A.3.3.57.

A.3.3.257.1 Alarm Signal. Examples of alarm signals include outputs of activated alarm initiating devices, the light and sound from actuated alarm notification appliances, alarm data transmission to a supervising station, and so forth.

A.3.3.257.5 Fire Alarm Signal. Examples include outputs from activated fire alarm initiating devices (manual fire alarm box, automatic fire detector, waterflow switch, etc.), the light and sound from actuated fire alarm notification appliances, fire alarm data transmission to a supervising station, and so forth.

A.3.3.257.6 Guard's Tour Supervisory Signal. The term *guard's tour supervisory signal*, associated with systems supporting guard's tour supervisory service, is a message indicating that a guard has activated a guard's tour reporting station (not in itself an indication of a supervisory condition). Guard's tour

supervisory signals are not a subset of the general category of supervisory signals as used in this Code.

A.3.3.257.7 Pre-Alarm Signal. Examples include outputs of analog initiating devices prior to reaching alarm levels, the light and sound from actuated pre-alarm notification appliances, aspiration system outputs indicating smoke at levels below the listed alarm threshold, and so forth.

A.3.3.257.9 Supervisory Signal. Examples include activated supervisory signal-initiating device outputs, supervisory data transmissions to supervising stations, the light and sound from actuated supervisory notification appliances, a delinquency signal indicating a guard's tour supervisory condition, and so forth.

The term *guard's tour supervisory signal*, associated with systems supporting guard's tour supervisory service, is a message indicating that a guard has activated a guard's tour reporting station (not in itself an indication of a supervisory condition). Guard's tour supervisory signals are not a subset of the general category of supervisory signals as used in this Code.

A.3.3.257.10 Trouble Signal. Examples include off-normal outputs from integrity monitoring circuits, the light and sound from actuated trouble notification appliances, trouble data transmission to a supervising station, and so forth.

A.3.3.269.2 Ionization Smoke Detection. Ionization smoke detection is more responsive to invisible particles (smaller than 1 micron in size) produced by most flaming fires. It is somewhat less responsive to the larger particles typical of most smoldering fires. Smoke detectors that use the ionization principle are usually of the spot type.

A.3.3.269.3 Photoelectric Light Obscuration Smoke Detection. The response of photoelectric light obscuration smoke detectors is usually not affected by the color of smoke.

Smoke detectors that use the light obscuration principle are usually of the line type. These detectors are commonly referred to as projected beam smoke detectors.

A.3.3.269.4 Photoelectric Light-Scattering Smoke Detection. Photoelectric light-scattering smoke detection is more responsive to the visible particles (larger than 1 micron in size) produced by most smoldering fires. It is somewhat less responsive to the smaller particles typical of most flaming fires. It is also less responsive to black smoke than to lighter colored smoke. Smoke detectors that use the light-scattering principle are usually of the spot type.

A.3.3.269.5 Video Image Smoke Detection (VISD). Video image smoke detection (VISD) is a software-based method of smoke detection that has become practical with the advent of digital video systems. Listing agencies have begun testing VISD components for several manufacturers. VISD systems can analyze images for changes in features such as brightness, contrast, edge content, loss of detail, and motion. The detection equipment can consist of cameras producing digital or analog (converted to digital) video signals and processing unit(s) that maintain the software and interfaces to the fire alarm control unit.

A.3.3.275 Spark. The overwhelming majority of applications involving the detection of Class A and Class D combustibles with radiant energy–sensing detectors involve the transport of particulate solid materials through pneumatic conveyor ducts or mechanical conveyors. It is common in the industries that include such hazards to refer to a moving piece of burning material as a *spark* and to systems for the detection of such fires as *spark detection systems.*

A.3.3.307 Unwanted Alarm. Unwanted alarms are any alarms that occur when there is no hazard condition present. These are sometimes also called false alarms. Because the term *false* has been used by many people to mean many different things, this Code is instead using the terms *unwanted, fault, nuisance, unintentional, unknown,* and *malicious* to categorize the different types of alarms. Unwanted alarms might be intentional, unintentional, or unknown. If they were caused intentionally, they might have been done by someone with the intent to cause disruption and should be classified as malicious. However, an unintentional alarm might occur when, for example, a child activated a manual fire alarm box not knowing the consequences. Similarly, someone accidentally causing mechanical damage to an initiating device that results in an alarm is causing an unintentional alarm.

A.3.3.307.2 Nuisance Alarm. Nuisance alarms are unwanted alarms. Sometimes nuisance alarms might be called false alarms. In this Code, any unwanted alarm is considered false because they are not indicative of real hazards. Because the term *false* has been used by many people to mean many different things, this Code is instead using the terms *unwanted, nuisance,* and *malicious* to categorize the different types of alarms. They occur when some condition simulates a fire or other hazardous condition. For example, cigarette smoke can activate smoke detectors and smoke alarms. In that case, there might not be anything wrong with the smoke detector or smoke alarm — it is doing its job responding to the condition or stimulus that it was designed to detect. Another example would be a heat detector or heat alarm that activates when someone inadvertently points a hair dryer towards it. A malicious alarm occurs when someone intentionally activates the detector or alarm when there is no fire hazard. See the definitions of malicious, unintentional, unknown, and unwanted alarms.

A.3.3.309 Video Image Flame Detection (VIFD). Video image flame detection (VIFD) is a software-based method of flame detection that can be implemented by a range of video image analysis techniques. VIFD systems can analyze images for changes in features such as brightness, contrast, edge content, loss of detail, and motion. The detection equipment can consist of cameras producing digital or analog (converted to digital) video signals and processing unit(s) that maintain the software and interfaces to the fire alarm control unit.

A.3.3.314 Wavelength. The concept of wavelength is extremely important in selecting the proper detector for a particular application. There is a precise interrelation between the wavelength of light being emitted from a flame and the combustion chemistry producing the flame. Specific subatomic, atomic, and molecular events yield radiant energy of specific wavelengths. For example, ultraviolet photons are emitted as the result of the complete loss of electrons or very large changes in electron energy levels. During combustion, molecules are violently torn apart by the chemical reactivity of oxygen, and electrons are released in the process, recombining at drastically lower energy levels, thus giving rise to ultraviolet radiation. Visible radiation is generally the result of smaller changes in electron energy levels within the molecules of fuel, flame intermediates, and products of combustion. Infrared radiation comes from the vibration of molecules or parts of molecules when they are in the superheated state associated with combustion. Each chemical compound exhibits a group of wavelengths at which it is resonant. These wavelengths constitute the chemical's infrared spectrum, which is usually unique to that chemical.

This interrelationship between wavelength and combustion chemistry affects the relative performance of various types of detectors with respect to various fires.

A.3.3.320.1 Evacuation Signaling Zone. A notification zone is the smallest discrete area used for any announcements or signaling. Depending on the emergency response plan, an evacuation signaling zone can encompass several notification zones. For example, in most high-rise buildings, each single floor (fire area) is a notification zone. Most emergency response plans call for the evacuation signaling zone to be the fire floor, floor above, and a floor below.

A.7.1.3 Unless otherwise identified, only the minimum documentation requirements of 7.2.1 apply. More stringent documentation requirements found in other chapters and other laws, codes, and standards, as well as project specifications, should identify any other documentation sections in this chapter that would be applicable.

A.7.2 It is not intended that all of the details outlined in Sections 7.3 through 7.5 be required for every project. In general, the more complex the system, the more stringent the requirements become for documentation. It is recognized that some projects would require only the minimum documentation listed in Section 7.2. Other projects might require more detailed documentation. Sections 7.3 through 7.5 provide menus of additional means of documenting a system. The intent is for other governing laws, codes, or standards; other parts of this Code; or project specifications or drawings to select the additional specific pieces of documentation from Sections 7.3 through 7.5.

A.7.2.1(1) The purpose for a written narrative is to provide a description of the work to be performed and could be as simple as "Install additional three smoke detectors to provide coverage for newly installed meeting room." However, it could be desirable to include why or by whose direction the work is being done, such as "at owner's request," "per specifications dated …," or "at the direction of … ." See also Section 23.3 for additional system feature documentation requirements.

A.7.2.1(9) It should be noted that the inspection and testing form can be modified as appropriate to reflect the scope of the project.

A.7.2.2 It is the intent that the system designer be identified on the drawings. For emergency public reporting systems, see 27.3.7.1.2 for additional requirements.

A.7.3.1 See Section 7.2 for the minimum documentation requirements.

A.7.3.2 Design (layout) documents should contain information related to the system that could include specifications, shop drawings, input/output matrix, battery calculations, notification appliance voltage drop calculations for strobes and speakers, and product technical data sheets.

Design (layout) documents could include such items as preliminary plans issued as guidance and direction, risk analysis, emergency response plan, or a combination of these.

Deviations from requirements of governing laws, codes, standards, or preliminary plan requirements specified by an engineer should be clearly identified and documented as such.

Documentation of equivalency, where applicable, should be provided in accordance with Section 1.5 and be included with the record drawings.

It is the intent that existing systems that are altered should have design (layout) documents prepared that are applicable only to the portion(s) of the system being altered.

A.7.3.3 Preliminary plans such as those used for bidding, solicitation, or for obtaining permits could contain information as follows:

Performance criteria required in support of alternative means and methods for other codes, standards, or construction features should be clearly identified on the design (layout) documentation.

Such information should reference applicable waivers, appeals, variances, or similarly approved deviations from prescriptive criteria.

Preliminary documents could include the following:

(1) Specifications and narrative applicable to the project
(2) When devices are located (spaced) on preliminary drawings, the devices should be located (spaced) in accordance with standards, listings, and limitations of the equipment specified. When devices are not located (spaced) on the preliminary documents, a note should be included directing that the spacing should be per listing(s) and this Code.
(3) Interface requirements between systems such as fire alarm, mass notification, security, HVAC, smoke control, paging, background music, audio visual equipment, elevators, access control, other fire protection systems, and so forth.
(4) Sequence of operation
(5) Survivability of system circuits and equipment, when applicable
(6) Notification zones, when applicable
(7) Message content for voice systems
(8) Means of system monitoring that is to be provided, when applicable
(9) Codes and editions applicable to the system(s)
(10) Special requirements of the owner, governing authority, or insurance carrier when applicable
(11) Voice delivery components beyond standard industry products required to achieve intelligibility

When known, acoustic properties of spaces should be indicated on the preliminary design (layout) documents.

A.7.3.4.1 See Section 7.2 for the minimum documentation requirements.

A.7.3.7 When a system or component is installed in accordance with performance-based design criteria, such systems should be reviewed and acceptance tested by a design professional to verify that performance objectives are attained.

Due to unique design and construction challenges, fire protection concepts are often established on performance-based engineering practices. When such practices have been approved by the authority having jurisdiction, the engineer of record should sign off on the final installation documents to ensure that all conditions have been satisfied. Such engineering analysis could be beyond the qualifications of the code authority. As such, it is imperative that the engineer of record review and accept final concepts as accepted by the authority having jurisdiction.

A.7.3.9.1 Evaluation documentation can also include documentation such as that associated with performance-based alternatives and documentation related to equivalencies as

well as any other special documentation that is specific to a particular system.

A.7.4.1 See Section 7.2 for the minimum documentation requirements.

A.7.4.2 It is important to note that shop drawings and particularly the word "sheets" do not necessarily mean physical paper sheets, but could be on electronic media.

A.7.4.9 For an example of an input/output matrix of operation, see A.14.6.2.4.

A.7.5.1 See Section 7.2 for the minimum documentation requirements.

A.7.5.3(1) Owner's Manual. An owner's manual should contain the following documentation:

(1) A detailed narrative description of the system inputs, evacuation signaling, ancillary functions, annunciation, intended sequence of operations, expansion capability, application considerations, and limitations.
(2) A written sequence of operation in matrix or narrative form.
(3) Operator instructions for basic system operations, including alarm acknowledgment, system reset, interpretation of system output (LEDs, CRT display, and printout), operation of manual evacuation signaling and ancillary function controls, and change of printer paper
(4) A detailed description of routine maintenance and testing as required and recommended and as would be provided under a maintenance contract, including testing and maintenance instructions for each type of device installed. This information shall include the following:
   (a) Listing of the individual system components that require periodic testing and maintenance
   (b) Step-by-step instructions detailing the requisite testing and maintenance procedures, and the intervals at which these procedures shall be performed, for each type of device installed
   (c) A schedule that correlates the testing and maintenance procedures
(5) A service directory, including a list of names and telephone numbers of those who provide service for the system.

A.7.5.5.2 For an example of an input/output matrix of operation, see A.14.6.2.4.

A.7.5.5.5 It is important that the documentation required by this section is available for technicians so they will be able to recognize variations of system configuration during acceptance, reacceptance, and periodic testing. It is also necessary for enforcement personnel in order to prevent confusion when they could otherwise misidentify an approved variation for being non-code compliant. This documentation is also necessary for those who might design additions or modifications.

A.7.5.6.1 It is the intent of this section to permit using forms other than Figure 7.8.2(a) through Figure 7.8.2(f) as long as they convey the same information.

A.7.5.6.2 Protected premises fire alarm systems are often installed under construction or remodeling contracts and subsequently connected to a supervising station alarm system under a separate contract. All contractors should complete the portions of the record of completion documentation for the portions of the connected systems for which they are responsible. Several partially completed documents might be accepted by the authority having jurisdiction provided that all portions of the connected systems are covered in the set of documents.

A.7.5.6.3 The requirements of Chapter 14 should be used to perform the installation wiring and operational acceptance tests required when completing the record of completion.

The record of completion form shall be permitted to be used to record decisions reached prior to installation regarding intended system type(s), circuit designations, device types, notification appliance type, power sources, and the means of transmission to the supervising station.

A.7.5.6.6.3 It is the intent that if an original or current record of completion is not available for the overall system, the installer would provide a new record of completion that addresses items discovered about the system. The installer will complete the respective sections related to the overall system that have been discovered under the current scope of work. It is not the intent of this section to require an in-depth evaluation of an existing system solely for the purpose of completing a system-wide record of completion.

A.7.5.8 This section is intended to provide a basis for the authority having jurisdiction to require third-party verification and certification that the authority having jurisdiction and the system owner can rely on to reasonably assure that the fire alarm system installation complies with the applicable requirements. Where the installation is an extension, modification, or reconfiguration of an existing system, the intent is that the verification be applicable only to the new work and that reacceptance testing be acceptable.

A.7.7.1.2 It is intended that archived records be allowed to be stored in electronic format as long as hard copies can be made from them when required.

A.7.7.1.6 Examples of system documents include the following:

(1) Record drawings (as-builts)
(2) Equipment technical data sheets
(3) Alternative means and methods, variances, appeals, and approvals, and so forth
(4) Performance-based design documentation in accordance with 7.3.7
(5) Risk analysis documentation in accordance with 7.3.6
(6) Emergency response plan in accordance with 7.3.8
(7) Evaluation documentation in accordance with 7.3.9
(8) Software and firmware control documentation in accordance with 23.2.2

A.7.7.2.2 The intent is that paper documents should not be stored inside the control unit because control units are not typically approved for the storage of combustible material.

A.7.7.3.2 It is recognized that there are circumstances in which the security and protection of some system documents will require measures other than that prescribed in this Code. Since a common expectation of a mass notification system is to function during security and/or terrorist events, it could be crucial that system design be protected.

Where such conditions have been identified, the stakeholders should clearly identify what and how system documents should be maintained to satisfy the integrity of this section regarding reviews, future service, modifications, and system support.

Due to freedom of information laws allowing for public access to documents submitted to and retained by code offi-

cials, it could be necessary for secure documents to be reviewed by code officials at alternate locations. Such conditions should be identified by the stakeholders and discussed with the authorities having jurisdiction(s) in advance.

A.7.8.1.1 See Section 7.2 for the minimum documentation requirements.

A.7.8.2 Examples of completed record of completion forms are shown in Figure A.7.8.2(a) through Figure A.7.8.2(f), and a risk analysis checklist form can be found in Figure A.7.8.2(g).

A.10.3.3 This requirement does not apply to notification appliance circuits.

A.10.3.5(1) The requirement of 10.3.5(1) does not preclude transfer to secondary supply at less than 85 percent of nominal primary voltage, provided the requirements of 10.6.7 are met.

A.10.4.1 Fire alarm specifications can include some or all of the following:

(1) Address of the protected premises
(2) Owner of the protected premises
(3) Authority having jurisdiction
(4) Applicable codes, standards, and other design criteria to which the system is required to comply
(5) Type of building construction and occupancy
(6) Fire department response point(s) and annunciator location(s)
(7) Type of fire alarm system to be provided
(8) Calculations (e.g., secondary supply and voltage drop calculations)
(9) Type(s) of fire alarm initiating devices, supervisory alarm initiating devices, and evacuation notification appliances to be provided
(10) Intended area(s) of coverage
(11) Complete list of detection, evacuation signaling, and annunciator zones
(12) Complete list of emergency control functions
(13) Complete sequence of operations detailing all inputs and outputs

A.10.4.4 The fire alarm control units that are to be protected are those that provide notification of a fire to the occupants and responders. The term *fire alarm control unit* does not include equipment such as annunciators and addressable devices. Requiring smoke detection at the transmitting equipment is intended to increase the probability that an alarm signal will be transmitted to a supervising station prior to that transmitting equipment being disabled due to the fire condition.

CAUTION: Exception No. 1 to 10.4.4 permits the use of a heat detector if ambient conditions are not suitable for smoke detection. It is important to also evaluate whether the area is suitable for the control unit.

Where the area or room containing the control unit is provided with total smoke detection coverage, additional smoke detection is not required to protect the control unit. Where total smoke detection coverage is not provided, the Code intends that only one smoke detector is required at the control unit even when the area of the room would require more than one detector if installed according to the spacing rules in Chapter 17. The intent of selective coverage is to address the specific location of the equipment.

The location of the required detection should be in accordance with 17.7.3.2.1.

SYSTEM RECORD OF COMPLETION

This form is to be completed by the system installation contractor at the time of system acceptance and approval.
It shall be permitted to modify this form as needed to provide a more complete and/or clear record.
Insert N/A in all unused lines.
Attach additional sheets, data, or calculations as necessary to provide a complete record.

Form Completion Date: __25 January 2011__   Supplemental Pages Attached: __0__

1. PROPERTY INFORMATION

Name of property: __World Storage and Transfer Headquarters__
Address: __27132 Santa Anita Boulevard, Hilo, HI__
Description of property: __Business and Office Building__
Name of property representative: __Joe Bago Donits__
Address: __As above__
Phone: __(743) 225-9768__   Fax: __(743) 225-9768__   E-mail: __jbago@WLST.net__

2. INSTALLATION, SERVICE, TESTING, AND MONITORING INFORMATION

Installation contractor: __Sparkee's Electric__
Address: __1954 Nimitz Highway, Honolulu, HI 76542__
Phone: __(978) 456-9876__   Fax: __(978) 456-9876__   E-mail: __shortcircuitguy@sparkee.net__
Service organization: __None__
Address: _____
Phone: _____   Fax: _____   E-mail: _____
Testing organization: __Jim's Protection, Inc.__
Address: __2300 Daly Boulevard, Austin, TX__
Phone: __(407) 738-4587__   Fax: __(407) 738-4598__   E-mail: __testerjim@JPI.com__
Effective date for test and inspection contract: __25 January 2011__
Monitoring organization: __Look the Other Way, Inc.__
Address: __995 Highway 35W, Minneapolis, MN__
Phone: __(412) 456-9078__   Fax: __(412) 456-7272__   E-mail: __Look@otherway.com__
Account number: __56734598__   Phone line 1: __(212) 978-6576__   Phone line 2: __(212) 978-9978__
Means of transmission: __POTS__
Entity to which alarms are retransmitted: __Honolulu FD__   Phone: __(808) 455-5555__

3. DOCUMENTATION

On-site location of the required record documents and site-specific software: __Building Mgrs. Office Room 203__

4. DESCRIPTION OF SYSTEM OR SERVICE

This is a: ☑ New system ❑ Modification to existing system   Permit number: __11-907645__
NFPA 72 edition: __2013__

4.1 Control Unit

Manufacturer: __Halter Cabinet__   Model number: __1019-7647__

4.2 Software and Firmware

Firmware revision number: __7.0 B   Executive Rev 9.11__

4.3 Alarm Verification

☑ This system does not incorporate alarm verification.

Number of devices subject to alarm verification: _____   Alarm verification set for _____ seconds

FIGURE A.7.8.2(a) Example of Completed System Record of Completion.

SYSTEM RECORD OF COMPLETION *(continued)*

5. SYSTEM POWER

5.1 Control Unit

5.1.1 Primary Power

Input voltage of control panel: ___120 VAC___   Control panel amps: _____

Overcurrent protection: Type: _____   Amps: ___1.8 A___

Branch circuit disconnecting means location: ___Breaker Panel — Room B-23___   Number: ___23___

5.1.2 Secondary Power

Type of secondary power: ___Engine Generator___

Location, if remote from the plant: ___Rear Yard — Adjacent to Trash Storage___

Calculated capacity of secondary power to drive the system:

In standby mode (hours): ___48___   In alarm mode (minutes): ___90___

5.2 Control Unit

❑ This system does not have power extender panels

❑ Power extender panels are listed on supplementary sheet A

6. CIRCUITS AND PATHWAYS

Pathway Type	Dual Media Pathway	Separate Pathway	Class	Survivability Level
Signaling Line				
Device Power				
Initiating Device	A			
Notification Appliance	Z			
Other (specify):				

7. REMOTE ANNUNCIATORS

Type	Location

8. INITIATING DEVICES

Type	Quantity	Addressable or Conventional	Alarm or Supervisory	Sensing Technology
Manual Pull Stations	12	Addressable		
Smoke Detectors	8	Addressable		
Duct Smoke Detectors				
Heat Detectors				
Gas Detectors	1	Conventional		
Waterflow Switches	2	Conventional		
Tamper Switches	4	Conventional		

NFPA 72 (p. 2 of 3)

FIGURE A.7.8.2(a) *Continued*

SYSTEM RECORD OF COMPLETION *(continued)*

9. NOTIFICATION APPLIANCES

Type	Quantity	Description
Audible	18	
Visible	24	
Combination Audible and Visible	6	

10. SYSTEM CONTROL FUNCTIONS

Type	Quantity
Hold-Open Door Releasing Devices	4
HVAC Shutdown	2
Fire/Smoke Dampers	
Door Unlocking	1
Elevator Recall	2
Elevator Shunt Trip	

11. INTERCONNECTED SYSTEMS

☑ This system does not have interconnected systems.

❏ Interconnected systems are listed on supplementary sheet _____ .

12. CERTIFICATION AND APPROVALS

12.1 System Installation Contractor

This system as specified herein has been installed according to all NFPA standards cited herein.

Signed: *Harry Johnson*   Printed name: Harry Johnson   Date: 11 January 2011

Organization: Sparkee's Electric   Title: Principal   Phone: (978) 456-9876

12.2 System Operational Test

This system as specified herein has tested according to all NFPA standards cited herein.

Signed: *Jim Riverbottom*   Printed name: Jim Riverbottom   Date: 14 January 2011

Organization: _____   Title: _____   Phone: _____

12.3 Acceptance Test

Date and time of acceptance test: 0830 hrs. — 26 January 2011

Installing contractor representative: Jim Johnson

Testing contractor representative: Reginald O'Haraquest

Property representative: Danny MacIntosh

AHJ representative: Inspector DiDonato

FIGURE A.7.8.2(a) *Continued*

EMERGENCY COMMUNICATIONS SYSTEMS
SUPPLEMENTARY RECORD OF COMPLETION

This form is a supplement to the System Record of Completion. It includes systems and components specific to emergency communications systems.
This form is to be completed by the system installation contractor at the time of system acceptance and approval. It shall be permitted to modify this form as needed to provide a more complete and/or clear record. Insert N/A in all unused lines.

Form Completion Date: __25 January 2011__   Number of Supplemental Pages Attached: _____

1. PROPERTY INFORMATION

Name of property: __World Storage and Transfer Headquarters__

Address: __27132 Santa Anita Boulevard, Hilo, HI__

2. DESCRIPTION OF SYSTEM OR SERVICE

❑ Fire alarm with in-building fire emergency voice alarm communication system (EVAC)

❑ Mass notification system

☑ Combination system, with the following components:

    ❑ Fire alarm   ❑ EVACS   ❑ MNS   ❑ Two-way, in-building, emergency communications system

❑ Other (specify): _____

NFPA 72 edition: __2013__   Additional description of system(s): _____

_____

2.1 In-Building Fire Emergency Voice Alarm Communications System

Manufacturer: __Halter Cabinet__   Model number: __1018-7648__

Number of single voice alarm channels: __2__   Number of multiple voice alarm channels: __0__

Number of speakers: __99__   Number of speaker circuits: __12__

Location of amplification and sound processing equipment: __Fire Control Room__

_____

_____

Location of paging microphone stations:

Location 1: __Fire Control Room__

Location 2: __Security Office__

Location 3: _____

2.2 Mass Notification System

2.2.1 System Type:

☑ In-building MNS–combination

❑ In-building MNS   ❑ Wide-area MNS   ❑ Distributed recipient MNS

❑ Other (specify): _____

© 2012 National Fire Protection Association   NFPA 72 (p. 1 of 3)

FIGURE A.7.8.2(b)   Example of Completed Emergency Communications System Supplementary Record of Completion.

EMERGENCY COMMUNICATIONS SYSTEMS
SUPPLEMENTARY RECORD OF COMPLETION *(continued)*

2. DESCRIPTION OF SYSTEM OR SERVICE *(continued)*

2.2.2 System Features:

☑ Combination fire alarm/MNS   ❏ MNS autonomous control unit   ❏ Wide-area MNS to regional national alerting interface

❏ Local operating console (LOC)   ❏ Distributed-recipient MNS (DRMNS)   ❏ Wide-area MNS to DRMNS interface

❏ Wide-area MNS to high power speaker array (HPSA) interface   ❏ In-building MNS to wide-area MNS interface

❏ Other (specify): _____

2.2.3 MNS Local Operating Consoles

Location 1: ___Fire Control Room_____

Location 2: ___Security Office_____

Location 3: _____

2.2.4 High-Power Speaker Arrays

Number of HPSA speaker initiation zones: ___0_____

Location 1: _____

Location 2: _____

Location 3: _____

2.2.5 Mass Notification Devices

Combination fire alarm/MNS visual devices: ___62_____   MNS-only visual devices: _____

Textual signs: _____   Other (describe): _____

Supervision class: _____

2.2.6 Special Hazard Notification

☑ This system does not have special suppression predischarge notification.

❏ MNS systems DO NOT override notification appliances required to provide special suppression predischarge notification.

3. TWO-WAY EMERGENCY COMMUNICATIONS SYSTEMS

3.1 Telephone System

Number of telephone jacks installed: ___15_____   Number of warden stations installed: ___3_____

Number of telephone handsets stored on site: ___6_____

Type of telephone system installed: ❏ Electrically powered   ☑ Sound powered

3.2 Two-Way Radio Communications Enhancement System

Percentage of area covered by two-way radio service: Critical areas ___5___ %   General building areas ___95___ %

Amplification component locations: ___Fire Control Room_____

_____

Inbound signal strength _____ dBm   Outbound signal strength _____ dBm

Donor antenna isolation is _____ dB above the signal booster gain.

Radio frequencies covered: _____

Radio system monitor panel location: _____

        NFPA 72 (p. 2 of 3)

FIGURE A.7.8.2(b) *Continued*

EMERGENCY COMMUNICATIONS SYSTEMS
SUPPLEMENTARY RECORD OF COMPLETION *(continued)*

3. TWO-WAY EMERGENCY COMMUNICATIONS SYSTEMS *(continued)*

3.3 Area of Refuge (Area of Rescue Assistance) Emergency Communications Systems

Number of stations:____0____ Location of central control point: _____

Days and hours when central control point is attended: _____

Location of alternate control point: _____

Days and hours when alternate control point is attended: _____

3.4 Elevator Emergency Communications Systems

Number of elevators with stations:____2____ Location of central control point: ___Fire Control Room_____

Days and hours when central control point is attended: ___24_____

Location of alternate control point: ___None_____

Days and hours when alternate control point is attended: ___None_____

3.5 Other Two-Way Communications System

Describe: _____

4. CONTROL FUNCTIONS

This system activates the following control functions specific to emergency communications systems:

Type	Quantity
Mass Notification Override of Alarm Signaling Systems or Appliances	1

See Main System Record of Completion for additional information, certifications, and approvals.

FIGURE A.7.8.2(b) *Continued*

POWER SYSTEMS
SUPPLEMENTARY RECORD OF COMPLETION

*This form is a supplement to the System Record of Completion. It includes systems and components specific
to power systems that incorporate generators, UPS systems, remote battery systems, or other complex power systems.
This form is to be completed by the system installation contractor at the time of system acceptance and approval.
It shall be permitted to modify this form as needed to provide a more complete and/or clear record.
Insert N/A in all unused lines.*

Form Completion Date: _25 January 2011_   Number of Supplemental Pages Attached: _0_

1. PROPERTY INFORMATION

Name of property: _World Storage and Transfer Headquarters_

Address: _27132 Santa Anita Boulevard, Hilo, HI_

2. SYSTEM POWER

2.1 Control Unit

2.1.1 Primary Power

Input voltage of control panel: _120 volt_   Control panel amps: _3.5_

Overcurrent protection: Type: _Circuit Breaker_   Amps: _20_

Location (of primary supply panelboard): _Main Electrical Room in Basement_

Disconnecting means location: _Panel E2 — Electric Room_

2.1.2 Engine-Driven Generator

Location of generator: _Basement_

Location of fuel storage: _Basement_   Type of fuel: _Diesel_

2.1.3 Uninterruptible Power System

Equipment powered by UPS system: _None_

Location of UPS system: _____

Calculated capacity of UPS batteries to drive the system components connected to it:

In standby mode (hours): _____   In alarm mode (minutes): _____

2.1.4 Batteries

Location: _FACP_   Type: _Gel Cell_   Nominal voltage: _24_   Amp/hour rating: _16_

Calculated capacity of batteries to drive the system:

In standby mode (hours): _86_   In alarm mode (minutes): _12_

2.2 In-Building Fire Emergency Voice Alarm Communications System or Mass Notification System

2.2.1 Primary Power

Input voltage of EVACS or MNS panel: _120 volt_   EVACS or MNS panel amps: _8.8_

Overcurrent protection: Type: _Circuit Breaker_   Amps: _20_

Location (of primary supply panelboard): _Main Electrical Room in Basement_

Disconnecting means location: _Panel E2 — Electric Room_

     NFPA 72 (p. 1 of 2)

FIGURE A.7.8.2(c) Example of Completed Power Systems Supplementary Record of Completion.

POWER SYSTEMS
SUPPLEMENTARY RECORD OF COMPLETION *(continued)*

2. SYSTEM POWER *(continued)*

2.2.2 Engine-Driven Generator

Location of generator: _Basement_

Location of fuel storage: _Basement_   Type of fuel: _Diesel_

2.2.3 Uninterruptible Power System

Equipment powered by UPS system: _None_

Location of UPS system: _N/A_

Calculated capacity of UPS batteries to drive the system components connected to it:

In standby mode (hours): _N/A_   In alarm mode (minutes): _N/A_

2.2.4 Batteries

Location: _ECS Panel_   Type: _Gel Cell_   Nominal voltage: _24_   Amp/hour rating: _20_

Calculated capacity of batteries to drive the system:

In standby mode (hours): _32_   In alarm mode (minutes): _8_

2.3 Notification Appliance Power Extender Panels

❏ This system does not have power extender panels.

2.3.1 Primary Power

Input voltage of power extender panel(s): _120 volt_   Power extender panel amps: _8_

Overcurrent protection: Type: _Circuit Breaker_   Amps: _20_

Location (of primary supply panelboard): _See Table_

Disconnecting means location: _____

2.3.2 Engine-Driven Generator

Location of generator: _Basement_

Location of fuel storage: _Basement_   Type of fuel: _Diesel_

2.3.3 Uninterruptible Power System

Equipment powered by UPS system: _None_

Location of UPS system: _____

Calculated capacity of UPS batteries to drive the system components connected to it:

In standby mode (hours): _____   In alarm mode (minutes): _____

2.3.4 Batteries

Location: _Power Panel_   Type: _Gel Cell_   Nominal voltage: _24_   Amp/hour rating: _12_

Calculated capacity of batteries to drive the system:

In standby mode (hours): _42_   In alarm mode (minutes): _11_

See Main System Record of Completion for additional information, certifications, and approvals.

© 2012 National Fire Protection Association   NFPA 72 (p. 2 of 2)

FIGURE A.7.8.2(c) *Continued*

NOTIFICATION APPLIANCE POWER PANEL
SUPPLEMENTARY RECORD OF COMPLETION

*This form is a supplement to the System Record of Completion. It includes a list of types and locations
of notification appliance power extender panels.*
*This form is to be completed by the system installation contractor at the time of system acceptance and approval.
It shall be permitted to modify this form as needed to provide a more complete and/or clear record.
Insert N/A in all unused lines.*

Form Completion Date: _25 January 2011_   Number of Supplemental Pages Attached: _0_

1. PROPERTY INFORMATION

Name of property: _World Storage and Transfer Headquarters_

Address: _27132 Santa Anita Boulevard, Hilo, HI_

2. NOTIFICATION APPLIANCE POWER EXTENDER PANELS

Make and Model	Location	Area Served	Power Source
Firelite W123	3rd Floor	3rd Floor	Panel 3E
SK + ABC	6th Floor	6th Floor	Panel 3G

See Main System Record of Completion for additional information, certifications, and approvals.

     NFPA 72

FIGURE A.7.8.2(d)   Example of Completed Notification Appliance Power Panel Supplementary Record of Completion.

INTERCONNECTED SYSTEMS
SUPPLEMENTARY RECORD OF COMPLETION

*This form is a supplement to the System Record of Completion. It includes a list of types and locations
of systems that are interconnected to the main system.*
This form is to be completed by the system installation contractor at the time of system acceptance and approval.
It shall be permitted to modify this form as needed to provide a more complete and/or clear record.
Insert N/A in all unused lines.

Form Completion Date: ___25 January 2011___   Number of Supplemental Pages Attached: _____

1. PROPERTY INFORMATION

Name of property: ___World Storage and Transfer Headquarters___

Address: ___27132 Santa Anita Boulevard, Hilo, HI___

2. INTERCONNECTED SYSTEMS

Description	Location	Purpose
Fan Shutdown	Roof	Shut down fans on fire alarm activation
Elevator Recall	Elevator Room	Recall elevators in case of alarm on lobby smoke detectors

See Main System Record of Completion for additional information, certifications, and approvals.

© 2012 National Fire Protection Association   NFPA 72

FIGURE A.7.8.2(e)   Example of Completed Interconnected Systems Suplementary Record of Completion.

DEVIATIONS FROM ADOPTED CODES AND STANDARDS
SUPPLEMENTARY RECORD OF COMPLETION

This form is a supplement to the System Record of Completion. It enables the designer and/or installer
to document and justify deviations from accepted codes or standards.
This form is to be completed by the system installation contractor at the time of system acceptance and approval.
It shall be permitted to modify this form as needed to provide a more complete and/or clear record.
Insert N/A in all unused lines.

Form Completion Date: __25 January 2011__   Number of Supplemental Pages Attached: _____

1. PROPERTY INFORMATION

Name of property: ___World Storage and Transfer Headquarters___

Address: ___27132 Santa Anita Boulevard, Hilo, HI___

2. DEVIATIONS FROM ADOPTED CODES OR STANDARDS

Description	Purpose

See Main System Record of Completion for additional information, certifications, and approvals.

© 2012 National Fire Protection Association   NFPA 72

FIGURE A.7.8.2(f)   Example of Completed Deviations from Adopted Codes and Standards Supplementary Record of Completion.

RISK ANALYSIS CHECKLIST

Facility name: _____   Facility location: _____

Prepared by: _____   Date prepared: _____ _____

Title and contact information: _____

ECS system type: _____

PART ONE: Identification of Assets or Operations at Risk
Use Part One of this checklist to identify the following assets or operations at risk at your facility

---

❏ **People**
- ❏ Employees
- ❏ Visitors and guests
- ❏ Contractors working on site
- ❏ Emergency responders
- ❏ Community surrounding the facility

❏ **Property**
- ❏ Physical property
  - ❏ Corporate offices
  - ❏ Manufacturing facilities
  - ❏ Call center
  - ❏ Distribution centers
  - ❏ Data-processing center
  - ❏ Research and development labs
  - ❏ Property on the premises of others
  - ❏ Vital papers, records, and drawings

- ❏ Intellectual property
  - ❏ Copyright and patent infringement
  - ❏ Trademark infringement
  - ❏ Theft of intellectual property
  - ❏ Theft of information

- ❏ Utilities
  - ❏ Telecommunications
  - ❏ Electricity
  - ❏ Water
  - ❏ Gas
  - ❏ Steam
  - ❏ Heating/ventilation/air conditioning
  - ❏ Pollution control
  - ❏ Sewerage system
  - ❏ Other critical infrastructure

- ❏ Computers and computer networks
  - ❏ Software applications
  - ❏ Electronic data

- ❏ Inventory
  - ❏ Raw materials
  - ❏ Finished product

❏ **Operations**
- ❏ Manufacturing processes
- ❏ Delivery of services
- ❏ Administrative support services
- ❏ Research and development
- ❏ Supply chain

❏ **Environment**
- ❏ Air
- ❏ Water
- ❏ Ground

❏ **Organization**
- ❏ Economic and financial condition
- ❏ Licenses, patents, or trademarks
- ❏ Reputation and image as well-managed company
- ❏ Contractual obligations
- ❏ Community relationships
- ❏ Regional and national impact
- ❏ Regulatory compliance and relationships with vendors

NFPA 72 (p. 1 of 2)

FIGURE A.7.8.2(g) Risk Analysis Checklist.

RISK ANALYSIS CHECKLIST *(continued)*

PART TWO: Determination of Facility Hazards

Use Part Two of this checklist to determine the potential hazards that may impact your facility.

❑ **Natural Hazards—Geological**
- ❑ Earthquake
- ❑ Tsunami
- ❑ Volcano
- ❑ Landslide, mudslide, subsidence
- ❑ Glacier, iceberg

❑ **Natural Hazards—Meteorological**
- ❑ Flood, flash flood, tidal surge
- ❑ Drought
- ❑ Windstorm, tropical cyclone, hurricane, tornado, water spout, dust/sand storm
- ❑ Extreme temperatures (heat, cold)
- ❑ Lightning strikes
- ❑ Famine
- ❑ Geomagnetic storm
- ❑ Snow, ice, hail, sleet, avalanche

❑ **Natural Hazards—Biological**
- ❑ Diseases (pandemic)
- ❑ Animal or insect infestation or damage

❑ **Human-Caused Accidental Events**
- ❑ Hazardous material (explosive, flammable liquid, flammable gas, flammable solid, oxidizer, poison, radiological, corrosive) spill or release
- ❑ Natural gas leak
- ❑ Nuclear power plant incident
- ❑ Hazmat incident off site
- ❑ Explosion/fire
- ❑ Wildfire (forest, range, urban, wildland, urban interface)
- ❑ Transportation accident (motor vehicle, railroad, watercraft, aircraft pipeline)
- ❑ Building/structure failure or collapse
- ❑ Entrapment
- ❑ Mechanical breakdown
- ❑ Energy/power/utility failure
- ❑ Fuel/resource shortage
- ❑ Air/water pollution, contamination
- ❑ Water control structure/dam/levee failure
- ❑ Communications systems interruptions
- ❑ Financial issues, economic depression, inflation, financial system collapse
- ❑ Misinformation

❑ **Human-Caused Intentional Events**
- ❑ Terrorism (explosive, chemical, biological, radiological, nuclear, cyber)
- ❑ Sabotage or vandalism
- ❑ Civil disturbance, public unrest, mass hysteria, riot
- ❑ Enemy attack, war
- ❑ Insurrection
- ❑ Strike or labor dispute
- ❑ Demonstration
- ❑ Disinformation
- ❑ Criminal activity (vandalism, arson, theft, fraud, embezzlement, data theft)
- ❑ Electromagnetic pulse
- ❑ Physical or information security breach
- ❑ Sniper incident
- ❑ Crime, theft, or robbery
- ❑ Product defect or contamination
- ❑ Harassment
- ❑ Arson
- ❑ Bomb threat
- ❑ Lost person
- ❑ Child abduction
- ❑ Kidnap
- ❑ Extortion
- ❑ Hostage incident
- ❑ Workplace violence

❑ **Technological-Caused Events**
- ❑ Telecommunications
- ❑ Central computer, mainframe, software, or application (internal/external)
- ❑ Energy/power/utility
- ❑ Ancillary support equipment

NFPA 72 (p. 2 of 2)

FIGURE A.7.8.2(g) *Continued*

A.10.5.3 It is not the intent to require personnel performing simple inspections or operational tests of initiating devices to require factory training or special certification, provided such personnel can demonstrate knowledge in these areas.

A.10.5.3.1 Inspection personnel knowledge should include equipment selection, placement, and installation requirements of this Code and the manufacturer's published documentation.

A.10.5.3.2 Testing personnel knowledge should include equipment selection, placement, and installation requirements of this Code and the manufacturer's published documentation.

A.10.5.3.3(1) Factory training and certification is intended to allow an individual to service equipment only for which he or she has specific brand and model training.

A.10.5.3.3(2) Nationally recognized fire alarm certification programs might include those programs offered by the International Municipal Signal Association (IMSA), National Institute for Certification in Engineering Technologies (NICET), and the Electronic Security Association (ESA). NOTE: These organizations and the products or services offered by them have not been independently verified by the NFPA, nor have the products or services been endorsed or certified by the NFPA or any of its technical committees.

A.10.5.3.3(3) Licenses and certifications offered at a state or local level are intended to recognize those individuals who have demonstrated a minimum level of technical competency in the area of fire alarm servicing.

A.10.5.4.1(2) An example of an organization providing alarm monitoring operator training is the Central Station Alarm Association (CSAA). Note that this reference is for information purposes only, information concerning the product or service has been provided by the manufacturer or other outside sources, and the information concerning the product or service has not been independently verified nor has the product or service been endorsed or certified by the NFPA or any of its technical committees.

A.10.6.6 Where a computer system of any kind is used to receive and process alarm or supervisory signals, an uninterruptible power supply (UPS) with sufficient capacity to operate the system until the secondary supply is capable of operating the fire alarm system might be required in order to prevent signal loss or a greater than 10-second signal delay.

UPS equipment often contains an internal bypass arrangement to supply the load directly from the line. These internal bypass arrangements are a potential source of failure. UPS equipment also requires periodic maintenance. It is, therefore, necessary to provide a means of promptly and safely bypassing and isolating the UPS equipment from all power sources while maintaining continuity of power supply to the equipment normally supplied by the UPS.

A.10.6.7.2 When a fire alarm system is used to alert occupants, the associated premises are generally evacuated during prolonged power outages. When this is not the case, as in emergency shelters or certain government facilities, additional secondary power should be required to address a more prolonged outage. These outages might be expected to result from weather or earthquake in locations subject to these events. Reasonable judgment should be employed when requiring additional secondary capacity.

When a fire alarm system is used to protect property, the associated premises might be vacant for prolonged periods (weekend, long holiday) or in very remote locations. When this is the case, and when the risk of loss is significant, additional secondary power should be required to address a more prolonged outage. These outages might be expected to result from weather or earthquake in locations subject to these events. Reasonable judgment should be employed when requiring additional secondary capacity.

A.10.6.7.3 The secondary power supply is not required to supply power to the fire alarm system through parallel distribution paths. Automatic transfer switches are commonly used to allow secondary power to be supplied over the same distribution system as the primary power.

The generator does not need to be dedicated to the fire alarm system.

A.10.6.8.1 Examples include the following:

(1) A building lighting power supply required for illumination in a required video image smoke detection means
(2) A notification appliance circuit power supply located remotely
(3) A power supply for transmitter required to transmit signals off premises
(4) Power over ethernet (PoE), where provided for control units, circuit interfaces, or other equipment essential to system operation, and located remotely from the main control unit

A.10.6.9.2 Because digital alarm communicator systems establish communications channels between the protected premises and the central station via the public switched telephone network, the requirement to supervise circuits between the protected premises and the central station (see 12.6.1 and 12.6.2) is considered to be met if the communications channel is periodically tested in accordance with 26.6.3.2.1.5.

A.10.6.9.3 This requirement is intended to prevent all of the supervising station alarm systems in a given geographic area from transmitting simultaneous trouble signals (and overwhelming the associated supervising stations) in the event of a widespread power failure. A trouble signal is not intended to be transmitted if primary power is restored within the time delay.

A.10.6.10 The following newer types of rechargeable batteries are normally used in protected premises applications:

(1) *Vented Lead-Acid, Gelled, or Starved Electrolyte Battery.* This rechargeable-type battery is generally used in place of primary batteries in applications that have a relatively high current drain or that require the extended standby capability of much lower currents. The nominal voltage of a single cell is 2 volts, and the battery is available in multiples of 2 volts (e.g., 2, 4, 6, 12). Batteries should be stored according to the manufacturer's published instructions.
(2) *Nickel-Cadmium Battery.* The sealed-type nickel-cadmium battery generally used in applications where the battery current drain during a power outage is low to moderate (typically up to a few hundred milliamperes) and is fairly constant. Nickel-cadmium batteries are also available in much larger capacities for other applications. The nominal voltage per cell is 1.42 volts, with batteries available in multiples of 1.42 (e.g., 12.78, 25.56). Batteries in storage

can be stored in any state of charge for indefinite periods. However, a battery in storage will lose capacity (will self-discharge), depending on storage time and temperature. Typically, batteries stored for more than 1 month require an 8-hour to 14-hour charge period to restore capacity. In service, the battery should receive a continuous, constant-charging current that is sufficient to keep it fully charged. (Typically, the charge rate equals 1/10 to 1/20 of the ampere-hour rating of the battery.) Because batteries are made up of individual cells connected in series, the possibility exists that, during deep discharge, one or more cells that are low in capacity will reach complete discharge prior to other cells. The cells with remaining life tend to charge the depleted cells, causing a polarity reversal resulting in permanent battery damage. This condition can be determined by measuring the open cell voltage of a fully charged battery (voltage should be a minimum of 1.28 volts per cell multiplied by the number of cells). Voltage depression effect is a minor change in discharge voltage level caused by constant current charging below the system discharge rate. In some applications of nickel-cadmium batteries (e.g., battery-powered shavers), a memory characteristic also exists. Specifically, if the battery is discharged daily for 1 minute, followed by a recharge, operation for 5 minutes will not result in the rated ampere-hour output because the battery has developed a 1-minute discharge memory.

(3) *Sealed Lead-Acid Battery.* In a sealed lead-acid battery, the electrolyte is totally absorbed by the separators, and no venting normally occurs. Gas evolved during recharge is internally recombined, resulting in minimal loss of capacity life. A high-pressure vent, however, is provided to avoid damage under abnormal conditions.

A.10.6.10.3.4 Batteries are trickle-charged if they are off-line and waiting to be put under load in the event of a loss of power.

Float-charged batteries are fully charged and connected across the output of the rectifiers to smooth the output and to serve as a standby source of power in the event of a loss of line power.

A.10.7.3 Mass notification signals might, at times, be more important to the building or area occupants than the fire alarm signal. Stakeholders should perform a risk analysis in accordance with 24.3.11 to determine which, if any, messages should receive priority.

A.10.7.9 In addition, the override of circuits should be indicated at the control panel of each system to ensure signals are restored to normal.

A.10.10.4 Control unit signals can be audible, visible, or both for any particular function. Some older systems used only audible indicators that had to be coded in order for users to know what the signal meant. Where a control unit uses both audible and visible indicators, the purpose of the audible signal is to get someone's attention. In large system configurations, there might be multiple control units with audible signals. Also, there might be several different functions requiring an audible alert as a part of the whole signal. Thus, there could be several different audible signals. It is not the intent of the Code to have separate and distinct audible signals where there is clear visual distinction that provides the user with the needed information. Visible signals, whether a lamp with a text label, an LCD screen, or a computer monitor, are a better form of human interface.

A.10.10.5 A valve supervisory, a low-pressure switch, or another device intended to cause a supervisory signal when actuated should not be connected in series with the end-of-line supervisory device of initiating device circuits, unless a distinctive signal, different from a trouble signal, is indicated.

A.10.11 Other locations could include the following:

(1) Building fire command center for in-building fire emergency voice/alarm communications systems
(2) Fire alarm control unit for network fire alarm systems
(3) Supervising station locations for systems installed in compliance with Chapter 26

A.10.12.2 The recommended coded signal designations for buildings that have four floors and multiple basements are provided in Table A.10.12.2.

Table A.10.12.2 Recommended Coded Signal Designations

Location	Coded Signal
Fourth floor	2–4
Third floor	2–3
Second floor	2–2
First floor	2–1
Basement	3–1
Sub-basement	3–2

A.10.12.4 Resetting of alarm signals should not require the simultaneous operation of multiple reset switches or the disconnection of any wiring or equipment to reset the alarm condition.

A.10.13 It is the intent that both visual and audible appliances are shut off when the notification appliance silence feature is activated on the fire alarm control unit.

Per the ADA, it is important not to provide conflicting signals for the hearing or visually impaired.

A.10.13.2.1 The intent to activate the strobes while voice instructions are being provided is to alert the hearing impaired of the fact that information is being provided and they should use the visual indication as an indication to seek out information.

A.10.15.9 The purpose of automatic trouble re-sound is to remind owners, or those responsible for the system, that the system remains in a fault condition. A secondary benefit is to possibly alert occupants of the building that the fire alarm system is in a fault condition.

A.10.15.10.7 In large, campus-style arrangements with proprietary supervising stations monitoring protected premises systems, and in other situations where off-premises monitoring achieves the desired result, the authority having jurisdiction is permitted to allow the re-actuation to occur only at the supervising station. Approval by the authority having jurisdiction is required so it can consider all fire safety issues and make a determination that there are procedures in place to ensure that the intent is met; in other words, someone is available to take action to correct the problem.

A.10.16.2 The operability of controlled mechanical equipment (e.g., smoke and fire dampers, elevator recall arrangements, and door holders) should be verified by periodic testing. Failure to test and properly maintain controlled mechanical equipment can result in operational failure during an emergency, with potential consequences up to and including loss of life.

A.10.17.2   Initially this requirement was meant to apply to notification appliance circuits (NACs) emanating from a single fire alarm control unit and did not contemplate the use of NAC extender panels. Acknowledging the control circuit concept allows NAC extender panels and relays to be connected to a control circuit.

A.10.18.3   The primary purpose of annunciation is to enable responding personnel to quickly and accurately determine the status of equipment or emergency control functions that might affect the safety of occupants.

A.10.18.5   Fire alarm system annunciation should, as a minimum, be sufficiently specific to identify a fire alarm signal in accordance with the following:

(1) If a floor exceeds 22,500 ft^2 (2090 m^2) in area, the floor should be subdivided into detection zones of 22,500 ft^2 (2090 m^2) or less, consistent with the existing smoke and fire barriers on the floor.
(2) If a floor exceeds 22,500 ft^2 (2090 m^2) in area and is undivided by smoke or fire barriers, detection zoning should be determined on a case-by-case basis in consultation with the authority having jurisdiction.
(3) Waterflow switches on sprinkler systems that serve multiple floors, areas exceeding 22,500 ft^2 (2090 m^2), or areas inconsistent with the established detection system zoning should be annunciated individually.
(4) In-duct smoke detectors on air-handling systems that serve multiple floors, areas exceeding 22,500 ft^2 (2090 m^2), or areas inconsistent with the established detection system zoning should be annunciated individually.
(5) If a floor area exceeds 22,500 ft^2 (2090 m^2), additional zoning should be provided. The length of any zone should not exceed 300 ft (91 m) in any direction. If the building is provided with automatic sprinklers throughout, the area of the alarm zone should be permitted to coincide with the allowable area of the sprinkler zone.

A.10.19.1   Amplifiers generally require significant power regardless of load. To reduce the secondary power demand, there is no requirement to monitor the integrity of amplifiers during non-alarm operation on secondary power. This allows the amplifiers to be shut down while the system is operating on secondary power until an alarm occurs. When an alarm occurs, monitoring of integrity must resume so that an operator is aware of current conditions and so that any backup amplifiers can be engaged.

Backup amplifying and evacuation signal–generating equipment is recommended with automatic transfer upon primary equipment failure to ensure prompt restoration of service in the event of equipment failure.

A.10.21   The term *impairments* encompasses a broad range of circumstances wherein a fire alarm system or portion thereof is taken out of service for a variety of reasons. Fire alarm systems are routinely impaired in order to perform hot work (e.g., open flame operations) in areas with automatic detection, construction, painting, etc., as well as to conduct normal fire alarm system maintenance and testing. Impairments can be limited to specific initiating devices and/or functions (e.g., disconnecting the supervising station connection during system testing), or they can involve taking entire systems or portions of systems out of service. This section is intended to help building owners control impairments of the fire alarm system(s) in their building(s) and to ensure that systems are restored to full operation and/or returned to service afterward.

Additional requirements for impairments and out-of-service conditions exist in 14.2.2.2.

A.10.21.4   It is important for the authority having jurisdiction, typically the local fire official, to be informed when fire alarm systems have been out of service for more than 8 hours so appropriate measures can be taken. Out of service is meant to be the entire system or a substantial portion thereof.

A.10.21.5   The need for mitigating measures is typically determined on a case-by-case basis. This considers the building, occupancy type, nature and duration of impairment, building occupancy level during impairment period, active work being conducted on the fire alarm system during the impairment, condition of other fire protection systems and features (i.e., sprinklers, structural compartmentation, etc.), and hazards and assets at risk.

Appropriate mitigating measures range from simple occupant notification to full-time fire watch. Determining factors vary from testing-related impairments and maintenance activities during normal business through extensive impairments to high-value, high-hazard situations.

A.10.22   See 3.3.307 for the definitions of unwanted alarms.

A.12.2.1   In the 2007 edition of *NFPA 72*, initiating device circuit, signaling line circuit, and notification appliance circuit performance class/style tables were rooted in "copper" wiring methods. Fire alarm control units use new communication technologies, such as Ethernet, fiber optics, and wireless, which do not fit in the "copper" wiring methods.

A.12.2.4.3   Fire alarm systems include fire detection and alarm notification, guard's tour, sprinkler waterflow, and sprinkler supervisory systems. Circuits controlled and powered by the fire alarm system include circuits for the control of building systems safety functions, elevator capture, elevator shutdown, door release, smoke doors and damper control, fire doors and damper control, and fan shutdown, but only where these circuits are powered by and controlled by the fire alarm system. [**70**:760.1 Informational Note No.1] (SIG-FUN)

Class 1, 2, and 3 circuits are defined in Article 725 (of *NFPA 70, National Electrical Code*). [**70**:760.1 Informational Note No. 2]

A.12.2.4.4   It is important for the intended functionality of circuit integrity cable or electrical circuit protective systems to follow manufacturer's installation instructions. An electrical circuit protective system has detailed installation requirements, and additional requirements can be found in the manufacturer's installation instructions, *NFPA 70, National Electrical Code*, or the listing organizations' guide information.

A.12.2.5.2   Technologies that do not use metallic conductors (e.g., wireless or optical fiber) are not affected by ground connections.

A.12.3   The intent of the circuit designations is not to create a hierarchal ranking; rather it is to provide guidance on the levels of performance.

The initiating device circuit, signaling line circuit, and notification appliance circuit performance class/style tables from previous editions of the Code have been included as Table A.12.3(a), Table A.12.3(b), and Table A.12.3(c) but have been modified to include the enhanced class references.

These tables reflect the classifications as applied to fire alarm systems. Some of the operations are a combination of the requirements of Chapter 12 in conjunction with the requirements of Chapters 10 and 23. Singular ground-fault conditions that do not affect operation of the pathway are not specifically covered in Chapter 12, but are covered by the requirements of other chapters. Users of the Chapter 12 designations should review whether there are other abnormal conditions not specified in Chapter 12 that the pathways need to annunciate and operate through for their application.

A.12.3.1 The Class A references for initiating device circuit and notification appliance circuit performance have been changed to eliminate the need for alarm receipt capability during a single ground or annunciation of a single ground fault. The signaling line circuit performance has changed to provide a clear separation between the Class A Style 6 and

Class A Style 7 performance. The Class A Style 7 performance is now defined as Class X.

Fiber optic or wireless pathways are examples of Class A circuitry not impaired by earth ground connection, and short-circuits, and therefore do not annunciate those conditions as a fault. Users of the code are advised that fire alarm circuits still require alarm receipt capability during a single ground. See Chapter 23.

A.12.3.2 The Class B references for initiating device circuit, signaling line circuit, and notification appliance circuit performance have been changed to eliminate the need for alarm receipt capability during a single ground or annunciation of a single ground fault. Users of the code are advised that fire alarm circuits still require alarm receipt capability during a single ground. *(See Chapter 23.)*

A.12.3.3 The Class C reference is new and is intended to describe technologies that supervise the communication pathway by polling or continuous communication "handshaking" such as the following:

(1) Fire alarm control unit or supervising station connections to a wired LAN, WAN, or Internet
(2) Fire alarm control unit or supervising station connections to a wireless LAN, WAN, and Internet
(3) Fire alarm control unit or supervising station connections to a wireless (proprietary communications)
(4) Fire alarm control unit digital alarm communicator transmitter or supervising station digital alarm communicator receiver connections to the public switched telephone network

Individual pathway segments are not required to be monitored. Supervision is accomplished by end to end communications.

A.12.3.4 The Class D reference is intended to describe pathways that are not supervised but have a fail-safe operation that performs the intended function when the connection is lost. Examples of such pathways include the following:

Table A.12.3(a) Performance of Initiating Device Circuits (IDCs)

NFPA 72-2007 Class	B			A		
NFPA 72-2010 Class	**B**			**A**		
	Alm	**Trbl**	**ARC**	**Alm**	**Trbl**	**ARC**
Abnormal Condition	**1**	**2**	**3**	**4**	**5**	**6**
Single open	—	X	—	—	X	R
Single ground	—	X	R	—	X	R

Alm: Alarm. Trbl: Trouble. ARC: Alarm receipt capability during abnormal condition. R: Required capability. X: Indication required at protected premises and as required by Chapter 26.

Table A.12.3(b) Performance of Signaling Line Circuits (SLCs)

NFPA 72-2007 Class	B			A			A		
Style	**4**			**6**			**7**		
NFPA 72-2010 Class	**B**			**A**			**X**		
	Alarm	**Trouble**	**ARC**	**Alarm**	**Trouble**	**ARC**	**Alarm**	**Trouble**	**ARC**
Abnormal Condition	**1**	**2**	**3**	**4**	**5**	**6**	**7**	**8**	**9**
Single open	—	X	—	—	X	R	—	X	R
Single ground	—	X	R	—	X	R	—	X	R
Wire-to-wire short	—	X	—	—	X	—	—	X	R
Wire-to-wire short and open	—	X	—	—	X	—	—	X	—
Wire-to-wire short and ground	—	X	—	—	X	—	—	X	—
Open and ground	—	X	—	—	X	R	—	X	R
Loss of carrier (if used)/channel interface	—	X	—	—	X	—	—	X	—

ARC: Alarm receipt capability during abnormal condition. R: Required capability. X: Indication required at protected premises and as required by Chapter 26.

Table A.12.3(c) Notification Appliance Circuits (NACs)

NFPA 72-2007 Class	B		A	
NFPA 72-2010 Class	B		A	
	Trouble Indications at Protective Premise	Alarm Capability During Abnormal Condition	Trouble Indications at Protective Premise	Alarm Capability During Abnormal Condition
Abnormal Condition	1	2	3	4
Single open	X	-	X	R
Single ground	X	R	X	R
Wire-to-wire short	X	-	X	-

X: Indication required at protected premises and as required by Chapter 26. R: Required capability.

(1) Power to door holders where interruption of the power results in the door closing
(2) Power to locking hardware that release upon an open circuit or fire alarm operation

A.12.3.5 The Class E reference is new and is intended to describe pathways that do not require supervision as described in Section 12.6.

A.12.3.6 The Class X reference is new and is intended to describe pathways as described as Class A Style 7 of the signaling line circuit performance of Table A.12.3(b). *(Also see A.12.3.)*

A.12.3.7 A goal of 12.3.7 is to provide adequate separation between the outgoing and return cables. This separation is required to help ensure protection of the cables from physical damage. The recommended minimum separation to prevent physical damage is 12 in. (300 mm) where the cable is installed vertically and 48 in. (1.22 m) where the cable is installed horizontally.

A.12.5 Shared pathway designations propose a list of shared pathways, some of which are only allowable for nonrequired functions. Other sections of this Code determine which of the shared pathways are allowed to be used as paths for required fire alarm signaling. Refer to 23.8.2.6 for shared communication requirements.

A.12.5.1 In a Shared Pathway Level 0, common equipment can be used to establish life safety and non–life safety pathways.

A.12.5.2 In a Shared Pathway Level 1, common equipment can be used to establish life safety and non–life safety pathways.

A.12.5.3 In a Shared Pathway Level 2, common equipment can be used to establish life safety and non–life safety pathways.

A.12.5.4 In a Shared Pathway Level 3, life safety equipment is not shared with equipment of non–life safety systems.

A.12.6 The provision of a double loop or other multiple path conductor or circuit to avoid electrical monitoring is not acceptable.

A.12.6.8 This Code does not have jurisdiction over the monitoring integrity of conductors within equipment, devices, or appliances.

A.14.2.1.1 Initial and re-acceptance inspections are performed to ensure compliance with approved design documents whatever the quality or origin. This involves inspection to ensure that the correct equipment has been used and properly located and installed. Ensuring compliance helps to assure both operational reliability and mission reliability. This concept applies to any type of system, not just fire alarm and signaling systems. At this stage of a system's life, the responsibilities for such inspections rest with the designers of the systems and with the various applicable authorities having jurisdiction.

A.14.2.1.2 If a system is designed to meet a specific mission or set of goals, then operational testing will assure that the system has mission reliability. For example, during acceptance testing, the design ambient noise level might not be present. Authorities having jurisdiction and technicians should not be trying to achieve the +5/15 dB or +5/10 dB requirements at acceptance, as they might not know what the maximum average or peak noise levels are. They need only measure the system and determine if it meets the required design level. Therefore, the design level needs to be documented and communicated to them.

Acceptance and re-acceptance testing includes proper operation, and non-operation, of the fire alarm or signaling system's ability to properly interface to other systems. The best way to ensure a proper interface operation is to observe the actual operation of the interfaced system. However, exercising an emergency control function every time a related initiating device is activated might not be desirable or practical, or in some cases may not even be permitted. *NFPA 72* permits testing of the fire alarm or signaling system up to the end point connection to the interfaced system or emergency control function. Refer to A.14.4.3.2 Table 14.4.3.2 Item 24.

A.14.2.1.3 Visual inspections contribute to the assurance of operational and mission reliability but do not ensure either.

A.14.2.1.4 Periodic testing of fire alarm and signaling systems is not necessarily done as a complete system test. *NFPA 72* requires parts of the systems to be tested at different frequencies. At any one particular test, only a fraction of the system can be tested. Periodic testing contributes to the assurance of operational and mission reliability but does not ensure either.

Periodic testing of the interface between a fire alarm or signaling system in some other system or emergency control function is permitted by *NFPA 72* to be performed without actually operating the interfaced system or function. Refer to A.14.4.3.2 Table 14.4.3.2 Item 24.

A.14.2.3.1 See definition of *Ownership* in 3.3.187.

A.14.2.3.6 Service personnel should be able to do the following:

(1) Understand the requirements contained in *NFPA 72, National Fire Alarm and Signaling Code*, and the fire alarm requirements contained in *NFPA 70, National Electrical Code*
(2) Understand basic job site safety laws and requirements
(3) Apply troubleshooting techniques, and determine the cause of fire alarm system trouble conditions
(4) Understand equipment specific requirements, such as programming, application, and compatibility
(5) Read and interpret fire alarm system design documentation and manufacturer's inspection, testing, and maintenance guidelines

(6) Properly use tools and test equipment required for testing and maintenance of fire alarm systems and their components

(7) Properly apply the test methods required by *NFPA 72, National Fire Alarm and Signaling Code*

A.14.2.4 Prior to any scheduled inspection or testing, the service company should consult with the building or system owner or the owner's designated representative. Issues of advance notification in certain occupancies, including advance notification time, building posting, systems interruption and restoration, evacuation procedures, accommodation for evacuees, and other related issues, should be agreed upon by all parties prior to any inspection or testing.

A.14.2.7.1 As an example, testing of the elevator fire service and shutdown functions will usually require a coordinated multi-discipline effort with presence of qualified service personnel for the fire alarm system, the elevator system, and other building systems. The presence of inspection authorities might also be needed in some jurisdictions. The development of a test plan should be considered to ensure that the testing of these features is accomplished in a coordinated and timely manner. This plan should also ensure that all appropriate parties and personnel are present when needed, and that the testing requirements for both the fire alarm system and the elevator system are fulfilled. See Section 21.3 and Section 21.4 for specific elevator emergency control functions.

A.14.2.9 This section provides the option to adopt a performance-based inspection and testing method as an alternate means of compliance for Sections 14.3 and 14.4. The prescriptive test and requirements contained in this Code are essentially qualitative. Equivalent or superior levels of performance can be demonstrated through quantitative performance-based analyses. This section provides a basis for implementing and monitoring a performance-based program acceptable under this option (provided that approval is obtained by the authority having jurisdiction). The concept of a performance-based inspection and testing program is to establish the requirements and frequencies at which inspection and testing must be performed to demonstrate an acceptable level of operational reliability. The goal is to balance the inspection and testing frequency with proven reliability of the system or component. The goal of a performance-based inspection program is also to adjust inspection and testing frequencies commensurate with historical documented equipment performance and desired reliability. Frequencies of inspection and testing under a performance-based program may be extended or reduced from the prescriptive inspection and testing requirements contained in this Code when continued inspection and testing has been documented indicating a higher or lower degree of reliability as compared to the authority having jurisdiction's expectations of performance. Additional program attributes should be considered when adjusting inspection and testing.

A fundamental requirement of a performance-based program is the continual monitoring of fire system/component failure rates and determining if they exceed the maximum allowable failure rates as agreed upon with the authority having jurisdiction. The process used to complete this review should be documented and be repeatable. Coupled with this ongoing review is a requirement for a formalized method of increasing or decreasing the frequency of inspection and testing when systems exhibit either a higher than expected failure

rate or an increase in reliability as a result of a decrease in failures. A formal process for reviewing the failure rates and increasing or decreasing the frequency of inspection and testing must be well documented. Concurrence from the authority having jurisdiction on the process used to determine test frequencies should be obtained in advance of any alterations to the inspection and testing program. The frequency required for future inspections and tests may be reduced to the next inspection frequency and maintained there for a period equaling the initial data review or until the ongoing review indicates that the failure rate is no longer being exceeded — for example, going from an annual to a semiannual testing when the failure rate exceeds the authority having jurisdiction's expectations, or from annual to every 18 months when the failure trend indicates an increase in reliability.

See also NFPA 551, *Guide for the Evaluation of Fire Risk Assessments*, for additional guidance.

A.14.2.10 The test plan is intended to clarify exactly what is to be tested and how it is to be tested. Testing of fire alarm and signaling systems is often done in a segmented fashion to accommodate the availability of testing or other personnel, or to minimize the interruption of building operations. Building operations can be affected by testing of the fire alarm or signaling system itself and by the operation of emergency control functions activated by the fire alarm or signaling system. The boundary of the fire alarm or signaling system extends up to and includes the emergency control function interface device. The testing requirements prescribed in *NFPA 72* for fire alarm and signaling systems end at the emergency control function interface device. The purpose of the test plan is to document what devices were and were not actually tested.

The testing of emergency control functions, releasing systems, or interfaced equipment is outside the scope of *NFPA 72*. Requirements for testing other systems are found in other governing laws, codes, or standards. Requirements for integrated testing of combined systems also fall under the authority of other governing laws, codes, standards, or authority having jurisdiction. NFPA 3, *Recommended Practice for Commissioning and Integrated Testing of Fire Protection and Life Safety Systems*, provides guidance for such testing. NFPA 3 recognizes the importance of the development of an integrated testing plan.

Further information on testing associated with emergency control functions can be found in Table 14.4.3.2, Item 24 and its related annex material in A.14.4.3.2.

A.14.3.1 Equipment performance can be affected by building modifications, occupancy changes, changes in environmental conditions, device location, physical obstructions, device orientation, physical damage, improper installation, degree of cleanliness, or other obvious problems that might not be indicated through electrical supervision.

The intent of 14.3.1 is to prevent an inspection being made at intervals exceeding those allowed by Table 14.3.1. Annual inspections should be made every 12 months; monthly inspections should be made every 30 days, and so forth. For example, it is not acceptable to conduct an annual inspection in January of year one, and December of year two (23 month frequency) just because Table 14.3.1 requires an inspection once each year.

A.14.4.2 Reacceptance testing is performed to verify the proper operation of added or replaced devices, appliances, emergency control function devices, control equipment, and so forth. It is not the intent of the committee to unduly burden the system owner with increased costs for repeated testing of devices not directly affected by the replacement of devices with like devices.

For example, if a 2 amp fuse is replaced with another 2 amp fuse in the fire alarm control unit, verification of the circuit(s) served by the fused supply is required, but it would not be necessary to test 10 percent of initiating devices not directly affected by replacing the fuse. Likewise, it is not necessary to test all these initiating devices whenever a smoke detector is replaced with a like smoke detector.

When wiring changes are made to correct improperly supervised circuits, a test of the affected device or appliance is required, but not a test of 10 percent of initiating devices not directly affected.

A.14.4.3 Fire alarm system testing can be conducted using silent testing and the bypassing of emergency control functions. All input signals should be verified according to the system matrix of operation to ensure they create the appropriate outputs. Tests of audible notification appliances and emergency control functions should be conducted at the conclusion of satisfactory tests of all inputs.

The intent is to reduce the amount of time spent causing audible and visible occupant notification during tests in an occupied building. This reduction will help reduce the negative (cry wolf) impact on occupants caused by excessive operation of notification appliances. System printouts or history logs are an effective way of verifying the correct receipt of signals. However, many outputs such as occupant notification and emergency control functions are tested for correct operation, because logs do not necessarily verify operation of the system output. Operation of audible and visible notification appliances could be accomplished in a lump sum fashion after all inputs are proven correct by silent testing. All inputs tested in this manner must be proved to cause the appropriate signal by verifying alarm receipt at the controls as each device is actuated. Manufacturer-specific protocols such as "walk test" or "alarm bypass" are an acceptable means of testing under this section. Other methods of mitigating the negative impact include off-hours tests when the building is not occupied.

A.14.4.3.1 If the authority having jurisdiction strongly suspects significant deterioration or otherwise improper operation by a central station, a surprise inspection to test the operation of the central station should be made, but extreme caution should be exercised. This test is to be conducted without advising the central station. However, the communications center must be contacted when manual alarms, waterflow alarms, or automatic fire detection systems are tested so that the fire department will not respond. In addition, persons normally receiving calls for supervisory alarms should be notified when items such as gate valves and functions such as pump power are tested. Confirmation of the authenticity of the test procedure should be obtained and should be a matter for resolution between plant management and the central station.

A.14.4.3.2 Table 14.4.3.2, Item 24. The extent of testing of a fire alarm or signaling system, including devices that were not tested, should be documented per the Test Plan in 14.2.10. *NFPA 72* does not require testing of an emergency control function, such as elevator recall, but does require testing of the emergency control function interface device, such as the relay powered by the fire alarm or signaling system. Where the emergency control function is not being tested concurrent with the fire alarm or signaling system testing, measurement of the emergency control function interface device output should be verified using the proper test devices. This might

require reading or observing the condition of a relay, a voltage measurement, or the use of another type of test instrument. Once testing is complete, verification that any disabled or disconnected interface devices have been restored to normal is essential and this verification should be documented in the testing results.

Testing of the emergency control functions themselves is outside of the scope of *NFPA 72*. A complete end-to-end test that demonstrates the performance of emergency control functions activated by the fire alarm or signaling system might be required by some other governing laws, codes, or standards, or the authority having jurisdiction. In that situation, other applicable installation standards and design documents, not *NFPA 72*, would address testing and performance of the emergency control functions. NFPA 3, *Recommended Practice for Commissioning and Integrated Testing of Fire Protection and Life Safety Systems*, provides guidance for integrated (end-to-end) testing of combined systems. The following excerpt from NFPA 3 includes guidance on when integrated testing should be performed.

7.2 Test Frequency. [**3**, 2012]

7.2.1 In new construction, integrated testing of fire protection and life safety systems should occur following:

(1) Verification of completeness and integrity of building construction

(2) Individual system functional operation and acceptance as required in applicable installation standards tests

(3) Completion of pre-functional tests of integrated systems [**3**, 2012]

7.2.2 Existing fire protection and life safety systems should have periodic integrated testing. [**3**, 2012]

7.2.2.1 Integrated systems that were commissioned upon installation in accordance with Chapter 6 should have integrated testing at the interval specified in the commissioning plan. [**3**, 2012]

7.2.2.2 For integrated systems that were not commissioned, an integrated testing plan should be developed to identify the appropriate extent and frequency of integrated system testing. [**3**, 2012]

7.2.3 In addition to periodic integrated testing, integrated system testing should be done when any of the following events occurs:

(1) New component fire protection or life safety systems are installed and interconnected to existing fire protection and life safety systems.

(2) Existing fire protection or life safety systems are modified to become components of interconnected systems.

(3) Interconnections or sequence of operations of existing integrated fire protection and life safety systems are modified. [**3**, 2012]

NFPA 3 also includes guidance on test methods for integrated testing. It is important to note that the appropriate NFPA standard would provide the acceptance criteria for the overall emergency control function operation requirements including performance and test methods while *NFPA 72* covers the required performance and testing of the emergency function interface device.

For instance, if an end-to-end test for a building with an engineered smoke control system is required by some other governing laws, codes, standards, or the authority having jurisdiction, the test protocol would have unique criteria for the smoke control system design and a special inspector would be responsible for the overall operation and performance of the smoke control system in accordance with the appropriate standard (NFPA 92, *Standard for Smoke Control Systems*, and NFPA *101, Life Safety Code*) during the testing, including measuring pressure differentials and ensuring proper fan and damper operation. Refer to the following extract from NFPA *101* on smoke control:

9.3.2 The engineer of record shall clearly identify the intent of the system, the design method used, the appropriateness of the method used, and the required means of inspecting, testing, and maintaining the system. [*101*, 2012]

9.3.3 Acceptance testing shall be performed by a special inspector in accordance with Section 9.9. [*101*, 2012]

Even though the fire alarm or signaling system initiating device might activate the smoke control system, the actual testing of the dampers and fan operation would be as required by the smoke control design and not part of the fire alarm or signaling system.

Other emergency control operation requirements might be as follows: For fan shutdown and smoke damper operation, the fan and damper operations would be in accordance with NFPA 90A, *Standard for the Installation of Air-Conditioning and Ventilating Systems*, and NFPA 105, *Standard for Smoke Door Assemblies and Other Opening Protectives*, respectively, and those equipment operations would be verified by those responsible for HVAC systems in combination with the fire alarm system personnel. Guidance for elevator inspection and testing can be found in ASME A.17.2, *Guide for Inspection of Elevators, Escalators and Moving Walks*. For elevator systems, the recall function, elevator power shutdown, and hat illumination would be done with the elevator mechanics present during the test. This operational test is often accomplished during routine periodic fire alarm testing. For fire door holder and fire shutter release, it would be expected that the emergency control function operation of the doors/shutters would be verified in accordance with NFPA 80, *Standard for Fire Doors and Other Opening Protectives*, and NFPA *101* during the test. In some cases, the door manufacturer representative might need to be present to reset the equipment.

Guidance on documenting and handling of faults, failures, and corrective action for integrated testing can be found in 7.4.5 of NFPA 3.

A.14.4.4 It is suggested that the annual test be conducted in segments so that all devices are tested annually.

The intent of 14.4.4 is to prevent a test from being made at intervals exceeding those allowed by Table 14.4.3.2. Annual tests should be made every 12 months; monthly tests should be made every 30 days, and so forth. For example, it is not acceptable to conduct an annual test in January of year one, and December of year two (23-month frequency), just because Table 14.4.3.2 requires a test once each year. See the definition of *frequency* in 3.3.115 for minimum and maximum time between testing events.

A.14.4.4.3 Detectors that cause unwanted alarms should be tested at their lower listed range (or at 0.5 percent obscuration if unmarked or unknown). Detectors that activate at less than this level should be replaced.

A.14.4.4.6 It is not intended to require testing the pathways at every device or circuit junctions.

A.14.4.7.2 Carbon monoxide alarm replacement is covered under NFPA 720, *Standard for the Installation of Carbon Monoxide (CO) Detection and Warning Equipment*.

A.14.4.10 In-building emergency radio communication systems where the ac power source is monitored for integrity should be tested annually. Systems where the ac power source is not monitored for integrity should be tested quarterly.

A.14.4.10.3 Testing procedures typically are done on a grid system. A grid is overlaid onto a floor area to provide 20 grid cells. Grid cells are provided with definite minimum and maximum dimensions. For most buildings, using a minimum grid dimension of 20 ft (6.1 m) and a maximum grid dimension of 80 ft (24.4 m) will suffice to encompass the entire floor area. Where a floor exceeds 128,000 ft^2 (11,890 m^2), which is the floor area that can be covered by the maximum grid dimension of 80 ft (24.4 m), it is recommended that the floor be subdivided into sectors, each having an area of less than or equal to 128,000 ft^2 (11,890 m^2), and that each sector be tested individually with 20 grid cells in each sector. Signal quality measurements should be taken at the center of each grid and should be performed using standardized parameters as specified in A.14.4.10.4. Signal quality typically is recorded on the delivered audio quality (DAQ) scale. This scale is a universal standard often cited in system designs and specifications, using the following measures:

(1) DAQ 1: Unusable speech present but unreadable
(2) DAQ 2: Understandable with considerable effort; frequent repetition due to noise/distortion
(3) DAQ 3: Speech understandable with slight effort; occasional repetition required due to noise/distortion
(4) DAQ 3.4: Speech understandable with repetition only rarely required; some noise/distortion
(5) DAQ 4: Speech easily understood; occasional noise/distortion
(6) DAQ 4.5: Speech easily understood; infrequent noise/distortion
(7) DAQ 5: Speech easily understood

The minimum allowable DAQ for each grid cell typically is DAQ 3 (17 ±1.5 dB SINAD).

The minimum downlink signal strength is specified in 24.5.2.3.1. The signal strengths are measured as per A.14.4.10.4 and will be recorded in each cell as well as the DAQ.

Not more than two nonadjacent grid cells should be allowed to fail the test. In the event that three of the areas fail the test, or if two adjacent areas fail the test, in order to be more statistically accurate, the testing grid resolution should be doubled. This would require decreasing the size to one-half the dimension used in the failed test to a minimum of 10 ft (3.0 m) and a maximum of 40 ft (12.2 m). Further, to cover the same floor area, the number of grids is quadrupled to 80. Not more than eight nonadjacent or five adjacent grid cells should then be allowed to fail the test. In the event that nine or more nonadjacent and/or six or more adjacent grid cells fail the test, consideration should be given to redesigning and reinstalling the public safety radio enhancement system to meet the minimum system design requirements. Failures should not be allowed in critical areas. Measurements should be made with the antenna held in a vertical position at (3 ft to 4 ft) [0.91 m to 1.22 m] above the floor. The DAQ and signal strength measurements should be recorded on small-scale drawings that are used for testing with the authority having jurisdiction. In addition, the gain values of all amplifiers should be measured, and the test measurement results should be kept on file with the building owner so that the measurements can be verified each year during annual tests.

A.14.4.10.4 Downlink measurements should be made with the following standardized parameters:

(1) Calibrated spectrum analyzer or calibrated automatic signal level measurement recording system to measure signal strength in dBm
(2) Receiving antennas of equal gain to the agency's standard portable radio antenna, oriented vertically, with a centerline between 3 ft (0.91 m) and 4 ft (1.22 m) above floor
(3) Resolution bandwidth nearest the bandwidth of the channel under test
(4) Levels recorded while walking an "X" pattern, with the center of the pattern located approximately in the center of each grid area
(5) Linear distance of each side of the "X" equal to at least 10 percent of the length of the grid's side and a minimum length of 10 ft (3.0 m)
(6) Measurement sampled in averaging mode to include a minimum of one sample per each 5 ft (1.52 m) traveled, recorded with not less than five samples per measurement recorded per side of the "X"

A.14.4.10.5 Typically, acceptance tests are required by the authority having jurisdiction prior to building occupancy. As-built drawings should be provided at the acceptance test along with other information required from the signal level and commissioning tests, including a full report with grid locations, DAQ and signal strength measurements, and amplifier gain values. The acceptance test typically entails a random test by the authority having jurisdiction of radio communication in various portions of the building, especially including the critical areas. The authority having jurisdiction can review any test documentation and ensure that the findings of the commissioning test with respect to DAQ and signal strength levels and gain values are supported by the acceptance test.

If amplification systems are utilized in the public safety radio enhancement system, a spectrum analyzer should be utilized to ensure spurious oscillations are not being generated or unauthorized carriers are being repeated in violation of FCC regulations. This testing should be conducted at time of installation and during subsequent inspections. Downlink and uplink spectrum should be recorded with a maximum-hold screen capture at the active system air interfaces, with the system under normal load and at least one uplink carrier active on the indoor portion of the system. Measurements should be analyzed for correct gains on both unlink and downlink paths, noise floor elevation from active components, intermodulation, and other parameters determined necessary by the authority having jurisdiction.

Gain values of all amplifiers should be measured and the results kept on file with the building owner and the authority having jurisdiction. In the event that the measurement results become lost, the building owner will need to repeat the acceptance test to reestablish the gain values.

A.14.4.10.6 Typically, annual tests require several items to be checked. Annual tests should include all procedures encompassed in 14.4.10.1 through 14.4.10.4. Signal boosters should be tested to ensure that the gain is the same as it was upon initial installation and acceptance. Backup batteries and power supplies should be tested under load for a period of 1 hour to verify that they will properly operate during an actual power outage. Other active components are typically checked to determine that they are operating within the manufacturer's specifications for the intended purpose.

A.14.4.11 See Annex D, Speech Intelligibility.

A.14.6.1 For final determination of record retention, see 14.4.4.3 for sensitivity options.

A.14.6.1.2 With many software-based fire systems, a copy of the site-specific software is required to restore system operation if a catastrophic system failure should occur. Without a back-up copy readily available on site, recovery of system operation by authorized service personnel can be substantially delayed.

The intent of this requirement is to provide authorized service personnel with an on-site copy of the site-specific software. The on-site copy should provide a means to recover the last installed and tested version of the site-specific operation of the system. This typically would be an electronic copy of the source files required to load an external programming device with the site-specific data. This requirement does not extend to the system executive software, nor does it require that the external programmer software if required be stored on site.

It is intended that this copy of the software be an electronic version stored on a nonrewritable media containing all of the file(s) or data necessary to restore the system and not just a printed version of the operation stored on electronic media. One example of a nonrewritable medium is a CD-R.

A.14.6.2.4 One method used to define the required sequence of operations and to document the actual sequence of operations is an input/output matrix (see Figure A.14.6.2.4).

A.17.1.2 The initiating devices chapter does not specify requirements for having or using any particular type of initiating device for a particular application. The requirements to have certain initiating devices are found in other NFPA codes and standards, or in other governing laws, codes, or standards. In a few instances other parts of this Code might require some minimal complement of initiating devices. For example, 10.4.4 requires a smoke detector at control unit locations but does not require complete smoke detection of any particular area. Similarly, 23.8.5.1.2 requires at least one manual fire alarm box on any fire alarm system that is connected to a supervising station and that also employs automatic fire detectors or waterflow detection devices. Thus, a system that might be required solely for the purpose of monitoring a sprinkler system and sending a signal off premises would still require a smoke detector at any control unit locations as well as a single manual pull station.

A.17.3 Annex B, Engineering Guide for Automatic Fire Detector Spacing, provides a detailed design guide for the implementation of the performance-based design of fire alarm systems.

A.17.4.6 The monitoring of circuit integrity relies on the interruption of the wiring continuity when the connection to the initiating device is lost. Terminals and leads, as illustrated in Figure A.17.4.6(a) and Figure A.17.4.6(b), monitor the presence of the device on the initiating device circuit.

A.17.4.8 Embossed plastic tape, pencil, ink, or crayon should not be considered to be a permanently attached placard.

A.17.4.10 There are some applications that do not require full area protection, but do require detection, to initiate action when specific objects or spaces are threatened by smoke or fire, such as at elevator landings that have ceilings in excess of 15 ft (4.6 m) and for protection of fire alarm control units. In high-ceiling areas, to achieve the desired initiation, such as for elevator recall and protection of fire alarm control units (FACUs), detection should be placed on the wall above and within 60 in. (1.52 m) from the top of the elevator door(s) or FACU.

System Outputs

Control Unit Annunciation | Notification | Required Fire Safety Control | Supplementary

System Inputs

A. Actuate common alarm signal indicator
B. Actuate audible alarm signal
C. Actuate common supervisory signal indicator
D. Actuate audible supervisory signal
E. Actuate common trouble signal indicator
F. Actuate audible common trouble signal
G. Actuate 1st floor (zone 1) alarm indicator
H. Actuate 1st floor (zone 2) alarm indicator
I. Actuate 1st floor (zone 3) alarm indicator
J. Actuate 2nd floor alarm indicator
K. Actuate 2nd floor evacuation signals
L. Actuate 3rd floor evacuation signals
M. Display/point change of status
N. Transmit fire alarm signal to supervising station
O. Transmit supervisory signal to supervising station
P. Transmit trouble signal to supervising station
Q. Release magnetically held smoke doors
R. Recall elevators to primary recall floor
S. Recall elevators to alternate recall floor
T. Close smoke/fire smoke dampers in rated walls
U. Actuate 1st floor smoke exhaust
V. Actuate 2nd floor smoke exhaust
W. Actuate 3rd floor smoke exhaust
X. Unlock exits
Y. Initiate suppression system predischarge alarms
Z. Energize releasing solenoids
AA. Actuate graphics system – display floor map
BB. Pressurize stairwells
CC. Shutdown process #1
DD. Shutdown process #2
EE. Shutdown process #3
FF. Actuate exterior strobe at I.d. response point
GG.

#	System Input
1	Manual fire alarm boxes – 1st floor
2	Manual fire alarm boxes – 2nd floor
3	Manual fire alarm boxes – 3rd floor
4	Smoke detectors – 1st floor
5	Smoke detectors – 3rd floor
6	Smoke detectors – 1st floor
7	Smoke detectors – 1st floor elev. lobby
8	2nd floor computer rm. smoke det.-zone 1
9	2nd floor computer rm. smoke det.-zone 2
10	In-duct smoke detector – supply fan 1
11	In-duct smoke detector – supply fan 2
12	In-duct smoke detector – 1st floor return
13	In-duct smoke detector – 2nd floor return
14	In-duct smoke detector – 3rd floor return
15	Heat detectors – 1st floor mech. rm.
16	Heat detectors – 2nd floor storage room
17	Heat detectors – 3rd floor janitor's closet
18	Waterflow – 1st floor
19	Waterflow – 2nd floor
20	Waterflow – 3rd floor
21	Sprinkler control valve – 1st floor
22	Sprinkler control valve – 2nd floor
23	Sprinkler control valve – 3rd floor
24	Fire pump running
25	Fire pump power failure/phase reversal
26	Fire alarm ac power failure
27	Fire alarm system low battery
28	Open circuit
29	Ground fault
30	Notification appliance circuit short

FIGURE A.14.6.2.4 **Typical Input/Output Matrix.**

A.17.5.2 This requirement is based on the generally accepted principle that the ceiling jet is approximately 10 percent of the distance from the base of the fire to the ceiling. To this figure, an additional safety factor of 50 percent has been added. Performance-based methods are available to predict the impact of partitions on the flow of smoke to detectors and can be used to substantiate a less restrictive design criterion.

A.17.5.3 The requirement of 17.5.3 recognizes that there are several different types of detector coverage.

A.17.5.3.1.4 Total coverage requires that a fire above the suspended ceiling be detected. Detector spacing and location for above ceiling spaces are addressed in 17.7.3.5.2. If that above-ceiling space is used as a air return plenum, this detection can be provided either by smoke detectors placed in accordance with 17.7.4.2 or where the air leaves the smoke compartment in accordance with 17.7.5.4.2.2.

A.17.5.3.2 If there are no detectors in the room or area of fire origin, the fire could exceed the design objectives before being detected by remotely located detectors. When coverage other than total coverage is required, partial coverage can be provided in common areas and work spaces such as corridors, lobbies, storage rooms, equipment rooms, and other tenant-less spaces. The intent of selective coverage is to address a specific hazard only.

Where a specific area is to be protected, all points within that area should be within 0.7 × the adjusted detector spacing for spot-type detectors as required by 17.6.3 and 17.7.3.2. Note that an area does not necessarily mean an entire room. It is possible to provide properly spaced detectors to provide detection for only part of a room. Similarly, the Code permits protection of a specific hazard. In that case, detectors within a radius of 0.7 × the adjusted detector spacing from the hazard provide the required detection. An example of protection of specific risk is the smoke detector required by Section 21.3 to be within 21 ft (6.4 m) of an elevator, where elevator recall is required.

It should also be noted that fire detection by itself is not fire protection. Also, protection goals could be such that detection being provided for a specific area or hazard might require a form of total coverage for that particular area or hazard. That is, it might be necessary to provide detectors above suspended ceilings or in small closets and other ancillary spaces that are a part of, or an exposure to, the area or hazard being protected.

A.17.5.3.3 The requirement of 17.5.3.3 recognizes there will be instances where, for example, a facility owner would want to apply detection to meet certain performance goals and to address a particular hazard or need, but that detection is not required. Once installed, of course, acceptance testing, annual testing, and ongoing maintenance in accordance with this Code is expected. The intent of this section is to allow the use of a single detector, or multiple detectors provided for specific protection, with spacing to meet specific fire safety objectives as determined in accordance with 17.6.1.1 and 17.7.1.1.

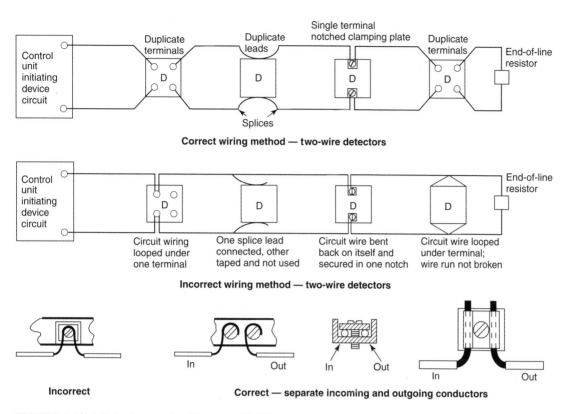

FIGURE A.17.4.6(a)   Correct (and Incorrect) Wiring Methods.

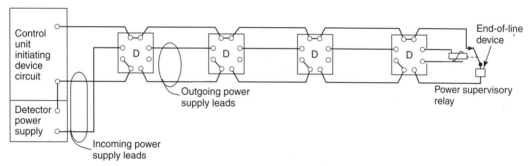

Illustrates four-wire smoke detector employing a three-wire connecting arrangement. One side of power supply is connected to one side of initiating device circuit. Wire run broken at each connection to smoke detector to provide supervision.

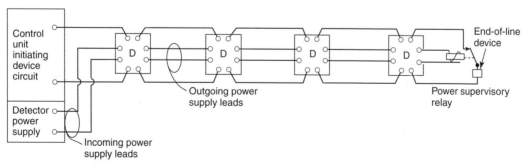

Illustrates four-wire smoke detector employing a four-wire connecting arrangement. Incoming and outgoing leads or terminals for both initiating device and power supply connections. Wire run broken at each connection to provide supervision.

D = Detector

FIGURE A.17.4.6(b)   Wiring Arrangements for Four-Wire Detectors.

A.17.6.1.1 The performance objective statement should describe the purpose of the detector placement and the intended response of the fire alarm control unit to the detector activation. This statement can include a narrative description of the required response time of the detectors, a narrative of the sequence of operations, a tabular list of programming requirements or some other method.

The performance objective of a fire detection system is usually expressed in terms of time and the size fire the system is intended to detect, measured in British thermal units per second (Btu/sec) or kilowatts (kW). Typically, the fire alarm system designer does not establish this criterion. It is usually obtained from the design documentation prepared by the designer responsible for the strategy of the structure as a whole. Where a prescriptive design is being provided, this requirement is fulfilled by stating in the design documentation that the design conforms to the prescriptive provisions of this Code.

A.17.6.1.3 In a performance-based design environment, the performance objectives for the fire alarm system are not established by the fire alarm system designer.

A fire protection strategy is developed to achieve those goals. General performance objectives are developed for the facility. These general objectives give rise to specific performance objectives for each fire protection system being employed in the facility. Consequently, the performance objectives and criteria for the fire alarm system are part of a much larger strategy that often relies on other fire protection features, working in concert with the fire alarm system to attain the overall fire protection goals for the facility.

In the performance-based design environment, the designer uses computational models to demonstrate that the spacing used for automatic fire detectors connected to the fire alarm system will achieve the objectives established by the system, by showing that the system meets the performance criteria established for the system in the design documentation. Consequently, it is imperative that the design objectives and performance criteria to which the system has been designed are clearly stated in the system documentation.

A.17.6.1.4 In order to predict the response of a heat detector using current fire modeling programs and currently published equations describing plume dynamics, two parameters must be known: operating temperature and response time index (RTI). The RTI is the quantification of the rate of heat transfer from the ceiling jet to the detector sensing element per unit of time, expressed as a function of ceiling jet temperature, ceiling jet velocity, and time. Spot-type heat detectors manufactured prior to July 1, 2008, were not required to be marked with an RTI.

A.17.6.2.3 Detectors should be selected to minimize this temperature difference in order to minimize response time. However, a heat detector with a temperature rating that is somewhat in excess of the highest normally expected ambient temperature is specified in order to avoid the possibility of premature operation of the heat detector to non-fire conditions.

A.17.6.3.1.1 Maximum linear spacings on smooth ceilings for spot-type heat detectors are determined by full-scale fire tests. *[See Figure A.17.6.3.1.1(c).]* These tests assume that the detectors are to be installed in a pattern of one or more squares, each side of which equals the maximum spacing as determined in the test, as illustrated in Figure A.17.6.3.1.1(a). The detector to be tested is placed at a corner of the square so that

it is positioned at the farthest possible distance from the fire while remaining within the square. Thus, the distance from the detector to the fire is always the test spacing multiplied by 0.7 and can be calculated as shown in Table A.17.6.3.1.1. Figure A.17.6.3.1.1(b) illustrates the smooth ceiling spacing layout for line-type heat detectors.

Table A.17.6.3.1.1 Test Spacing for Spot-Type Heat Detectors

Test Spacing		Maximum Test Distance from Fire to Detector (0.7D)	
ft	m	ft	m
50 × 50	15.2 × 15.2	35.0	10.7
40 × 40	12.2 × 12.2	28.0	8.5
30 × 30	9.1 × 9.1	21.0	6.4
25 × 25	7.6 × 7.6	17.5	5.3
20 × 20	6.1 × 6.1	14.0	4.3
15 × 15	4.6 × 4.6	10.5	3.2

Once the correct maximum test distance has been determined, it is valid to interchange the positions of the fire and the detector. The detector is now in the middle of the square, and the listing specifies that the detector is adequate to detect a fire that occurs anywhere within that square — even out to the farthest corner.

In laying out detector installations, designers work in terms of rectangles, as building areas are generally rectangular in shape. The pattern of heat spread from a fire source, however, is not rectangular in shape. On a smooth ceiling, heat spreads out in all directions in an ever-expanding circle. Thus, the coverage of a detector is not, in fact, a square, but rather a circle whose radius is the linear spacing multiplied by 0.7.

This is graphically illustrated in Figure A.17.6.3.1.1(d). With the detector at the center, by rotating the square, an infinite number of squares can be laid out, the corners of which create the plot of a circle whose radius is 0.7 times the listed spacing. The detector will cover any of these squares and, consequently, any point within the confines of the circle.

So far this explanation has considered squares and circles. In practical applications, very few areas turn out to be exactly square, and circular areas are extremely rare. Designers deal generally with rectangles of odd dimensions and corners of rooms or areas formed by wall intercepts, where spacing to one wall is less than one-half the listed spacing. To simplify the rest of this explanation, the use of a detector with a listed spacing of 30 ft × 30 ft (9.1 m × 9.1 m) should be considered. The principles derived are equally applicable to other types.

Figure A.17.6.3.1.1(g) illustrates the derivation of this concept. In Figure A.17.6.3.1.1(g), a detector is placed in the center of a circle with a radius of 21 ft (0.7 × 30 ft) [6.4 m (0.7 × 9.1 m)]. A series of rectangles with one dimension less than the permitted maximum of 30 ft (9.1 m) is constructed within the circle. The following conclusions can be drawn:

(1) As the smaller dimension decreases, the longer dimension can be increased beyond the linear maximum spacing of the detector with no loss in detection efficiency.

(2) A single detector covers any area that fits within the circle. For a rectangle, a single, properly located detector may be permitted, provided the diagonal of the rectangle does not exceed the diameter of the circle.

(3) Relative detector efficiency actually is increased, because the area coverage in square meters is always less than the 900 ft^2 (84 m^2) permitted if the full 30 ft × 30 ft (9.1 m × 9.1 m) square were to be utilized. The principle illustrated here allows equal linear spacing between the detector and the fire, with no recognition for the effect of reflection from walls or partitions, which in narrow rooms or corridors is of additional benefit. For detectors that are not centered, the longer dimension should always be used in laying out the radius of coverage.

Areas so large that they exceed the rectangular dimensions given in Figure A.17.6.3.1.1(g) require additional detectors. Often proper placement of detectors can be facilitated by breaking down the area into multiple rectangles of the dimensions that fit most appropriately *[see Figure A.17.6.3.1.1(e) and Figure A.17.6.3.1.1(f)]*. For example, refer to Figure A.17.6.3.1.1(h). A corridor 10 ft (3.0 m) wide and up to 82 ft (25.0 m) long can be covered with two 30 ft (9.1 m) spot-type detectors. An area 40 ft (12.2 m) wide and up to 74 ft (22.6 m) long can be covered with four spot-type detectors. Irregular areas need more careful planning to make certain that no spot on the ceiling is more than 21 ft (6.4 m) away from a detector. These points can be determined by striking arcs from the remote corner. Where any part of the area lies beyond the circle with a radius of 0.7 times the listed spacings, additional detectors are required.

Figure A.17.6.3.1.1(h) illustrates smoke or heat detector spacing layouts in irregular areas.

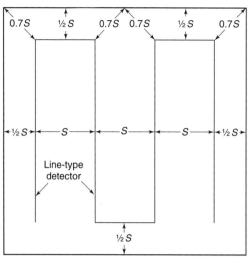

S = Space between detectors

FIGURE A.17.6.3.1.1(b) Line-Type Detectors — Spacing Layouts, Smooth Ceiling.

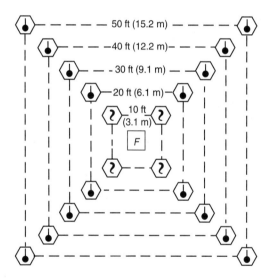

F = Test fire, denatured alcohol, 190 proof. Pan located approximately 36 in. (0.9 m) above floor.

⟨?⟩ = Indicates normal sprinkler spacings on 10 ft (3.1 m) schedules.

⟨•⟩ = Indicates normal heat detector spacing on various spacing schedules.

FIGURE A.17.6.3.1.1(c) Fire Test Layout.

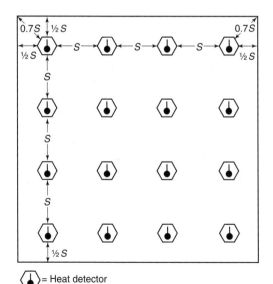

⟨•⟩ = Heat detector

S = Space between detectors

FIGURE A.17.6.3.1.1(a) Spot-Type Heat Detectors.

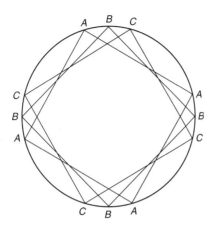

FIGURE A.17.6.3.1.1(d) Detector Covering any Square Laid Out in Confines of Circle in Which Radius Is 0.7 Times Listed Spacing.

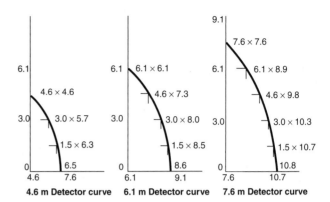

4.6 m Detector curve   6.1 m Detector curve   7.6 m Detector curve

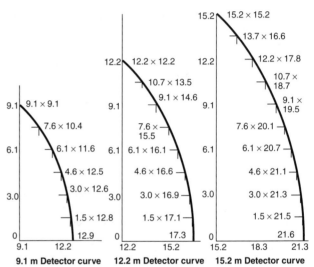

9.1 m Detector curve   12.2 m Detector curve   15.2 m Detector curve

Note: All measures are in meters.

FIGURE A.17.6.3.1.1(f) Typical Rectangles for Detector Curves of 4.6 m to 15.2 m.

A.17.6.3.1.3.1 Figure A.17.6.3.1.3.1 illustrates the proper mounting placement for detectors.

A.17.6.3.2 In addition to the special requirements for heat detectors that are installed on ceilings with exposed joists, reduced spacing also could be required due to other structural characteristics of the protected area, such as possible drafts or other conditions that could affect detector operation.

See Figure A.17.6.3.2 for an example of reduced spacing for solid joist construction.

A.17.6.3.3 The location and spacing of heat detectors should consider beam depth, ceiling height, beam spacing, and fire size.

If the ratio of beam depth (D) to ceiling height (H), (D/H), is greater than 0.10 and the ratio of beam spacing (W) to ceiling height (H), (W/H), is greater than 0.40, heat detectors should be located in each beam pocket.

If either the ratio of beam depth to ceiling height (D/H) is less than 0.10 or the ratio of beam spacing to ceiling height (W/H) is less than 0.40, heat detectors should be installed on the bottom of the beams.

A.17.6.3.4 Figure A.17.6.3.4(a) illustrates smoke or heat detector spacing for peaked-type sloped ceilings.

Figure A.17.6.3.4(b) illustrates smoke or heat detector spacing for shed-type sloped ceilings.

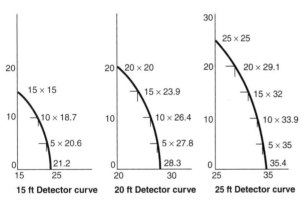

15 ft Detector curve   20 ft Detector curve   25 ft Detector curve

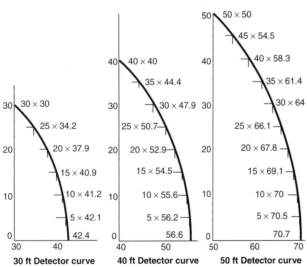

30 ft Detector curve   40 ft Detector curve   50 ft Detector curve

Note: All measures are in feet.

FIGURE A.17.6.3.1.1(e) Typical Rectangles for Detector Curves of 15 ft to 50 ft.

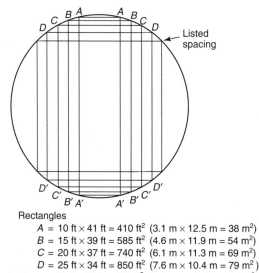

Rectangles

A = 10 ft × 41 ft = 410 ft² (3.1 m × 12.5 m = 38 m²)
B = 15 ft × 39 ft = 585 ft² (4.6 m × 11.9 m = 54 m²)
C = 20 ft × 37 ft = 740 ft² (6.1 m × 11.3 m = 69 m²)
D = 25 ft × 34 ft = 850 ft² (7.6 m × 10.4 m = 79 m²)
Listed spacing for   = 30 ft × 30 ft = 900 ft² (9.1 m × 9.1 m = 84 m²)
heat detectors only

Note: Smoke detectors are not listed for spacing. Use manufacturer's
coverage recommendations and this figure.

FIGURE A.17.6.3.1.1(g) Detector Spacing, Rectangular Areas.

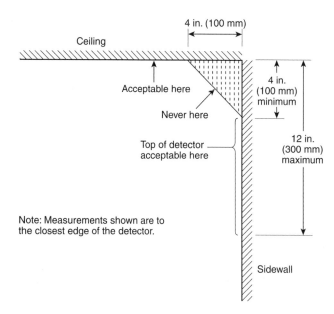

Note: Measurements shown are to
the closest edge of the detector.

FIGURE A.17.6.3.1.3.1 Example of Proper Mounting for Heat Detectors.

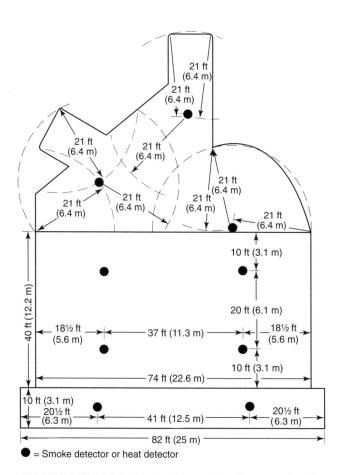

● = Smoke detector or heat detector

FIGURE A.17.6.3.1.1(h) Smoke or Heat Detector Spacing Layout in Irregular Areas.

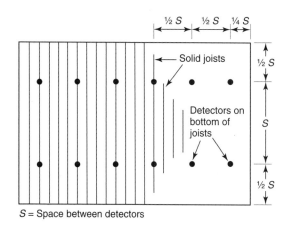

S = Space between detectors

FIGURE A.17.6.3.2 Detector Spacing Layout, Solid Joist Construction.

A.17.6.3.5.1 Both 17.6.3.5.1 and Table 17.6.3.5.1 are constructed to provide detector performance on higher ceilings [to 30 ft (9.1 m) high] that is essentially equivalent to that which would exist with detectors on a 10 ft (3.0 m) ceiling.

The Fire Detection Institute Fire Test Report [see Annex G.1.2.13(16)] is used as a basis for Table 17.6.3.5.1. The report does not include data on integration-type detectors. Pending development of such data, the manufacturer's published instructions will provide guidance.

Table 17.6.3.5.1 provides for spacing modification to take into account different ceiling heights for generalized fire conditions. Information regarding a design method that allows the designer to take into account ceiling height, fire size, and ambient temperatures is provided in Annex B.

A.17.6.3.5.2 The width of uniform temperature of the plume when it impinges on the ceiling is approximately 0.4 times the height above the fire, so reducing spacing below this level will

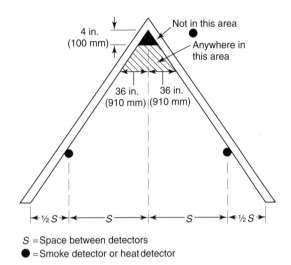

FIGURE A.17.6.3.4(a) Smoke or Heat Detector Spacing Layout, Sloped Ceilings (Peaked Type).

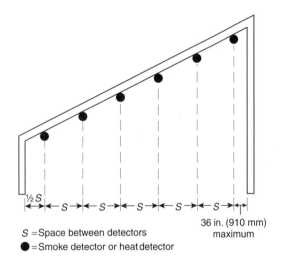

FIGURE A.17.6.3.4(b) Smoke or Heat Detector Spacing Layout, Sloped Ceilings (Shed Type).

not increase response time. For example, a detector with a listed spacing of 15 ft (4.6 m) or 225 ft² (21 m²) need not be spaced closer than 12 ft (3.7 m) on a 30 ft (9.1 m) ceiling, even though Table 17.6.3.5.1 states that the spacing should be 0.34 × 15 ft (0.34 × 4.6 m), which equals 5.1 ft (1.6 m).

A.17.6.3.6 The linear space rating is the maximum allowable distance between heat detectors. The linear space rating is also a measure of the heat detector response time to a standard test fire where tested at the same distance. The higher the rating, the faster the response time. This Code recognizes only those heat detectors with ratings of 50 ft (15.2 m) or more.

A.17.7.1.1 The performance objective statement should describe the purpose of the detector placement and the intended response of the fire alarm control unit to the detector activation. This statement can include a narrative description of the required response time of the detectors, a narrative of the sequence of operations, a tabular list of programming requirements, or some other method.

The performance objective of a fire detection system is usually expressed in terms of time and the size fire the system is intended to detect, measured in British thermal units per second (Btu/sec) or kilowatts (kW). Typically, the fire alarm system designer does not establish this criterion. It is usually obtained from the design documentation prepared by the designer responsible for the strategy of the structure as a whole. Where a prescriptive design is being provided, this requirement is fulfilled by stating in the design documentation that the design conforms to the prescriptive provisions of this Code.

A.17.7.1.2 The person designing an installation should keep in mind that, in order for a smoke detector to respond, the smoke has to travel from the point of origin to the detector. In evaluating any particular building or location, likely fire locations should be determined first. From each of these points of origin, paths of smoke travel should be determined. Wherever practicable, actual field tests should be conducted. The most desired locations for smoke detectors are the common points of intersection of smoke travel from fire locations throughout the building.

NOTE: This is one of the reasons that specific spacing is not assigned to smoke detectors by the testing laboratories.

A.17.7.1.3 In a performance-based design environment, the performance objectives for the fire alarm system are not established by the fire alarm system designer.

A fire protection strategy is developed to achieve those goals. General performance objectives are developed for the facility. These general objectives give rise to specific performance objectives for each fire protection system being employed in the facility. Consequently, the performance objectives and criteria for the fire alarm system are part of a much larger strategy that often relies on other fire protection features, working in concert with the fire alarm system to attain the overall fire protection goals for the facility.

In the performance-based design environment, the designer uses computational models to demonstrate that the spacing used for automatic fire detectors connected to the fire alarm system will achieve the objectives established by the system, by showing that the system meets the performance criteria established for the system in the design documentation. Consequently, it is imperative that the design objectives and performance criteria to which the system has been designed are clearly stated in the system documentation.

A.17.7.1.8 Product-listing standards include tests for temporary excursions beyond normal limits. In addition to temperature, humidity, and velocity variations, smoke detectors should operate reliably under such common environmental conditions as mechanical vibration, electrical interference, and other environmental influences. Tests for these conditions are also conducted by the testing laboratories in their listing program. In those cases in which environmental conditions approach the limits shown in Table A.17.7.1.8, the detector manufacturer's published instructions should be consulted for additional information and recommendations.

Table A.17.7.1.8 Environmental Conditions that Influence Smoke Detector Response

Detection Protection	Air Velocity >300 ft/min (>91.44 m/min)	Altitude >3000 ft (>914.4 m)	Humidity >93% RH	Temperature <32°F >100°F (<0°C >37.8°C)	Color of Smoke
Ion	X	X	X	X	O
Photo	O	O	X	X	X
Beam	O	O	X	X	O
Air sampling	O	O	X	X	O

X: Can affect detector response. O: Generally does not affect detector response.

A.17.7.1.9 Smoke detectors can be affected by electrical and mechanical influences and by aerosols and particulate matter found in protected spaces. The location of detectors should be such that the influences of aerosols and particulate matter from sources such as those in Table A.17.7.1.9(a) are minimized. Similarly, the influences of electrical and mechanical factors shown in Table A.17.7.1.9(b) should be minimized. While it might not be possible to isolate environmental factors totally, an awareness of these factors during system layout and design favorably affects detector performance.

Table A.17.7.1.9(a) Common Sources of Aerosols and Particulate Matter Moisture

Moisture	Humid outside air
	Humidifiers
	Live steam
	Showers
	Slop sink
	Steam tables
	Water spray
Combustion products and fumes	Chemical fumes
	Cleaning fluids
	Cooking equipment
	Curing
	Cutting, welding, and brazing
	Dryers
	Exhaust hoods
	Fireplaces
	Machining
	Ovens
	Paint spray
Atmospheric contaminants	Corrosive atmospheres
	Dust or lint
	Excessive tobacco smoke
	Heat treating
	Linen and bedding handling
	Pneumatic transport
	Sawing, drilling, and grinding
	Textile and agricultural processing
Engine exhaust	Diesel trucks and locomotives
	Engines not vented to the outside
	Gasoline forklift trucks
Heating element with abnormal conditions	Dust accumulations
	Improper exhaust
	Incomplete combustion

Table A.17.7.1.9(b) Sources of Electrical and Mechanical Influences on Smoke Detectors

Electrical Noise and Transients	Airflow
Vibration or shock	Gusts
Radiation	Excessive velocity
Radio frequency	
Intense light	
Lightning	
Electrostatic discharge	
Power supply	

A.17.7.1.10 Stratification of air in a room can hinder air containing smoke particles or gaseous combustion products from reaching ceiling-mounted smoke detectors or fire–gas detectors.

Stratification occurs when air containing smoke particles or gaseous combustion products is heated by smoldering or burning material and, becoming less dense than the surrounding cooler air, rises until it reaches a level at which there is no longer a difference in temperature between it and the surrounding air.

Stratification also can occur when evaporative coolers are used, because moisture introduced by these devices can condense on smoke, causing it to fall toward the floor. Therefore, to ensure rapid response, it might be necessary to install smoke detectors on sidewalls or at locations below the ceiling.

In installations where detection of smoldering or small fires is desired and where the possibility of stratification exists, consideration should be given to mounting a portion of the detectors below the ceiling. In high-ceiling areas, projected beam–type or air sampling–type detectors at different levels also should be considered. (*See Figure A.17.7.1.10.*)

A.17.7.1.11 Construction debris, dust (especially gypsum dust and the fines resulting from the sanding of drywall joint compounds), and aerosols can affect the sensitivity of smoke detectors and, in some instances, cause deleterious effects to the detector, thereby significantly reducing the expected life of the detector.

A.17.7.2 Throughout this Code, smoke detector sensitivity is referred to in terms of the percent obscuration required to alarm or produce a signal. Smoke detectors are tested using various smoke sources that have different characteristics (e.g., color, particle size, number of particles, particle shape). Unless otherwise specified, this Code, the manufacturers, and the listing agencies report and use the percent obscuration produced using a specific type of gray smoke.

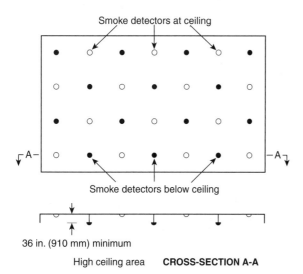

FIGURE A.17.7.1.10 Smoke Detector Layout Accounting for Stratification.

Actual detector response will vary when the characteristics of the smoke reaching the detector are different from the smoke used in testing and reporting detector sensitivity.

A.17.7.2.1 The production sensitivity range should only be used as a benchmark for testing and should not be used as the sole basis for selection of devices. The percent per foot sensitivity marked on the smoke detector is derived from testing in a smoke chamber, usually referred to as the ANSI/UL 268 Smoke Box. The measurements derived from this measurement apparatus are only valid in the context of the apparatus and cannot be used outside the context of the smoke box. The polychromatic light source employed in the smoke box results in measurements that are highly dependent upon smoke color and does not account for variations in light transmission as a function of wavelength that occurs as fuels and fire ventilation rates change or as smoke ages. Furthermore, the measurement apparatus uses a measurement of light obscuration by smoke to infer a measure of light reflectance when there is no correlation between these two optical characteristics.

A.17.7.3.1 Except in the case of smoldering, low-energy fires, all smoke detectors, regardless of the type of technology, usually rely on the plume and ceiling jet produced by the fire to transport the smoke upward and across the ceiling to the detector, sampling port, or projected sensing light beam. Once sufficient concentration is attained at the detector, sampling port, or sensing light beam location and, in the case of spot-type detectors, sufficient flow velocity is attained to overcome the flow resistance into the sensing chamber, the detector responds with an alarm signal. Detectors are usually mounted at the ceiling plane to take advantage of the flow provided by the plume and the ceiling jet. A hot, energetic fire produces large plume velocities and temperatures and hot, fast ceiling jets. This minimizes the time it takes for the smoke to travel to the detector. A smoldering fire produces little, if any, plume and no appreciable ceiling jet. Far more time elapses between ignition and detection under this circumstance.

A.17.7.3.2 In high-ceiling areas, such as atriums, where spot-type smoke detectors are not accessible for periodic mainte-nance and testing, projected beam–type or air sampling–type detectors should be considered where access can be provided.

A.17.7.3.2.1 Refer to Figure A.17.7.3.2.1 for an example of proper mounting for detectors. Sidewall detectors mounted closer to the ceiling will respond faster.

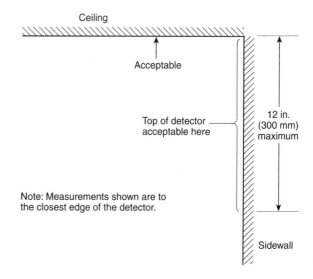

FIGURE A.17.7.3.2.1 Example of Proper Mounting of Smoke Detectors.

A.17.7.3.2.2 Figure A.17.7.3.2.2 illustrates underfloor mounting installations.

A.17.7.3.2.3.1 The 30 ft (9.1 m) spacing is a guide for prescriptive designs. The use of such a spacing is based upon customary practice in the fire alarm community.

Where there are explicit performance objectives for the response of the smoke detection system, the performance-based design methods outlined in Annex B should be used.

For the purposes of this section, "nominal 30 ft (9.1 m)" should be determined to be 30 ft (9.1 m) ±5 percent [±18 in. (460 mm)].

A.17.7.3.2.3.1(2) This is useful in calculating locations in corridors or irregular areas [see 17.6.3.1.1 and Figure A.17.6.3.1.1(h)]. For irregularly shaped areas, the spacing between detectors can be greater than the selected spacing, provided the maximum spacing from a detector to the farthest point of a sidewall or corner within its zone of protection is not greater than 0.7 times the selected spacing (0.7S).

A.17.7.3.2.4 Detectors are placed at reduced spacings at right angles to joists or beams in an attempt to ensure that detection time is equivalent to that which would be experienced on a flat ceiling. It takes longer for the combustion products (smoke or heat) to travel at right angles to beams or joists because of the phenomenon wherein a plume from a relatively hot fire with significant thermal lift tends to fill the pocket between each beam or joist before moving to the next beam or joist.

Though it is true that this phenomenon might not be significant in a small smoldering fire where there is only enough thermal lift to cause stratification at the bottom of the joists, reduced spacing is still recommended to ensure that detection time is equivalent to that which would exist on a flat ceiling, even in the case of a hotter type of fire.

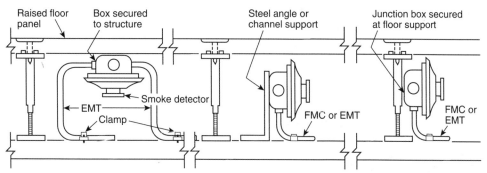

Underfloor mounting orientations — permitted

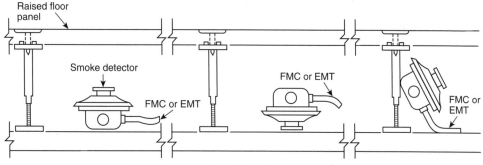

Underfloor mounting orientations — not permitted

FIGURE A.17.7.3.2.2 Mounting Installations Permitted *(top)* **and Not Permitted** *(bottom).*

A.17.7.3.2.4.2(3) The geometry and reservoir effect is a significant factor that contributes to the development of velocity, temperature, and smoke obscuration conditions at smoke detectors located on the ceiling in beam pocket areas or at the bottom of beams as smoke collected in the reservoir volume spills into adjacent pockets. The waffle- or pan-type ceiling created by beams or solid joists, although retarding the initial flow of smoke, results in increased optical density, temperature rise, and gas velocities comparable to unconfined smooth ceilings.

For waffle- or pan-type ceilings with beams or solid joists, an alternative smoke detector grid arrangement (such as a shifted grid), with detectors located to take advantage of the channeling effect due to the reservoirs created by the beam pockets, will improve detector response and might allow greater spacing. See Figure A.17.7.3.2.4.2(3)(a) and Figure A.17.7.3.2.4.2(3)(b) for an example of shifted grids. The alternative smoke detector grid arrangement and spacing should be justified by an engineering analysis comparing the alternative smoke detector grid arrangement with the performance of smoke detectors on a level ceiling of equal height using 30 ft (9.1 m) smoke detector spacing.

Figure A.17.7.3.2.4.2(3)(a) illustrates the reservoir and channeling effect that results from the deep beam configuration. The strongest gas flows occur in a direction perpendicular to the beam opposite the fire location. The weaker flow occurs in a directional 45 degrees off the beam grid; however, the reservoir effect accounts for higher concentrations of smoke eventually flowing from the strong area reservoirs into the weak area reservoirs.

Figure A.17.7.3.2.4.2(3)(b) is a generic example illustrating how a smoke detection grid using 30 ft (9.1 m) spacing can be shifted to take advantage of the channeling and reservoir effect to optimize detection response. In the circle, the fire is split into four beam bays that must fill with smoke before ap-

preciable flows occur into the next adjoining eight beam bays. This represents the worst case scenario for smoke to reach the detectors on the circle. The three other fire locations shown require the fire to initially fill only one or two bays before spilling to adjacent bays.

A.17.7.3.2.4.2(4) Corridor geometry is a significant factor that contributes to the development of velocity, temperature, and smoke obscuration conditions at smoke detectors located along a corridor. This is based on the fact that the ceiling jet is confined or constrained by the nearby walls without opportunity for entrainment of air. For corridors of approximately 15 ft (4.6 m) in width and for fires of approximately 100 kW or greater, modeling has demonstrated that the performance of smoke detectors in corridors with beams has been shown to be comparable to spot smoke detector spacing on an unconfined smooth ceiling surface.

A.17.7.3.2.4.3 A smoke detector should be placed within each beam channel. Computer modeling has shown that parallel beams (upslope) are very effective at channeling smoke, and smoke spillover is rarely detectable in adjacent parallel pockets.

A.17.7.3.2.4.4 Irregular area spacing guidance for level beam ceilings can be used. Computer modeling has shown that spot-type detectors should be located on the bottom of perpendicular beams.

A.17.7.3.2.4.5 Computer modeling has shown that spot-type detectors should be located on the bottom of perpendicular beams and should be aligned with the center of pocket, as shown, in Figure A.17.7.3.2.4.5.

A.17.7.3.3 Refer to Figure A.17.6.3.4(a).

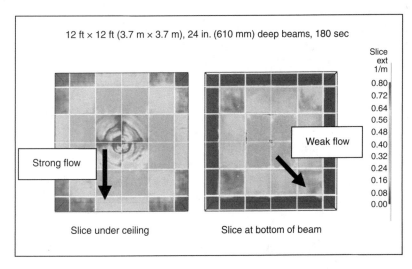

12 ft × 12 ft (3.7 m × 3.7 m), 24 in. (610 mm) deep beams, 180 sec

FIGURE A.17.7.3.2.4.2(3)(a)   Reservoir and Channeling Effect of Deep Beams.

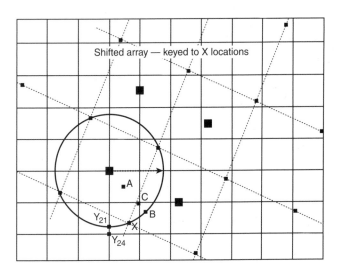

FIGURE A.17.7.3.2.4.2(3)(b)   Shifted Smoke Detection Grid to Optimize Detection for Deep Beam Effects.

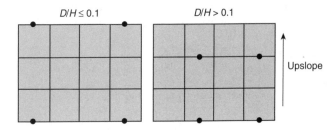

FIGURE A.17.7.3.2.4.5   Spot-Type Detector Spacing for Sloping Ceilings with Beam Pockets.

A.17.7.3.4   Refer to Figure A.17.6.3.4(b).

A.17.7.3.6.3   A single-pipe network has a shorter transport time than a multiple-pipe network of similar length pipe; however, a multiple-pipe system provides a faster smoke transport time than a single-pipe system of the same total length. As the number of sampling holes in a pipe increases, the smoke transport time increases. Where practicable, pipe run lengths in a multiple-pipe system should be nearly equal, or the system should be otherwise pneumatically balanced.

A.17.7.3.6.6   The air sampling–type detector system should be able to withstand dusty environments by air filtering, electronic discrimination of particle size, or other listed methods or combinations thereof. The detector should be capable of providing optimal time delays of alarm outputs to eliminate nuisance alarms due to transient smoke conditions. The detector should also provide facilities for the connection of monitoring equipment for the recording of background smoke level information necessary in setting alert and alarm levels and delays.

A.17.7.3.7   On smooth ceilings, a spacing of not more than 60 ft (18.3 m) between projected beams and not more than one-half that spacing between a projected beam and a sidewall (wall parallel to the beam travel) should be used as a guide. Other spacing should be determined based on ceiling height, airflow characteristics, and response requirements.

In some cases, the light beam projector is mounted on one end wall, with the light beam receiver mounted on the opposite wall. However, it is also permitted to suspend the projector and receiver from the ceiling at a distance from the end walls not exceeding one-quarter the selected spacing (S). *(See Figure A.17.7.3.7.)*

A.17.7.3.7.8   Where the light path of a projected beam–type detector is abruptly interrupted or obscured, the unit should not initiate an alarm. It should give a trouble signal after verification of blockage.

A.17.7.4.1   Detectors should not be located in a direct airflow or closer than 36 in. (910 mm) from an air supply diffuser or return air opening. Supply or return sources larger than those commonly found in residential and small commercial establishments can require greater clearance to smoke detectors. Similarly, smoke detectors should be located farther away from high velocity air supplies. See B.4.10.

A.17.7.4.3   Smoke might not be drawn into the duct or plenums when the ventilating system is shut down. Furthermore, when the ventilating system is operating, the detector(s) can

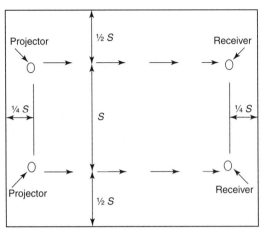

FIGURE A.17.7.3.7 **Maximum Distance at Which Ceiling-Suspended Light Projector and Receiver Can Be Positioned from End Wall Is One-Quarter Selected Spacing** *(S)*.

be less responsive to a fire condition in the room of fire origin due to dilution by clean air.

A.17.7.5 Refer to NFPA *101, Life Safety Code,* for the definition of smoke compartment; NFPA 90A, *Standard for the Installation of Air-Conditioning and Ventilating Systems,* for the definition of duct systems; and NFPA 92, *Standard for Smoke Control Systems,* for the definition of smoke zone.

A.17.7.5.1 Smoke detectors located in an open area(s) should be used rather than duct-type detectors because of the dilution effect in air ducts. Active smoke management systems installed in accordance with NFPA 92, *Standard for Smoke Control Systems,* should be controlled by total coverage open area detection.

A.17.7.5.2 Dilution of smoke-laden air by clean air from other parts of the building or dilution by outside air intakes can allow high densities of smoke in a single room with no appreciable smoke in the air duct at the detector location. Smoke might not be drawn from open areas if air-conditioning systems or ventilating systems are shut down.

A.17.7.5.3 Smoke detectors can be applied in order to initiate control of smoke spread for the following purposes:

(1) Prevention of the recirculation of dangerous quantities of smoke within a building
(2) Selective operation of equipment to exhaust smoke from a building
(3) Selective operation of equipment to pressurize smoke compartments
(4) Operation of doors and dampers to close the openings in smoke compartments

A.17.7.5.4.2 Smoke detectors are designed to sense the presence of particles of combustion, but depending on the sensing technology and other design factors, different detectors respond to different types of particles. Detectors based on ionization detection technology are most responsive to smaller, invisible sub-micron sized particles. Detectors based on photoelectric technology, by contrast, are most responsive to larger visible particles.

It is generally accepted that particle size distribution varies from sub-micron diameter particles predominant in the proximity of the flame of a flaming fire to particles one or more orders of magnitude larger, which are characteristic of smoke from a smoldering fire. The actual particle size distribution depends on a host of other variables including the fuel and its physical make-up, the availability of oxygen including air supply and fire–gas discharge, and other ambient conditions, especially humidity. Moreover, the particle size distribution is not constant, but as the fire gases cool, the sub-micron particles agglomerate and the very large ones precipitate. In other words, as smoke travels away from the fire source, the particle size distribution shows a relative decrease in smaller particles. Water vapor, which is abundantly present in most fires, when cooled sufficiently will condense to form fog particles — an effect frequently seen above tall chimneys. Because water condensation is basically clear in color, when it is mixed with other smoke particles, it can be expected to lighten the color of the mixture.

In almost every fire scenario in an air-handling system, the point of detection will be some distance from the fire source; therefore, the smoke will be cooler and more visible because of the growth of sub-micron particles into larger particles due to agglomeration and recombination. For these reasons, photoelectric detection technology has advantages over ionization detection technology in air duct system applications.

A.17.7.5.4.2.2 Detectors listed for the air velocity present can be permitted to be installed at the opening where the return air enters the common return air system. The detectors should be installed up to 12 in. (300 mm) in front of or behind the opening and spaced according to the following opening dimensions [*see Figure A.17.7.5.4.2.2(a) through Figure A.17.7.5.4.2.2(c)*]:

(1) *Width.*
   (a) Up to 36 in. (910 mm) — One detector centered in opening
   (b) Up to 72 in. (1.83 m) — Two detectors located at the one-quarter points of the opening
   (c) Over 72 in. (1.83 m) — One additional detector for each full 24 in. (610 mm) of opening
(2) *Depth.* The number and spacing of the detector(s) in the depth (vertical) of the opening should be the same as those given for the width (horizontal) in A.17.7.5.4.2.2(1).
(3) *Orientation.* Detectors should be oriented in the most favorable position for smoke entry with respect to the direction of airflow. The path of a projected beam–type detector across the return air openings should be considered equivalent in coverage to a row of individual detectors.

Additional duct smoke detection is not required where the air leaves each smoke compartment or in the duct system before the air enters the return air system in the return air of a smoke compartment provided with total (complete) smoke detection compliant with 17.5.3 because the addition of duct smoke detection would essentially not add any substantial detection benefit.

A.17.7.5.5.2 Where duct detectors are used to initiate the operation of smoke dampers, they should be located so that the detector is between the last inlet or outlet upstream of the damper and the first inlet or outlet downstream of the damper.

In order to obtain a representative sample, stratification and dead air space should be avoided. Such conditions could be caused by return duct openings, sharp turns, or connections, as well as by long, uninterrupted straight runs.

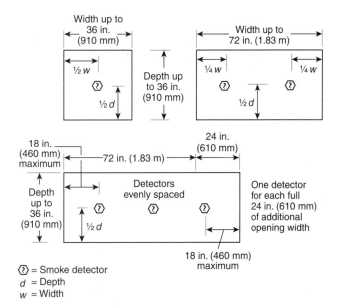

⟨?⟩ = Smoke detector
d = Depth
w = Width

FIGURE A.17.7.5.4.2.2(a) Location of Smoke Detector(s) in Return Air System Openings for Selective Operation of Equipment.

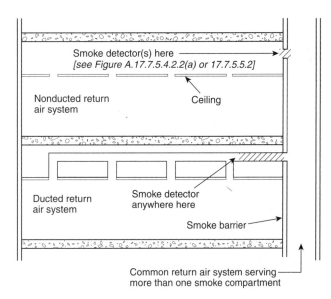

FIGURE A.17.7.5.4.2.2(b) Location of Smoke Detector(s) in Return Air Systems for Selective Operation of Equipment.

In return air systems, the requirements of 17.7.5.4.2.2 take precedence over these considerations. *[See Figure A.17.7.5.5.2(a) and Figure A.17.7.5.5.2(b).]*

Usually, it is necessary to manage smoke flow in buildings. Duct smoke detectors are used to shut down HVAC systems or initiate smoke management.

Filters have a serious effect on the performance of duct smoke detectors. The location of the detector relative to the filter and the source of smoke must be considered during the design process. Where smoke detectors are installed downstream from filters, they should be deemed to serve the purpose of providing an alarm indication of the occurrence of a

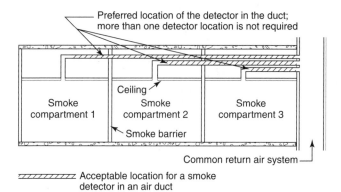

━━━━━ Acceptable location for a smoke detector in an air duct

FIGURE A.17.7.5.4.2.2(c) Detector Location in Duct that Passes Through Smoke Compartments Not Served by Duct.

fire in the HVAC unit (filters, belts, heat exchangers, etc.). These detectors usually serve the purpose of protecting building occupants from the smoke produced by an HVAC unit fire, or smoke ingress via the fresh air intake for the unit. They cannot be expected to serve the purpose of providing detection for the return side of the system.

Where return side detection is required, that requirement should be fulfilled with separate detectors from those monitoring the supply side. In order to be effective, return air duct smoke detectors should be located such that there are no filters between them and the source of the smoke.

Sampling tubes should be oriented to overcome thermal stratification due to buoyancy of the smoke in the upper half of the duct. This condition occurs where duct velocities are low, buoyancy exceeds flow inertia, or the detector is installed close to the fire compartment. A vertical orientation of sampling tubes overcomes the effects of differential buoyancy.

Where a detector is installed on a duct serving a single fire compartment, where the buoyancy exceeds the flow inertia of the air in the duct and the sampling tube cannot be oriented vertically, then the effects of thermal stratification can be minimized by locating the detector sampling tube in the upper half of the duct.

The thermal stratification is not a concern where the detector is installed far from the fire compartment or where the smoke is at or close to the average temperature in the duct.

A.17.7.5.6.5.1(C) If the depth of wall section above the door is 60 in. (1.52 m) or greater, additional detectors might be required as indicated by an engineering evaluation.

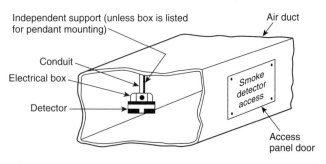

FIGURE A.17.7.5.5.2(a) Pendant-Mounted Air Duct Installation.

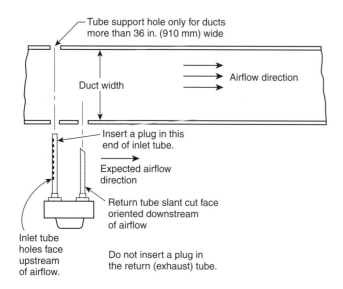

FIGURE A.17.7.5.5.2(b) Inlet Tube Orientation.

A.17.7.6.1.2 Airflow through holes in the rear of a smoke detector can interfere with smoke entry to the sensing chamber. Similarly, air from the conduit system can flow around the outside edges of the detector and interfere with smoke reaching the sensing chamber. Additionally, holes in the rear of a detector provide a means for entry of dust, dirt, and insects, each of which can adversely affect the detector's performance.

A.17.7.6.2 For the most effective detection of fire in high-rack storage areas, detectors should be located on the ceiling above each aisle and at intermediate levels in the racks. This is necessary to detect smoke that is trapped in the racks at an early stage of fire development when insufficient thermal energy is released to carry the smoke to the ceiling. Earliest detection of smoke is achieved by locating the intermediate level detectors adjacent to alternate pallet sections as shown in Figure A.17.7.6.2(a) and Figure A.17.7.6.2(b). The detector manufacturer's published instructions and engineering judgment should be followed for specific installations.

A projected beam–type detector can be permitted to be used in lieu of a single row of individual spot-type smoke detectors.

Sampling ports of an air sampling–type detector can be permitted to be located above each aisle to provide coverage that is equivalent to the location of spot-type detectors. The manufacturer's published instructions and engineering judgment should be followed for the specific installation.

A.17.7.6.3.3 Smoke detector spacing depends on the movement of air within the room.

A.17.7.7.3 Facility owners and managers might desire to use cameras and their images for purposes other than smoke detection. The intent of this paragraph is not to prohibit additional uses, but to ensure the integrity of the life safety smoke detection mission of the equipment.

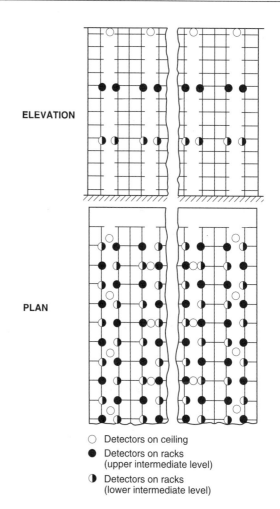

○ Detectors on ceiling
● Detectors on racks (upper intermediate level)
◑ Detectors on racks (lower intermediate level)

FIGURE A.17.7.6.2(a) **Detector Location for Solid Storage (Closed Rack) in Which Transverse and Longitudinal Flue Spaces Are Irregular or Nonexistent, as for Slatted or Solid Shelved Storage.**

A.17.7.7.4 Video image smoke detection control and software should be protected from tampering by passwords, software keys, or other means of limiting access to authorized/qualified personnel. Component settings include any control or programming that might affect the operation of coverage of the detection. This includes, but is not limited to, camera focus, field of view, motion sensitivity settings, and change of camera position. Any changes in component settings or ambient conditions that affect the design performance of the detector should initiate a trouble signal.

A.17.8.1 For the purpose of this Code, radiant energy includes the electromagnetic radiation emitted as a by-product of the combustion reaction, which obeys the laws of optics. This includes radiation in the ultraviolet, visible, and infrared portions of the spectrum emitted by flames or glowing embers. These portions of the spectrum are distinguished by wavelengths as shown in Table A.17.8.1.

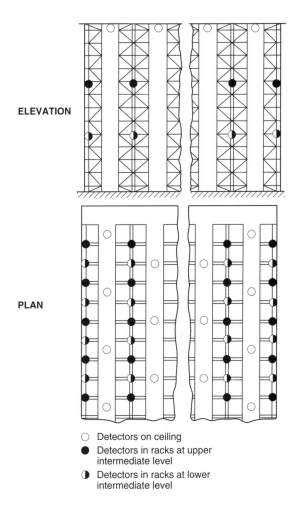

ELEVATION

PLAN

○ Detectors on ceiling

● Detectors in racks at upper
  intermediate level

◑ Detectors in racks at lower
  intermediate level

FIGURE A.17.7.6.2(b) Detector Location for Palletized Storage (Open Rack) or No Shelved Storage in Which Regular Transverse and Longitudinal Flue Spaces Are Maintained.

Table A.17.8.1 Spectrum Wavelength Ranges

Radiant Energy	μm
Ultraviolet	0.1–0.35
Visible	0.36–0.75
Infrared	0.76–220

Conversion factors: 1.0 μm = 1000 nm = 10,000 Å.

A.17.8.2 Following are operating principles for two types of detectors:

(1) *Flame Detectors.* Ultraviolet flame detectors typically use a vacuum photodiode Geiger–Muller tube to detect the ultraviolet radiation that is produced by a flame. The photodiode allows a burst of current to flow for each ultraviolet photon that hits the active area of the tube. When the number of current bursts per unit time reaches a predetermined level, the detector initiates an alarm. A single wavelength infrared flame detector uses one of several different photocell types to detect the infrared emissions in a single wavelength band that are produced by a flame. These detectors generally in-

clude provisions to minimize alarms from commonly occurring infrared sources such as incandescent lighting or sunlight. An ultraviolet/infrared (UV/IR) flame detector senses ultraviolet radiation with a vacuum photodiode tube and a selected wavelength of infrared radiation with a photocell and uses the combined signal to indicate a fire. These detectors need exposure to both types of radiation before an alarm signal can be initiated. A multiple wavelength infrared (IR/IR) flame detector senses radiation at two or more narrow bands of wavelengths in the infrared spectrum. These detectors electronically compare the emissions between the bands and initiate a signal where the relationship between the two bands indicates a fire.

(2) *Spark/Ember Detectors.* A spark/ember-sensing detector usually uses a solid state photodiode or phototransistor to sense the radiant energy emitted by embers, typically between 0.5 microns and 2.0 microns in normally dark environments. These detectors can be made extremely sensitive (microwatts), and their response times can be made very short (microseconds).

A.17.8.2.1 The radiant energy from a flame or spark/ember is comprised of emissions in various bands of the ultraviolet, visible, and infrared portions of the spectrum. The relative quantities of radiation emitted in each part of the spectrum are determined by the fuel chemistry, the temperature, and the rate of combustion. The detector should be matched to the characteristics of the fire.

Almost all materials that participate in flaming combustion emit ultraviolet radiation to some degree during flaming combustion, whereas only carbon-containing fuels emit significant radiation at the 4.35 micron (carbon dioxide) band used by many detector types to detect a flame. (*See Figure A.17.8.2.1.*)

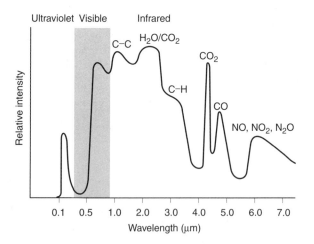

FIGURE A.17.8.2.1 Spectrum of Typical Flame (Free-Burning Gasoline).

The radiant energy emitted from an ember is determined primarily by the fuel temperature (Planck's law emissions) and the emissivity of the fuel. Radiant energy from an ember is primarily infrared and, to a lesser degree, visible in wavelength. In general, embers do not emit ultraviolet energy in significant quantities (0.1 percent of total emissions) until the ember achieves temperatures of 3240°F (1727°C or 2000°K). In most cases, the emissions are included in the band of 0.8 microns to 2.0 microns, corresponding to temperatures of approximately 750°F to 1830°F (398°C to 1000°C).

Most radiant energy detectors have some form of qualification circuitry within them that uses time to help distinguish between spurious, transient signals and legitimate fire alarms. These circuits become very important where the anticipated fire scenario and the ability of the detector to respond to that anticipated fire are considered. For example, a detector that uses an integration circuit or a timing circuit to respond to the flickering light from a fire might not respond well to a deflagration resulting from the ignition of accumulated combustible vapors and gases, or where the fire is a spark that is traveling up to 328 ft/sec (100 m/sec) past the detector. Under these circumstances, a detector that has a high-speed response capability is most appropriate. On the other hand, in applications where the development of the fire is slower, a detector that uses time for the confirmation of repetitive signals is appropriate. Consequently, the fire growth rate should be considered in selecting the detector. The detector performance should be selected to respond to the anticipated fire.

The radiant emissions are not the only criteria to be considered. The medium between the anticipated fire and the detector is also very important. Different wavelengths of radiant energy are absorbed with varying degrees of efficiency by materials that are suspended in the air or that accumulate on the optical surfaces of the detector. Generally, aerosols and surface deposits reduce the sensitivity of the detector. The detection technology used should take into account those normally occurring aerosols and surface deposits to minimize the reduction of system response between maintenance intervals. It should be noted that the smoke evolved from the combustion of middle and heavy fraction petroleum distillates is highly absorptive in the ultraviolet end of the spectrum. If using this type of detection, the system should be designed to minimize the effect of smoke interference on the response of the detection system.

The environment and ambient conditions anticipated in the area to be protected impact the choice of detector. All detectors have limitations on the range of ambient temperatures over which they will respond, consistent with their tested or approved sensitivities. The designer should make certain that the detector is compatible with the range of ambient temperatures anticipated in the area in which it is installed. In addition, rain, snow, and ice attenuate both ultraviolet and infrared radiation to varying degrees. Where anticipated, provisions should be made to protect the detector from accumulations of these materials on its optical surfaces.

A.17.8.2.2 Normal radiant emissions that are not from a fire can be present in the hazard area. When selecting a detector for an area, other potential sources of radiant emissions should be evaluated. Refer to A.17.8.2.1 for additional information.

A.17.8.3.1.1 All optical detectors respond according to the following theoretical equation:

$$S = \frac{kP^{-e\zeta d}}{d^2}$$

where:
S = radiant power reaching the detector
k = proportionality constant for the detector
P = radiant power emitted by the fire
e = Naperian logarithm base (2.7183)
ζ = extinction coefficient of air
d = distance between the fire and the detector

The sensitivity (S) typically is measured in nanowatts. This equation yields a family of curves similar to the one shown in Figure A.17.8.3.1.1.

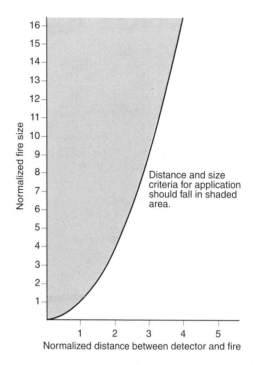

FIGURE A.17.8.3.1.1 **Normalized Fire Size vs. Distance.**

The curve defines the maximum distance at which the detector consistently detects a fire of defined size and fuel. Detectors should be employed only in the shaded area above the curve.

Under the best of conditions, with no atmospheric absorption, the radiant power reaching the detector is reduced by a factor of 4 if the distance between the detector and the fire is doubled. For the consumption of the atmospheric extinction, the exponential term zeta (ζ) is added to the equation. Zeta is a measure of the clarity of the air at the wavelength under consideration. Zeta is affected by humidity, dust, and any other contaminants in the air that are absorbent at the wavelength in question. Zeta generally has values between −0.001 and −0.1 for normal ambient air.

A.17.8.3.2.1 The following are types of application for which flame detectors are suitable:

(1) High-ceiling, open-spaced buildings such as warehouses and aircraft hangars
(2) Outdoor or semioutdoor areas where winds or drafts can prevent smoke from reaching a heat or smoke detector
(3) Areas where rapidly developing flaming fires can occur, such as aircraft hangars, petrochemical production areas, storage and transfer areas, natural gas installations, paint shops, or solvent areas
(4) Areas needing high fire risk machinery or installations, often coupled with an automatic gas extinguishing system
(5) Environments that are unsuitable for other types of detectors

Some extraneous sources of radiant emissions that have been identified as interfering with the stability of flame detectors include the following:

(1) Sunlight
(2) Lightning
(3) X-rays
(4) Gamma rays
(5) Cosmic rays
(6) Ultraviolet radiation from arc welding
(7) Electromagnetic interference (EMI, RFI)
(8) Hot objects
(9) Artificial lighting

A.17.8.3.2.3 The greater the angular displacement of the fire from the optical axis of the detector, the larger the fire must become before it is detected. This phenomenon establishes the field of view of the detector. Figure A.17.8.3.2.3 shows an example of the effective sensitivity versus angular displacement of a flame detector.

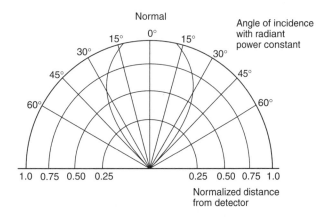

FIGURE A.17.8.3.2.3 Normalized Sensitivity vs. Angular Displacement.

A.17.8.3.2.4 Virtually all radiant energy–sensing detectors exhibit some kind of fuel specificity. If burned at uniform rates [W (J/sec)], different fuels emit different levels of radiant power in the ultraviolet, visible, and infrared portions of the spectrum. Under free-burn conditions, a fire of given surface area but of different fuels burns at different rates [W (J/sec)] and emits varying levels of radiation in each of the major portions of the spectrum. Most radiant energy detectors designed to detect flame are qualified on the basis of a defined fire under specific conditions. If employing these detectors for fuels other than the defined fire, the designer should make certain that the appropriate adjustments to the maximum distance between the detector and the fire are made consistent with the fuel specificity of the detector.

A.17.8.3.2.6 This requirement has been satisfied by the following means:

(1) Lens clarity monitoring and cleaning where a contaminated lens signal is rendered
(2) Lens air purge

The need to clean detector windows can be reduced by the provision of air purge devices. These devices are not foolproof, however, and are not a replacement for regular inspection and testing. Radiant energy–sensing detectors should not

be placed in protective housings (e.g., behind glass) to keep them clean, unless such housings are listed for the purpose. Some optical materials are absorptive at the wavelengths used by the detector.

A.17.8.3.3.1 Spark/ember detectors are installed primarily to detect sparks and embers that could, if allowed to continue to burn, precipitate a much larger fire or explosion. Spark/ember detectors are typically mounted on some form of duct or conveyor, monitoring the fuel as it passes by. Usually, it is necessary to enclose the portion of the conveyor where the detectors are located, as these devices generally require a dark environment. Extraneous sources of radiant emissions that have been identified as interfering with the stability of spark/ember detectors include the following:

(1) Ambient light
(2) Electromagnetic interference (EMI, RFI)
(3) Electrostatic discharge in the fuel stream

A.17.8.3.3.2 There is a minimum ignition power (watts) for all combustible dusts. If the spark or ember is incapable of delivering that quantity of power to the adjacent combustible material (dust), an expanding dust fire cannot occur. The minimum ignition power is determined by the fuel chemistry, fuel particle size, fuel concentration in air, and ambient conditions such as temperature and humidity.

A.17.8.3.3.4 As the distance between the fire and the detector increases, the radiant power reaching the detector decreases. Refer to A.17.8.3.1.1 for additional information.

A.17.8.3.3.5 The greater the angular displacement of the fire from the optical axis of the detector, the larger the fire must become before it is detected. This phenomenon establishes the field of view of the detector. Figure A.17.8.3.2.3 shows an example of the effective sensitivity versus angular displacement of a flame detector.

A.17.8.3.3.6 This requirement has been satisfied by the following means:

(1) Lens clarity monitoring and cleaning where a contaminated lens signal is rendered
(2) Lens air purge

A.17.8.5.3 Facility owners and managers might desire to use cameras and their images for purposes other than flame detection. The intent of this paragraph is not to prohibit additional uses, but to ensure the integrity of the life safety flame detection mission of the equipment.

A.17.8.5.4 Video image flame detection control and software should be protected from tampering by passwords, software keys, or other means of limiting access to authorized/qualified personnel. Component settings include any control or programming that might affect the operation of coverage of the detection. This includes, but is not limited to, camera focus, field of view, motion sensitivity settings, and change of camera position. Any changes in component settings or ambient conditions that affect the design performance of the detector should initiate a trouble signal.

A.17.10.2.4 The engineering evaluation should include, but is not limited to, the following:

(1) Structural features, size, and shape of the rooms and bays
(2) Occupancy and uses of areas
(3) Ceiling heights
(4) Ceiling shape, surface, and obstructions

(5) Ventilation
(6) Ambient environment
(7) Gas characteristics of the gases present
(8) Configuration of the contents in the area to be protected
(9) Response time(s)

A.17.11.2 Examples of such combustion effects are water vapor, ionized molecules, or other phenomena for which they are designed. The performance characteristics of the detector and the area into which it is to be installed should be evaluated to minimize nuisance alarms or conditions that would interfere with operation.

A.17.12.1 Piping between the sprinkler system and a pressure actuated alarm-initiating device should be galvanized or of nonferrous metal or other approved corrosion-resistant material of not less than ⅜ in.(9.5 mm) nominal pipe size.

A.17.12.2 The waterflow device should be field adjusted so that an alarm is initiated no more than 90 seconds after a sustained flow of at least 10 gpm (40 L/min).

Features that should be investigated to minimize alarm response time include the following:

(1) Elimination of trapped air in the sprinkler system piping
(2) Use of an excess pressure pump
(3) Use of pressure drop alarm-initiating devices
(4) A combination thereof

Care should be used when choosing waterflow alarm-initiating devices for hydraulically calculated looped systems and those systems using small orifice sprinklers. Such systems might incorporate a single point flow of significantly less than 10 gpm (40 L/min). In such cases, additional waterflow alarm-initiating devices or the use of pressure drop-type waterflow alarm-initiating devices might be necessary.

Care should be used when choosing waterflow alarm-initiating devices for sprinkler systems that use on–off sprinklers to ensure that an alarm is initiated in the event of a waterflow condition. On–off sprinklers open at a predetermined temperature and close when the temperature reaches a predetermined lower temperature. With certain types of fires, waterflow might occur in a series of short bursts of a duration of 10 seconds to 30 seconds each. An alarm-initiating device with retard might not detect waterflow under these conditions. An excess pressure system or a system that operates on pressure drop should be considered to facilitate waterflow detection on sprinkler systems that use on–off sprinklers.

Excess pressure systems can be used with or without alarm valves. The following is a description of one type of excess pressure system with an alarm valve.

An excess pressure system with an alarm valve consists of an excess pressure pump with pressure switches to control the operation of the pump. The inlet of the pump is connected to the supply side of the alarm valve, and the outlet is connected to the sprinkler system. The pump control pressure switch is of the differential type, maintaining the sprinkler system pressure above the main pressure by a constant amount. Another switch monitors low sprinkler system pressure to initiate a supervisory signal in the event of a failure of the pump or other malfunction. An additional pressure switch can be used to stop pump operation in the event of a deficiency in water supply. Another pressure switch is connected to the alarm outlet of the alarm valve to initiate a waterflow alarm signal when waterflow exists. This type of system also inherently prevents false alarms due to water surges. The sprinkler retard chamber

should be eliminated to enhance the detection capability of the system for short duration flows.

A.17.13 Alarm initiation can be accomplished by devices that detect the following:

(1) Flow of water in foam systems
(2) Pump activation
(3) Differential pressure
(4) Pressure (e.g., clean agent systems, carbon dioxide systems, and wet/dry chemical systems)
(5) Mechanical operation of a release mechanism

A.17.14.7 Protective covers, also called pull station protectors can be installed over manually actuated alarm initiating devices to provide mechanical protection, environmental protection, and to reduce the likelihood of accidental or malicious activation. The protective covers must be listed to ensure that they do not hinder the operation of the pull stations and to ensure that they meet accessibility requirements for activation by persons with physical disabilities. The Code explicitly permits installing them over single- or double-action devices. When installed over a double-action device, the assembly effectively becomes a triple-action device. Some units include battery-operated audible warning signals that have been shown to deter malicious activations. To be effective, it is important that the regular staff or occupants be aware of the sound and investigate immediately in order to catch someone who might otherwise activate the device without cause or to ensure that the device is activated if there is a legitimate reason.

A.17.14.8.3 In environments where red paint or red plastic is not suitable, an alternative material, such as stainless steel, could be used as long as the box meets the requirements of 17.14.8.2.

A.17.14.8.5 It is not the intent of 17.14.8.5 to require manual fire alarm boxes to be attached to movable partitions or to equipment, nor to require the installation of permanent structures for mounting purposes only.

A.18.1 Notification appliances should be sufficient in quantity, audibility, intelligibility, and visibility so as to reliably convey the intended information to the intended personnel during an emergency.

Notification appliances in conventional commercial and industrial applications should be installed in accordance with the specific requirements of Section 18.4 and Section 18.5.

The Code recognizes that it is not possible to identify specific criteria sufficient to ensure effective occupant notification in every conceivable application. If the specific criteria of Section 18.4 and Section 18.5 are determined to be inadequate or inappropriate to provide the performance recommended, approved alternative approaches or methods are permitted to be used.

A.18.1.5 Chapter 18 establishes the means, methods, and performance requirements of notification appliances and systems. Chapter 18 does not require the installation of notification appliances or identify where notification signaling is required. Authorities having jurisdiction, other codes, other standards, and chapters of this Code require notification signaling and might specify areas or intended audiences.

For example, Chapter 10 requires audible and visible trouble signals at specific locations. A building or fire code might require audible and visible occupant notification throughout all occupiable areas. In contrast, a building or fire code might require complete coverage with audible signaling, but might only require specific areas or spaces to have visible signaling. It is also possible that a referring code or standard might require compliance with mounting and notification appliance performance requirements without requiring complete notification signaling system performance. An example might be where an appliance is specifically located to provide information or notification to a person at a specific desk within a larger room.

A.18.3.3.2 The intent is to prohibit labeling that could give an incorrect message. Wording such as "Emergency" would be acceptable for labeling because it is generic enough not to cause confusion. Fire alarm systems are often used as emergency notification systems, and therefore attention should be given to this detail.

Combination audible and visible units may have several visible appliances, each labeled differently or not labeled at all.

A.18.3.4 Situations exist where supplemental enclosures are necessary to protect the physical integrity of a notification appliance. Protective enclosures should not interfere with the performance characteristics of the appliance. If the enclosure degrades the performance, methods should be detailed in the manufacturer's published instructions of the enclosure that clearly identify the degradation. For example, where the appliance signal is attenuated, it might be necessary to adjust the appliance spacings or appliance output.

A.18.3.6 For hardwired appliances, terminals or leads, as described in 18.3.6, are necessary to ensure that the wire run is broken and that the individual connections are made to the leads or other terminals for signaling and power.

A common terminal can be used for connection of incoming and outgoing wires. However, the design and construction of the terminal should not permit an uninsulated section of a single conductor to be looped around the terminal and to serve as two separate connections. For example, a notched clamping plate under a single securing screw is acceptable only if separate conductors of a notification circuit are intended to be inserted in each notch. *[See Figure A.17.4.6(a).]*

Another means to monitor the integrity of a connection is to establish communication between the appliance and the control unit. The integrity of the connection is verified by the presence of communication. Monitoring integrity in this fashion might not require multiple terminals or leads, as previously described.

It should be noted that monitoring the integrity of the installation conductors and their connection to an appliance does not guarantee the integrity of the appliance or that it is operational. Appliances can be damaged and become inoperable or a circuit can be overloaded, resulting in failure when the appliances are called upon to work. Presently, only testing can establish the integrity of an appliance.

A.18.4.1.1 The Code does not require that all audible notification appliances within a building be of the same type. However, a mixture of different types of audible notification appliances within a space is not the desired method. Audible notification appliances that convey a similar audible signal are preferred. For example, a space that uses mechanical horns and bells might not be desirable. A space that is provided with mechanical horns and electronic horns with similar audible signal output is preferred.

However, the cost of replacing all existing appliances to match new appliances can impose substantial economic impact where other methods can be used to avoid occupant con-

fusion of signals and signal content. Examples of other methods used to avoid confusion include, but are not limited to, training of occupants, signage, consistent use of temporal code signal pattern, and fire drills.

Hearing protection can attenuate both the ambient noise level and the audible signal. Specifications from hearing protection manufacturers might allow the effect of hearing protection devices to be evaluated. In spaces where hearing protection is worn due to high ambient noise conditions, visible signal appliances should be considered.

In addition, where hearing protection is worn due to high ambient noise conditions, the audible signal and ambient noise measurements can be analyzed and the audible signal can be adjusted to account for attenuation caused by the hearing protection devices.

A.18.4.1.2 The maximum sound pressure level permitted in a space is 110 dBA, reduced from 120 dBA in previous editions. The change from 120 dBA to 110 dBA is to coordinate with other laws, codes, and standards.

In addition to the danger of exposure to a high sound level, long-term exposure to lower levels may also be a problem when, for example, occupants must traverse long egress paths to exit or technicians test large systems over extended time periods.

This Code does not presume to know how long a person will be exposed to an audible notification system. The limit of 110 dBA has been set as a reasonable upper limit for the performance of a system. For workers who may be exposed to high sound levels over the course of a 40-year employment history, OSHA (Occupational, Health and Safety Administration) has established a maximum permitted dose before a hearing conservation program must be implemented. A worker exposed to 120 dBA for 7.5 minutes a day for 40 years might be in danger of suffering a hearing impairment. The OSHA regulation includes a formula to calculate a dose for situations where a person is exposed to different sound levels for different periods of time. The maximum permitted by the regulation is an 8-hour equivalent dose of 90 dBA. It is possible to calculate the dose a person experiences when traversing an egress path where the sound pressure level varies as he/she passes close to, then away from, audible appliances. Table A.18.4.1.2 depicts OSHA permissible noise exposures.

Table A.18.4.1.2 Permissible Noise Exposures

Duration (hr)	L_A (dBA)
8	90
6	92
4	95
3	97
2	100
1.5	102
1	105
0.5	110
0.25	115
0.125 (7.5 minutes)	120

Source: OSHA, 29 CFR 1910.5, Table G-16, Occupational Noise Exposure.

A.18.4.1.3 In determining maximum ambient sound levels, sound sources that should be considered include air-handling equipment and background music in a typical office environment, office cleaning equipment (vacuum cleaner), noisy children in a school auditorium, car engines in an auto shop, conveyor belts in a warehouse, and a running shower and fan in a hotel bathroom. Temporary or abnormal sound sources that can be excluded would include internal or external construction activities (i.e., office rearrangements and construction equipment).

A.18.4.1.4.1 Audibility of a fire or emergency signal might not be required in all rooms and spaces. For example, a system that is used for general occupant notification should not require audibility of the signal in closets and other spaces that are not considered as occupiable spaces. However, a space of the same size used as a file room would be considered occupiable and should have coverage by notification appliances. Also, signaling intended only for staff or emergency forces might only have to be effective in very specific locations.

A.18.4.1.4.2 See 3.3.177 for the definition of occupiable.

A.18.4.1.5 Because voice is composed of modulated tones, it is not valid to compare loudness measurements of tone signals with loudness measurements of voice signals. A voice signal that is subjectively judged to be equally as loud as a tone signal will actually produce a dB reading below that of the tone signal. The modulated tones of a voice signal can have the same or greater peak amplitude as that of a tone signal. However, because they are modulated meters with fast or slow time, constants will show a lower dB or dBA reading.

A voice signal must have sufficient audibility to result in intelligible communication. Intelligibility modeling/measurements (subject based and instrument based) include audibility as well as many other factors when determining whether a voice signal is adequate or not adequate.

Where a voice signal includes an audible alert or evacuation tone, the tone portion of the signal should meet the audible signal requirements listed in 18.4.3.

A.18.4.2.1 Paragraph 10.10 requires that alarm signals be distinctive in sound from other signals and that this sound not be used for any other purpose. The use of the distinctive three-pulse temporal pattern signal required by 18.4.2.1 became effective July 1, 1996, for new systems installed after that date. It is not the intent to prohibit continued use of an existing consistent evacuation signaling scheme, subject to approval by the authority having jurisdiction. It is also not the intent that the distinct pattern be applied to visible appliances.

Prior to the 2013 edition, the use of the temporal code 3 distinctive evacuation signal was intended only where evacuation of the building was the intended response. In order to eliminate the need for additional signals to mean "relocate," the signal is now permitted to be used where relocation or partial evacuation is the intended response. The simple result is people should not be in any area where the signal is sounding and that it is safe to be anywhere that signal is not sounding.

The temporal pattern can be produced by any audible notification appliance, as illustrated in Figure A.18.4.2.1(a) and Figure A.18.4.2.1(b).

A.18.4.2.4 Coordination or synchronization of the audible signal within a notification zone is needed to preserve the temporal pattern. It is unlikely that the audible signal in one evacuation/notification zone will be heard in another at a level that will destroy the temporal pattern. Thus, it would not

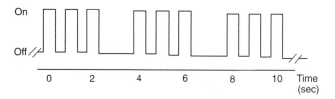

FIGURE A.18.4.2.1(a) Temporal Pattern Imposed on Signaling Appliances That Emit Continuous Signal While Energized.

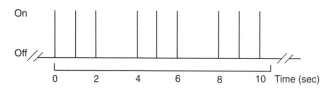

FIGURE A.18.4.2.1(b) Temporal Pattern Imposed on Single-Stroke Bell or Chime.

normally be necessary to provide coordination or synchronization for an entire system. Caution should be used in spaces such as atriums, where the sounds produced in one notification zone can be sufficient to cause confusion regarding the temporal pattern.

A.18.4.3 The typical average ambient sound level for the occupancies specified in Table A.18.4.3 are intended only for design guidance purposes. The typical average ambient sound levels specified should not be used in lieu of actual sound level measurements.

Table A.18.4.3 Average Ambient Sound Level According to Location

Location	Average Ambient Sound Level (dBA)
Business occupancies	55
Educational occupancies	45
Industrial occupancies	80
Institutional occupancies	50
Mercantile occupancies	40
Mechanical rooms	85
Piers and water-surrounded structures	40
Places of assembly	55
Residential occupancies	35
Storage occupancies	30
Thoroughfares, high-density urban	70
Thoroughfares, medium-density urban	55
Thoroughfares, rural and suburban	40
Tower occupancies	35
Underground structures and windowless buildings	40
Vehicles and vessels	50

Sound levels can be significantly reduced due to distance and losses through building elements. Every time the distance from the source doubles, the sound level decreases by about 6 decibels (dB). Audible notification appliances are typically rated by manufacturers' and testing agencies at 10 ft (3 m) from the appliance. Subsequently, at a distance of 20 ft (6.1 m) from an audible appliance rated at 84 dBA, the sound level might be reduced to 78 dBA. At a closed door, the loss might be about 10 dB to 24 dB or more depending on construction. If the opening around the door is sealed, this might result in a loss of 22 dB to 34 dB or more.

A.18.4.3.1 Audio levels are commonly measured using units of decibels, or $\frac{1}{10}$ Bell, abbreviated dB. When measured using a sound level meter, the operator can select either an A-weighted, B-weighted, or C-weighted measurement. The C-weighted measurement is nominally flat from 70 Hz to 4000 Hz, and the B-weighted measurement is nominally flat from 300 Hz to 4000 Hz. The A-weighted measurement filters the input signal to reduce the measurement sensitivity for frequencies to which the human ear is less sensitive and is relatively flat from 600 Hz to 7000 Hz. This results in a measurement that is weighted to simulate the segment of the audio spectrum that provides the most significant intelligibility components heard by the human ear. The units used for measurement are still dB, but the shorthand for specifying use of the A-weighted filter is typically dBA. The difference between any two sound levels measured on the same scale is always expressed in units of dB, not dBA.

The constantly changing nature of pressure waves, which are detected by ear, can be measured by electronic sound meters, and the resulting electronic waveforms can be processed and presented in a number of meaningful ways. Most simple sound level meters have a fast or slow time constant (125 ms and 1000 ms, respectively) to quickly average a sound signal and present a root mean square (RMS) level to the meter movement or display. This is the type of measurement used to determine the maximum sound level having a duration of at least 60 seconds. Note that Chapter 14 requires this measurement to be made using the FAST time setting on the meter. However, this quick average of impressed sound results in fast movements of the meter's output that are best seen when talking into the microphone; the meter quickly rises and falls with speech. However, when surveying the ambient sound levels to establish the increased level at which a notification appliance will properly function, the sound source needs to be averaged over a longer period of time. See 3.3.29, Average Ambient Sound Level. Moderately priced sound level meters have such a function, usually called L_{eq} or equivalent sound level. For example, an L_{eq} of speech in a quiet room would cause the meter movement to rise gradually to a peak reading and slowly fall well after the speech is over. L_{eq} measurements are made over a specified time period and reported as $L_{eq,t}$, where t is the time period. For example, a measurement taken over 24 hours is reported as L_{eq24}.

L_{eq} readings can be misapplied in situations where the background ambient noises vary greatly during a 24-hour period. L_{eq} measurements should be taken over the period of occupancy. This is clarified by the definition of average ambient sound level (see 3.3.29). Note that average in this context is the integrated average at a particular measurement location, not the average of several readings taken at different locations. For example, it would be incorrect to take a reading in a quiet bathroom and average it with a reading taken near a noisy machine to get an average to use for the alarm signal design. The alarm would probably be excessively loud in the quiet bathroom and not loud enough near the noisy machine.

In areas where the background noise is generated by machinery and is fairly constant, a frequency analysis can be warranted. It might be found that the high sound levels are predominantly in one or two frequency bandwidths — often lower frequencies. Notification appliances producing sound in one or two other frequency bandwidths can adequately penetrate the background noise and provide notification. The system would still be designed to produce or have a sound level at the particular frequency or frequency bandwidth of at least 15 dB above the average ambient sound level or 5 dB above the maximum sound level having a duration of at least 60 seconds, whichever is greater.

In very high noise areas, such as theaters, dance halls, nightclubs, and machine shops, sound levels during occupied times can be 100 dBA and higher. Peak sounds might be 110 dBA or greater. At other occupied times, the sound level might be below 50 dBA. A system designed to have a sound level of at least 15 dB above the average ambient sound level or 5 dB above the maximum sound level having a duration of at least 60 seconds might result in a required sound pressure level in excess of the maximum of 115 dBA. A viable option is to reduce or eliminate the background noise. Professional theaters or other entertainment venues can have road show connection control units (see NFPA 70, National Electrical Code, Section 520.50) to which troupes can connect their light and sound systems. These power sources can be controlled by the system. In less formal applications, such as many nightclubs, designated power circuits could be controlled. Diligence needs to be exercised to ensure that the controlled circuits are used.

Also, in occupancies such as machine shops or other production facilities, care must be exercised in the design to ensure that the removal of power to the noise source does not create some other hazard. As with other emergency control functions, control circuits and relays would be monitored for integrity in accordance with Chapter 10, Chapter 12, and Chapter 23.

Appropriate audible signaling in high ambient noise areas is often difficult. Areas such as automotive assembly areas, machining areas, paint spray areas, and so on, where the ambient noise is caused by the manufacturing process itself, require special consideration. Adding additional audible notification appliances that merely contribute to the already noisy environment might not be appropriate. Other alerting techniques such as visible notification appliances, for example, could be more effectively used.

Other codes, standards, laws, or regulations, and the authority having jurisdiction determine where a signal must be audible. This Code section describes the performance requirement needed for a signal to be considered reliably audible.

A.18.4.4.1 See A.18.4.3.1 for additional information on sound measurements and weighting scales.

A.18.4.4.2 For example, in critical care patient areas, it is often desirable to not have an audible alarm even at reduced private mode levels. Each case requires consideration by the governing authority. Another example would be high noise work areas where an audible signal needed to overcome background noise at one time of day would be excessively loud and potentially dangerous at another time of lower ambient noise. A sudden increase of more than 30 dB over 0.5 seconds is considered to cause sudden and potentially dangerous fright.

A.18.4.5.1 See A.18.4.3.1 for additional information on sound measurements and weighting scales.

A.18.4.5.3 The intent of this section is to require the use of the low frequency signal in areas intended for sleeping and in areas that might reasonably be used for sleeping. For example, this section requires a low frequency audible signal in a bedroom of an apartment and also in the living room area of an apartment as it might have sleeping occupants. However, it would not be required to use the low frequency signal in the hallways, lobby, and other tenantless spaces. In hotels, the guest rooms would require use of the low frequency signals, but other spaces that might require audible signals could use any listed audible appliances regardless of the frequency content of the signal being produced. This chapter of the Code addresses notification appliances connected to and controlled by a fire alarm or emergency communications system. This chapter does not address dwelling unit protection such as smoke alarms and their audible signal characteristics. Requirements for single- and multiple-station alarms and household fire alarm systems can be found in Chapter 29.

It is not the intent of this section to preclude devices that have been demonstrated through peer-reviewed research to awaken occupants with hearing loss as effectively as those using the frequency and amplitude specified in this section.

Non-voice (e.g., horns) notification appliances should be listed as a "low frequency alarm" alarm appliance. Voice appliances and systems should be capable of 520 Hz ±10 percent with the appropriate harmonics.

For increased protection in the sleeping area, tactile notification in accordance with Section 18.10 might be an effective means of awakening those who have normal hearing, as well as those who are hearing impaired.

A.18.4.6 This subsection permits a more rigorous analysis and design for audible signaling. Acoustic design practice and psychoacoustic research have long recognized that for a signal to be audible, it need only penetrate the background noise in a one-third or a one octave band. The averaging resulting from A-weighted analysis and design is a simplification that often results in systems being overdesigned. This overdesign is not dangerous but can be costly and is certainly not needed for effective system performance.

A.18.4.6.2 Noise at a lower frequency can mask a signal at an adjacent higher frequency. Thus, it is necessary to calculate the effective masked level of the noise in accordance with established procedures. Figure A.18.4.6.2 shows an example of an octave band analysis of noise along with the calculated effective masked threshold and the proposed alarm signal.

A.18.4.7.1 The sound content of directional sounders is very different from that of the traditional fire alarm sounders. Traditional fire alarm sounders have a strong tonal content, usually centered near the 3 kHz region. Directional sounders use broadband frequency content, usually covering most of the human audible frequency range, 20 Hz to 20 kHz. Figure A.18.4.7.1(a) compares the frequency content of a traditional fire alarm sounder to a directional sounder. This figure shows that while the fire alarm sounder clearly dominates the 3 kHz and upper harmonics, the broadband content of the directional sounder is 20 dB to 30 dB in other frequency bands or ranges. The fire alarm has an overall A-weighted sound level greater than the directional sounder and will be perceived as being louder. However, since the directional sounder has a wide spectral range, the signal penetrates the fire alarm signal in several other frequency bands as permitted by 18.4.6.

There are three main types of information that allow the brain to identify the location of a sound. The first two are known as binaural cues because they make use of the fact that we have two ears, separated by the width of our head. A sound that emanates from either side of the mid-line will arrive first at the ear closer to it and will be loudest at the ear closer to it. At low frequencies the brain recognizes differences in the arrival time of sound between the ears (interaural time differences). At higher frequencies the salient signal is the loudness/intensity difference between the

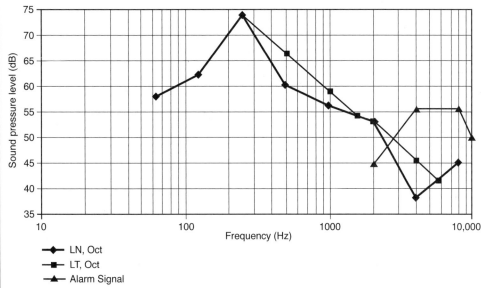

At the first octave band center frequency, the masked threshold of hearing, LT, Oct is equal to the noise level. For each subsequent center frequency, LT, Oct is the greater of either the noise level at that octave band, LN, Oct, or the masked threshold of the previous band less 7.5 dB.

FIGURE A.18.4.6.2 Threshold Masking Level Example.

Directional sound = 66 dB(A)*; Fire alarm = 86 dB(A)*

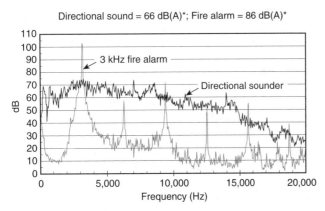

* Measured at 10 ft in an anechoic room.

FIGURE A.18.4.7.1(a) Comparison of Frequency Content of Traditional Fire Alarm Sounder to Directional Sounder.

sounds at each ear (interaural intensity differences). Refer to Figure A.18.4.7.1(b). For single frequencies, these cues are spatially ambiguous.

The inherent ambiguity has been described as the "cone of confusion." This arises from the fact that for any given frequency there are numerous spatial positions that generate identical timing/intensity differences. These can be graphically represented in the form of a cone, the apex of which is at the level of the external ear. The cone of confusion is the main reason for our not being able to localize pure tones.

The final piece of sound localization information processed by the brain is the head-related transfer function (HRTF). The HRTF refers to the effect the external ear has on sound. As a result of passing over the bumps or convolutions of the pinna, the sound is modified so that some frequencies are attenuated and others are amplified. Refer to Figure A.18.4.7.1(c). Although there are certain generalities in the way the pinnae modify sound, the HRTF is unique to each individual. The role of the HRTF is particularly important when determining whether a sound is in front of or behind us. In this instance the timing and intensity differences are negligible, and there is consequently very little information available to the central nervous system on which to base this decision. To locate the direction of a sound source, the larger the frequency content to overcome the ambiguities inherent to single tones, the better the accuracy.

A.18.4.7.2 *ITD*: A difference in arrival times of waveform features (such as peaks and positive-going zero crossings) at the two ears is known as the interaural time difference, or ITD. The binaural physiology is capable of using phase information from ITD cues only at low frequencies below about 1500 Hz. However, the binaural system can successfully register an ITD that occurs at a high frequency such as 4000 Hz if the signal is modulated. The modulation, in turn, must have a rate that is less than about 1000 Hz.

ILD: Comparison between intensities in the left and right ears is known as the interaural level difference, or ILD. ILD cues exist physically only for frequencies above about 500 Hz. They become large and reliable for frequencies above 3000 Hz, making ILD cues most effective at high frequencies.

ATF: The anatomical transfer function (ATF), also known as the head-related transfer function (HRTF), is used by listeners to resolve front–back confusion and to determine elevation. Waves that come from behind tend to be boosted in the

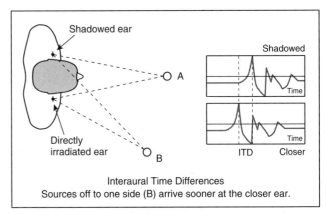

Interaural Time Differences
Sources off to one side (B) arrive sooner at the closer ear.

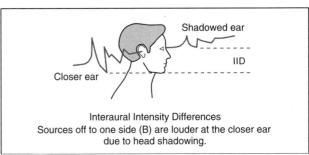

Interaural Intensity Differences
Sources off to one side (B) are louder at the closer ear due to head shadowing.

FIGURE A.18.4.7.1(b) Interaural Time and Intensity Differences of Sound.

1000 Hz frequency region, whereas waves that come from the forward direction are boosted near 3000 Hz. The most dramatic effects occur above 4000 Hz.

These localization cues can be implemented simultaneously when the source signal is a broadband sound containing a range of low to high frequencies. For example, octave bands of 1 kHz (707–1414 Hz) for ITD, 4 kHz (2828–5856 Hz) for ILD, and 8 kHz (5657–11,314 Hz) for ATF would fall within the effective frequency ranges required in 18.4.6.

Additional information on sound localization and auditory localization cues is contained in the following article: http://www.aip.org/pt/nov99/locsound.html, G.1.2.12.1.

The ability to pinpoint the location of a sound source is based on the physics of sound and the physiology of the human hearing mechanism. The brain processes a large amount of neural signals, some of which provide cues to the sound source's location. People are able to hear sound ranging from about 20 Hz to 20,000 Hz. Unfortunately, pure tones in this frequency range provide only limited localization information. The primary localization cues are provided by interaural time differences (ITDs) (lower frequencies), interaural intensity differences (IIDs) (mid to higher frequencies), and the head-related transfer function (HRTF) (higher frequencies). In enclosed spaces that can be somewhat reverberant, the precedence effect (PE) also provides directional information.

The interaural time difference (ITD) and interaural intensity difference (IID) are termed binaural cues because they depend on both ears separated by the width of the head. At lower frequencies (longer wavelength), the time delay between arriving sound signals is detectable. ITD is most evident in frequencies below about 500 Hz with clicks or short bursts of sound. At higher frequencies (shorter wavelength), the loudness/intensity differences between the ears is more no-

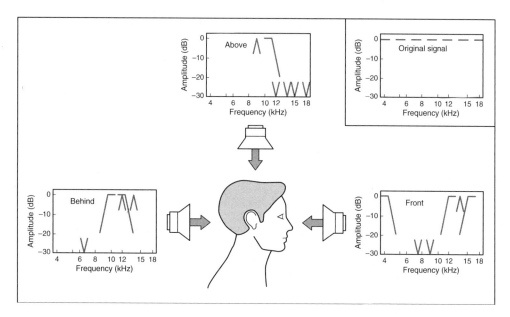

FIGURE A.18.4.7.1(c) Examples of Frequency-Dependent Attenuation for Sources in Front, Above, and Behind Listener.

ticeable because of partial shielding of the more distant ear by the head. IID is most evident for frequencies above 3000 Hz.

The head-related transfer function (HRTF) relies on the effect of the external ear on perceived sound. The HRTF describes the transforming effect of the head, torso, and external ear on sound as it travels from the sound source to the ear canals. The HRTF changes depending on sound source location, providing an additional localization cue. HRTF operates over a range of frequencies but seems to be most effective in the 5000 Hz to 10,000 Hz range. Combined with the listener's head motion, HRTF provides an independent localization method to complement ITD and IID capabilities.

The precedence effect (PE) is important for discriminating between the direct sound signal and reflected sound, a common situation within buildings. The ear is capable of discerning and fixating on the first sound received (line-of-sight direct signal) and disregarding later signals (reflected sound). The acoustical signal arriving first at the ears suppresses the ability to hear other signals (including reverberation) that arrive up to about 40 milliseconds after the initial signal.

All of the preceding cues are utilized simultaneously when the source signal is broadband sound containing a range of low and high frequencies, and when the sound arrives in bursts rather than as steady state sound. The combination of different cues provides reinforcement and redundancy of information to enhance the ability to locate the sound source. Broadband sound tends to eliminate potential ambiguities that occur for pure tone or narrowband sound sources.

Other types of sound patterns can be used as directional sounders that can be used for audible exit marking. Some scientific research has been performed to develop a directional sounder that utilizes a tonal sound different from the example above. As with the directional sound example presented above, the development of this alternative signal is similarly rooted in the vast research data that exists for sound localization and directional auditory cues.

An example of an alternative directional sound signal can be a sequence of two harmonic two-tone complexes. This sequence starts with a complex of low fundamental frequencies

of 262 and 330 Hz having duration of 200 ms. This sound is then followed by a 200-ms silence. Next the sequence continues with a second sound that is a complex of low fundamental frequencies of 330 and 392 Hz having a duration of 200 ms. After another 200-ms silence, this whole pattern is repeated.

Localizability was ensured by the dense harmonic structure of the signal, with closely spaced harmonics up to 20 kHz. In addition sharp signal onsets were included to aid the detection of interaural time differences, thus increasing localizability.

A.18.4.7.4 Where directional sounders are used, they should not be located on only a single exit. They should be located at all of the identified exits in the building. This is to ensure that in an evacuation or relocation the occupants utilize all of the exits and areas of refuge, not just those that have directional sounders located near them. Some examples of exits would include the following:

(1) Code-complying exterior doors and exit discharge
(2) Code-complying exit passageway
(3) Code-complying interior stairs, including smokeproof enclosures
(4) Code-complying outside stairs
(5) Code-complying ramps
(6) Code-complying fire escapes
(7) Code-complying horizontal exits

A.18.4.10 See Annex D, Speech Intelligibility.

A.18.4.10.1 See the definition of acoustically distinguishable space in 3.3.6.

A.18.4.10.2.1 For example, based on the system design the following locations might not require intelligibility. See also Annex D.

(1) Private bathrooms, shower rooms, saunas, and similar rooms/areas
(2) Mechanical, electrical, elevator equipment rooms, and similar rooms/areas
(3) Elevator cars
(4) Individual offices

(5) Kitchens
(6) Storage rooms
(7) Closets
(8) Rooms/areas where intelligibility cannot reasonably be predicted

A.18.4.10.3 ADS assignments should be a part of the original design process. See the discussion in A.3.3.6. The design drawings should be used to plan and show the limits of each ADS where there is more than one.

All areas that are intended to have audible occupant notification, whether by tone only or by voice should be designated as one or more ADSs. Drawings or a table listing all ADSs should be used to indicate which ADSs will require intelligible voice communications and those that will not. The same drawings or table could be used to list audibility requirements where tones are used and to list any forms of visual or other notification or communications methods being employed in the ADS.

A.18.5 The mounting height of the appliances affects the distribution pattern and level of illumination produced by an appliance on adjacent surfaces. It is this pattern, or effect, that provides occupant notification by visible appliances. If mounted too high, the pattern is larger but at a lower level of illumination (measured in lumens per square foot or foot-candles). If mounted too low, the illumination is greater (brighter) but the pattern is smaller and might not overlap correctly with that of adjacent appliances.

A qualified designer could choose to present calculations to an authority having jurisdiction showing that it is possible to use a mounting height greater than 96 in. (2.44 m) or less than 80 in. (2.03 m), provided that an equivalent level of illumination is achieved on the adjacent surfaces. This can be accomplished by using listed higher intensity appliances or closer spacing, or both.

Engineering calculations should be prepared by qualified persons and should be submitted to the authority having jurisdiction, showing how the proposed variation achieves the same or greater level of illumination provided by the prescriptive requirements of Section 18.5.

The calculations require knowledge of calculation methods for high-intensity strobes. In addition, the calculations require knowledge of the test standards used to evaluate and list the appliance.

A.18.5.1 There are two methods of visible signaling. These are methods in which notification of an emergency condition is conveyed by direct viewing of the illuminating appliance or by means of illumination of the surrounding area.

Visible notification appliances used in the public mode must be located and must be of a type, size, intensity, and number so that the operating effect of the appliance is seen by the intended viewers regardless of the viewer's orientation.

A.18.5.1.2 Visible appliances for fire or emergency signaling might not be required in all rooms or spaces. For example, a system that is used for general occupant notification should not require visible signaling in closets and other spaces that are not considered as occupiable areas. However, a space of the same size used as a file room could be considered occupiable and should have coverage by notification appliances. Also, signaling intended only for staff or emergency forces might only have to be effective in very specific locations.

A.18.5.2.2 Occupant notification by visible signaling is not required by *NFPA 72* except in high noise areas *(see 18.4.1.1)*. Just as with audible occupant notification, the requirement to

have such signaling originates from other governing laws, codes, or standards. Those other governing laws, codes, or standards specify the areas or spaces that require either audible, visible, or both types of occupant notification. *NFPA 72* then provides the standards for those systems.

A.18.5.3.4 Effective intensity is the conventional method of equating the brightness of a flashing light to that of a steady-burning light as seen by a human observer. The units of effective intensity are expressed in candelas (or candlepower, which is equivalent to candelas). For example, a flashing light that has an effective intensity of 15 cd has the same apparent brightness to an observer as a 15 cd steady-burning light source.

Measurement of effective intensity is usually done in a laboratory using specialized photometric equipment. Accurate field measurement of effective intensity is not practical. Other units of measure for the intensity of flashing lights, such as peak candela or flash energy, do not correlate directly to effective intensity and are not used in this standard.

Strobe lights might be used to signal fire or other emergencies and might be intended to initiate evacuation, relocation, or some other behavior. Lights intended to initiate evacuation due to fire are required by the Code to be clear or white. Colored lights, such as amber/yellow lights, might be used in a combination system for any emergency (fire, bomb, chemical, weather, etc.) when the intent is for the signal recipient to seek additional information from other sources (voice, text displays, and so on).

Example Scenario 1: A building has a fire alarm system used for general evacuation. A separate mass notification system is used to provide voice instructions and information in the event of non-fire emergencies. The fire alarm system would have white/clear strobes intended to alert occupants of the need to evacuate. The mass notification system would have amber/yellow strobes that are intended to signal the need to get additional information from either audible voice announcements, text or graphical displays, or other information sources controlled or operated from the mass notification system. In the event that both systems are activated at the same time, the strobes should be synchronized per 18.5.5.4.2.

Example Scenario 2: A building has a mass notification system that provides information and instructions for a variety of emergency situations, including fire. Fire alarm initiation might be by a stand-alone fire detection system or might be an integral part of the mass notification system. In the event of an emergency, textual audible appliances are used to provide information. Visible alerting could be accomplished using one set of clear or colored strobes to indicate the need to get additional information. Visible textual information can be provided by text or graphic display or other visible information appliances. The content of the audible and visible messages will vary depending on the emergency.

A.18.5.3.6 It is not the intent to establish viewing and synchronization requirements for viewing locations outdoors. As an example, there is no need for Floor No. 1 to be synchronized with Floor No. 2 if there is no visible coupling as in an atrium.

Studies have shown that the effect of strobes on photosensitive epilepsy lessens with distance and viewing angle.

As long as the composite flash rate is no greater than that produced by two listed strobes as allowed by 18.5.5.4.2, compliance is achieved.

Example: A ballroom has multiple synchronized strobes operating during an emergency, the doors exiting the ballroom are opened, and the strobes outside in the lobby and corridor are also operating. The strobes in the corridor and lobby are synchronized with each other, but the strobes outside the ballroom are not synchronized with the strobes inside the ballroom. This would be an acceptable application because the composite flash rate does not exceed that allowed by 18.5.5.4.2.

A.18.5.4 The prescriptive requirements of Section 18.5 assume the use of appliances having very specific characteristics of light color, intensity, distribution, and so on. The appliance and application requirements are based on extensive research. However, the research was limited to typical residential and commercial applications such as school classrooms, offices, hallways, and hotel rooms. While these specific appliances and applications will likely work in other spaces, their use might not be the most effective solution and might not be as reliable as other visible notification methods.

For example, in large warehouse spaces and large distribution spaces such as super stores, it is possible to provide visible signaling using the appliances and applications of this chapter. However, mounting strobe lights at a height of 80 in. to 96 in. (2.03 m to 2.44 m) along aisles with rack storage subjects the lights to frequent mechanical damage by forklift trucks and stock. Also, the number of appliances required would be very high. It might be possible to use other appliances and applications not specifically addressed by this chapter at this time. Alternative applications must be carefully engineered for reliability and function and would require permission of the authority having jurisdiction.

Tests of a system in large warehouse/super stores designed using the prescriptive approach of 18.5.5.4 showed that high ambient light levels resulted in both indirect and direct signaling effects. The signal-to-noise ratio produced by the operating visible notification appliances was low in many locations. However, with visible notification appliances located over the aisles or unobstructed by stock, indirect and some direct notification was sometimes achieved. Direct notification occurs even when occupants do not look up toward the ceiling-mounted visible notification appliances due to the extended cone of vision shown in Figure A.18.5.4(a). The visible notification appliance intensity and spacing resulting from the prescriptive design was generally sufficient for occupant notification by a combination of direct and indirect signaling. Testing showed that the best performance was achieved where visible notification appliances were directly over aisles or where visible notification appliances in adjacent aisles were not obstructed by stock. The performance-based design method will almost always result in aisles not having a line of visible notification appliances in them, because the spacing of visible notification appliances can be greater than the spacing of aisles. Also, it is recognized that aisles might be relocated after installation of the system. Good design practice is to place visible notification appliances over aisles, especially those that are

likely to remain unchanged such as main aisles, and over checkout areas. Where reorganization of aisles results in visible notification appliances not in or over an aisle, or where that is the base design, it is important to have a clear view from that aisle to a nearby visible notification appliance. See Figure A.18.5.4(b). Some spaces might have marginal visible notification appliance effect (direct or indirect). However, occupants in these large stores and storage occupancies move frequently and place themselves in a position where they receive notification via the visible notification appliances. In addition, complete synchronization of the visible notification appliances in the space produced a desirable effect.

Visible notification using the methods contained in 18.5.5.4 is achieved by indirect signaling. This means the viewer need not actually see the appliance, just the effect of the appliance. This can be achieved by producing minimum illumination on surfaces near the appliance, such as the floor, walls, and desks. There must be a sufficient change in illumination to be noticeable. The tables and charts in Section 18.5 specify a certain candela-effective light intensity for certain size spaces. The data were based on extensive research and testing. Appliances do not typically produce the same light intensity when measured off-axis. To ensure that the appliance produces the desired illumination (effect), it must have some distribution of light intensity to the areas surrounding the appliance. ANSI/UL 1971, *Standard for Signaling Devices for the Hearing Impaired*, specifies the distribution of light shown to provide effective notification by indirect visible signaling.

A.18.5.5.1 The requirements for the location of appliances within a building or structure are intended to apply to strobe lights applied in accordance with 18.5.5.4, 18.5.5.5, and 18.5.5.7. The mounting and location of appliances installed using the performance-based alternative of 18.5.5.6 can be located differently, provided they meet the intended performance requirements. Other appliances, such as graphic displays, video screens, and so on, should be located so that they meet their intended performance.

Where low ceiling heights or other conditions do not permit mounting at a minimum of 80 in. (2.03 m), visible appliances can be mounted at a lower height. However, lowering the mounting height reduces the area of coverage for that strobe. The performance-based methods of 18.5.5.6 can be used to determine the area of coverage. Strobe light mounting height should not be lowered below the plane of normal human viewing [approximately 5 ft (1.5 m)] except where ceiling heights limit the mounting position.

The mounting height requirement of 80 in. to 96 in. (2.03 m to 2.44 m) does not address the possibility of conditions where ceiling heights are less than 80 in. (2.03 m). The range that is permitted [80 in. to 96 in. (2.03 m to 2.44 m)] ensures that strobes are not mounted too high, which would result in lower

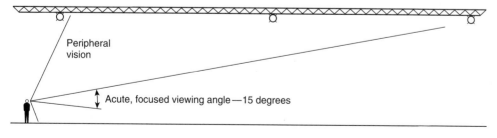

FIGURE A.18.5.4(a) Extended Cone of Vision. (*Courtesy of R. P. Schifiliti Associates, Inc.*)

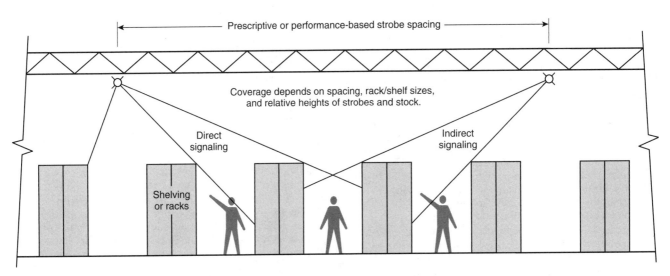

FIGURE A.18.5.4(b)   Visible Notification Appliances in Stores. *(Courtesy of R. P. Schifiliti Associates, Inc.)*

levels of illumination on surrounding walls and on the floor. The lower limit of the range ensures that a minimum percentage of the surrounding surfaces is illuminated and that the top of the illuminated pattern is at or above the plane of normal human viewing [approximately 5 ft (1.5 m)]. Wall mounting of strobe lights, which are listed only for wall mounting, can result in little or no illumination above the plane of the strobe light. In the case of lower ceiling heights and mounting close to the ceiling, the level of illumination on the floor and surrounding walls is not reduced but the walls have a near 100 percent illuminated or "painted" area because the strobe is close to the ceiling. That is, there is little or no wall surface above the plane of the strobe that is not illuminated when the strobe is mounted close to the ceiling. Thus, when a strobe is mounted lower than the minimum [80 in. (2.03 m)] but still close to the ceiling, the only loss of signal is the smaller pattern produced on the horizontal plane (floor).

In the case where the only change is a lower mounting height due to a lower ceiling height, the room size covered by a strobe of a given value should be reduced by twice the difference between the minimum mounting height of 80 in. (2.03 m) and the actual, lower mounting height. For example, if a 15 cd effective strobe that normally covers a 20 ft (6.1 m) square space is being used and the height of the space is 63 in. (1.6 m) and the strobe is mounted at 59 in. (1.5 m), the strobe can only cover a 16.5 ft (5.03 m) square space: 20 ft − 2 (80 in. − 59 in.) (1 ft/12 in.) = 16.5 ft (5.03 m).

The room size reduction assumes that the horizontal pattern on each side of the strobe is reduced by the same amount that the strobe height is reduced.

A.18.5.5.3 Visible appliances must be listed for either wall mounting or ceiling mounting. The effectiveness of ceiling-mounted appliances does not depend on them being mounted on a surface. Therefore, the Code permits them to be suspended below the ceiling using proper electrical installation methods. Appliances mounted parallel to the floor, whether on a ceiling or suspended, can sometimes significantly reduce installation costs and provide better coverage.

In convention spaces and areas with racking and shelving, wall-mounted appliances are frequently obstructed or subjected to mechanical damage. Ceiling mounting (or suspending) the appliances can prevent problems and increases the ability for the appliance to cover the floor area through direct and indirect signaling. See A.18.5.4.

A.18.5.5.4 The strobe intensities listed in Table 18.5.5.4.1(a) or Table 18.5.5.4.1(b), 18.5.5.5, or Table 18.5.5.7.2 or determined in accordance with the performance requirements of 18.5.5.6 are the minimum required intensities. It is acceptable to use a higher intensity strobe in lieu of the minimum required intensity.

Areas large enough to exceed the rectangular dimensions given in Figure A.18.5.5.4(a) through Figure A.18.5.5.4(c) require additional appliances. Often, proper placement of appliances can be facilitated by breaking down the area into multiple squares and dimensions that fit most appropriately *[see Figure A.18.5.5.4(a) through Figure A.18.5.5.4(d)]*. An area that is 40 ft (12.2 m) wide and 80 ft (24.4 m) long can be covered with two 60 cd appliances. Irregular areas and areas with dividers or partitions need more careful planning to make certain that at least one 15 cd appliance is installed for each 20 ft × 20 ft (6.1 m × 6.1 m) area and that light from the appliance is not blocked.

A.18.5.5.4.2(2) The field of view is based on the focusing capability of the human eye specified as 120 degrees in the *Illuminating Engineering Society (IES) Lighting Handbook Reference and Application.* The apex of this angle is the viewer's eye. In order to ensure compliance with the requirements of 18.5.5.4.2, this angle should be increased to approximately 135 degrees.

Testing has shown that high flash rates of high-intensity strobe lights can pose a potential risk of seizure to people with photosensitive epilepsy. To reduce this risk, more than two visible appliances are not permitted in any field of view unless their flashes are synchronized. This does not preclude synchronization of appliances that are not within the same field of view.

A.18.5.5.4.6 This subsection is also intended to permit ceiling-mounted strobes to be suspended below the ceiling, provided the strobe height is not below the viewing plane for any ceiling height.

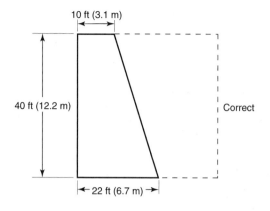

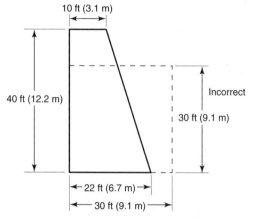

Note: Broken lines represent imaginary walls.

FIGURE A.18.5.5.4(a)   Irregular Area Spacing.

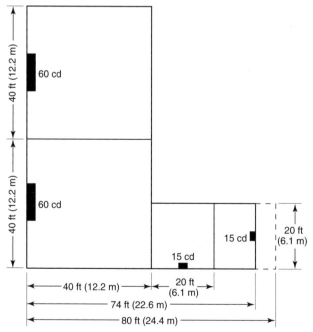

Note: Broken lines represent imaginary walls.

FIGURE A.18.5.5.4(b)   Spacing of Wall-Mounted Visible Appliances in Rooms.

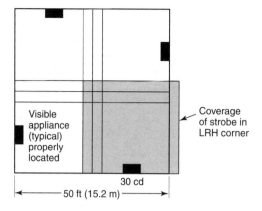

FIGURE A.18.5.5.4(c)   Room Spacing Allocation — Correct.

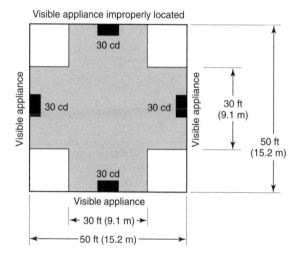

FIGURE A.18.5.5.4(d)   Room Spacing Allocation — Incorrect.

A.18.5.5.5 Because the occupants are usually alert and moving, and because their vision is focused by the narrowness of the space, corridor signaling is permitted to be by direct viewing of lower-intensity (15 cd) appliances. That is, the alerting is intended to be done by direct viewing of the strobe, not necessarily by its reflection off of surfaces (indirect viewing) as required for rooms in 18.5.5.4.

Note that it is acceptable to use 18.5.5.4 (Spacing in Rooms) to determine the number and location of strobes in corridors. If 18.5.5.4 is used, it is not necessary to have a corridor strobe within 15 ft (4.5 m) of the end of the corridor.

See Figure A.18.5.5.5 for corridor spacing for visible appliances.

A.18.5.5.5.5 Visible appliances in corridors are permitted to be mounted on walls or on ceilings in accordance with 18.5.5.5. Where there are more than two appliances in a field of view, they need to be synchronized.

Note that it is acceptable to use 18.5.5.4 (Spacing in Rooms) to determine the number and location of strobes in corridors. If 18.5.5.4 is used, it is not necessary to have a corridor strobe within 15 ft (4.5 m) of the end of the corridor. It is not the intent of this section to require strobes at or near every exit or exit access from a corridor.

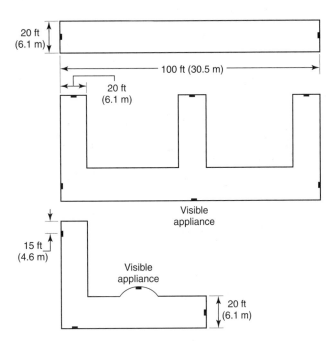

FIGURE A.18.5.5.5 Corridor Spacing for Visible Appliances.

A.18.5.5.6 A design that delivers a minimum illumination of 0.0375 lumens/ft² (footcandles) [0.4037 lumens/m² (lux)] to all occupiable spaces where visible notification is required is considered to meet the minimum light intensity requirements of 18.5.5.4.2(1). This level of illumination has been shown to alert people by indirect viewing (reflected light) in a large variety of rooms with a wide range of ambient lighting conditions.

The illumination from a visible notification appliance at a particular distance is equal to the effective intensity of the appliance divided by the distance squared (the inverse square law). Table 18.5.5.4.1(a) and Table 18.5.5.4.1(b) are based on applying the inverse square law to provide an illumination of at least 0.0375 lumens/ft² (0.4037 lumens/m²) throughout each room size. For example, a 60 cd effective intensity appliance in a 40 ft × 40 ft (12.2 m × 12.2 m) room produces 0.0375 lumens/ft² (0.4037 lumens/m²) on the opposite wall 40 ft (12.2 m) away [60 ÷ (40 ft)² or (60 ÷ (12.2 m)²)]. This same 60 cd effective intensity appliance produces 0.0375 lumens/ft² (0.4037 lumens/m²) on the adjacent wall 20 ft (6.1 m) away [60 × 25% ÷ (20 ft)² or (60 × 25% ÷ (12.2 m)²)] where the minimum light output of the appliance at 90 degrees off-axis is 25 percent of rated output per ANSI/UL 1971, *Standard for Signaling Devices for the Hearing Impaired.* Similarly, a 110 cd strobe will produce at least 0.0375 lumens/ft² (0.4037 lumens/m²) in a 54 ft × 54 ft (16.5 m × 16.5 m) room. Calculated intensities in Table 18.5.5.4.1(a) and Table 18.5.5.4.1(b) have been adjusted to standardize the intensity options of presently available products and take into account additional reflections in room corners and higher direct viewing probability when there is more than one appliance in a room.

The application of visible notification appliances in outdoor areas has not been tested and is not addressed in this standard. Visible appliances that are mounted outdoors should be listed for outdoor use (under ANSI/UL 1638, *Standard for Visual Signaling Appliances — Private Mode Emergency and General Utility Signaling,*

for example) and should be located for direct viewing because reflected light will usually be greatly reduced.

A.18.5.5.7.2 For sleeping areas, the use of lights with other intensities at distances different than within 16 ft (4.9 m) has not been researched and is not addressed in this Code.

This section on strobes for alerting sleeping persons intends that stand-alone strobes be located in accordance with 18.5.5. If the strobe is an integral part of a smoke detector or smoke alarm, the unit must be mounted in accordance with the requirements for the smoke detector or smoke alarm. In either case (stand-alone or combination), Table 18.5.5.7.2 is then consulted to determine the minimum required intensity. Where the appliance is mounted less than 24 in. (610 mm) from the ceiling, it must have a minimum 177 cd effective rating because it might be in a smoke layer at the time it is called upon to operate. If the appliance is 24 in. (610 mm) or more from the ceiling, it is permitted to be rated 110 cd effective or more. Note that the requirement for increasing the intensity when mounted close to the ceiling applies only to strobes used in sleeping areas to awaken sleeping people. It is assumed that in nonsleeping situations, a strobe is not needed to alert someone if there is a developing smoke layer.

A.18.6 Though the number of visible notification appliances might be reduced in private operating mode settings, visible notification appliances might still need to be considered in spaces occupied by the public or the hearing impaired or subject to other laws or codes.

A.18.8.1.2 The tone signal is used to evaluate the sound pressure level produced by speaker appliances because of the fluctuating sound pressure level of voice or recorded messages.

A.18.9 Textual and graphical visible appliances are selected and installed to provide temporary text, permanent text, or symbols. Textual and graphical visible appliances are most commonly used in the private mode for fire alarm systems. The use of microprocessors with computer monitors and printers has resulted in the ability to provide detailed information in the form of text and graphics to persons charged with directing emergency response and evacuation. Textual and graphical visible appliances are also used in the public mode to communicate emergency response and evacuation information directly to the occupants or inhabitants of the area protected by the system. For both private mode and public mode signaling, text and graphic annunciators can provide information about pre-alarm, alarm, trouble, and supervisory conditions. Because textual and graphical visible appliances do not necessarily have the ability to alert, they should only be used to supplement audible or visible notification appliances.

Textual and graphical visible information should be of a size and visual quality that is easily read. Many factors influence the readability of textual visible appliances, including the following:

(1) Size and color of the text or graphic
(2) Distance from the point of observation
(3) Observation time
(4) Contrast
(5) Background luminance
(6) Lighting
(7) Stray lighting (glare)
(8) Shadows
(9) Physiological factors

While many of these factors can be influenced by the equipment manufacturer and by the building designers, there is no readily available method to measure legibility.

A.18.9.4 Parts of this section on text characteristics are based on Section 703.5 of the updated accessibility guidelines in the U.S. Access Board's ADA-ABA-AG, released in 2004.

A.18.9.4.2 Signs are more legible for persons with low vision when characters contrast as much as possible with their background. Additional factors affecting the ease with which the text can be distinguished from its background include shadows cast by lighting sources, surface glare, and the uniformity of the text and its background colors and textures.

Stroke width-to-height ratios are an important part of character legibility and are affected by contrast. Ratios for light characters on a dark background and dark characters on a light background differ because light characters or symbols tend to spread or bleed into the adjacent dark background. To accommodate these differences, recommendations for symbol stroke width-to-character height ratios are as follows:

(1) Positive image — Dark characters on a light background, ratio of 1:6 to 1:8
(2) Negative image — Light characters on a dark background, ratio of 1:8 to 1:10

Source: Federal Aviation Administration (FAA) Human Factors Awareness Course available at http://www.hf.faa.gov/webtraining/Intro/Intro1.htm.

A.18.9.4.4 The use of all uppercase characters in messages should be avoided as it decreases legibility. The exception is one- or two-word commands or statements such as stop, go, or exit stair.

A.18.9.4.7 Paragraph 18.9.4.7 and the associated table does not apply to text and graphics displayed on desktop monitors. The Code does not list any specific sizing requirements for desktop monitors. However, 18.9.3 does require them to be clear and legible at the intended viewing distance. Other requirements in 18.9.4 such as contrast, sans serif fonts, and so forth should still apply to desktop displays. The specific requirements of Table 18.9.4.7 are taken directly from Section 703.5 of the updated accessibility guidelines in the U.S. Access Board's ADA-ABA-AG, released in 2004. The table has been reformatted to be consistent with other parts of *NFPA 72*.

A.18.9.4.8 The minimum height for textual and graphic visible appliances is given as 40 in. (1.02 m) above the ground or finished floor. However, the character or symbol sizes should be based on the height of the highest character or symbol displayed by the appliance.

A.18.10.2 Notification appliances are available for the deaf and hard of hearing. These appliances include, but are not limited to, supplemental tactical notification appliances. Such tactile notification appliances can be capable of awakening people. Tactile appliances can initiate in response to the activation of an audible smoke alarm, through hard wiring into the fire alarm system or by wireless methods.

Some tests show that strobes might not be effective in awakening some sleeping individuals during an emergency. Some tactile devices can be more effective in awakening individuals, regardless of hearing levels, from sleep.

A.18.11 *Standard Emergency Service Interface.* Annunciators, information display systems, and controls for portions of a system provided for use by emergency service personnel should be designed, arranged, and located in accordance with the needs of the organizations intended to use the equipment.

Where annunciators, information display systems, and controls for portions of the system are provided for use by emergency service personnel, these should have a common design and operation to avoid confusion of users.

A.21.2.1 The performance of automatic emergency control functions refers to their normal operation. For instance, it is all right to shut down elevator mainline power when the system has been designed to do so.

A.21.2.4 Emergency control function interface devices can be located far from the device to be activated, such as air-handling units and exhaust fans located on the roof. The requirement for monitoring installation wiring for integrity only applies to the wiring between the fire alarm control unit and the emergency control function interface device. For example, it does not apply to the wiring between the emergency control function interface device and a motor stop/start control relay, or between the emergency control function interface device and the equipment to be controlled (e.g., air-handling units and exhaust fans). The location of the emergency control function interface device within 3 ft (0.9 m) applies to the point of interface and not to remotely located equipment.

A.21.3 The terms *machinery space, control space, machine room,* and *control room* are defined in *NFPA 70, National Electrical Code,* and ANSI/ASME A17.1/CSA B44.

A.21.3.2 In facilities without a building alarm system, dedicated function fire alarm control units are required by 21.3.2 for elevator recall in order that the elevator recall systems be monitored for integrity and have primary and secondary power meeting the requirements of this Code.

The fire alarm control unit used for this purpose should be located in an area that is normally occupied and should have audible and visible indicators to annunciate supervisory (elevator recall) and trouble conditions; however, no form of general occupant notification or evacuation signal is required or intended by 21.3.2.

A.21.3.5 Smoke detectors should not be installed in outdoor locations or locations that are open to the weather (such as unenclosed elevator lobbies in open parking structures), because such environments can exceed the parameters of the detector listing and can result in unwanted alarms. *(See 21.3.9.)*

A.21.3.7 This requirement applies to smoke and heat detectors installed in the hoistway. It is important to note that the hoistway includes the pit. The location of smoke or heat detectors will, most likely, require special consideration in order to provide the intended response of early detection of fire in the elevator pit. The location of these detectors will likely need to be below the lowest level of recall in order to provide an adequate response. Since there is no real ceiling at this location to allow installation using the spacing provisions of Chapter 17, the provisions of 17.7.3.1.3 and 17.4.10 should be considered, which allows detectors to be placed closer to the hazard in a position where the detector can intercept the smoke or heat. Also refer to A.21.3.14.2(3).

A.21.3.8 It should be noted that smoke detectors installed in hoistways can be a source of nuisance activation. Therefore, hoistways need smoke detectors specifically intended for those types of spaces (environments).

A.21.3.9 The objective of Phase I Emergency Recall Operation is to have the elevator automatically return to the recall level before fire can affect the safe operation of the elevator. This includes both the safe mechanical operation of the elevator, as well as the delivery of passengers to a safe lobby location. Where ANSI/ASME A17.1/CSA B44, *Safety Code for Elevators and Escalators*, specifies the use of smoke detectors, these devices are expected to provide the earliest response to situations that would require Phase I Emergency Recall Operations. The use of other automatic fire detection is only intended where smoke detection would not be appropriate due to the environment. Where ambient conditions prohibit the installation of smoke detectors, the selection and location of other automatic fire detection should be evaluated to ensure the best response is achieved. When heat detectors are used, consideration should be given to both detector temperature and time lag characteristics. The consideration of a low temperature rating alone might not provide the earliest response.

A.21.3.14 It is recommended that the installation be in accordance with Figure A.21.3.14(a) and Figure A.21.3.14(b). Figure A.21.3.14(a) should be used where the elevator is installed at the same time as the building fire alarm system. Figure A.21.3.14(b) should be used where the elevator is installed after the building fire alarm system.

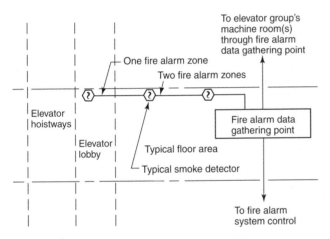

FIGURE A.21.3.14(a) Elevator Zone — Elevator and Fire Alarm System Installed at Same Time.

A.21.3.14.2(3) Where initiating devices are located in the elevator hoistway at or below the lowest level of recall, ANSI/ASME A17.1/CSA B44, *Safety Code for Elevators and Escalators*, requires that the elevator be sent to the upper recall level. Note that the lowest level of recall could be the designated level or alternate level as determined by the local authority for the particular installation. Also note that the elevator hoistway, as defined in ASME A17.1, includes the elevator pit.

A.21.3.14.3 ANSI/ASME A17.1/CSA B44, *Safety Code for Elevators and Escalators*, requires differentiation between separate hoistways that share a common elevator machine room. For instance, in a situation where there is more than one single hoistway sharing the same elevator machine room, a separate signal must be derived from each hoistway.

A.21.4.1 When determining desired performance, consideration should be given to the temperature and time lag characteristics of both the sprinkler head and the heat detector to ensure as much as possible that the heat detector will operate prior to the sprinkler head, because a lower temperature rating alone

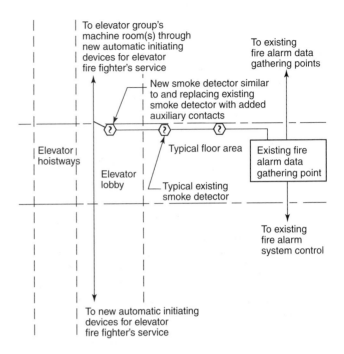

FIGURE A.21.3.14(b) Elevator Zone — Elevator Installed After Fire Alarm System.

might not provide earlier response. The listed spacing rating of the heat detector should be 25 ft (7.6 m) or greater.

A.21.4.2 Upon activation of the heat detector used for elevator power shutdown, there can be a delay in the activation of the power shunt trip. When such a delay is used, it is recommended that the delay should be approximately the time that it takes the elevator car to travel from the top of the hoistway to the lowest recall level. The purpose of the delay of the shunt trip is to increase the potential for elevators to complete their travel to the recall level. It is important to be aware that the requirements of A17.1/B44, *Safety Code for Elevators and Escalators*, relative to sprinkler water release and power shutdown would still apply.

A.21.4.3 Care should be taken to ensure that elevator power cannot be interrupted due to water pressure surges in the sprinkler system. The intent of the Code is to ensure that the switch and the system as a whole do not have the capability of introducing a time delay into the sequence. The use of a switch with a time delay mechanism set to zero does not meet the intent of the Code, because it is possible to introduce a time delay after the system has been accepted. This might occur in response to unwanted alarms caused by surges or water movement, rather than addressing the underlying cause of the surges or water movement (often due to air in the piping). Permanently disabling the delay in accordance with the manufacturer's printed instructions should be considered acceptable. Systems that have software that can introduce a delay in the sequence should be programmed to require a security password to make such a change.

A.21.4.4 Figure A.21.4.4 illustrates one method of monitoring elevator shunt trip control power for integrity.

A.21.5.1(2) Signals to the standard emergency service interface providing the status of the elevator(s), including location within

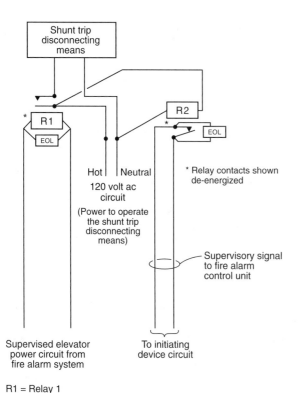

R1 = Relay 1
R2 = Relay 2
EOL = End-of-line device

FIGURE A.21.4.4 Typical Method of Providing Elevator Power Shunt Trip Supervisory Signal.

the hoistway, direction of travel, and whether they are occupied should be provided by the elevator management system.

A.21.6.2.1.1(2) The manual means is intended in lieu of automatic initiating devices that are impaired or out of service and would otherwise have actuated to provide automatic initiation in accordance with 21.6.2.1.1(2). Manual fire alarm boxes location throughout the building are not included because they are typically activated at locations remote from the fire and could lead to misinformation about the location of the fire.

A.21.6.2.1.2 The fire alarm system uses the floor identification to automatically establish a contiguous block of floors to be evacuated consistent with 21.6.2.1.2(B). The established block of floors is updated to reflect changing conditions as indicated by the output signal(s). This information is sent to the elevator system and also used for occupant notification. The output signals from the fire alarm system can be in the form of contact closures or serial communications. Coordination needs to be provided between the fire alarm system installer and the elevator system installer.

A.21.6.2.1.4 Messages need to be coordinated with the operation of the elevators so that occupants understand what to expect and how to react. Additional visual information will be provided in each elevator lobby by the elevator management system to further inform occupants of the status of the elevators.

A.21.6.2.1.4(C) This new message will require a signal from the elevator management system to the fire alarm system.

A.21.7.2 See A.21.7.3.

A.21.7.3 This standard does not specifically require detection devices used to cause the operation of HVAC system smoke dampers, fire dampers, fan control, smoke doors, and fire doors to be connected to the fire alarm system.

A.21.9.1 Doors are commonly locked for various security reasons. Though doors are permitted to be locked to prevent ingress, doors are generally not permitted to be locked to restrict egress unless specifically permitted by governing laws, codes, and standards. Examples of special locking arrangements include delayed egress locking and access control locking. Approved locking requirements by governing laws, codes, and standards can vary extensively. For example, some might require all fire alarm initiating devices to immediately unlock electrically locked egress doors, while others might permit such doors to remain locked when a single manual fire alarm box is activated. Some codes might also permit electrically locked doors to remain locked when a single smoke detector has activated. These allowances are typically permitted only in sprinklered buildings and are generally used as additional safeguards to counter efforts to breach security, without compromising occupant safety.

A.21.9.3 A problem could exist when batteries are used as a secondary power source if a fire alarm control unit having 24 hours of standby operating power were to lose primary power and be operated for more than 24 hours from the secondary power source (batteries). It is possible that sufficient voltage would be available to keep the doors locked, but not enough voltage would be available to operate the fire alarm control unit to release the locks.

A.21.10 When a fire alarm evacuation signal activates, the exit marking system will be activated. In some cases, the activation might be sequenced to meet the fire safety plan of the property.

A.23.1.1 It is intended that fire alarm systems and their components used for mass notification applications be covered by Chapter 23.

A.23.2.1 Systems can be installed for the purposes of life safety, property protection, or both. Evacuation or relocation is not a required output action for every system installed in accordance with Chapter 23.

A.23.2.2.1.1 Compatibility between software systems is necessary to ensure that the systems can communicate correctly and that the overall system can function as intended. Unfortunately, software that is compatible can become incompatible when the software is updated. Newer revisions of software might not maintain compatibility with older revisions. This paragraph requires that the fire alarm software or firmware that interfaces with software or firmware in another system is compatible. An example might be a smoke control system that gets information from the fire alarm system. The term "required" indicates that this compatibility requirement is intended for required functions (e.g., smoke control) and not for supplemental functions that are not part of the required operation of the fire alarm system. An example of a supplemental function might be an RS-232 port that connects to a terminal emulator program used for maintenance purposes. The term "functionally" is intended to ensure that the intended functionality is maintained by the software. It is trying to avoid a situation where a change in software revision might still be compatible but changes the available functionality so that the two systems no longer perform the intended functions, even though the software communicates correctly.

A.23.2.2.1.2 Compatibility between systems will be documented in one or the other (or both) of the manufacturer's installation documents for the compatible products and controlled by the listings agencies. This documentation will be referenced in the marking on the product. The documentation might be paper copy or electronic media (disk, website, etc.). When a software revision changes, the documentation can be consulted to ensure that it is still compatible with the software or firmware on the other side of the interface.

A.23.2.2.2 A commonly used method of protecting against unauthorized changes can be described as follows (in ascending levels of access):

(1) *Access Level 1.* Access by persons who have a general responsibility for safety supervision, and who might be expected to investigate and initially respond to a fire alarm or trouble signal

(2) *Access Level 2.* Access by persons who have a specific responsibility for safety, and who are trained to operate the control unit

(3) *Access Level 3.* Access by persons who are trained and authorized to do the following:
   (a) Reconfigure the site-specific data held within the control unit, or controlled by it
   (b) Maintain the control unit in accordance with the manufacturer's published instructions and data

(4) *Access Level 4.* Access by persons who are trained and authorized either to repair the control unit or to alter its site-specific data or operating system program, thereby changing its basic mode of operation

A.23.3.2 Nonrequired fire alarm features are defined in 3.3.171. These are fire alarm systems or components that are not required by the building or fire codes and are installed voluntarily by a building owner to meet site-specific fire safety objectives. There is a need to properly document the nonrequired system and components. Nonrequired components must be operationally compatible in harmony with other required components and must not be detrimental to the overall system performance. It is for this reason that 23.3.2.1 mandates that nonrequired (voluntary) systems and components meet the applicable installation, testing, and maintenance requirements of this Code. It is not the intent of the Code to have the installation of nonrequired (voluntary) systems or components trigger a requirement for the installation of additional fire alarm components or features in the building. For example, if a building owner voluntarily installs a fire alarm control unit to transmit sprinkler waterflow signals to a central station, that does not trigger a requirement to install other fire alarm system components or features, such as manual fire alarm boxes, occupant notification, or electronic supervision of sprinkler control valves. See also A.17.5.3.3 and A.18.1.5.

Alternatively, supervision and power requirements are required to be taken into account for the nonrequired components/systems on the required fire alarm systems.

A.23.3.3.1 The following functions are included in Annex A to provide guidelines for utilizing building systems and equipment in addition to proprietary fire alarm equipment in order to provide life safety and property protection. Building functions that should be initiated or controlled during a fire alarm condition include, but should not be limited to, the following:

(1) Elevator operation consistent with ANSI/ASME A17.1/CSA B44, *Safety Code for Elevators and Escalators*

(2) Unlocking of stairwell and exit doors (*see* NFPA 80, *Standard for Fire Doors and Other Opening Protectives,* and NFPA *101, Life Safety Code*)

(3) Release of fire and smoke dampers (*see* NFPA 90A, *Standard for the Installation of Air-Conditioning and Ventilating Systems,* and NFPA 90B, *Standard for the Installation of Warm Air Heating and Air-Conditioning Systems*)

(4) Monitoring and initiating of self-contained automatic fire extinguishing system(s) or suppression system(s) and equipment (*see* NFPA 11, *Standard for Low-, Medium-, and High-Expansion Foam;* NFPA 12, *Standard on Carbon Dioxide Extinguishing Systems;* NFPA 12A, *Standard on Halon 1301 Fire Extinguishing Systems;* NFPA 13, *Standard for the Installation of Sprinkler Systems;* NFPA 14, *Standard for the Installation of Standpipe and Hose Systems;* NFPA 15, *Standard for Water Spray Fixed Systems for Fire Protection;* NFPA 17, *Standard for Dry Chemical Extinguishing Systems;* NFPA 17A, *Standard for Wet Chemical Extinguishing Systems; and* NFPA 750, *Standard on Water Mist Fire Protection Systems*)

A.23.3.3.2 Examples of dedicated function fire alarm systems would include an elevator recall control and supervisory control unit, as addressed in 21.3.2, or a system used specifically to monitor sprinkler waterflow and supervisory functions.

A.23.4.2.2 The intent of this paragraph is to prevent situations where the signaling line circuit to a device is required to be one class of operation, while the power circuits, running in the same raceways and subject to the same threats, are wired to a lower class of operation. This means that it is possible to have power wiring connected to a device that is of a different class than the signaling line or initiating device circuits. One example of where meeting the same minimum performance requirements would still allow different classes of wiring is where the performance requirements are based on distance or the number of devices attached to the wires. For example, if the signaling line circuit supplies 200 devices and the performance requirement is that not more than 10 devices be lost to a wiring fault, then the class of wiring on the signaling line circuit will be Class A, with isolators to protect against shorts. Where the power wires never supply more than 10 devices, the power wires could be wired as Class B.

> Paragraph A.23.6 was deleted by a tentative interim amendment (TIA). See page 1.

A.23.6.1 The intent is to clarify that this requirement applies only to SLCs that connect to addressable devices and not to SLCs that interconnect fire alarm control units (FACU).

Fire incidents have occurred where substantial losses were incurred due to the shorting and failure of an SLC damaged by fire prior to the activation of an alarm. In addition SLC shorts caused inadvertently as part of building operations, and activities can cause a catastrophic failure of the fire and life system to operate if a fire occurs subsequently to the occurrence of a fault that had not been corrected. A single short on an SLC of an *NFPA 72 2013* fully code compliant system not only can disable the capability of the system to activate an alarm. But, in addition, the alarm notification appliances and critical life safety emergency control functions including atrium smoke control, stairwell pressurization, door unlocking, and HVAC shutdown can all be disabled as well. In some configurations, even off-premises alarm, trouble, and supervisory reporting functions can be disabled.

When an SLC is shorted, the results can be catastrophic in terms of loss of lives and property if a fire occurs.

A.23.8.1.1 Actuation of an initiating device is usually the instant at which a complete digital signal is achieved at the device, such as a contact closure. For smoke detectors or other automatic initiating devices, which can involve signal processing and analysis of the signature of fire phenomena, actuation means the instant when the signal analysis requirements are completed by the device or fire alarm control unit software.

A separate fire alarm control unit contemplates a network of fire alarm control units forming a single large system as defined in Section 23.8.

For some analog initiating devices, actuation is the moment that the fire alarm control unit interprets that the signal from an initiating device has exceeded the alarm threshold programmed into the fire alarm control unit.

For smoke detectors working on a system with alarm verification, where the verification function is performed in the fire alarm control unit, the moment of actuation of smoke detectors is sometimes determined by the fire alarm control unit.

It is not the intent of this paragraph to dictate the time frame for the local fire safety devices to complete their function, such as fan wind-down time, door closure time, or elevator travel time.

A.23.8.1.2 A system provided with an alarm verification feature as permitted by 23.8.5.4.1 is not considered a presignal system, since the delay in the signal produced is 60 seconds or less and requires no human intervention.

A.23.8.1.3.1.1(6) "Immediately activated" means there are no delays imposed by the system other than the processing of the signal in accordance with 23.8.1.1.

A.23.8.1.3.1.2 The bypass means is intended to enable automatic or manual day, night, and weekend operation.

A.23.8.2 This Code addresses field installations that interconnect two or more listed control units, possibly from different manufacturers, that together fulfill the requirements of this Code.

Such an arrangement should preserve the reliability, adequacy, and integrity of all alarm, supervisory, and trouble signals and interconnecting circuits intended to be in accordance with the provisions of this Code.

Where interconnected control units are in separate buildings, consideration should be given to protecting the interconnecting wiring from electrical and radio frequency interference.

A.23.8.4.1 The provisions of 23.8.4.1 apply to types of equipment used in common for fire alarm systems, such as fire alarm, sprinkler supervisory, or guard's tour service, and for other systems, such as burglar alarm or coded paging systems, and to methods of circuit wiring common to both types of systems. The intent of connecting non-fire systems with the fire alarm system is often to cause the non-fire systems to react appropriately when signaled by the fire alarm system.

A.23.8.4.3 For systems such as carbon monoxide detection, fire extinguisher electronic monitoring device, emergency communication (mass notification), or intrusion, much of the benefit of a combination system comes from being able to use common wiring. If the equipment in the combination system is of equivalent quality to fire alarm equipment, and the system monitors the wiring and equipment in the same way as fire alarm equipment, then sharing of wiring is permitted. If the equipment is not of equivalent quality, isolation between the systems would be required.

A.23.8.4.6 Examples of signal classification are provided in Table A.23.8.4.6. This is not all-inclusive or prescriptive but is meant to illustrate a potential classification scheme. Actual schemes may vary depending upon the response plan and/or requirements of the authority having jurisdiction. Mass notification systems are allowed to take priority over the fire alarm audible notification message or signal. This is intended to allow the mass notification system to prioritize emergency signals on the basis of risk to building occupants. The designer should specify the desired operation, in particular, as to what should occur immediately after the mass notification message has completed.

Table A.23.8.4.6 Examples of Signal Classification

Life Safety	Property Protection	Trouble	Other
Fire alarm signals	Security signals	Battery fault	HVAC signals
Carbon monoxide alarm signals	Supervisory signals	AC power failure	Occupancy
Code blue signals	Access control	IDC faults	
Panic alarms		NAC faults	
Hazmat signals		SLC faults	
Severe weather warnings			
Flood alarms			
Mass notification signals			
Holdup alarm signals			

A.23.8.4.8 See NFPA 720, *Standard for the Installation of Carbon Monoxide (CO) Detection and Warning Equipment,* for more information.

A.23.8.4.8.2 Response to carbon monoxide alarm signals could include, but not be limited to, any one of the following: immediate evacuation of occupants, immediate call to the fire department or other responding authorities, relocation of occupants to another portion of the building, investigation of the area identified, and/or opening of all doors and windows to the outside in the area identified.

A.23.8.4.9 See NFPA 10, *Standard for Portable Fire Extinguishers,* for more information on portable fire extinguishers.

A.23.8.5.1.2 The manual means required by 23.8.5.1.2 is intended to provide a backup means to manually activate the fire alarm system when the automatic fire detection system or waterflow devices are out of service due to maintenance or testing, or where human discovery of the fire precedes automatic sprinkler system or automatic detection system activation.

The manual fire alarm box required by 23.8.5.1.2 should be connected to a separate circuit that is not placed "on test" when the detection or sprinkler system is placed "on test." The manual means is only intended for use by the system technician or the building owner and should be located by the sprinkler riser or fire alarm control unit.

A.23.8.5.3.2 Where power is supplied separately to the individual initiating device(s), multiple initiating circuits are not prohibited from being monitored for integrity by a single power supervision device.

A.23.8.5.4.1 The alarm verification feature should not be used as a substitute for proper detector location/applications or regular system maintenance. Alarm verification features are intended to reduce the frequency of false alarms caused by transient conditions. They are not intended to compensate for design errors or lack of maintenance.

A.23.8.5.4.6.3 Where a separate power source is provided for a duct smoke detector, consideration should be given to provide a secondary power source for the duct detector power source as a power failure to the duct detector will (or should) indicate a trouble condition on the fire panel. If the system is connected to an off-premises monitoring station, a trouble signal will be sent immediately upon power failure. This is in contrast to the intent and requirements to delay the off-premises reporting of primary power failures.

A.23.8.5.5 This Code does not specifically require a waterflow alarm initiating device to be connected to the building fire alarm system. Connection to the building fire alarm system would be determined by the requirements established by the authority having jurisdiction. See A.1.2.4.

A.23.8.5.5.2 Circuits connected to a signaling line circuit interface are initiating device circuits and are subject to these limitations.

A.23.8.5.6 This Code does not specifically require supervisory signal initiating devices to be connected to the building fire alarm system. Connections to the building fire alarm system would be determined by the requirements established by the authority having jurisdiction. See A.1.2.4. Some systems utilize nonelectrical methods to supervise conditions of the system such as chains on sprinkler control valves.

Supervisory signals are not intended to provide indication of design, installation, or functional defects in the supervised systems or system components and are not a substitute for regular testing of those systems in accordance with the applicable standard. Supervised conditions should include, but not be limited to, the following:

(1) Control valves 1½ in. (38.1 mm) or larger
(2) Pressure, including dry pipe system air, pressure tank air, preaction system supervisory air, steam for flooding systems, and public water
(3) Water tanks, including water level and temperature
(4) Building temperature, including areas such as valve closet and fire pump house
(5) Electric fire pumps, including running (alarm or supervisory), power failure, and phase reversal
(6) Engine-driven fire pumps, including running (alarm or supervisory), failure to start, controller off "automatic," and trouble (e.g., low oil, high temperature, overspeed)
(7) Steam turbine fire pumps, including running (alarm or supervisory), steam pressure, and steam control valves

A.23.8.5.6.2 Circuits connected to a signaling line circuit interface are initiating device circuits and are subject to these limitations.

A.23.8.5.8 See A.23.8.5.6.

A.23.8.6.2 The general purpose of the fire alarm audible and visual notification appliances is to alert occupants that there is a fire condition and for occupants to exit from the building.

Once the occupants are in the exit enclosures, high noise levels and light intensity from notification appliances could cause confusion and impede egress. There could be conditions that warrant the installation of notification appliances in exit passageways, but careful analysis is necessary to avoid impeding exiting from the building.

A.23.10.2 One or more of the following means might be considered acceptable to provide a level of survivability consistent with the intent of this requirement:

(1) Installing a fire alarm system in a fully sprinklered building in accordance with NFPA 13, *Standard for the Installation of Sprinkler Systems*
(2) Routing notification appliance circuits separately
(3) Using short-circuit fault-tolerant signaling line circuits for controlling evacuation signals

The requirement for notification appliances to operate in those evacuation signaling zones that are not attacked by fire will also require that circuits and equipment that are common to more than one evacuation signaling zone be designed and installed such that the fire will not disable them. For instance, a signaling line circuit used to control notification appliances in multiple evacuation signaling zones should be properly designed and installed so that one fire would not impair the signaling line circuit, rendering the notification appliances serving more than one evacuation signaling zone inoperative. Power supply requirements of Chapter 10 apply to these systems. The secondary power supply requirements of that chapter meet the intent of these survivability requirements.

A.23.11.7 Automatic fire suppression systems referred to in 23.11.7 include, but are not limited to, preaction and deluge sprinkler systems, carbon dioxide systems, Halon systems, and dry chemical systems.

A.23.12.4 Off-site logging of fire alarm data can be useful to preserve information in the face of fire or building failure to facilitate accurate reconstruction of the event. It can also be beneficial to send data off-premises to incident command personnel to enhance situational awareness and response decisions and to maintain safe and efficient operations.

A.23.16 The term *wireless* has been replaced with the term *low-power radio* to eliminate potential confusion with other transmission media such as optical fiber cables.

Low-power radio devices are required to comply with the applicable *low-power* requirements of Title 47, Code of Federal Regulations, Part 15.

A.23.16.1 Equipment listed solely for dwelling unit use would not comply with this requirement.

A.23.16.3.1 This requirement is not intended to preclude verification and local test intervals prior to alarm transmission.

A.23.16.3.5 Trouble and supervisory signals are not required to latch. Self-restoring trouble and supervisory signals are acceptable.

A.24.1.2 An emergency communications system could target the general building, area, space, campus, or region.

A.24.3.1 In certain situations, it is important to provide a distributed sound level with minimal sound intensity variations to achieve an intelligible voice message. This differs from past fire alarm design practice that used fewer notification appliances, but with each having greater sound pressure output levels. Non-emergency system design practice is to use more speakers and less sound intensity from each speaker. Besides improving intelligibility of the message, this approach minimizes annoyance to building occupants from the system and lessens the likelihood of tampering with the system by occupants because of speakers being too loud. In other applications, such as outdoor signaling where reverberation is not a problem, intelligibility can be achieved by using fewer appliances or clusters of appliances covering larger areas.

Intelligibility is a complex function of the source audio, the acoustic response of the architectural features and materials of the immediate vicinity, and the dynamics created by the room's occupants. Refer to Annex D for more information on speech intelligibility and how it is predicted. Spacing speakers closely can be an intelligibility-enhancing technique but can occasionally lead to opposite results when improperly designed. There are several techniques using directionality features that do not use closely spaced speakers but rather use the room/space acoustic response in their favor.

Based upon a detailed risk analysis and emergency response plan, certain recorded or live mass notification voice messages could take priority over fire alarm messages and signals. If the fire alarm system is in the alarm mode when recorded voice message or audible signals are sounding, and the mass notification system is actuated with a signal of higher priority, it should temporarily cause deactivation of all fire alarm-initiated audible and visible notification appliances during the time period required to transmit the mass notification emergency message.

A.24.3.2.1 Users who speak too softly, too loudly, or who hold a microphone too close, too far, or at an incorrect angle can introduce distortion or cause reduced intelligibility of the spoken message. The characteristics of the system microphone are important ergonomic factors that affect voice intelligibility. Some microphones need to be held close to the mouth, perhaps an inch or less. Others need to be three or four inches away. How is the user to know what's ideal? A simple diagram next to the microphone can help. Some microphones are very directional and must be held flat in front of the speaker's mouth. These microphones are useful in small command centers, since they are less likely to pick up conversations off to the sides. On the other hand, microphones with a wider polar sensitivity are more forgiving for a user to hold comfortably while moving and doing other tasks. Their downside is that they will pick up extraneous noise in poorly designed command centers introduced into the microphone.

A.24.3.3 The requirements found in *NFPA 70, National Electrical Code*, Article 708, should be considered for emergency communications systems that are installed in vital infrastructure facilities classified as a designated critical operations area (DCOA). This includes facilities that, if destroyed or incapacitated, would disrupt national security, the economy, public health or safety and where enhanced electrical infrastructure for continuity of operation has been deemed necessary by governmental authority.

A.24.3.4 The features for a nonrequired system should be established by the system designer on the basis of the goals and objectives intended by the system owner.

A.24.3.5.2 Dedicated in-building fire emergency voice/alarm communications systems are not required to monitor the integrity of the notification appliance circuits while active for emergency purposes. However, these circuits have to be monitored for integrity while active for non-emergency purposes.

The building operator, system designer, and authority having jurisdiction should be aware that, in some situations, such a system could be subject to deliberate tampering. Tampering is usually attempted to reduce the output of a sound system that is in constant use, such as background music or a paging system, and that could be a source of annoyance to employees.

The likelihood of tampering can be reduced through proper consideration of loudspeaker accessibility and system operation.

Access can be reduced through the use of hidden or non-adjustable transformer taps (which can reduce playback levels), use of vandal-resistant listed loudspeakers, and placement in areas that are difficult to access, such as high ceilings (any ceiling higher than could be reached by standing on a desk or chair). Non-emergency operation of the system should always consider that an audio system that annoys an employee potentially reduces employee productivity and can also annoy the public in a commercial environment. Most motivations for tampering can be eliminated through appropriate use of the system and employee discipline. Access to amplification equipment and controls should be limited to those authorized to make adjustments to such equipment. It is common practice to install such equipment in a manner that allows adjustment of non-emergency audio signal levels while defaulting to a fixed, preset level of playback when operating in emergency mode. Under extreme circumstances, certain zones of a protected area might require a dedicated in-building fire emergency voice/alarm communications zone.

A.24.3.6.3 This section is not meant to preclude a performance-based pathway survivability approach. As with most performance-based approaches, documentation should be provided by the designer and maintained with system documentation for the life of the system. Written documentation of the approval from the authority having jurisdiction should also be maintained. A performance-based approach to pathway survivability could be equivalent to, less stringent than, or more stringent than the prescriptive approach in 24.3.6. Often a performance-based approach will result from a risk analysis.

This section is also not meant to preclude less stringent pathway survivability requirements supported by a risk analysis for those unique occupancies that employ voice alarm/emergency communication systems for relocation or partial evacuation as part of their fire safety plan where relocation or partial evacuation could be readily superseded by total evacuation and where buildings are of a type other than Type I or Type II (222) construction where the pathway survivability performance requirement does not need to be for two hours. Examples include low rise education and day care occupancies, nursing homes, ambulatory health care occupancies, hotel and dormitory occupancies, and residential board and care occupancies.

A.24.3.6.8.1 Extensive searches and discussions with cable manufacturers have not been able to identify a source of listed 2-hour-rated coaxial or fiber cables. Listed fire-rated 75 ohm coaxial cables for security cameras exist but are not adaptable to distributed antenna systems operating at much higher radio frequencies. Coaxial cable with characteristics similar to low loss 50 ohm, ½ in. (13 mm) diameter, coaxial cables are available in plenum and riser ratings. Past installations have used these plenum and riser rated coaxial cables prior to this Code.

The fiber component of fiber-optic cables melts at temperatures well below the 1825°F (996°C) test specification for listed 2-hour cable.

Using 2-hour-rated cable enclosures throughout each floor of most structures is impractical, especially when added to existing structures.

A.24.3.6.8.3 Examples of 2-hour-rated enclosures could include stairwells and elevator hoistways for first responders–use elevators.

A.24.3.6.9 Although in some instances areas of refuge (areas of rescue assistance) might be installed in buildings that use general evacuation and not relocation/partial evacuation, it is still crucial that people awaiting assistance can communicate with emergency responders to facilitate their evacuation. Thus, their evacuation time might be prolonged, and therefore the emergency communications systems should be capable of operating reliably during a fire incident.

A.24.3.7 One-way emergency communications systems are intended to broadcast information, in an emergency, to personnel in one or more specified indoor or outdoor areas. It is intended that emergency messages be conveyed either by audible or visible textual means or both. This section does not apply to bells, horns, or other sounders and lights, except where used in conjunction with the desired operation of emergency messages and signaling.

Two-way emergency communications systems are divided into two categories, those systems that are anticipated to be used by building occupants and those systems that are to be used by fire fighters, police, and other emergency services personnel. Two-way emergency communications systems are used both to exchange information and to communicate information, such as, but not limited to, instructions, acknowledgement of receipt of messages, condition of local environment, and condition of persons, and to give assurance that help is on its way.

NFPA 72 contains requirements that can impact the application of emergency communications systems. For instance, coordination of the functions of an emergency communications system with other systems that communicate audibly and/or visibly [such as fire alarm systems, security systems, public address (PA) systems] is essential in order to provide effective communication in an emergency situation. Conflicting or competing signals or messages from different systems could be very confusing to occupants and have a negative impact on the intended occupant response. Where independent systems using audible and/or visible notification are present, the emergency communications system needs to interface with those systems to effect related control actions such as deactivating both audible and visible notification appliances. The use of a single integrated combination system might offer both economic and technical advantages. In any case, coordination between system functions is essential. The coordination of emergency communications systems with other systems should be considered part of the risk analysis for the emergency communications system. *(See Figure A.24.3.7.)*

Additional documents such as NEMA Standard SB 40, *Communications Systems for Life Safety in Schools*, can also be used as supplemental resources to provide help with risk assessment and application considerations.

A.24.3.8 The layers can be used in combination. In all cases, the system design needs to follow the risk analysis and be integrated into the emergency response plan. Research has shown that more than one layer has been used to be effective. Multiple layers provide an extra level of notification (a safety net). The overall MNS application is likely to exploit a number of public and individual systems or components that combine to produce a reliable and robust solution to achieve emergency notification objectives.

Layer 1 could consist of elements such as the following:

(1) Emergency voice/alarm communications systems (EVACS)
(2) One-way voice communication systems (PA)
(3) Two-way voice communication systems
(4) Visible notification appliances
(5) Textual/digital signage/displays

Layer 2 could consist of elements such as the following:

(1) Wide-area outdoor mass notification systems (MNS)
(2) High power speaker arrays (HPSA)

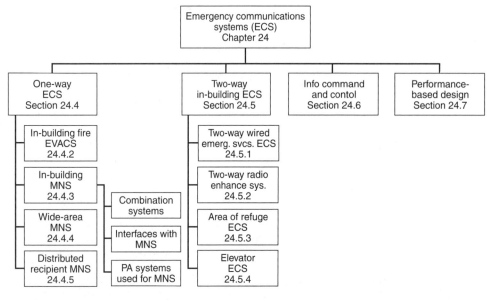

FIGURE A.24.3.7　Emergency Communications Systems.

Layer 3 could consist of elements such as the following:

(1) Short message service (SMS)
(2) Email
(3) Computer pop-ups
(4) Smartphone applications (Apps)
(5) Reverse 911/automated dialing

Layer 4 could consist of elements such as the following:

(1) Radio broadcast (satellite, AM/FM)
(2) Television broadcast (satellite, digital)
(3) Location specific messages/notifications
(4) Weather radios
(5) Social networks

Also see *Optimizing Fire Alarm Notification for High Risk Groups* research project.

A.24.3.9 The design documents might include, but are not limited to, shop drawings, input/output matrix, battery calculations, notification appliance voltage drop calculations for strobes and speakers, and product data sheets.

A.24.3.11 There are many credible risk assessment methodologies that can be utilized and/or referenced in conducting the risk assessment required in 24.3.11, some of which are listed as follows:

(1) *CARVER — Target Analysis and Vulnerability Assessment Methodology*, Washington, DC: U.S. Department of Defense (see Field Manual 34-36, Special Operation Forces Intelligence and Electronics Warfare Operation, Sept. 30, 1991), www.defense.gov
(2) *General Security Risk Assessment Guidelines*. Alexandria, VA: American Society for Industrial Security International, www.asisonline.org
(3) *NFPA 1600, Standard on Disaster/Emergency Management and Business Continuity Programs*, Quincy, MA: National Fire Protection Association, www.nfpa.org
(4) NFPA 730, *Guide for Premises Security*, Quincy, MA: National Fire Protection Association, www.nfpa.org
(5) *Responsible Care Code*, Washington, DC: American Chemistry Council, www.americanchemistry.com
(6) *Risk and Resilience Management of Water & Wastewater Systems*, Denver, CO: American Water Works Association, www.awwa.org
(7) *VAMCAP® Vulnerability Assessment Methodology for Critical Asset Protection*, Wilmington, DE: SafePlace Corporation, www.safeplace.com
(8) *Vulnerability Assessment Methodologies*, Albuquerque, NM: Sandia National Laboratories, www.sandia.gov

Refer to A.7.8.2 and Figure A.7.8.2(g) for a risk analysis checklist.

A.24.3.11.1 Although this chapter outlines some specific criteria and/or limitations, each application should be based on recognized performance-based design practices and the emergency response plan developed for the specific facility.

Here are the general categories of questions that might be presented to the senior manager responsible for mass notification decisions. The actual questions for each project must be tailored to the area, the building, the campus, and the culture of the user organization. Following is a brief description of potential content within the mass notification event questions:

(1) What is the type of emergency event — that is, is it fire, security, safety, health, environmental, geological, meteorological, utility service disruption, or another type of event?
(2) What is the urgency of the emergency event — that is, does it represent immediate danger, has it already occurred, is it expected to occur soon, is it expected to occur in the future, or is its occurrence unknown?
(3) What is the anticipated or expected severity of the emergency event that is, how will it impact our facility and its functions, is it expected to be extreme, severe, etc.?
(4) What is the certainty of the emergency event that is, is it happening now, is it very likely to occur, is it likely to occur, is it possible that it will occur in the future, is it unlikely to occur, or is its occurrence unknown?
(5) What is the location of the event, or from what direction is the emergency event approaching — that is, has it or will it be approaching from the north, south, east, or west?
(6) What zone or areas should receive the emergency message(s) — that is, is it a floor of a building, multiple floors of a building, the entire building, multiple buildings, a campus of buildings, an entire town or city, an entire state, an entire region of states, or an entire country?
(7) What is the validity of the emergency event — that is, has the emergency event been investigated and/or confirmed?
(8) What instructions should we send to our personnel — that is, should they evacuate the facility, should they shelter-in-place, should they shelter-in-place at a special location, should they proceed to a safe haven area, and other action oriented items?
(9) Are there any special instructions, procedures, or special tasks that we need to remind personnel about or to accomplish — that is, close your office door, open your office door, stay away from windows, do not use elevators, and other information relating to personnel actions?

The questions suggested in items (1) through (9) are offered for consideration, and not all of them might be appropriate for every mass notification system installation. It is important to remember that when an emergency event occurs, the response must be immediate and deliberate. Therefore, there is no time for indecision. So the questions selected to reside in the emergency messaging decision tree illustrated in items (1) through (9) must be straightforward and as simple as possible. They must also be tailored to the specific organization, culture, site, and unique requirements of each local environment.

A.24.3.12 The emergency response plan should include, but not be limited to, the following elements:

(1) Emergency response team structure
(2) Emergency response procedures, as follows:
   (a) Building system related emergencies
   (b) Human-related emergencies
   (c) Terrorism-related emergencies
   (d) Weather-related emergencies
(3) Emergency response equipment and operations
(4) Emergency response notification, as follows:
   (a) Emergency message content
   (b) Emergency notification approval process
   (c) Emergency notification initiation process
(5) Emergency response training and drills, as follows:
   (a) Classroom training
   (b) Table-top training
   (c) Live drills

A.24.4.1.1 The fundamental structure of the prerecorded or live messages is critical for providing information and instructions that are intelligible. Prerecorded messages created in a controlled environment are considerably more intelligible than live messages and should be developed and provided to handle as many of the probable emergencies that a particular facility will encounter.

The voice instructions (live or prerecorded) should be preceded by a tone to get attention and prepare the target audience for voice instructions. This tone should be differentiated for specific emergencies, based on the standards for that facility. The actual voice message (live or pre-recorded) should be delivered in a well-enunciated, clear, calm, and deliberate manner, using respectful language. Focus the message on the action to be taken and minimize wasting words on the cause. For the voice itself, best results will vary, depending on the specific location — for example, in outdoor applications, it has been shown that a male voice will provide better intelligibility, as the naturally lower frequency of the male voice travels better. Inversely, in an interior application, where the background ambient noise is typically in the same lower frequencies, a female voice tends to penetrate better, as it is more distinct from the ambient. Messages should be constructed using 2-second to 3-second bursts of information and brief periods of quiet between the bursts of information. This methodology facilitates better processing of information by the brain and minimizes the negative effects of reverberation and echo.

Generally, the emergency message should consist of an alert tone of 1 second to 3 seconds, followed by a voice message that is repeated at least three times. The alert tone can be used in between repeats of the voice message.

For live instructions, it is critical that the message be delivered in a clear and calm manner. When possible, the following procedure is recommended:

(1) Think about what information must be delivered in the live announcement, keep it brief, and write down the message
(2) Read the message out loud for a practice round in a clear and projecting voice
(3) When you are ready to announce, key the microphone and read the message at least three times
(4) When possible, use an alert tone, such as a Code 3, 1000 Hz signal preceding the message, and then announce over the live microphone
(5) Repeat the message a few times more as the emergency warrants

A.24.4.1.2 A well-crafted, evidence-based message (incentive to response) with content that includes the following:

(1) What: Guidance on what people should do
(2) When: An idea of when they need to act
(3) Where: Description of the location of the risk of hazard (who should be taking action and who should not be)
(4) Why: Information on the hazard and danger/consequences
(5) Who: The name of the source of the warning (who is giving it)

Warning style is also crucial and should be specific, consistent, certain, clear, and accurate with attention paid to the frequency — the more it is repeated, the better.

A.24.4.2 Where used, recorded voice messages for fire emergency alarm systems should be prepared in accordance with this Code by persons who are experienced with the operation of building fire emergency alarm systems and are knowledge-able of the building's construction, layout, and fire protection plan, including evacuation procedures. The proposed voice messages should be approved by the authority having jurisdiction prior to being implemented. Persons who record the messages for fire emergency alarm systems should be able to read and speak the language used for the message clearly, concisely, and without an accent that would have an adverse affect on intelligibility.

It is not the intention that in-building fire emergency voice/alarm communications service be limited to English-speaking populations. Emergency messages should be provided in the language of the predominant building population. If there is a possibility of isolated groups that do not speak the predominant language, multilingual messages should be provided. It is expected that small groups of transients unfamiliar with the predominant language will be picked up in the traffic flow in the event of an emergency and are not likely to be in an isolated situation.

A.24.4.2.2.2.2 Generally speaking, in a standard building configuration with normal ceiling height [8 ft to 12 ft (2.4 m to 3.7 m)], normal ceiling construction (e.g., drop acoustical ceiling tiles), standard wall configurations, and finishes and carpeted floors, ceiling-mounted speakers should be installed in all normally occupiable spaces and in corridors spaced at a maximum of twice the ceiling height or as determined by a commercially available computer acoustical/speaker modeling program. Where wall-mounted speakers are used, manufacturer recommendations should be reviewed and/or computer modeling should be employed. One of the goals of speaker placement is to provide the shortest practical distance from the source (speaker) to the recipient (person hearing the signal). In many applications, a combination of wall- and ceiling-mounted speakers might be required. The audibility and intelligibility of the speakers can be impacted by the tap/setting at which the speaker is connected and should meet the audibility requirements of the Code while still having the message intelligible. Connecting to a high setting to meet the audibility requirements of the code could distort the intelligibility of the signal.

In an ADS that is a non-acoustically challenging area, designing for audibility will typically result in an intelligible system provided minimum speaker guidelines are followed. Areas typically considered to be non-acoustically challenging include traditional office environments, hotel guest rooms, dwelling units, and spaces with carpeting and furnishings.

Special attention must be given to acoustically challenging ADSs. Such areas might incorporate appreciable hard surfaces (e.g., glass, marble, tile, metal, etc) or appreciably high ceilings (e.g., atriums, multiple ceiling heights). These conditions will require more stringent design guidelines to ensure intelligibility (e.g., a closer than normal speaker spacing with lower taps). This can help reduce the effect of excessive reverberation and result in better intelligibility. In extreme cases there could be areas where intelligibility is not attainable, but this can be acceptable if there is an ADS within 30 ft (9.1 m) where the intelligibility of the system is deemed adequate.

In an ADS where the ambient noise level exceeds 85 dB it is acknowledged that intelligibility might not be attainable and an alternate means of notification is required.

Design guidance is provided in the NEMA Standards Publication SB 50-2008, *Emergency Communications Audio Intelligibility Applications Guide.*

A.24.4.2.4.2 The intent of this low frequency tone is to accommodate those with mild to severe hearing loss. See also 18.4.5, A.18.4.5.1, and A.29.3.8.2. The effective date listed in Chapter 18 for using a low frequency signal has not been allowed in 24.4.2.4 because voice systems are easily adapted to comply, whereas the requirements of 18.4.5 also apply to stand-alone tone signaling appliances.

A.24.4.2.4.3 Sleeping accommodations are provided in occupancies such as healthcare, detention and correction, and other occupancies where it would not be necessary to utilize a low frequency tone that awakens those sleeping. For example, in a hospital, the voice message is used to notify staff members who are already awake. The staff will then respond to the appropriate location in the hospital to carry out their duties that could include awakening and relocating patients who could be in danger. In addition, fire drills are required to be conducted on a regular basis and providing a low frequency tone could unnecessarily awaken patients, which would be detrimental to their care.

A.24.4.2.5.1 The choice of the location(s) for the in-building fire emergency voice/alarm communications control equipment should also take into consideration the ability of the fire alarm system to operate and function during any probable single event. Although NFPA 72 does not regulate either building construction or contents, system designers should consider the potential for an event that could damage the equipment, including remotely located control devices, to disable the system or a portion thereof. Where practical, it is prudent to minimize unnecessary fire exposures of fire alarm control equipment through the use of fire-rated construction or enclosures, by limiting adjacent combustibles and ignition sources, or other appropriate means.

A.24.4.2.6.1 Speakers located in the vicinity of the in-building fire emergency voice/alarm communications control equipment should be arranged so they do not cause audio feedback when the system microphone is used. Speakers installed in the area of two-way telephone stations should be arranged so that the sound pressure level emitted does not preclude the effective use of the two-way telephone system. Circuits for speakers and telephones should be separated, shielded, or otherwise arranged to prevent audio cross-talk between circuits.

A.24.4.2.7.1 Special suppression systems that are delivered through a total flooding or localized application include, but are not limited to, carbon dioxide, clean agents, halons, and other extinguishing agents. Special suppression systems require audible and visible warning alarms to provide personnel the opportunity to evacuate or to alert personnel not to enter the area of discharge that could be hazardous to life. A special suppression system discharge can be a life-threatening hazard for personnel who are not notified and, therefore, fail to react to the pre-discharge alarm. In such cases, pre-discharge and discharge alarms should be independent of the fire alarm speakers that are used as part of the mass notification system. A special suppression system discharge could pose a greater threat to personnel that are located in the protected area, or that could enter the protected area, if the local signals were to be overridden and they did not receive the appropriate warning.

A.24.4.2.8 When a fire or other emergency occurs in a building, the usual goal is to evacuate the occupants or relocate them so that they are not exposed to hazardous conditions. The exception occurs in occupancies using stay-in-place/ defend-in-place (SIP/DIP) [1] strategies. It might also be nec-essary to alert and provide information to trained staff responsible for assisting evacuation or relocation. Figure A.24.4.2.8 shows several key steps in a person's reaction and decision-making process [2].

Occupants rarely panic in fire situations [3,4]. The behavior that they adopt is based on the information they have, the perceived threat, and the decisions they make. The entire decision path is full of thought and decisions on the part of the occupant, all of which take time before leading to the development of adaptive behavior. In hindsight, the actions of many occupants in real fires are sometimes less than optimal. However, their decisions might have been the best choices given the information they had. Fire alarm systems that only use audible tones and/or flashing strobe lights impart only one bit of information: fire alarm. It has long been recognized that environments having complex egress situations or high hazard potentials require occupant notification systems that provide more than one bit of information [5]. To reduce the response time of the occupants and to effect the desired behavior, the message should contain several key elements [3,6].

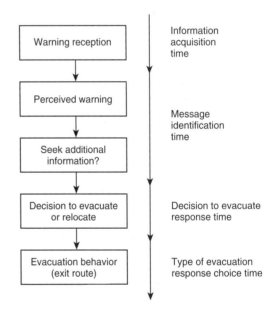

FIGURE A.24.4.2.8 Key Steps in Person's Reaction.

The key elements include the following:

(1) Tell occupants what has happened and where
(2) Tell occupants what they should do
(3) Tell occupants why they should do it

There does not seem to be any research that has tested actual message content to determine the best way to inform occupants. The problem is that each building and each fire is unique. Messaging is further complicated by the need to give different information to different people, depending on their location relative to the fire, their training, and their physical/ mental capabilities.

Messages should use positive language and avoid negative instructions that could be misinterpreted due to unintelligible communications. For example, if you want people to leave an area, say so: "A fire has been reported in the area. For your safety, use the stairs to evacuate the area immediately." A bad example is: "The signal tone you have just heard indicated a report of an emergency. If your floor evacuation signal sounds after this message, do not use the elevator, walk to the nearest stairway and leave the floor. While the report is being verified, occupants on other floors should await further instructions." This message is too long, ambiguous, and subject to misunderstanding if not heard clearly. The word "not" might not be heard clearly, or it might be heard to apply to the entire remaining sentence. Similarly, care should be used in selecting and clearly enunciating words such as "fifth" and "sixth," which can sound the same if the system and environment lead to low intelligibility.

See A.24.4.1.1 for more information on methodology for improved message content, structure, and intelligibility. Refer to Annex D for more information on speech intelligibility and how it is predicted.

Content of the message should be predicated on the building fire safety plan, the nature of the building and its occupants, the design of the fire alarm system, and testing of the occupant reaction to the message. Caution is advised that the fire alarm system operation and message actuation might be initiated by a manual pull station or detector remote from the fire.

[1] Schifiliti, R. P., "To Leave or Not to Leave — That is the Question!", National Fire Protection Association, World Fire Safety Congress & Exposition, May 16, 2000, Denver, CO.

[2] Ramachandran, G., "Informative Fire Warning Systems," *Fire Technology*, vol. 47, no. 1, February 1991, National Fire Protection Association, 66–81.

[3] J., Bryan, "Psychological Variables That May Affect Fire Alarm Design," *Fire Protection Engineering*, Society of Fire Protection Engineers, Issue No. 11, Fall 2001.

[4] Proulx, G., "Cool Under Fire," *Fire Protection Engineering*, Society of Fire Protection Engineers, Issue No. 16, Fall 2002.

[5] General Services Administration, Proceedings of the Reconvened International Conference on Fire Safety in High Rise Buildings, Washington, D.C., October 1971.

[6] Proulx, G., "Strategies for Ensuring Appropriate Occupant Response to Fire Alarm Signals," National Research Council of Canada, Ottawa, Ontario, *Construction Technology Update*, No. 43, 1–6, December 2000.

A.24.4.2.8.5.1 Along with the pathway survivability requirements, one or more of the following means could be considered acceptable to provide a level of survivability consistent with the intent of this requirement:

(1) Routing notification appliance circuits separately
(2) Using short-circuit, fault-tolerant signaling line circuits for controlling evacuation signals

The requirement for notification appliances to operate in those evacuation signaling zones that are not attacked by fire will also require that circuits and equipment that are common to more than one evacuation signaling zone be designed and installed such that the fire will not disable them. For instance, a signaling line circuit used to control notification appliances in multiple evacuation signaling zones should be properly designed and installed so that one fire would not impair the signaling line circuit, rendering the notification appliances serving more than one evacuation signaling zone inoperative.

A.24.4.2.8.5.3 Paragraph 24.4.2.8.5.3 requires the protection of circuits as they pass through fire areas other than the one served. The purpose of this is to delay possible damage to the circuits from fires in areas other than those served by the circuits and to increase the likelihood that circuits serving areas remote from the original fire will have the opportunity to be

actuated and serve their purpose. Note that the protection requirement would also apply to a signaling line circuit that extends from a master fire alarm control unit to another remote fire alarm control unit where notification appliance circuits might originate.

A.24.4.2.9.1 Paragraph 24.4.2.9.1 does not prohibit the provision of multiple notification appliance circuits within an evacuation signaling zone.

A.24.4.3 This section covers the application, installation, location, performance, and maintenance of mass notification systems used for emergency purposes.

An in-building mass notification system is considered to be a system used to provide information and instructions to people in a building(s) or other space using intelligible voice communications and including visible signals, text, graphics, tactile, or other communication methods.

Mass notification systems can consist of fully independent systems with minimal or no interface with the building fire alarm system, systems that report trouble and supervisory signals through the fire alarm system, systems that share audible and visible notification circuits and appliances with the fire alarm system, or combination mass notification and fire alarm systems.

A.24.4.3.1 Although some minimum criteria are outlined for a particular feature, the feature might not be applicable for every project.

The information and instructions delivered by a mass notification system could be initiated manually by an operator or automatically by sensors or other systems and might be delivered to the target audience using prerecorded messages or live messages, or both, tailored to the situation and the audience.

Each mass notification system could be different, depending on the anticipated threat and the level of protection intended. As an example, a particular project might not require secure radio transmissions. As such, criteria for such would not apply. However, if the authority having jurisdiction or design professional has specified secure radio transmissions, the minimum applicable criteria within this document would be required. Deviation from these minimum criteria would require approval of the stakeholders.

Mass notification systems can consist of fully independent systems with minimal or no interface with the building fire alarm system, systems that report trouble and supervisory signals through the fire alarm system, systems that share audible and visible notification circuits and appliances with the fire alarm system, or combination mass notification and fire alarm systems.

A.24.4.3.1.2(6) Other systems could include wide-area mass notification, distributed recipient mass notification, and regional and national alerting.

A.24.4.3.2.1 Authorized personnel could include building occupants who can readily access and originate messages in emergency situations. Depending on the individual facility, use of the mass notification system to originate non-emergency messages could also be permitted. The selection of authorized personnel should be based on a risk assessment and the building emergency response plan.

A.24.4.3.2.2 Authorized personnel could effect message initiation over the mass notification system from either a emergency command center or a secondary (backup) control station(s). In cases where clusters of facilities within the same geographical region exist, one or more regional control stations could effect message initiation. The mass notification system could permit activation of messages originated by mobile sentries and roving patrols using wireless activation devices. Since it is common practice to allow mass notification systems to be utilized for "nonemergency" messages, the emergency command center should incorporate a clearly marked and easy to operate means to distinguish between emergency and non-emergency use. Comprehensive training and a fail-safe default to the emergency mode of operation should be employed to ensure that no actual emergency message gets transmitted as a non-emergency broadcast.

A.24.4.3.2.3 As a general practice, the number of message selection switches included as part of the operating controls should be limited, so that authorized personnel can utilize the system with only minimal familiarity. This, of course, could be a different matter on an industrial or college campus where trained individuals are likely to be very familiar with the operation and use of the system. In that case, more selection switches could be beneficial.

A.24.4.3.2.5 It is recognized that there can be benefit for users at the ACU to identify which specific location is currently in control. This can be indicated through visual means or through an audible location code. This can be especially useful for emergency responders utilizing the ACU to know which remote location is in control. If incorporated into a system, such features can be enabled or disabled by authorized personnel or as directed through the risk analysis.

A.24.4.3.2.10 During emergencies, building occupants should periodically receive an audible clue that the emergency notification given by the mass notification system is still in effect. This also can help building occupants and emergency response personnel recognize that the mass notification system is overriding fire alarm notification appliances. The audible signal could consist of a simple signal such as a chirp of sufficient duration to be recognized by the usual building occupants and, typically, by occupants who are not hearing disabled.

A.24.4.3.3.1 The mass notification system could permit activation of messages originated by mobile sentries and roving patrols using wireless activation devices.

A.24.4.3.3.4 Generally, each separate building should be provided with a separate in-building mass notification system; however, some facilities (such as a campus-type high school with multiple separate buildings) might be more effectively served by a single in-building mass notification system. Alternately, a risk analysis could determine that a wide-area mass notification system provides the optimal capability for mass notification.

A.24.4.3.4.1 Alternate methods that achieve the desired statistical availability could be deemed acceptable in lieu of monitoring the integrity of circuits, signaling channels, or communication pathways where consistent with the risk analysis and emergency response plan.

A.24.4.3.5.1 It is recognized that there are circumstances in which the security and protection of system documents could require measures other than as prescribed in 24.4.3.5. Where such conditions have been identified, the stakeholders should clearly identify what and how system documents should be maintained to satisfy the integrity of this section.

A.24.4.3.5.2.1 A customized form developed around the particular system that contains applicable information might be used. The form should not contain information or items that are not applicable to the particular system.

A.24.4.3.8 The risk analysis should identify what emergency situations will take priority over the fire alarm evacuation signal. Should a tornado warning for the area take priority over an active fire in the building? Should a breach of security at the campus entry gate take priority over an active fire in the building? If a manual fire alarm pull box has been activated, it might be a terrorist action to have people leave the building and walk into an exterior threat. In such a case, mass notification input is intended to override the fire alarm evacuation signals to redirect the occupants based on the conditions.

A.24.4.3.10.2 Devices such as gas or chemical sensors and detectors, weather alert signals, or other such signals can be desirable to connect to the mass notification system to provide a faster response to emergency conditions.

A.24.4.3.11 Refer to 24.4.3.2 for requirements related to operation of the system by authorized personnel. It is recognized that, based on the risk analysis, control equipment and circuits could need different levels of protection for different facilities. Access to the fire alarm/mass notification interface should be consistent with the action outlined in the emergency response plan. It could have been prior practice in some jurisdictions to locate the fire alarm control unit in the main lobby of a facility. However, it might not be appropriate to locate the mass notification system autonomous control unit within the lobby if the general public would have access to deactivate mass notification system components. Based on the risk analysis, it could be appropriate to locate the autonomous control unit within a secured room while providing local operating consoles for use by other authorized personnel.

A.24.4.3.13.1 Mass notification systems can include a system local operating console(s) for authorized occupants to readily access and originate messages in emergency and non-emergency situations. The quantity and location(s) of an LOC(s) should be determined by the risk analysis and the facilities emergency response plan.

A.24.4.3.14.1 The following is an example scheme for message prioritization, from highest (1) to lowest (5), for consideration during the risk analysis:

(1) Live voice messages from personnel in the building should be the highest priority. If systems provide control locations that are usable by nonauthorized personnel, these controls should be disabled or overridden during emergency operations.

(2) Automatic fire alarm messages/other high priority messages as determined by risk analysis criteria.

(3) External messages originated by a wide-area mass notification system.

(4) Message priority for emergency conditions such as severe weather warnings, gas leaks, chemical spills, and other hazardous conditions should be determined by risk analysis criteria and defined in the emergency response plan.

(5) Non-emergency messages, such as general announcements and time function signaling (work breaks, class change, etc.), should have the lowest priority.

A.24.4.3.14.6(2) Unless the risk analysis determines otherwise, the fire alarm system should always be automatically returned to normal functionality. If the fire alarm system is automatically returned to normal functionality, the building emergency response plan should state that no user intervention is required. When manual intervention is required to return the fire alarm system to normal, specific instructions should be in place in the emergency response plan explaining how the fire alarm system notification appliances should be reactivated. These instructions should be located at the fire alarm and mass notification control units. Individuals responsible for manually returning the fire alarm system to normal should be properly trained in the procedure.

A.24.4.3.18 Care in location and placement is critical to the survivability of the textual visible appliance and maximizing its effectiveness. Locate the textual visible appliance away from direct sunlight or direct local area lighting. Avoid locating the textual visible appliance near heating and air-conditioning ducts.

A.24.4.3.20 The video display can be a video appliance used to facilitate mass notification. Information displayed could be video, graphic, text, or audio. Information can be transmitted over a video distribution network, MATV, or CATV system. These messages can be standardized or customized for specific applications or situations. Dynamic text elements can be derived from secure data or updated in real time, either locally or remotely. Messages can be controlled by authorities to update and alter content with manual overrides from authorized security, police, and so forth to ensure up-to-date and real-time information. The same can be accomplished with remote control from an emergency command center. Examples of interfaces used for real-time control include USB, Ethernet, RS-232, and GPI.

A.24.4.3.22.1.3 Where automatic transmission is required to a supervisory station, it should be performed in accordance with the emergency response plan. The purpose for disabling or overriding the fire alarm system notification appliances during simultaneous fire and mass notification events is so that occupants will not receive conflicting messages and fail to respond correctly. Fire alarm notification that should be overridden during a mass notification system activation could include audible notification appliances, visible notification appliances, textual notification appliances, and video notification appliances.

A.24.4.3.22.3.1 As part of the risk analysis and emergency response plan, consideration should be given to future interfacing in-building mass notification systems with a wide-area mass notification system if it does not presently exist. In-building mass notification systems should be designed to allow future interface with a wide-area mass notification system.

A.24.4.3.23.1 A combined system can include an autonomous control unit and fire alarm control unit supplied from different manufacturers or placed in separate equipment enclosures; however, the autonomous control unit and fire alarm control unit should be integrated in their controls and performance to meet the requirements of this Code.

A.24.4.4 Wide-area mass notification systems are generally installed to provide real-time information to outdoor areas. These systems are normally provided with, and operated from, two or more emergency command centers. Communications between emergency command centers and in-building mass notification systems is provided. Communications between the emergency command centers and regional or national command systems could also be provided. Wide-area mass notification systems are often those such as campus giant voice systems, military base public address systems, civil defense warning systems, large outdoor visible displays, and so forth.

A.24.4.4.2 A commonly used method of protecting against unauthorized changes using multiple levels of password protection can be described as follows (in ascending levels of access):

(1) *Access Level 1.* Access by persons who have a general responsibility for safety supervision, and who might be expected to investigate and initially respond to an alarm or trouble signal.
(2) *Access Level 2.* Access by persons who have a specific responsibility for safety, and who are trained to operate the control unit.
(3) *Access Level 3.* Access by persons who are trained and authorized to take control over a given area of a site to allow local paging, which might be different from that of another area. Note: This might require a higher form of access to the local control.
(4) *Access Level 4.* Access by persons that serve in a system administrator capacity and are authorized to make changes to the system and its associated software.

A.24.4.4.3 A wide-area mass notification system could have the capability to communicate with other notification systems on the site, such as the telephone alerting system, paging system, cell phone, pager, PDA activation, e-Blast, message scrolling, reverse 911, fax transmission, and highway advisory radio and sign control system (used for dynamic control of radio information and traffic signs for emergency information and traffic management).

A.24.4.4.4.2 High power speaker arrays should be designed with directional characteristics that will minimize the distortion of voice signals by interface from other zones and will minimize the transmission of voice or tone signals into environmentally sensitive areas or off the site.

A.24.4.4.4.2.1(B) Refer to Annex D for more information on speech intelligibility and how it is predicted.

Normal weather conditions should be specified as appropriate for the geographic location.

In outdoor areas, such as in industrial areas with many multi-story buildings, the maximum distance of personnel from an outdoor speaker often has to be significantly reduced to retain acceptable intelligibility of the voice message. Speakers that provide directional capability should be used. These can be mounted on building exteriors if the speakers do not radiate unacceptable levels of sound into the building on which they are mounted.

At some sites, it could be necessary to control the amount of sound that propagates in undesirable directions, such as into civilian communities adjacent to the site boundaries or into wildlife areas with protected or endangered animal species. Additionally, in some areas, it might be necessary to mount wide-area mass notification speakers on the side of a building while simultaneously preventing an unacceptable increase in that building's interior noise levels.

A.24.4.4.4.2.4 At a minimum, the high power speaker array controller should be located above known high water level during historic floods. In northern states, the high power speaker array should be located above known snow levels. When selecting high power speaker arrays, care should be taken to ensure the equipment is rated to operate between the high and low temperature range and other anticipated environmental conditions for the geographical location of installation. The system designer should inquire about this information as part of the risk analysis.

A.24.4.4.4.4.2 High power speaker arrays should be mounted not to exceed the OSHA and FEMA Publication CPG-17 for occupational noise exposure limits or an absolute limit of 123 C-weighted decibels (dBC) as referenced in FEMA to anyone in the immediate vicinity of the speakers.

A.24.4.4.4.6 High power speaker arrays and their supporting structures should have a minimum design wind speed of 100 miles/hr [161 km/hr (86.8 kn)]. The supporting structure should be sized to accommodate the static and dynamic loads produced by the sound systems and all attachments. Seismic loads are generally site specific.

A.24.4.5 Distributed recipient mass notification systems are enterprise-class systems for the management of, and mass distribution of, emergency notification messages within buildings, throughout installations, across entire geographical regions, or throughout a worldwide military command. Using distributed recipient mass notification systems, designated system operators would be able to rapidly and reliably inform appropriate personnel of homeland security levels (including chemical, biological, radiological, and nuclear threats; hazardous weather conditions; and many other critical events), possibly with near real-time response capability.

A distributed recipient mass notification system is meant to communicate to a wide range of targeted individuals and groups. These systems might use mass dialing systems, including reverse 911, email, SMS, or other directed communications methods to broadcast information. They might also use wired or wireless networks for one- or two-way communications and/or control between a building or area and an emergency services organization (information, command, and control).

Distributed recipient mass notification systems could be capable of centrally tracking, in real time, all alerting activities for each individual recipient, including sending, receiving, and responding to alerts, and be able to generate reports based on tracked information.

Distributed recipient mass notification systems could incorporate a predefined library of signals and messaging appropriate for, but not limited to, the following:

(1) Presidential alert message
(2) Homeland security levels
(3) Terrorism threats, watches, or warnings
(4) Evacuation routes
(5) Emergency directives
(6) Personnel recall requirements
(7) Federal, DOD, police, fire, or locally /installation-specific warning and notification requirements
(8) Amber alerts

The distributed recipient mass notification system could be capable of monitoring emergency notifications from multiple data sources [Commercial Mobile Alert System (CMAS), National Weather Service, Emergency Managers Weather Information Network (EMWIN), Naval Meteorology and Oceanography (METOC), and others as determined locally] and automatically sending out notifications to designated facilities and personnel based on predefined rules.

A mass notification system could also be capable of reaching out to all online personnel by leveraging a highly secure, redundant, Web-based IP network architecture to manage the entire mass notification process. Agencies and organizations can create role-based uses such as operators, administrators, and recipients, based on their access rights across multiple facilities, campuses, and installations. System rules could be established to determine operator permissions and actions such as creating and activating scenarios, as well as the extent and geography of alerts and delivery systems and devices that should be used. Such a Web-based mass notification system would employ an open, standards-based architecture. The system could be integrated with existing user directories to support organizational hierarchy and emergency response groups. It could be structured to allow emergency criteria–based targeting of emergency alerts.

Additionally, this annex material provides information on ongoing development of system requirements for net-centric alerting systems (NCAS) that will be based on IP technologies. This annex is not mandatory, but is provided to stimulate development of suitable requirements and standards. Consequently, user suggestions and feedback on this annex are highly encouraged and requested. Methods to ensure reliability and robustness in off-normal or emergency conditions are of particular concern. The required amount of and method for isolating alerting functions from normal, non-alerting system functions needs development.

NCAS leverage the IP network infrastructure to instantly reach those personnel who have access to nearly any IP-connected devices [such as pop-up alerts on personal computers (PC), text messages to personal data assistants (PDA) and cellular telephones, electronic mail to IP-capable cellular telephones, and voice messages to voiceover-IP (VoIP) telephones and PCs]. Additionally, NCAS could be used to activate, through a single interface, other (IP based and non-IP based) alerting systems, such as wide-area alerting systems and traditional dial-up telephone alerting systems.

NCAS can be installed independently or at a central location. In a centrally managed NCAS configuration, personnel and facilities in the regional operations center's particular area of coverage could be alerted instantly by events, either from any individual installation, or centrally from the regional operations center. Using management tools, designated operators from each installation in the region could log in via a web browser and have complete access to their own portion of the NCAS. The regional operations center would retain the ability to centrally monitor and manage all portions of the system, including supervisory and trouble conditions of the different system components and integrated components.

The NCAS would incorporate a Web-based management and alert activation application through which all operators and administrators could gain access to the system's capabilities, based on the users' permissions and the defined access policy. Such a management application would incorporate management of the alert activation flow through all delivery methods, as well as end-user management, operators' permission and access, tracking and reporting, and all administrative aspects of the system.

Distributed recipient mass notification systems could interface and interoperate with other types of mass notification capabilities, including wide-area and in-building mass notification systems. During emergencies, systems operators should not need to send notifications using multiple alerting systems. The distributed recipient mass notification system, particularly NCAS, might be able to provide the capability to integrate user interfaces and consolidate access to multiple mass notification and alerting systems.

A.24.4.5.1 Distributed recipient mass notification systems could enable the management of the notification flow, including users' management, groups targeting, operators' permissions, access policies, predefined emergency scenarios, and response tracking and reporting.

A.24.4.5.2 Distributed recipient mass notification systems could be capable of sending alert messages in a prioritized method to target recipients according to the following:

(1) Hierarchical organizational structure (as would be imported from an active directory)
(2) Organizational roles
(3) Specific distribution lists [e.g., hazardous materials (HAZMAT) response teams]
(4) Specific distribution (e.g., hearing impaired or others with impairments that warrant prioritized notification)
(5) Dynamic groups created through on-the-fly queries of the user directory
(6) Geographical locations (e.g., entire bases, zones within bases)
(7) IP addresses (required for targeting devices in specific physical locations)

A.24.4.5.2.1 Distributed recipient mass notification systems should provide mechanisms to update user and targeting data; for example, user data import, integration with personnel directories, and self-user registration.

A.24.4.5.3 Distributed recipient mass notification systems could use a Web-based user interface, support locally designated standard network ports and protocols, and provide open interfaces to support interoperability, such as eXtensible markup language (XML) and common alerting protocol (CAP) based emergency messages. *(See OASIS Standard CAP-V1.2, OASIS Common Alerting Protocol version 1.2.)*

A.24.4.5.5 Distributed recipient mass notification systems would be capable of sending alert messages to end-users (recipients) via multiple delivery methods, including the following:

(1) Audio-visual network alerts to desktops and laptops via desktop pop-up
(2) Text alerts to mobile phones and pagers
(3) Text alerts to electronic mail (e-mail) clients
(4) Audio alerts to phones
(5) Audio alerts to existing wide-area or building voice and or mass notification systems
(6) Network alerts to any other IP-connected devices via standard XML and CAP protocols

The system could be extendable to support additional delivery methods in the future as this technology develops.

A.24.4.5.6 A distributed recipient mass notification system could support multiple server and multiple site configurations to achieve a "hot standby" failover configuration (i.e., no down time in case of failure in a single server), as well as to support higher load scenarios (e.g., more users). This could be accomplished with premises-based systems or hosted configurations.

Backup configuration can either be a net-centric system architecture located behind internet firewalls or hosted off-site, outside the owner's internet firewall utilizing a hosted software and hardware configuration operated and maintained by DRMNS provider(s), or incorporate features of both configurations.

A.24.5.1 Two-way, in-building emergency services communications systems are used by fire fighters, police, and other emergency services personnel. This does not preclude equipment outside of the protected premises.

A.24.5.1.6 Consideration should be given to the type of telephone handset that fire fighters use in areas where high ambient noise levels exist or areas where high noise levels could exist during a fire condition. Push-to-talk handsets, handsets that contain directional microphones, or handsets that contain other suitable noise-canceling features, can be used.

A.24.5.1.19 Two-way, in-building wired emergency services communications systems are intended to provide emergency service personnel and designated building occupants with a supervised, reliable communication system that is completely independent of other in-building communication systems. The survivability of two-way, in-building wired emergency services communications systems is paramount as they are intended for use during and throughout the duration of a fire or other emergency event. This kind of functionality requires that measures are taken to ensure that the system is designed, installed, and maintained in such a manner that they can survive and function under extreme conditions.

A.24.5.2 The use of radio communication enhancement systems has become prevalent throughout the country.

Safety features and flexibilities of radio systems include:

(1) Allowing full building coverage to facilitate communications from any point within the building, in case access to the telephone jack is compromised.
(2) Allowing communications to be conducted between emergency responders in the field to allow quicker dissemination of safety and emergency information.
(3) Each emergency responder typically will carry an individual radio, allowing for each individual to provide information or request assistance individually, which can be important if members of crews separate from each other during an incident.
(4) Radio systems allow for "fire fighter down" emergency calls in case of injury, where, by pushing a single button, a call is placed to a central location to initiate a roll call in order to determine the emergency responder who has been injured and requires assistance.
(5) Radio systems can employ an emergency call where, by pushing a single button, an emergency responder call jump to the next radio given system access to allow wide-range communication of a superseding emergency, such as building structure failure, failure of a fire pump or standpipe system, or other emergency that could cause a change in operational strategies.

A.24.5.2.4 Modulation technologies include analog and digital modulation.

It is important that interoperability be developed and maintained when implementing analog and digital two-way radio systems. The simplest means to gaining a measure of interoperability with analog two-way radio systems is programming into a radio existing, operational channels from agencies that are adjacent to each other geographically and that operate in the same public safety frequency band. To gain interoperability with digital two-way radio systems, systems and devices that are (APCO) Project 25 (P25) compatible can be used. Project 25 is a standard for the manufacturing of interpretable digital two-way wireless communications systems and devices. A P25 radio system provides interoperability, because it incorporates a common air interface and a multi-band excitation vocoder that converts speech into a digital bit stream. P25 defines standard modes of radio operation to enable multi-vendor interoperability such as trunking, encryption, over-the-air rekeying, and so forth. Formally, P25 specifications are defined in the ANSI/TIA/EIA 102 suite of standards.

All homeland security funding promotes interoperable communications and recommends adherence to open architecture technologies and P25 standards.

A.24.5.2.4.2 There is currently an ongoing national effort to eliminate current interference issues between cellular carriers and public safety bands in the 800 MHz band. This effort could revise the actual frequencies for public agencies within this band. The public safety radio enhancement system design should be capable of being changed to accommodate updated frequencies in order to allow maintenance of the minimum system design criteria.

A.24.5.2.5.4(1) All repeaters, transmitters, receivers, and signal boosters should be installed and operated in a manner consistent with Title 47, CFR. Within these regulations is a mandatory requirement that repeaters, transmitters, and signal boosters have Federal Communications Commission (FCC) "certification." Receivers do not normally have a FCC certification requirement but must comply with other applicable FCC regulations. FCC certification is a formal procedure that verifies the equipment meets certain minimum FCC technical specifications. Each brand and model type is issued a distinct FCC certification number. Use of repeaters, transmitters, or signal boosters that do not have an existing FCC-issued certification is a violation of federal law, and users are subject to fine and/or imprisonment. A label displaying the exact FCC certification number must be placed in a visible place on the equipment itself.

FCC certification verification can be obtained from any FCC office or online (https://fjallfoss.fcc.gov/oetcf/eas/reports/genericsearch.cfm).

A.24.5.2.5.5.2 The battery requirement of 12 hours for the public safety radio enhancement system is purposely longer than the 5-minute performance requirement for general evacuation and the 15-minute performance requirement for emergency voice/alarm communication systems. This is due to the primary mission of these systems, where the fire alarm system's primary mission is to assist fire detection and occupant egress, and the public safety radio enhancement system's primary mission is to assist fire department operations, which might take longer than occupant egress.

A.24.5.2.6.2 Due to the longer backup battery requirement for the public safety radio communications enhancement system, it is recognized that the fire alarm system might not be available to provide monitoring of radio system signals, including low-battery signals. Therefore, redundant status annunciation is required to provide local signals to the incident commander or his/her designee at the fire command center.

A.24.5.3 "Areas of refuge" or "areas of rescue assistance" are areas that have direct access to an exit, where people who are unable to use stairs can remain temporarily in safety to await further instructions or assistance during emergency evacuation or other emergency situation. It is, therefore, important that a method to communicate between that remote location and a central control point where appropriate action for assistance can be initiated.

A.24.5.3.1 Generally, the building code or engineer specification will provide the specifics on the required locations of the remote area of refuge (area of rescue assistance) stations, as well as the central control point. Requirements found in 24.5.3 should be coordinated with the requirements of the building code in force.

A.24.5.3.4 In order to ensure a timely response to a call for assistance, the call is to be forwarded to a constantly attended approved location, such as a supervising station, 911 communications center, or other monitoring location.

A.24.6 An emergency communications system information, command, and control is intended to include wired or wireless networks for one- or two-way communications and/or control between a building or area and an emergency command center and could include an emergency services organization or public alarm reporting system. In a very basic configuration, a system and the receiving facility could be a supervising station system. However, there can be more complex systems that allow control of building systems and communication to building occupants from a remote location, including a municipal or other public alarm reporting command center or possibly even from a mobile command vehicle using secure communications.

A.24.6.1 For the purposes of this chapter, an emergency command center is considered to be a mass notification system facility(s), with communications and control equipment serving more than one building, where responsible authorities receive information from premises sources or systems, or from (higher level) regional or national sources or systems, and then disseminate appropriate information to a building, multiple buildings, outside campus areas, municipalities, or a combination of these in accordance with the emergency response plan established for the premises. A mass notification system could include at least one emergency command center with optional secondary/alternate emergency command centers.

A.24.6.1.1 The location of the emergency command center should be coordinated with the first responders. The primary emergency command center should be located at the command post, emergency operations center, or some such similar location. A redundant emergency command center, if required, should be located at a physically separate location, such as a police station, fire station, or similar facility.

Generally, the primary emergency command center should be housed in a building or portion of a building separated from the rest of the facility and having a 2-hour fire-resistive-rated separation.

The mass notification system might require activation of messages originated by mobile sentries and roving patrols using wireless activation devices. In cases where clusters of facilities within the same geographical region exist, one or more regional control stations might also exercise control.

A.24.6.1.4 The emergency command center should be staffed by qualified personnel who would monitor the system and take action appropriate to the emergency response plan established for the specific premises.

A.24.6.1.4.2 It is imperative that individuals expected to initiate or deliver emergency messages be properly trained in the expected operations. Individuals must be familiar with the equipment, its location, and functions if they will be expected to react properly in an emergency. In an emergency situation, people only react according to instinct or habit. If the individual has not had proper and repeated training over the emergency expectations, they could lack the proper instinct or habit.

Reading an employee manual is generally not an effective means of training for an emergency. To be effective, training must be reinforced with multiple means such as text, audio, visual, and, most importantly, hands-on experience. Regular drills allowing for delivery of live messages indicating an emergency condition is important. Many people have a very difficult time communicating clearly and effectively in an emergency situation when they are excited or fearful. If live messages are to be effective, they must be short, to the point, and in a calm tone conveying exactly what is expected. Screaming into the microphone, for instance, would not be appropriate. Actual message content will depend on the emergency response plan in place for the respective business and the response to an unfolding event. Situations such as an intruder in a building have become more common today and, as such, should be considered and planned for.

A.24.6.3 Different messages or signals could be prerecorded or live voice, tones, and so forth.

A.24.6.6 Text notification via wireless devices and desktop computer notification could be an effective means for delivering mass notification messages to multiple recipient groups. Supplementary wireless text messaging could be effective in reaching remote personnel. Desktop notification is particularly effective when more complex information must be conveyed, and it can be a cost-effective interim solution prior to, but not in lieu of, installing an in-building mass notification system.

A.24.7 The risk analysis forms the basis for the emergency response plan.

Ensuring accurate information dissemination to the right people, at the right place, and at the right time is essential to the mitigation of threat actions and consequences. Trained personnel are charged with making such decisions in real time. Quite often, the instructions provided to personnel in affected areas pertain to acting in specific defensive ways so as not to expose them to danger. A typical example is the case of a chemical or biological agent attack wherein the right response is to relocate to secure areas within the building while sealing doors and windows and shutting down air intakes, rather than to leave the building and be exposed to the attacking agent.

In cases of bomb threats, where specific information is available, directions for evacuation are to be given; these directions require more specificity than simply the instruction "Evacuate the building." In most cases, the evacuation route might depend on threat intelligence and is likely to be different from that specified in an emergency response plan. Most people can tell where the fire comes from but do not always know where the bomb is. Automatic evacuation of a building, a common procedure in cases of a fire, is to be avoided, since it might expose personnel to even greater danger.

One of the reasons for implementing a mass notification system is the threat of terrorism. Terrorism attacks tend to be well organized and are often planned with details to inflict the widest degree of damage that is possible. The mass notification system must be designed to withstand various attack scenarios and survive even if some damage has already occurred.

Each design of a mass notification system should be specific to the nature and anticipated risks of each facility for which it is designed. Although this chapter outlines some specific criteria and/or limitations, each design should be based on recognized performance-based design practices.

The mass notification system should take into account various considerations, such as those indicated in this chapter.

The particular design might or might not incorporate these provisions.

Considerations for developing a mass notification system are as follows:

(1) Specific design for the facility
(2) Account for anticipated risks
(3) Use of live and/or prerecorded messaging
(4) Interfacing with other building emergency communications systems
(5) Interfacing with wide-area notification systems
(6) Ability to control the HVAC and access control systems
(7) Access to system components
(8) Survivability of the system
(9) Communication link redundancy and security
(10) Redundancy and security of the emergency command center
(11) Ability to customize and add to prerecorded message library
(12) Messages should be tailored to the situation and audience
(13) Scripted messages for live voice messages
(14) Proper training of individuals that operate the system

A.24.7.2 The design professional(s) as part of the design team should be experienced in multiple areas considered essential for conducting the risk analysis and performance design based on the scope and size of the project. Areas of experience can include, but are not limited to:

(1) Applying recognized performance-based design concepts,
(2) Conducting hazard and operability studies
(3) Technical aspects of fire alarm system design
(4) Technical aspects of emergency communication systems
(5) Security risks and/or terrorist threats
(6) Building code requirements and limitations with respect to egress
(7) Human response to emergency conditions
(8) Development of emergency response plans
(9) Other qualifications relative to the needs of the user/risk

The design professional(s) will often be a part of the engineering design team preparing project documents and specifications. However, the design professional can work for or be obtained by a qualified installation company. The design professional should be bound by professional licensing guidelines to ensure that the risk analysis is conducted in an objective manner based on user needs and not based on product or employment.

A.24.7.6.3 Communication and coordination between and among the various members of the design team is an important element to achieving the goals for performance of the system.

A.24.7.6.6 The *Guide to Performance Based Design*, published by the Society of Fire Protection Engineers, provides guidance on the elements of a design brief.

A.24.8.2 The minimum documentation requirements of 24.8.1 should be used as a guide to include sufficient documentation depending on the size and complexity of the additions or modifications.

A.26.1 Table A.26.1 provides a tool for users of the Code to easily and systematically look up requirements for protected premises, central station service, remote supervising station, and proprietary supervising station alarm systems.

Table A.26.1 Alarm System Performance Criteria

Attribute	Protected Premises Fire Alarm System	Central Station Service Alarm System	Remote Supervising Station Alarm System	Proprietary Supervising Station Alarm System
Applicability	All fire alarm systems	Supervising station service provided by a prime contractor. There is a subscriber (26.3.2, 26.3.3, and 26.3.4).	Where central station service is neither required nor elected, properties under various ownership monitored by a remote supervising station (26.5.1.1 and 26.5.1.2)	Supervising station monitoring contiguous or noncontiguous properties under one ownership and responsible to the owner of the protected property (26.4.2.1 and 26.4.2.2)
Listing	Equipment listed for the use intended (10.3)	Equipment listed for the use intended (10.3). Compliance documentation (26.3.4).	Equipment listed for use intended (10.3)	Equipment listed for use intended (10.3)
Design	According to Code by experienced persons (10.5.1)	According to Code by experienced persons (10.5.1)	According to Code by experienced persons (10.5.1)	According to Code by experienced persons (10.5.1)
Compatibility	Detector devices pulling power from initiating or signaling circuits listed for control unit (10.3.3)	Detector devices pulling power from initiating or signaling circuits listed for control unit (10.3.3)	Detector devices pulling power from initiating or signaling circuits listed for control unit (10.3.3)	Detector devices pulling power from initiating or signaling circuits listed for control unit (10.3.3)
Performance and limitations	85% and 110% of the nameplate rated input voltage, 32°F (0°C) and 120°F (49°C) ambient temperature, 85% relative humidity at 85°F (29.4°C) (10.3.5)	85% and 110% of the nameplate rated input voltage, 32°F (0°C) and 120°F (49°C) ambient temperature, 85% relative humidity at 85°F (29.4°C) (10.3.5)	85% and 110% of the nameplate rated input voltage, 32°F (0°C) and 120°F (49°C) ambient temperature, 85% relative humidity at 85°F (29.4°C) (10.3.5)	85% and 110% of the nameplate rated input voltage, 32°F (0°C) and 120°F (49°C) ambient temperature, 85% relative humidity at 85°F (29.4°C) (10.3.5)
Documentation	Authority having jurisdiction notified of new or changed specifications, wiring diagrams, battery calculations, floor plans. Statement from contractor that system meets manufacturer's published instructions and NFPA requirements (7.5.2). Record of completion (7.5.6). Results of evaluation required in 23.4.3.3.	Authority having jurisdiction notified of new or changed specifications, wiring diagrams, battery calculations, floor plans. Statement from contractor that system meets manufacturer's published instructions and NFPA requirements (7.5.2). Record of completion (7.5.6). Results of evaluation required in 23.4.3.3.	Authority having jurisdiction notified of new or changed specifications, wiring diagrams, battery calculations, floor plans. Statement from contractor that system meets manufacturer's published instructions and NFPA requirements (7.5.2). Record of completion (7.5.6). Results of evaluation required in 23.4.3.3.	Authority having jurisdiction notified of new or changed specifications, wiring diagrams, battery calculations, floor plans. Statement from contractor that system meets manufacturer's published instructions and NFPA requirements (7.5.2). Record of completion (7.5.6). Results of evaluation required in 23.4.3.3.
Supervising station facilities	None	UL 827-compliant for the supervising station and any subsidiary station (26.3.5.1 and 26.3.5.2)	Communications centers or other location acceptable to the authority having jurisdiction (26.5.3)	Fire-resistive, detached building or cut-off room not near or exposed to hazards. Access restricted, NFPA 10, 26-hour emergency lighting (26.4.3).
Testing and maintenance	Chapter 14	Chapter 14. Pass code must be provided to place system into test mode (26.3.8.5.6).	Chapter 14	Chapter 14

(continues)

Table A.26.1 *Continued*

Attribute	Protected Premises Fire Alarm System	Central Station Service Alarm System	Remote Supervising Station Alarm System	Proprietary Supervising Station Alarm System
Runner service	No	Yes Alarm — arrive at the protected premises within 2 hours where equipment needs to be reset. Guard's tour — 30 minutes. Supervisory — 2 hours. Trouble — 4 hours. *(26.3.8)*	No	Yes Alarm — arrive at the protected premises within 2 hours where equipment needs to be reset. Guard's tour — 30 minutes. Supervisory— 2 hours. Trouble — 4 hours. *(26.4.6.6)*
Operations and management requirements	None	Prime contractor provides all elements of central station service under a variety of contractual arrangements *(26.3.2)*	None	Supervising station is under same ownership and management responsibility as premises being supervised
Staff	None	Minimum of two persons on duty at supervising station. Operation and supervision primary task *(26.3.7)*.	Minimum of two persons on duty at supervising station at all times. Other duties permitted per the authority having jurisdiction *(26.5.5)*.	Two operators of which one may be the runner. When runner is not in attendance at station, time between contact not to exceed 15 minutes. Primary duties are monitoring alarms and operations of station *(26.4.5)*.
Monitor supervisory signals	Control unit and command center *(10.14.1 and 10.14.2)*	Control unit, command center, and central station *(10.14.1 and 10.14.2)*	Control unit, command center, and remote supervising station *(10.14.1 and 10.14.2)*	Control unit, command center, and proprietary supervising station *(10.14.1 and 10.14.2)*
Retransmission of signals	None	Alarm to public service communications center and subscriber. Supervisory, trouble, and guard service to designated personnel *(26.3.8)*.	Alarm to public service communications center when monitored privately. Supervisory and trouble signals to owner's designated representative *(26.5.6)*.	Alarm to public service communications center and plant brigade. Supervisory, trouble, and guard service to designated personnel *(26.4.6.6)*.
Retransmission time	None	Alarm — immediate. Supervisory — immediate. Guard's tour supervisory — without unreasonable delay. Trouble — immediate. *(26.3.8)*	Alarm — immediate. Supervisory — immediate. Trouble — immediate. *(26.5.6)*	Alarm — immediate. Supervisory — immediate. Guard's tour supervisory — at once. Trouble — immediate. *(26.4.6.6)*
Records	Current year and 1 year after *(7.7.1)*	Complete records of all signals received must be retained for at least 1 year. Reports provided of signals received to authority having jurisdiction in a form it finds acceptable *(10.3.9)*.	At least 1 year *(26.5.7.1)*.	Complete records of all signals received shall be retained for at least 1 year. Reports provided of signals received to authority having jurisdiction in a form it finds acceptable *(26.4.7)*.

A.26.1.1 Supervising station alarm systems include the equipment at the protected premises as well as the equipment at the supervising station itself. While the operational requirements relating to the signals sent off-premises fall under the scope of Chapter 26, the requirements of Chapter 23 also apply. For example, for protected premises fire alarm systems, refer to Figure A.26.1.1.

A.26.2.1 The term *immediately* in this context is intended to mean "without unreasonable delay." Routine handling should take a maximum of 90 seconds from receipt of an alarm signal.

A.26.2.3.1(1) It is recognized that individual fire departments will have preference on whether verification is used in certain occupancies based on many variables such as department-specific staffing or response protocols, occupancy staffing, and occupancy risk. This section allows the fire authority to specifically select those occupancies where verification is allowed.

A.26.2.3.1(4) The 90-second allowance for a supervising station to call the protected premise to verify the validity of the received alarm signal is independent from the time allowed for the supervising station to initiate the retransmission to the communications center.

A.26.2.3.1(6) It is important to notify the communications center that an alarm signal was verified and that fire conditions exist at the protected premises or that some other type of an emergency exists. Fire departments typically have a substantially larger response for confirmed structure fires.

A.26.2.3.1(7) If an alarm signal cannot be reliably confirmed as a nuisance alarm, then it should be immediately retransmitted. This might include situations where no contact is made within the premises, or where the persons within the premises cannot verify the source of the alarm within the allowable 90 seconds, or other related scenarios.

A.26.2.3.2 When verification of a fire alarm signal results in a signal not being reported to the communications center, it is important that fire department personnel be made aware of the alarm and the reason for nondispatch so that problematic systems can be identified.

A.26.2.5.2 Scheduled impairments include interruptions caused by construction or building damage. In addition, natural disasters can result in long-term system impairments that are not intended to require 24-hour reminders.

A.26.2.7 Changing where signals go from an existing to a new or different supervising station facility is sometimes done simply by changing a call-forward phone number. Or, within a supervising station, a new receiving computer and software can be constructed and lines changed over. Often, the account data are manually entered into the new system. Sometimes the data are transferred electronically. Errors can be made, causing the supervising station to get undefined alarms or incorrect account data, resulting in incorrect response by the supervising station. When such changes are made, the only viable way to ensure correct operation is to conduct an end-to-end test.

A.26.3.2 There are related types of contract service that often are provided from, or controlled by, a central station but that are neither anticipated by, nor consistent with, the provisions of 26.3.2. Although 26.3.2 does not preclude such arrangements, a central station company is expected to recognize, provide for, and preserve the reliability, adequacy, and integrity of those supervisory and alarm services intended to be in accordance with the provisions of 26.3.2.

A.26.3.4 The terms *certificated* and *placarded*, which appeared in previous editions of *NFPA 72*, were considered by some to be too specific to two listing organizations and were replaced with more generic wording. The concept of providing documentation to indicate ongoing compliance of an installed system continues to be reflected by the current language.

A.26.3.4.2(2) The record of completion (*see Chapter 10*) can be used to fulfill this requirement.

A.26.3.4.5 It is the prime contractor's responsibility to remove all compliance markings (certification markings or placards) when a service contract goes into effect that conflicts in any way with the requirements of 26.3.4.

A.26.3.4.6 The prime contractor should be aware of statutes, public agency regulations, or certifications regarding alarm systems that might be binding on the subscriber. The prime contractor should identify for the subscriber which agencies could be an authority having jurisdiction and, if possible, advise the subscriber of any requirements or approvals being mandated by these agencies.

The subscriber has the responsibility for notifying the prime contractor of those private organizations that are being designated as an authority having jurisdiction. The subscriber also has the responsibility to notify the prime contractor of changes in the authority having jurisdiction, such as where there is a change in insurance companies. Although the responsibility is primarily the subscriber's, the prime contractor should also take responsibility for seeking out these private authority(ies) having jurisdiction through the subscriber. The prime contractor is responsible for maintaining current records on the authority(ies) having jurisdiction for each protected premises.

The most prevalent public agency involved as an authority having jurisdiction with regard to alarm systems is the local fire department or fire prevention bureau. These are normally city or county agencies with statutory authority, and their approval of alarm system installations might be required. At the state level, the fire marshal's office is most likely to serve as the public regulatory agency.

The most prevalent private organizations involved as authorities having jurisdiction are insurance companies. Others include insurance rating bureaus, insurance brokers and agents, and private consultants. It is important to note that these organizations have no statutory authority and become authorities having jurisdiction only when designated by the subscriber.

With both public and private concerns to satisfy, it is not uncommon to find multiple authorities having jurisdiction involved with a particular protected premises. It is necessary to identify all authorities having jurisdiction in order to obtain all the necessary approvals for a central station alarm system installation.

A.26.3.6.6 Two telephone lines (numbers) at the central station connected to the public switched telephone network, each having its own telephone instrument connected, and two telephone lines (numbers) available at the communications center to which a central station operator can retransmit an alarm meet the intent of this requirement.

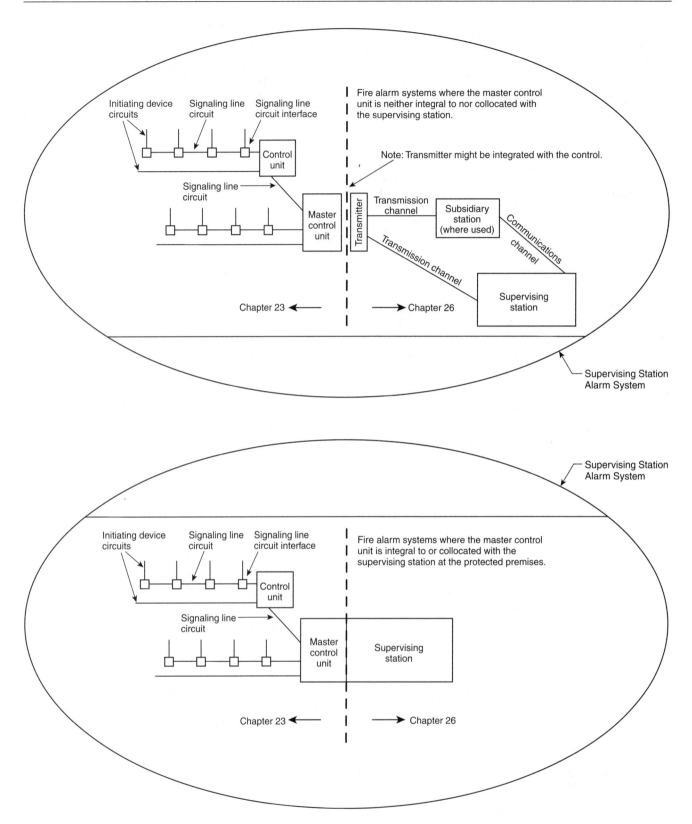

FIGURE A.26.1.1 Supervising Station Alarm System.

A.26.3.8.1.2(1) The term *immediately* in this context is intended to mean "without unreasonable delay." Routine handling should take a maximum of 90 seconds from receipt of an alarm signal by the central station until the initiation of retransmission to the communications center.

A.26.3.8.3 It is anticipated that the central station will first attempt to notify designated personnel at the protected premises. When such notification cannot be made, it might be appropriate to notify law enforcement or the fire department, or both. For example, if a valve supervisory signal is received where protected premises are not occupied, it is appropriate to notify the police.

A.26.3.8.3(1) The term *immediately* in this context is intended to mean "without unreasonable delay." Routine handling should take a maximum of 4 minutes from receipt of a supervisory signal by the central station until the initiation of communications with a person(s) designated by the subscriber.

A.26.3.8.4(1) The term *immediately* in this context is intended to mean "without unreasonable delay." Routine handling should take a maximum of 4 minutes from receipt of a trouble signal by the central station until initiation of the investigation by telephone.

A.26.3.8.5.3 The term *immediately* in this context is intended to mean "without unreasonable delay." Routine handling should take a maximum of 4 minutes from receipt of a trouble signal by the central station until initiation of the investigation by telephone.

A.26.4.3.1 Consideration should be given to providing the following features for a proprietary supervising station location:

(1) Fire resistive construction meeting the requirements of adopted building codes
(2) Air handling systems isolated from common building systems

A.26.4.4.3 Proprietary station procedures should include periodic review of nonrestored signals. One method for such a review could be by the use of equipment that would automatically redisplay the information.

A.26.4.6.4 It is the intent of this Code that the operator within the proprietary supervising station should have a secure means of immediately retransmitting any signal indicative of a fire to the public fire department communications center. Automatic retransmission using an approved method installed in accordance with Sections 26.3 through 26.5, and Chapter 27 is the best method for proper retransmission. However, a manual means can be permitted to be used, consisting of either a manual connection following the requirements of Section 26.3, Section 26.5, and Chapter 27, or, for proprietary supervising stations serving only contiguous properties, a means in the form of a municipal fire alarm box installed within 50 ft (15 m) of the proprietary supervising station in accordance with Chapter 27 can be permitted.

A.26.4.6.5 Regardless of the type of retransmission facility used, telephone communications between the proprietary supervising station and the fire department should be available at all times and should not depend on a switchboard operator.

A.26.5.2(1) Chapter 14 permits the building owner or his designated representative to perform these services if they are qualified. In this situation, the documentation could be a declaration of qualification signed by the building owner. Multiple service providers are permitted.

A.26.5.3 As a minimum, the room or rooms containing the remote supervising station equipment should have a 1-hour fire rating, and the entire structure should be protected by an alarm system complying with Chapter 23.

A.26.5.3.1.3 A listed central station might be considered an acceptable alternate location for receipt of fire alarm, supervisory, and trouble signals.

A.26.5.3.2 A listed central station might be considered an acceptable alternate location for receipt of trouble signals.

A.26.6.1 Refer to Table A.26.6.1 for communications methods.

Table A.26.6.1 was revised by a tentative interim amendment (TIA). See page 1.

A.26.6.2.2 It is not the intent of Section 26.6 to limit the use of listed equipment using alternate communications methods, provided these methods demonstrate performance characteristics that are equal to or superior to those technologies described in Section 26.6. Such demonstration of equivalency is to be evidenced by the equipment using the alternate communications methods meeting all the requirements of Chapter 10, including those that deal with such factors as reliability, monitoring for integrity, and listing. It is further expected that suitable proposals stating the requirements for such technology will be submitted for inclusion in subsequent editions of this Code.

A.26.6.2.3 The communications cloud is created by multiple telephone lines and multiple paths on the Internet. Under these circumstances, the requirements of Chapters 10 and 14, as required by 26.1.2, do not apply to devices comprising the communications cloud.

Table A.26.6.1 Communications Methods for Supervising Stations

Criteria	Performance-Based Technologies 26.6.3.1	Digital Alarm Communicator Systems 26.6.3.2	Two-Way Radio Frequency (RF) Multiplex Systems 26.6.3.3.1	One-Way Private Radio Alarm Systems 26.6.3.3.2
FCC approval when applicable	Yes	Yes	Yes	Yes
Conform to *NFPA 70, National Electrical Code*	Yes	Yes	Yes	Yes
Monitoring for integrity of the transmission and communications channel	Monitor for integrity	Both the premises unit and the system unit monitor for integrity in a manner approved for the means of transmission employed. A single signal received on each incoming DACR line once every 6 hours.	Systems are periodically polled for end-to-end communications integrity.	Test signal from every transmitter once every 24 hours
Annunciate, at the supervising station, the degradation and restoration of the transmission or communications channel	Within 60 minutes for a single communication path and within 6 hours for multiple communication paths	Within 4 minutes using alternate phone line to report the trouble	Not exceed 90 seconds from the time of the actual failure	Only monitor the quality of signal received and indicate if the signal falls below minimum signal quality specified in Code
Redundant communication path where a portion of the transmission or communications channel cannot be monitored for integrity		Employ a combination of two separate transmission channels alternately tested at intervals not exceeding 6 hours	Redundant path not required — supervising station always indicates a communications failure	Minimum of two independent RF paths must be simultaneously employed
Interval testing of the backup path(s)		When two phone lines are used, test alternately every 6 hours. Testing for other back-up technologies, see 26.6.3.2.1.4(B).	Backup path not required	No requirement, because the quality of the signal is continuously monitored
Annunciation of communication failure or ability to communicate at the protected premises	Systems where the transmitter at the local premises unit detects a communication failure, the premises unit will annunciate the failure within 200 seconds of the failure.	Indication of failure at premises due to line failure or failure to communicate after from 5 to 10 dialing attempts	Not required — always annunciated at the supervising station that initiates corrective action	Monitor the interconnection of the premises unit elements of transmitting equipment, and indicate a failure at the premises or transmit a trouble signal to the supervising station.
Time to restore signal-receiving, processing, display, and recording equipment	Where duplicate equipment not provided, spare hardware required so a repair can be effected within 30 minutes.	Spare digital alarm communicator receivers required for switchover to backup receiver in 30 seconds. One backup system unit for every five system units.	Where duplicate equipment not provided, spare hardware required so a repair can be effected within 30 minutes	Where duplicate equipment not provided, spare hardware required so a repair can be effected within 30 minutes
Loading capacities for system units and transmission and communications channels	512 independent alarm systems on a system unit with no backup. Unlimited if you can switch to a backup in 30 seconds.	See Table 26.6.3.2.2.2(C) for the maximum number of transmitters on a hunt group in a system unit	512 buildings and premises on a system unit with no backup. Unlimited if you can switch to a backup in 30 seconds.	512 buildings and premises on a system unit with no backup. Unlimited if you can switch to a backup in 30 seconds.
End-to-end communication time for an alarm	90 seconds from initiation of alarm until displayed to the operator and recorded on a medium from which the information can be retrieved	Off-hook to on-hook not to exceed 90 seconds per attempt. 10 attempts maximum. 900 seconds maximum for all attempts.	90 seconds from initiation until it is recorded	90% probability to receive an alarm in 90 seconds, 99% probability in 180 seconds, 99.999% probability in 450 seconds
Record and display rate of subsequent alarms at supervising station	Not slower than one every 10 additional seconds	Not addressed	When any number of subsequent alarms come in, record at a rate not slower than one every additional 10 seconds	When any number of subsequent alarms come in, record at a rate not slower than one every additional 10 seconds

Table A.26.6.1 *Continued*

Criteria	Performance-Based Technologies 26.6.3.1	Digital Alarm Communicator Systems 26.6.3.2	Two-Way Radio Frequency (RF) Multiplex Systems 26.6.3.3.1	One-Way Private Radio Alarm Systems 26.6.3.3.2
Signal error detection and correction	Signal repetition, parity check, or some equivalent means of error detection and correction must be used.	Signal repetition, digital parity check, or some equivalent means of signal verification must be used.	Not addressed	Not addressed
Path sequence priority	No need for prioritization of paths. The requirement is that both paths are equivalent.	The first transmission attempt uses the primary channel.	Not addressed	Not addressed
Carrier diversity		Where long distance service (including WATS) is used, the second telephone number must be provided by a different long distance service provider where there are multiple providers.	Not addressed	Not addressed
Throughput probability		Demonstrate 90% probability of a system unit immediately answering a call or follow the loading Table 16.6.3.2.2.2(C). One-way radio backup demonstrates 90% probability of transmission.	Not addressed	90% probability to receive an alarm in 90 seconds, 99% probability in 180 seconds, 99.999% in probability 450 seconds
Unique premises identifier	If a transmitter shares a transmission or communication channel with other transmitters, it must have a unique transmitter identifier.	Yes	Yes	Yes
Unique flaws	From time to time, there may be unique flaws in a communication system. Unique requirements must be written for these unique flaws.	If call forwarding is used to communicate to the supervising station, verify the integrity of this feature every 4 hours.	None addressed	None addressed
Signal priority	If the communication methodology is shared with any other usage, all alarm transmissions must preempt and take precedence over any other usage. Alarm signals take precedence over supervisory signals.	Chapter 1 on fundamentals requires that alarm signals take priority over supervisory signals unless there is sufficient repetition of the alarm signal to prevent the loss of an alarm signal.	Chapter 1 on fundamentals requires that alarm signals take priority over supervisory signals unless there is sufficient repetition of the alarm signal to prevent the loss of an alarm signal.	Chapter 1 on fundamentals requires that alarm signals take priority over supervisory signals unless there is sufficient repetition of the alarm signal to prevent the loss of an alarm signal.
Sharing communications equipment on premises	If the transmitter is sharing on-premises communications equipment, the shared equipment must be listed for the purpose (otherwise the transmitter must be installed ahead of the unlisted equipment).	Disconnect outgoing or incoming telephone call and prevent its use for outgoing telephone calls until signal transmission has been completed.	Not addressed	Not addressed

A.26.6.3.1 Certain legacy technologies (active multiplex, McCulloh, directly connected non-coded and private microwave) have been removed from the text of the document. Existing systems utilizing these technologies are acceptable, because all these technologies also comply with the general provisions of 26.6.3.1.

The object of 26.6.3.1 is not to give details of specific technologies but rather give basic operating parameters of the transmission supervison rates of technologies. The following list represents examples of current technologies that can be configured to meet the requirements and the intent of 26.6.3.1:

(1) Transmitters using IP (Internet Protocol)
(2) IP transmission over the public open Internet or over private IP facilities maintained by an organization for its own use
(3) Transmitters using various (non-dialup) digital cellular technology

Wired IP Transmission. There are two types of wired IP transmission devices. One where the IP network is connected directly to the fire alarm control unit (integrated IP or native IP). The second uses an intermediary module that can include the following:

(1) IP dialer capture module
(2) IP data capture module (such as RS-232, keypad bus, RS-485)
(3) Relay contact monitoring module

Devices referred to as "IP dialer capture modules" (an IP communicator used with a DACT) are transmission devices that connect to the DACT output of the fire alarm control unit and convert the output data stream to IP (Internet protocol). As such, they are considered to use IP technology in their connection to the IP network. Therefore they should be treated in this Code under the requirements of 26.6.3.1, performanced-based technologies, and not under the requirements of 26.6.3.2, digital alarm communicator systems.

Digital Cellular. To accommodate an increase in the demand for mobile wireless communications as well as introducing new services over that same network, wireless voice communications no longer utilizes dedicated connections to pass voice band frequencies. Current ubiquities methods such as 2G and 3G have established a new and different environment to operate. In place of the voice band, the voice conversation is converted into a stream of bits and packaged within data packets that conform to messaging protocols, packets are addressed to a destination point, delivered into the network, received by the destination point, and are converted back into an intelligible voice-grade message. The message exchange through this wireless data network is done through well known defined protocols such as "Global System for Mobile" communications (GSM) for voice communications as well as Code Division Multiple Access (CDMA) for both voice and data and General Packet Radio Service (GPRS) mobile data services. These protocols have been developed to operate in an optimal way for the intended application. For example, GSM is used to efficiently establish voice-grade connections that deliver an appropriate level of intelligible voice quality, but might not be good enough to pass tones that represent data. Data transmission is better served by GPRS and CDMA where a connection into the wireless network is always available without having to "dial," and large amounts of data can be efficiently transmitted. However the data passed using GPRS or CDMA is not that of coded tones such as DTMF (Contact ID), but is computer type messages similar to IP.

When using digital cellular, a DACT might or might not be used.

For example, the digital cellular device might be used to backup the DACT or, if properly supervised, be used as a stand-alone device. If used, the DACT is connected to a digital cellular radio device that connects to the cellular network by means of an antenna. The digital cellular radio device is constantly connecting to the wireless network and is always ready to attempt to transmit to a destination address without having to "dial" a number. The radio device recognizes that the alarm panel is attempting to place a call by the DACT's "off-hook" signaling. The radio device accepts the DACT tone signaling, converts it into a packeted data stream, and sends the packets into the wireless network for delivery to a pre-assigned destination address.

A.26.6.3.1.7 When considering a fire alarm system utilizing a single communication path to the supervising station, consideration should be given to the risk exposure that results from the loss of that path for any period of time and for any reason. Some of these outages can be regular and predicable and others transitory.

A.26.6.3.1.14 Most communications equipment is not specifically listed for fire alarm applications, but is listed in accordance with applicable product standard for general communications equipment and is acceptable.

A.26.6.3.1.15 This requirement is to ensure that communications equipment will operate for the same period of time on secondary power as the alarm control unit.

A.26.6.3.2.1.1 Special care should be used when connecting a DACT to a digital service such as DSL or ADSL. Filters or other special equipment might be needed to communicate reliably.

A.26.6.3.2.1.3 To give the DACT the ability to disconnect an incoming call to the protected premises, telephone service should be of the type that provides for timed-release disconnect. In some telephone systems (step-by-step offices), timed-release disconnect is not provided.

A.26.6.3.2.1.3(C) A DACT can be programmed to originate calls to the DACR telephone lines (numbers) in any alternating sequence. The sequence can consist of single or multiple calls to one DACR telephone line (number), followed by transmissions on the alternate path or any combination thereof that is consistent with the minimum/maximum attempt requirements in 26.6.3.2.1.3(C).

A.26.6.3.2.1.4(B)(6) Where two telephone lines (numbers) are used, care should be taken to assign the primary DACT telephone line (number) to a nonessential telephone line (number) at the protected premises so that the primary line used in the premises is not unnecessarily interrupted.

A.26.6.3.2.1.5(4) Where two telephone lines (numbers) are used, care should be taken to assign the primary DACT telephone line (number) to a nonessential telephone line (number) at the protected premises so that the primary line used in the premises is not unnecessarily interrupted.

A.26.6.3.2.1.5(7) Because call forwarding requires equipment at a telephone company central office that could occasionally interrupt the call forwarding feature, a signal should be initiated whereby the integrity of the forwarded telephone line (number) that is being called by DACTs is verified every 4 hours. This can be accomplished by a single DACT, either in service or used solely for verification, that automatically initiates and completes a transmission sequence to its associated DACR every 4 hours. A successful signal transmission sequence of any other type within the same 4-hour period should be considered sufficient to fulfill this requirement.

Call forwarding should not be confused with WATS or 800 service. The latter, differentiated from the former by dialing the 800 prefix, is a dedicated service used mainly for its toll-free feature; all calls are preprogrammed to terminate at a fixed telephone line (number) or to a dedicated line.

A.26.6.3.2.2.2(A) The timed-release disconnect considerations as outlined in A.26.6.3.2.1.3 apply to the telephone lines (numbers) connected to a DACR at the supervising station.

It might be necessary to consult with appropriate telephone service personnel to ensure that numbers assigned to the DACR can be individually accessed even where they are connected in rotary (a hunt group).

> Paragraph A.26.6.3.2.2.2(C)(1)(d) was revised and A.26.6.3.2.2.2(F) was deleted by a tentative interim amendment (TIA). See page 1.

A.26.6.3.2.2.2(C) In determining system loading, Table 26.6.3.2.2.2(C) can be used, or it should be demonstrated that there is a 90 percent probability of incoming line availability. Table 26.6.3.2.2.2(C) is based on an average distribution of calls and an average connected time of 30 seconds per message. Therefore, where it is proposed to use Table 26.6.3.2.2.2(C) to determine system loading, if any factors are disclosed that could extend DACR connect time so as to increase the average connect time, the alternate method of determining system loading should be used. Higher (or possibly lower) loadings might be appropriate in some applications.

(1) Some factors that could increase (or decrease) the capacity of a hunt group follow:

   (a) Shorter (or longer) average message transmission time can influence hunt group capacity.
   (b) The use of audio monitoring (listen-in) slow-scan video or other similar equipment can significantly increase the connected time for a signal and reduce effective hunt group capacity.
   (c) The clustering of active burglar alarm signals can generate high peak loads at certain hours.
   (d) Inappropriate scheduling of 6-hour test signals can generate excessive peak loads.

(2) Demonstration of a 90 percent probability of incoming line availability can be accomplished by the following in-service monitoring of line activity:

   (a) Incoming lines are assigned to telephone hunt groups. When a DACT calls the main number of a hunt group, it can connect to any currently available line in that hunt group.
   (b) The receiver continuously monitors the "available" status of each line. A line is available when it is waiting for an incoming call. A line is unavailable for any of the following reasons:
       i. Currently processing a call
       ii. Line in trouble
       iii. Audio monitoring (listen-in) in progress
       iv. Any other condition that makes the line input unable to accept calls

   (c) The receiver monitors the "available" status of the hunt group. A hunt group is available when any line in it is available.
   (d) A message is emitted by the receiver when a hunt group is unavailable for more than 1 minute out of 10 minutes. This message references the hunt group and the degree of overload.

A.26.6.3.3.1.4 The intent of the plurality of control sites is to safeguard against damage caused by lightning and to minimize the effect of interference on the receipt of signals. The control sites can be co-located.

A.26.6.3.3.2 Originally the concept of one-way private radio was codified for a one-way system requiring at least two receiving towers or repeaters. Other similar systems have been developed that use this basic principle. Among them is the concept of the "mesh network" where a premises transmitter can access multiple nearby transmitters.

It is difficult to reliably test redundant paths on a mesh radio network without significant impact on the system and considerable efforts of time and personnel.

A remedy is to have the mesh network system equipment generate a report at the protected premises or supervising station showing redundant pathways. Additionally, the mesh system equipment at the protected premises and at the supervising station periodically determine the number of viable redundant paths and generate a trouble signal whenever the number falls below two paths, as is required by 26.6.3.3.2.

A.26.6.3.3.2.2 It is intended that each RAT communicate with two or more independently located RARSRs. The location of such RARSRs should be such that they do not share common facilities.

NOTE: All probability calculations required for the purposes of Chapter 17 should be made in accordance with established communications procedures, should assume the maximum channel loading parameters specified, and should further assume that 25 RATs are actively in alarm and are being received by each RARSR.

A.26.6.4.1 The signal information can be permitted to be provided in coded form. Records can be permitted to be used to interpret these codes.

A.26.6.4.1(4) Any signal that would dictate a different response, such as carbon monoxide alarms or mass notification alarms, should be individually identifiable so the appropriate response to the event can be initiated. There are more types of alarms and other signals that are being received at supervising stations and that require different responses by supervising station operators. These signals could be other than fire, but still life safety in nature, and must be uniquely identified because their signal is indicative of a different response.

A.26.6.4.2 In order to expedite repairs, it is recommended that spare modules, such as printed circuit boards, displays, or printers, be stocked at the supervising station.

A.26.6.4.3 For all forms of transmission, the maximum time to process an alarm signal should be 90 seconds. The maximum time to process a supervisory signal should be 4 minutes. The time to process an alarm or supervisory signal is defined as that time measured from receipt of a signal until retransmission or subscriber contact is initiated.

When the level of traffic in a supervising station system reaches a magnitude such that delayed response is possible, even if the loading tables or loading formulas of this Code are not exceeded, it is envisioned that it will be necessary to employ an enhanced method of processing.

For example, in a system where a single DACR instrument provided with fire and burglar alarm service is connected to multiple telephone lines, it is conceivable that, during certain periods of the day, fire alarm signals could be delayed by the security signaling traffic, such as opening and closing signals. Such an enhanced system would perform as follows, upon receipt of a signal:

(1) Automatically process the signals, differentiating between those that require immediate response by supervising station personnel and those that need only be logged
(2) Automatically provide relevant subscriber information to assist supervising station personnel in their response
(3) Maintain a timed, unalterable log of the signals received and the response of supervising station personnel to such signals

A.27.1.8 Auxiliary alarm systems include the equipment at the protected premises as well as the equipment connecting it to the public emergency alarm reporting system. While the operational requirements relating to the signals sent off-premises fall under the scope of Chapter 27, the requirements of Chapter 23 also apply.

A.27.2.1 When choosing from available options to implement a public emergency alarm reporting system, the operating agency should consider which of the choices would facilitate the maximum reliability of the system, where such a choice is not cost prohibitive.

A.27.2.3 Consideration should be given to the fact that devices could be installed in areas that are exposed to higher or lower temperatures, moisture, or other environmental conditions that could be more severe than ambient conditions found in a typical building. As an example, equipment could be installed inside a building in a boiler room, basement, attic, and so forth, where temperatures actually exceed ambient conditions outside the building. It is recommended that the authority having jurisdiction consider all possible installation locations and environmental conditions and that the equipment selected be designed to operate within the most extreme conditions to which it could be exposed.

A.27.3.7.4.1(2) An example of an organization providing public emergency alarm reporting system certification is the International Municipal Signal Association. Note that this reference is for information purposes only. Information concerning the product or service has been provided by the manufacturer or other outside sources, and the information concerning the product or service has not been independently verified, nor has the product or service been endorsed or certified by NFPA or any of its technical committees.

A.27.4.3.3 Nonfederal radio frequencies are licensed by the Federal Communications Commission. Federal radio frequencies are assigned by the NTIA. Most frequencies available for FCC licensing require frequency coordination in order to limit interference from other users. Authorities having jurisdiction should use licensed, coordinated radio frequencies for wireless networks in order to minimize interference.

Outside of the United States similar regulatory bodies provide coordination and licensing such as Industry Canada.

A.27.5.2.5.1(1) Figure A.27.5.2.5.1(1) illustrates a Form 4A arrangement.

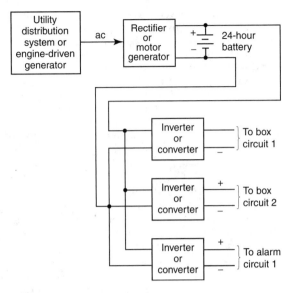

FIGURE A.27.5.2.5.1(1) Form 4A.

A.27.5.2.5.1(2) Figure A.27.5.2.5.1(2) illustrates a Form 4B arrangement.

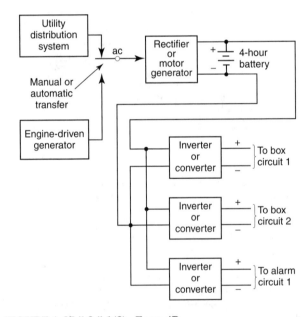

FIGURE A.27.5.2.5.1(2) Form 4B.

A.27.5.2.5.1(3) Figure A.27.5.2.5.1(3) illustrates a Form 4C arrangement. Refer to NFPA 1221, *Standard for the Installation, Maintenance, and Use of Emergency Services Communications Systems.*

A.27.5.5.1.1.1 Figure A.27.5.5.1.1.1 illustrates a Type A receiving network.

A.27.5.5.1.4 Figure A.27.5.5.1.4 illustrates the separate functional requirements and power source requirements for systems that function with wireless network repeater systems in accordance with 27.5.5.1.4.

A.27.5.5.3.3 See A.27.6.6.2.

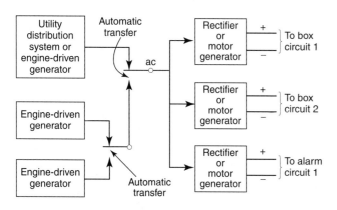

FIGURE A.27.5.2.5.1(3) Form 4C.

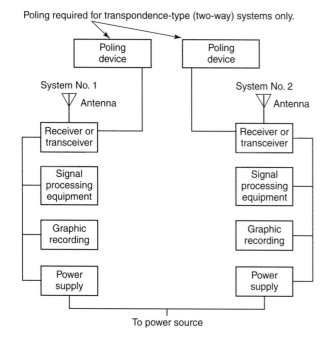

FIGURE A.27.5.5.1.1.1 Type A System Receiving Networks.

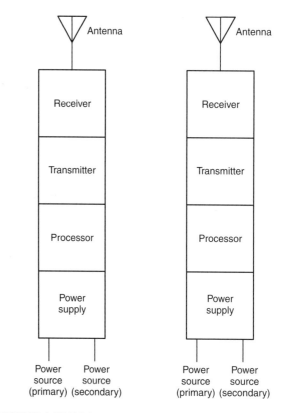

FIGURE A.27.5.5.1.4 Repeater Wireless Network/System.

A.27.6.1.4 If the operating mechanism of a box creates sufficient sound to be heard by the user, the requirements are satisfied.

A.27.6.2 Publicly accessible alarm boxes were commonly referred to as "street boxes" in previous editions of the Code. Applications of these boxes are no longer limited to street locations.

A.27.6.2.1.6 Where the intent is for complete coverage, it should not be necessary to travel in excess of one block or 500 ft (150 m) to reach a box. In residential areas, it should not be necessary to travel in excess of two blocks or 800 ft (240 m) to reach a box.

A.27.6.2.1.10 The current supply for designating lights at boxes should be secured at lamp locations from the local electric utility company.

Alternating-current power can be permitted to be superimposed on metallic fire alarm circuits for supplying designating lamps or for control or actuation of equipment devices for fire alarm or other emergency signals, provided that the following conditions exist:

(1) Voltage between any wire and ground or between one wire and any other wire of the system does not exceed 150 volts, and the total resultant current in any line circuit does not exceed ¼ ampere.
(2) Components such as coupling capacitors, transformers, chokes, or coils are rated for 600-volt working voltage and have a breakdown voltage of at least twice the working voltage plus 1000 volts.
(3) There is no interference with fire alarm service under any conditions.

A.27.6.1 There are three types of alarm boxes covered under Chapter 27. They are the publicly accessible box, auxiliary box, and master box.

(1) The publicly accessible box has a manual control that can be operated by the public. This type of alarm box is typically located outside on a pole or building and was previously called a street box. The box type was renamed because it is not necessarily located on or near a street.
(2) An auxiliary box is part of an auxiliary alarm system and can be automatically activated either by initiating devices in limited applications or by a protected premises alarm system (Chapter 23). An auxiliary box can be located inside or outside a building.
(3) The master box is a combination box that can be manually operated (publicly accessible) and automatically activated by the auxiliary alarm system (auxiliary box). The master box is typically located outside on a pole or building.

A.27.6.3.1.3 Figure A.27.6.3.1.3 shows the interconnecting wiring that is intended to meet Level 2 survivability.

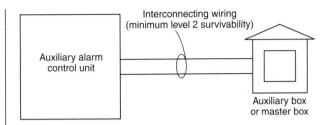

FIGURE A.27.6.3.1.3 Interconnecting Wiring from Auxiliary Alarm System to Auxiliary Box or Master Box.

A.27.6.3.2.2.1(1) The local energy-type system [*see Figure A.27.6.3.2.2.1(1)(a) and Figure A.27.6.3.2.2.1(1)(b)*] is electrically isolated from the public emergency alarm reporting system and has its own power supply. The tripping of the transmitting device does not depend on the current in the system. In a wired circuit, receipt of the alarm by the communications center when the circuit is accidentally opened depends on the design of the transmitting device and the associated communications center equipment (i.e., whether or not the system is designed to receive alarms through manual or automatic ground operational facilities). In a radio box–type system, receipt of the alarm by the communications center depends on the proper operation of the radio transmitting and receiving equipment.

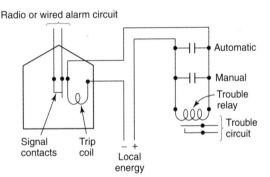

FIGURE A.27.6.3.2.2.1(1)(a) Local Energy-Type Auxiliary Alarm System — Radio or Wired.

A.27.6.3.2.2.1(2) The shunt-type system [*see Figure A.27.6.3.2.2.1(2)(a) and Figure A.27.6.3.2.2.1(2)(b)*] is electrically connected to, and is an integral part of, the public emergency alarm reporting system. A ground fault on the auxiliary circuit is a fault on the public emergency alarm reporting system circuit, and an accidental opening of the auxiliary circuit sends a needless (or false) alarm to the communications center. An open circuit in the transmitting device trip coil is not indicated either at the protected property or at the communications center. Also, if an initiating device is operated, an alarm is not transmitted, but an open circuit indication is given at the communications center. If a public emergency alarm reporting system circuit is open when a connected shunt-type system is operated, the transmitting device does not trip until the public emergency alarm reporting system circuit returns to normal, at which time the alarm is transmit-

ted, unless the auxiliary circuit is first returned to a normal condition.

Additional design restrictions for shunt-type systems are found in laws or ordinances.

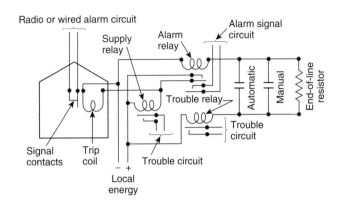

FIGURE A.27.6.3.2.2.1(1)(b) Local Energy-Type Auxiliary Alarm System with Supply and Alarm Relay — Radio or Wired.

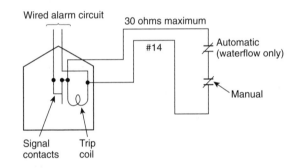

FIGURE A.27.6.3.2.2.1(2)(a) Shunt-Type Auxiliary Alarm System (Permitted).

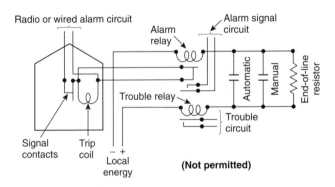

FIGURE A.27.6.3.2.2.1(2)(b) Shunt-Type Auxiliary Alarm System (Not Permitted).

A.27.6.3.2.2.1(2)(g) See Figure A.27.6.3.2.2.1(2)(b).

A.27.6.6.2 The transmission of an actual emergency-related message, initiated at the same time it is preselected for a test message, and, in turn, preempts said test message, must satisfy the intent of 27.6.6.2.

A.27.6.6.7 Examples of priority levels as follows:

(1) Priority 1 — fire
(2) Priority 2 — ECS
(3) Priority 3 — medical
(4) Priority 4 — supervisory
(5) Priority 5 — monitored for integrity signals
(6) Priority 6 — tamper
(7) Priority 7 — test

Additionally, within each signal category, additional priorities can be required such as Fire 1, Fire 2, Fire 3, and so forth.

A.27.7.1.6.2 There could be environmental conditions that neccessitate the use of rigid nonmetallic conduit.

A.27.7.3 All requirements for circuit protection do not apply to coded radio reporting systems. These systems do not use metallic circuits.

A.27.8.1 The public emergency alarm reporting system infrastructure could be used to facilitate the operation of wide area signaling, as is currently being done for emergency notification to the public in some communities and as has been done in the past for civil defense notification.

A.29.1.1 Chapter 29 does not attempt to cover all equipment, methods, and requirements that might be necessary or advantageous for the protection of lives and property from fire.

NFPA 72 is a "minimum code." This chapter provides a number of requirements related to single- and multiple-station alarms and household fire alarm systems that are deemed to be the practical and necessary minimum for average conditions at the present state of the art.

Currently Available Smoke Alarm Technology. The technologies used in currently available smoke alarms include ionization smoke detection and photoelectric detection. These detection types are defined in 3.3.269.2 and 3.3.269.4 and are further explained in A.3.3.269.2 and A.3.3.269.4. Ionization smoke detection is more responsive to invisible particles produced by most flaming fires. Photoelectric smoke detection is more responsive to the visible particles produced by most smoldering fire. Residential smoke alarms and commercial smoke detectors are currently available with either ionization technology or photoelectric technology or a combination of both technologies. The use of both technologies generally offers the advantage of providing a faster response to both flaming and smoldering fires, and is recommended for those who desire a higher level of protection than the minimum requirements of this Code.

Fatal home fires involving smoldering fires and flaming fires occur at night and during the day. It is not possible to reliably predict what type of fire will occur or at what hour of the day it will occur. Therefore, the preference of one technology over the other on the basis of the expectation of a particular type of fire (predominately smoldering or flaming) is not a sound basis for selection. While the current consensus of experts suggests that neither technology offers an advantage when the fire type is not known, there is a consensus that there would be a benefit to having both technologies since the type of fire cannot be predicted.

Based on recent analysis of the full scale fire tests documented by the National Institute of Standards and Technology in Report TN 1455-1-2008, *Performance of Home Smoke Alarms, Analysis of the Response of Several Available Technologies in Residential Fire Settings*, the minimum provisions of the Code using either technology are considered to provide an adequate level of protection for most individuals who are not intimate with the fire and are capable of self rescue. This would include occupants in the room of fire origin for both flaming and smoldering fires who escape through the normal path of egress. Protection beyond the minimum provisions of the Code using both technologies should be considered for situations involving individuals who are not capable of self rescue or who might need additional time for escape. These situations might include families where extra time is needed to awaken or assist others.

While it is true that ionization detection technology is more susceptible to nuisance alarms due to cooking, the use of this technology should not be dismissed, particularly where the additional protection of both technologies is suggested. In addition, there is no substantial evidence that suggests that either technology is more susceptible to nuisance alarms from bathroom steam. Provisions and guidance have been added to 29.8.3.4 to help minimize nuisance alarms from both sources. This is important since smoke alarms that are disabled due to frequent nuisance alarms offer no protection whatsoever. A higher level of protection would be afforded by using both technologies in all locations required by this Code with additional locations in other rooms of the dwelling. In considering this, pending the availability of smoke alarms specifically designed for nuisance alarm immunity, additional locations within 20 ft of a cooking appliance should be minimized, especially for smoke alarms using ionization technology.

While these considerations reflect the consensus of experts based on currently available test data that allows analysis of tenability along with alarm response, full scale fire testing and nuisance alarm testing of current technologies has continued and analysis of this data will also continue. In addition, new technologies are being considered with the prospect of enhanced detection response along with a higher immunity to nuisance activations. The work of the industry and the NFPA technical committee responsible for smoke alarm provisions will be ongoing.

A.29.1.2 An example of the applicable code within the NFPA set of codes and standards is NFPA *101, Life Safety Code.* Other codes such as local building codes are other examples to be considered.

The requirements of Chapter 29 are intended to apply to installations in the following new and existing locations:

(1) One- and two-family dwelling units
(2) Sleeping rooms of lodging and rooming houses
(3) Individual dwelling units of apartment buildings
(4) Guest rooms, sleeping rooms, and living areas within guest suites of hotels and dormitories
(5) Day-care homes
(6) Residential board and care facilities
(7) Other locations where applicable laws codes or standards specify a requirement for the installation of smoke alarms

A.29.1.4 Installations in manufactured homes are under the jurisdiction of The Department of Housing and Urban Development (HUD). The rules for installation are addressed in the Federal Manufactured Housing Construction Safety Standards (available at http://www.hud.gov/offices/hsg/sfh/mhs/mhshome.cfm).

A.29.2 *Fire Danger in the Home.* In 2005, fire was the third leading cause of unintentional injury deaths in the home, and the sixth leading cause of unintentional injury deaths overall (*Injury Facts*, 2007 edition, National Safety Council).

Eighty-four (84.4) percent of the fire fatalities in 2007 resulted from residential fires — 68.5 percent resulted from fires in one- and two-family dwellings, including manufactured homes, 15.0 percent were caused by apartment fires, and 0.9 percent resulted from fires in other residential occupancies ("Fire Loss in the United States during 2007," Michael J. Karter, NFPA Fire Analysis and Research Division).

Approximately half (53 percent) of the home (dwellings and apartments) fire fatalities resulted from fires reported between 11:00 p.m. and 7:00 a.m., the common sleeping hours ("Home Structure Fires," Marty Ahrens, NFPA Fire Analysis and Research Division, February 2007).

Over three-quarters (76.9 percent) of all reported fire injuries occurred in the home, with more than one-half (54.6 percent) in one- and two-family dwellings (including manufactured housing), and more than one-fifth (22.3 percent) in apartments ("Fire Loss in the United States during 2007," Michael J. Karter, NFPA Fire Analysis and Research Division).

It is estimated that each household will experience three (usually unreported) fires per decade and two fires serious enough to report to a fire department per lifetime ("A Few Fire Facts at the Household Level," NFPA Fire Analysis Division, *Fire Journal*, May 1986).

Fire Safety in the Home. NFPA 72 is intended to provide reasonable fire safety for persons in family living units. Reasonable fire safety can be produced through the following three-point program:

(1) Minimizing fire hazards
(2) Providing fire-warning equipment
(3) Having and practicing an escape plan

Minimizing Fire Hazards. This Code cannot protect all persons at all times. For instance, the application of this Code might not provide protection against the following three traditional fatal fire scenarios:

(1) Smoking in bed
(2) Leaving children home alone
(3) Cleaning with flammable liquids, such as gasoline

However, Chapter 29 can lead to reasonable safety from fire when the three-point program is observed.

Fire-Warning Equipment. There are two types of fire to which household fire-warning equipment needs to respond. One is a rapidly developing, high-heat fire. The other is a slow, smoldering fire. Either can produce smoke and toxic gases.

Family Escape Plan. There often is very little time between the detection of a fire and the time it becomes deadly. This interval can be as little as 1 or 2 minutes. Thus, this Code requires detection means to give a family some advance warning of the development of conditions that become dangerous to life within a short period of time. Such warning, however, could be wasted unless the family has planned in advance for rapid exit from their residence. Therefore, in addition to the fire-warning equipment, this Code assumes that the residents have developed and practiced an exit plan.

Planning and practicing for fire conditions with a focus on rapid exit from the residence are important. Drills should be held so that all family members know the action to be taken. Each person should plan for the possibility that exit out of a bedroom window could be necessary. An exit out of the residence without the need to open a bedroom door is essential.

Household fires are especially dangerous at night when the occupants are asleep. Fires produce smoke and deadly gases that can overcome occupants while they are asleep. Furthermore, dense smoke reduces visibility. Most fire casualties are victims of smoke and gas inhalation rather than burns. To warn against a fire, Chapter 29 provides smoke detector (alarm) requirements in accordance with 29.5.1, and the associated annex recommends heat or smoke detectors (alarms) in all other major areas.

A.29.3.3 This Code establishes minimum standards for the use of fire-warning equipment. The use of additional alarms or detectors over and above the minimum standard is encouraged. The use of additional devices can result in a combination of equipment (e.g., a combination of single- and multiple-station alarms or a combination of smoke alarms or smoke detectors that are part of a security/fire system and existing multiple-station alarms). Though a combination is allowed, one type of equipment must independently meet the requirements of the Code. Compliance with the requirements of the Code cannot rely on the combination of the following fire-warning equipment:

(1) Single-station alarms
(2) Multiple-station alarms
(3) Household fire alarm system (includes a security/fire system with smoke alarms or smoke detectors)

It is encouraged that the highest level of protection be used where possible. For example, if multiple-station alarms are added to an occupancy with compliant single-station alarms, the multiple-station alarms should be installed to replace all of the single-station alarms. Similarly, if a monitored household fire alarm system is added to a house that has compliant multiple-station alarms, monitored smoke alarms or smoke detectors should be installed to replace the multiple-station alarms or be installed to provide the same required coverage.

The responsiveness of ionization- and photoelectric-type smoke alarms depends on a number of factors, including the type of fire (smoldering, flaming), the chemistry of materials involved in the fire, and the properties of the resulting smoke. Several fire safety organizations recommend that a consumer utilize both ionization and photoelectric technologies in their home smoke alarm systems to permit the longest potential escape times for nonspecific fire situations. This will not preclude the development of new technology with equivalent performance.

A.29.3.5 The use of the distinctive three-pulse temporal pattern fire alarm evacuation signal has been recommended by this Code since 1979. It has since been adopted as both an American National Standard (ANSI S3.41, *American National Standard Audible Emergency Evacuation Signal*) and an International Standard (ISO 8201, *Audible Emergency Evacuation Signal*).

Copies of both of these standards are available from either of the following:

(1) The web at asastore.aip.org
(2) Standards Publication Fulfillment, P.O., Box 1020, Sewickly, PA 15143-9998, Tel. 412-741-1979

For information about the Acoustical Society of America, or for how and why the three-pulse temporal pattern signal was chosen as the international standard evacuation signal, contact Standards Secretariat, Acoustical Society of America, 35 Pinelawn Road, Suite 114E, Melville, NY 11747, Tel. 531-490-0215, Email: asastds@aip.org.

The standard fire alarm evacuation signal is a three-pulse temporal pattern using any appropriate sound. The pattern consists of the following in this order:

(1) An "on" phase lasting 0.5 second ±10 percent.
(2) An "off" phase lasting 0.5 second ±10 percent for three successive "on" periods.
(3) An "off" phase lasting 1.5 seconds ±10 percent *[see Figure A.29.3.5(a) and Figure A.29.3.5(b)]*. The signal should be repeated for a period appropriate for the purposes of evacuation of the building, but for not less than 180 seconds. A single-stroke bell or chime sounded at "on" intervals lasting 1 second ±10 percent, with a 2-second ±10 percent "off" interval after each third "on" stroke, is permitted *[see Figure A.29.3.5(c)]*.

The minimum repetition time is permitted to be manually interrupted.

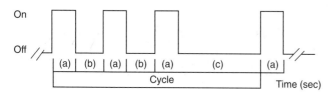

FIGURE A.29.3.5(a)   Temporal Pattern Parameters.

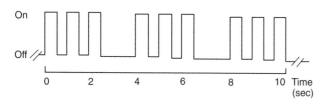

FIGURE A.29.3.5(b)   Temporal Pattern Imposed on Signaling Appliances That Emit Continuous Signal While Energized.

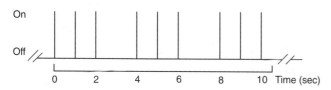

FIGURE A.29.3.5(c)   Temporal Pattern Imposed on Single-Stroke Bell or Chime.

A.29.3.5.2 It is recommended that the voice notification message be intelligible, audible, and appropriate for the hazard. Care should be taken to avoid excessive silence during the message. Figure A.29.3.5.2(a) through Figure A.29.3.5.2(c) provide examples of acceptable combinations of the emergency evacuation signal and voice messages.

A.29.3.7 Low frequency or tactile notification appliances such as bed shakers have been shown to be effective in waking those with normal hearing to profound hearing loss

[CSE NIH report, 2005; Bruck and Thomas, 2009; Bruck, Thomas, and Ball, NFPA RF report, 2007].

A.29.3.8.1 As an example, governing laws, codes, or standards might require a certain number of accommodations be equipped for those with hearing loss or other disability.

A.29.3.8.1(2) It is not the intent of this section to preclude devices that have been demonstrated through peer-reviewed research to awaken occupants with hearing loss as effectively as those using the frequency and amplitude specified in this section.

A.29.3.8.2 Tactile notification appliances such as bed shakers have been shown to be effective in waking those with normal hearing to profound hearing loss [Ashley et al., 2005, UL 1971, 1991]. Tactile signaling has been studied and found to be an effective way to alert and notify sleeping persons. However, there are many variables that have not been tested that might affect the reliability of their performance. Some of the appliance variables include the mass of the appliance, frequency of vibration, and the throw or displacement of the vibrating mass. Occupant variables that might affect the reporting of test results and the effectiveness of the appliance include the person's age, how long a person has lived with their hearing loss, and what sleep stage the person is experiencing when the appliance operates. The type of mattress might also have an effect of the performance of certain tactile appliances. Mattress variables can include thickness, firmness, memory foam, pillow tops, water beds, air beds, and motion isolation mattresses. Users of tactile appliances should be cautioned to test how well they might sense the effect of the appliance.

The Code requires both strobes and tactile appliances. Strobes can awaken sleeping persons, provide verification that there is a fire alarm condition, and serve to alert persons when they are not in contact with a tactile appliance.

A.29.3.8.2(1) As an example, governing laws, codes, or standards might require a certain number of accommodations be equipped for those with hearing loss or other disability.

A.29.4.1 Working smoke alarms cut the risk of dying in reported home structure fires in half. Victims who are intimate with the fire or are incapable of taking action to escape might not benefit from the early warning. For these people, other strategies such as protection in-place or assisted escape or rescue would be necessary.

A.29.4.2 *Family Escape Plan.* There often is very little time between the detection of a fire and the time it becomes deadly. This interval can be as little as 1 or 2 minutes. Thus, this Code requires detection means to give a family some advance warning of the development of conditions that become dangerous to life within a short period of time. Such warning, however, could be wasted unless the family has planned in advance for rapid exit from their residence. Therefore, in addition to the fire-warning equipment, this Code requires exit plan information to be furnished.

Planning and practicing for fire conditions with a focus on rapid exit from the residence are important. Drills should be held so that all family members know the action to be taken. Each person should plan for the possibility that exit out of a bedroom window could be necessary. An exit out of the residence without the need to open a bedroom door is essential.

Special Provisions for the Disabled. For special circumstances where the life safety of an occupant(s) depends on prompt rescue by others, the fire-warning equipment should include means of prompt automatic notification to those who are to be depended on for rescue.

Alarm initiation — eight T3 cycles minimum.								Two T3 cycles minimum — repeat as desired.		
T3 cycle	T3 cycle	T3 cycle	T3 cycle	T3 cycle	T3 cycle	T3 cycle	T3 cycle	Voice — 10-sec maximum	T3 cycle	T3 cycle
(1)	(2)	(3)	(4)	(5)	(6)	(7)	(8)		(1)	(2)

FIGURE A.29.3.5.2(a)   Temporal Pattern Parameters with 10-Second Voice Allowance.

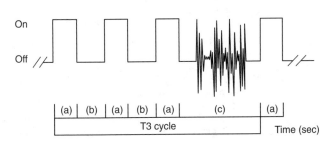

Key:
Phase (a) signal is on for 0.5 sec ±10%
Phase (b) signal is off for 0.5 sec ±10%
Phase (c) signal is off for 1.5 sec ±10% [(c) = (a) + 2(b)]
Phase (c) signal can incorporate voice notification.
Total cycle lasts for 4 sec ±10%

FIGURE A.29.3.5.2(b)   Temporal Pattern Parameters with 1.5-Second Voice Allowance.

A.29.4.2.3   The normal path of egress does not include windows or other means of escape.

A.29.4.3   Assumptions — equipment is as follows:

(1) Maintenance. Good fire protection requires that the equipment be maintained periodically. If the system owner or responsible party is unable to perform the required maintenance, a maintenance agreement should be considered.

(2) Reliability of fire alarm systems. Fire alarm systems located in dwelling units and having all of the following features are considered to have a functional reliability of 95 percent:
  (a) Utilizes a control unit
  (b) Has at least two independent sources of operating power
  (c) Monitors all initiating and notification circuits for integrity
  (d) Transmits alarm signals to a constantly attended, remote monitoring location
  (e) Is tested regularly by the homeowner and at least every 3 years by a qualified service technician

(3) Reliability of fire alarm systems without remote monitoring or with wireless transmission. Fire alarm systems for dwelling units with all of the preceding features except (d) or systems that use low-power wireless transmission from initiating devices within the dwelling units are considered to have a functional reliability of 90 percent.

(4) Reliability of other systems. Fire alarm systems for dwelling units comprised of interconnected smoke alarms where the interconnecting means is monitored for integrity are considered to have a functional reliability of 88 percent. If the interconnecting means is not supervised or the alarms are not interconnected, such systems are considered to have a functional reliability of 85 percent.

A.29.5.1   All hostile fires in dwelling units generate smoke and heat. However, the results of full-scale experiments conducted over the last several decades in the United States, using typical fires in dwelling units, indicate that detectable quantities of smoke precede detectable levels of heat in nearly all cases (NBS GCR 75-51, *Detector Sensitivity and Siting Requirements for Dwellings*, 1975; NBS GCR 77-82, *Detector Sensitivity and Siting Requirements for Dwellings Phase 2*, 1977; and NIST Technical Note 1455-1, *Performance of Home Smoke Detectors Analysis of the Response of Several Available Technologies in a Residential Setting*, 2007). In addition, slowly developing, smoldering fires can produce smoke and toxic gases without a significant increase in the room's temperature. Again, the results of experiments indicate that detectable quantities of smoke precede the development of hazardous thermal atmospheres in nearly all cases.

For the preceding reasons, the required protection in this Code utilizes smoke alarms as the primary life safety equipment for providing a reasonable level of protection against fire.

The installation of additional alarms of either the smoke or heat type should result in a higher degree of protection. Adding alarms to rooms that are normally closed off from the required alarms increases the escape time because the fire does not need to build to the higher level necessary to force smoke out of the closed room to the required alarms. As a consequence, it is recommended that the householder consider the installation of additional fire protection devices. However, it should be understood that Chapter 29 does not require additional smoke alarms over and above those called for in 29.5.1. Refer to Figure A.29.5.1(a) through Figure A.29.5.1(d) where required smoke alarms are shown.

Alarm initiation — eight T3 cycles minimum. Optional voice allowed in any T3 cycle.								Two T3 cycles minimum — repeat as desired.		
T3 cycle with voice	T3 cycle with voice	T3 cycle with voice	T3 cycle with voice	T3 cycle with voice	T3 cycle with voice	T3 cycle with voice	T3 cycle with voice	Voice — 10-sec maximum	T3 cycle with voice	T3 cycle with voice
(1)	(2)	(3)	(4)	(5)	(6)	(7)	(8)		(1)	(2)

FIGURE A.29.3.5.2(c)   Temporal Pattern Parameters with 10-Second Voice Allowance.

Where to Locate the Required Smoke Alarms. Fifty-three percent of home fire deaths were reported between 11:00 p.m. and 7:00 a.m. Persons in sleeping areas can be threatened by fires in the remainder of the unit; therefore, smoke alarms are best located in each bedroom and between the bedroom areas and the rest of the unit as shown in Figure A.29.5.1(b). In dwelling units with more than one bedroom area or with bedrooms on more than one floor, more than one smoke alarm is required, as shown in Figure A.29.5.1(c).

In addition to smoke alarms outside of the sleeping areas and in each bedroom, Chapter 29 requires the installation of a smoke alarm on each additional level of the dwelling unit, including the basement. These installations are shown in Figure A.29.5.1(d). The living area smoke alarm should be installed in the living room or near the stairway to the upper level, or in both locations. The basement smoke alarm should be installed in close proximity to the stairway leading to the floor above. Where installed on an open-joisted ceiling, the smoke alarm should be placed on the bottom of the joists. The smoke alarm should be positioned relative to the stairway so as to intercept smoke coming from a fire in the basement before the smoke enters the stairway.

Are More Smoke Alarms Desirable? The required number of smoke alarms might not provide reliable early warning protection for those areas separated by a door from the areas protected by the required smoke alarms. For this reason, the use of additional smoke alarms for those areas for increased protection is recommended. The additional areas include dining room, furnace room, utility room, and hallways not protected by the required smoke alarms. The installation of smoke alarms in kitchens, attics (finished or unfinished), or garages is not normally recommended, because these locations occasionally experience conditions that can result in improper operation.

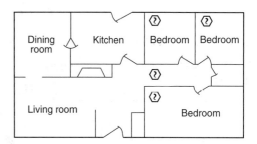

FIGURE A.29.5.1(b)   Smoke Alarm Should Be Located Between Sleeping Area and Rest of Dwelling Unit, as Well as in Each Bedroom.

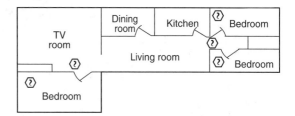

FIGURE A.29.5.1(c)   In Dwelling Units with More Than One Sleeping Area, Smoke Alarm Should Be Provided to Protect Each Sleeping Area in Addition to Smoke Alarms Required in Bedrooms.

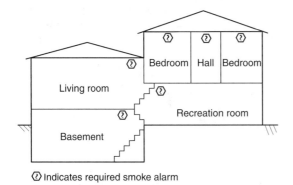

FIGURE A.29.5.1(a)   Split Level Arrangement.

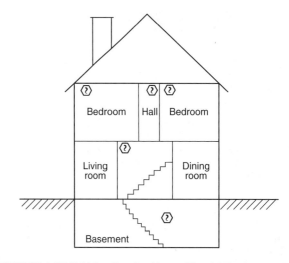

FIGURE A.29.5.1(d)   Smoke Alarm Should Be Located on Each Level in Addition to Each Bedroom.

A.29.5.1.1 Occupancies where smoke alarms are typically required include residential, residential board and care, or day-care home. The term *residential occupancy* is defined in 3.3.243 and includes one- and two-family dwellings; lodging or rooming houses; hotels, motels, and dormitories; and apartment buildings. The term *residential board and care occupancy* is defined in 3.3.242 and includes both small and large facilities. NFPA *101, Life Safety Code,* specifies a small facility to be one with sleeping accommodations for not more than 16 residents. The term *day-care home,* defined in 3.3.60, is a specific category of day-care occupancy. It should be noted that applicable laws, codes, or standards might include conditions that could impact the applicability of these requirements. The local authority should be consulted for specific details.

A.29.5.1.1(1) The term *sleeping room* applies to several occupancies including: one- and two-family dwellings; lodging or rooming houses; hotels, motels, and dormitories; apartment buildings; residential board and care facilities; and day-care homes. The term *guest room,* defined in 3.3.120, is an accommodation that includes sleeping facilities. It applies in the context of hotel and dormitory occupancies.

A.29.5.1.1(2) The term *dwelling unit* is defined in 3.3.81 and applies to one- and two-family dwellings and dwelling units of apartment buildings (including condominiums).

A.29.5.1.1(5) The term *guest suite* is defined in 3.3.121, and the term *living area* is defined in 3.3.143.

A.29.5.1.3.1 The requirements do not preclude the installation of smoke alarms on walls in accordance with 29.8.3.3. Some building configurations, such as division of rooms and open foyers or great rooms, dictate that alarms be located so that they do not cover distinctly separate 500 ft² (46 m²) areas but rather provide overlapping coverage relative to this spacing requirement.

A.29.5.2.1.1 Fire-warning performance is improved when all alarms are interconnected so that alarm notification is achieved throughout the occupiable areas. In some cases for existing construction, interconnection of alarms is specifically exempted by jurisdictional requirements. This allowance takes into consideration the cost of hard-wired interconnection.

A.29.5.2.2 One of the common problems associated with smoke alarms and detectors is the nuisance alarms that are usually triggered by products of combustion from cooking, smoking, or other household particulates. While an alarm for such a condition is anticipated and tolerated by the occupant of a dwelling unit through routine living experience, the alarm is not permitted where it also sounds alarms in other dwelling units or in common use spaces. Nuisance alarms caused by cooking are a very common occurrence, and inspection authorities should be aware of the possible ramifications where the coverage is extended beyond the limits of the dwelling unit.

A.29.7.2 The UL listing for smoke alarms addresses two categories of these devices: one for applications where sensitivity testing is not required (UTGT), and one for applications where sensitivity testing is required (UTHA). Refer to the testing requirements for these devices in Chapter 14.

A.29.7.4 The linear space rating is the maximum allowable distance between heat detectors. The linear space rating is also a measure of detector response time to a standard test fire when tested at the same distance. A higher rating corresponds to a faster response time. This Code recognizes only those heat detectors with ratings of 50 ft (15.2 m) or more.

A.29.7.4.2 A heat detector with a temperature rating somewhat in excess of the highest normally expected ambient temperature is specified in order to avoid the possibility of premature response of the heat detector to non-fire conditions.

Some areas or rooms of the dwelling unit can experience ambient temperatures considerably higher than those in the normally occupied living spaces. Examples are unfinished attics, the space near hot air registers, and some furnace rooms. This fact should be considered in the selection of the appropriate temperature rating for fixed-temperature heat detectors to be installed in these areas or rooms.

A.29.7.7.7 Such input and output devices include, but are not limited to, relay modules, notification appliances, phone dialers, system control units, heat detectors, and manual fire alarm boxes.

A.29.7.8.2.1 For RF waves traveling along the earth surface, the signal power loss (in dB), L_p, can be calculated using the following plane-earth propagation loss model:

$$L_p = 10\log\left[\frac{D_p^4}{h_{TX}^2 h_{RX}^2}\right] \quad \textbf{(A.29.7.8.2.1a)}$$

where D_p represents the distance between the transmitter and receiver and h_{TX} and h_{RX} are the heights of the transmitter and receiver, respectively, above the earth.

The plane earth propagation model is a practical simplification and requires that h_{TX}, $h_{RX} \ll D_p$. It reflects the average expected attenuation due to distance of the RF carrier for a stationary set of radios with an essentially clear line of sight. It predicts maximum communications range only in the UHF band (300 MHz to 3 GHz) and is not dependent on frequency.

Inside a building, the model can be expanded to determine the total path loss, L_T, which includes the plane earth loss, L_p (equation A.29.7.8.2.1a), and the loss due to the building materials in the propagation path, L_b, as follows:

$$L_T = 10\log\left[\frac{D_p^4}{\left(h_{TX}h_{RX}\right)^2}\right] + L_b \quad \textbf{(A.29.7.8.2.1b)}$$

If an equivalent open area test distance D_{EOAT} is defined as follows:

$$L_T = 10\log\left[\frac{D_{EOAT}^4}{\left(h_{TX}h_{RX}\right)^2}\right] \quad \textbf{(A.29.7.8.2.1c)}$$

then D_{EOAT} can be shown to be:

$$D_{EOAT} = 10^{\frac{-L_T}{40}}\sqrt{h_{TX}}\sqrt{h_{RX}} = D_p \cdot 10^{\frac{L_b}{40}} \quad \textbf{(A.29.7.8.2.1d)}$$

The D_{EOAT} function is used to calculate a test distance required to verify the functional range of wireless alarm products. As noted above in the right side of equation A.29.7.8.2.1d, the function represents two factors — one that describes the attenuation of a radio frequency signal due to plane earth propagation path loss (D_p), and one that describes the dwelling material losses (L_b) in the signal's propagation path. It is the combination of dwelling loss and propagation path loss that is used in the calculation of the test distance D_{EOAT}. The losses are expressed in dB, and the unit for distances is meter.

In reviewing average home sizes, a reliable (indoor) communication of 100 ft (30.5 m) is adequate for a majority of dwellings, based on an average house size of 2200 ft² (204 m²) [National Association of Home Builders]. Construction materials of a home (walls and floors) can attenuate an RF signal, with the RF signal being attenuated more at higher frequencies [Stone, 1997]. Communication specifications for devices of this type are typically specified as open field (no obstructions) test distances, and not in terms of attenuation. Therefore, the standard specifies a minimum open area test distance, D_{EOAT}, that the RF products must communicate. This distance is equal to 100 ft (30.5 m) (the longest straight line distance within a majority of homes) plus an additional distance that is equivalent to the attenuation of four walls and two floors (the most straight line obstructions in a majority of homes). The additional distance varies depending on the operating frequency of the product. Formulas for calculating D_{EOAT} are included below, along with examples for a number of different frequencies. These criteria are expected to yield reliable indoor communications at 100 ft (30.5 m) when used inside a majority of dwellings.

The building attenuation factor, L_b, represents the maximum attenuation value of typical floors and walls within a majority of structures. L_b is calculated using attenuation values of different materials. The following method is used to calculate L_b. The building materials attenuation coefficients specified in this application are taken from Stone, 1977. Other sources of appropriate building material attenuation coefficients may be used; however, testing organizations should apply values consistently for all products tested.

L_L = Frequency dependent attenuation value for ½ in. (13 mm) drywall

L_2 = Frequency dependent attenuation value for 1½ in. (38 mm) structural lumber

L_3 = Frequency dependent attenuation value for ¾ in. (19 mm) plywood

L_4 = Frequency dependent attenuation value for ½ in. (13 mm) glass/tile floor

L_w = Attenuation value of a wall = $2 \times L_1 + L_2$

L_f = Attenuation value of a floor = $L_1 + L_2 + L_3 + L_4$

Assuming four walls and two floors,

$$L_b = 4 \times L_w + 2 \times L_f$$

The source for the equation in 29.7.8.2.1 is Stone, W. "Electromagnetic Attenuation in Construction Materials," National Institute of Standards and Technology, NISTIR 6055, 1997.

A.29.7.8.2.4 Receiving units that stay in alarm for 30 seconds or 1 minute longer than the transmitting alarm would provide additional protection if the first alarm is damaged due to a very fast growing fire. The persisting alarm signal would provide additional notification to occupants. This option needs to be considered in light of the potential for the longer alarm signals on receiving smoke alarms being a potential nuisance to occupants during test and other nuisance alarm events.

A.29.7.9.2 Where 29.7.9.2, which provides for screening alarm signals to minimize response to false alarms, is to be implemented, the following should be considered:

(1) Was the verification call answered at the protected premises?
(2) Did the respondent provide proper identification?
(3) Is it necessary for the respondent to identify the cause of the alarm signal?
(4) Should the public service fire communications center be notified and advised that an alarm signal was received, including the response to the verification call, when an authorized respondent states that fire service response is not desired?
(5) Should the public service fire communications center be notified and advised that an alarm signal was received, including the response to the verification call, for all other situations, including both a hostile fire and no answer to the verification call?
(6) What other actions should be required by a standard operating procedure?

A.29.8.2.2 Once these limits have been exceeded, a fire alarm system should be installed.

A.29.8.3 One of the most critical factors of any fire alarm system is the location of the fire detecting devices. This annex is not a technical study. It is an attempt to provide some fundamentals on fire-warning equipment location. For simplicity, only those types of alarms or detectors recognized by Chapter 29 (e.g., smoke and heat alarms or smoke and heat detectors) are discussed. Specific mounting locations of fire-warning equipment in unoccupied or architecturally unique

areas (e.g., as in attics or in rooms with high ceilings) should be evaluated by a qualified professional.

The conclusions of the Kemano Study and FPRF Smoke Detector Spacing Requirements Report (2008) have determined revisions to smoke alarm and smoke detector mounting within 4 in. (100 mm) of a flat ceiling/wall corner are now acceptable. The studies have shown that acceptable detection performance does not depend on the 4 in. (100 mm) separation. Figure A.29.8.3 illustrates acceptable smoke alarm and smoke detector mounting locations.

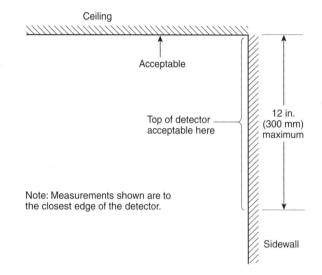

FIGURE A.29.8.3 Example of Proper Mounting for Smoke Alarms and Smoke Detectors.

A.29.8.3.1 Figure A.29.8.3.1 illustrates acceptable smoke alarm or smoke detector mounting locations for a peaked ceiling.

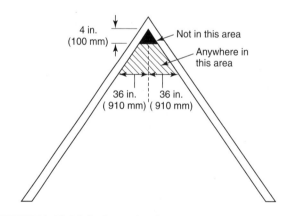

FIGURE A.29.8.3.1 Example of Proper Mounting for Alarms and Detectors with Peaked Ceilings.

A.29.8.3.2 Figure A.29.8.3.2 illustrates acceptable smoke alarm or smoke detector mounting locations for a sloped ceiling.

A.29.8.3.3 Figure A.29.8.3 illustrates acceptable smoke alarm or smoke detector mounting locations.

In those dwelling units employing radiant heating in the ceiling, the wall location is the recommended location. Radiant heating in the ceiling can create a hot air boundary layer

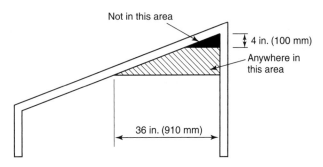

FIGURE A.29.8.3.2 Example of Proper Mounting for Alarms and Detectors with Sloped Ceilings.

along the ceiling surface, which can seriously restrict the movement of smoke and heat to a ceiling-mounted detector.

A.29.8.3.4(3) Smoke detectors and smoke alarms should be installed in those locations recommended by the manufacturer's published instructions, except in those cases where the space above the ceiling is open to the outside and little or no insulation is present over the ceiling. Such cases result in the ceiling being excessively cold in the winter or excessively hot in the summer. Where the ceiling is significantly different in temperature from the air space below, smoke and heat have difficulty reaching the ceiling and a detector that is located on that ceiling.

A.29.8.3.4(4) As per annex material located in A.29.5.1, it is not normally recommended that smoke alarms or smoke detectors be placed in kitchen spaces. This section of the code provides guidelines for safe installation if a need exists to install a smoke alarm or smoke detector in a residential kitchen space or cooking area.

Within this Code section, a fixed cooking appliance is any appliance that is intended to be permanently connected electrically to the wiring system or the fuel source. A stationary cooking appliance is any appliance that is intended to be fastened in place or located in a dedicated space, and is connected to the supply circuit or fuel source.

Smoke alarms and smoke detectors that are currently available to consumers are susceptible to particles released into the air during normal cooking procedures. If smoke alarms and smoke detectors are placed too close to the area where the cooking source originates, a high level of nuisance alarms can occur. Frequent nuisance alarms can result in an occupant disabling the smoke alarm or smoke detector.

Nuisance alarm studies show that commercially available residential smoke alarms and smoke detectors are susceptible to nuisance alarms when installed too close to cooking appliances. As the horizontal distance between the smoke alarm or smoke detectors and the cooking appliance increases, the frequency of nuisance alarms decreases. Smoke alarms or smoke detectors that use ionization smoke detection have been shown to be more susceptible to cooking nuisance alarms than those that use photoelectric smoke detection when the alarms or detectors are installed within 10 ft (3.0 m) along a horizontal smoke travel path from a cooking appliance. Smoke alarms or smoke detectors that use photoelectric smoke detection produce nuisance alarms when installed less than 10 ft (3.0 m) from a cooking appliance, though to a lesser degree.

The occurrence of the higher frequency of nuisance alarms observed in smoke alarms or smoke detectors that use ionization detection have been documented in the fire research data. Due to the differences in technology between ionization detection

and photoelectric detection, the sensitivity typically used for ionization detection is much higher than that used for photoelectric detection. This sensitivity difference is a result of each type of the detection being required to satisfy UL 217 performance tests. Removing detection technology from consideration, the frequency of nuisance alarms is solely due to the sensitivity of the detection method used. Thus, both ionization and photoelectric detector technologies will produce nuisance alarms due to cooking, but currently available smoke alarms and smoke detectors that use ionization detection typically produce more cooking-related nuisance alarms.

The higher sensitivities of currently available smoke alarms and smoke detectors that use ionization detection do provide a benefit at the expense of a potentially higher rate of cooking-related nuisance alarms. Research has demonstrated that ionization detection will typically respond faster than photoelectric detection to flaming fires, providing earlier warning to occupants that might allow for quicker intervention or faster egress. In general, the installation of smoke alarms or smoke detectors that use ionization detection will result in increased fire safety at the risk of a higher frequency of nuisance alarms. The installation of smoke alarms or smoke detectors that use photoelectric detection will result in reduced fire safety for flaming fires and a reduced risk of nuisance alarms. Based on the trade-off between faster response to fires and the frequency of nuisance alarms, detectors that utilize both technologies (i.e., ionization, photoelectric, and a combination) are allowed to be installed between 10 ft (3.0 m) and 20 ft (6.1 m) along a horizontal flow path from a standard or fixed cooking appliance if the specific detector is equipped with an alarm silencing means or is of the photoelectric-type.

Nuisance alarm studies provide data on cooking nuisances that emanate from both fixed cooking appliances and stationary cooking appliances (e.g., stove, oven) as well as portable cooking appliances (e.g., toaster). Based on these studies, which demonstrate the potential of all cooking appliances to generate nuisance sources, a zone of exclusion has been specified surrounding each stationary or fixed cooking appliance. The purpose of this zone is to limit the installation of smoke alarms and detectors in areas where stationary, fixed, or portable cooking appliances will be located within the residential kitchen space such that potential nuisance alarms are minimized. The size of the zone of exclusion is specified to attempt to take into account the unknown and transitory locations of portable cooking appliances. This zone of exclusion is determined by measuring a 10 ft (3.0 m) radial distance from the closest edge of a stationary or fixed cooking appliance. The zone of exclusion is not intended to pass through walls or doorways. Figure A.29.8.3.4(4)(a) provides an example of the zone of exclusion in a generalized residential kitchen.

If other areas of this code require that a smoke alarm or smoke detector be placed within a horizontal flow path distance between 10 ft (3.0 m) and 20 ft (6.1 m) from a stationary or fixed cooking appliance, the following method should be used to determine the distance, and only photoelectric detection or smoke alarms/detectors with alarm silencing means can be installed in this area.

To install a smoke alarm or detector between 10 ft (3.0 m) and 20 ft (6.1 m) from the cooking appliance, an installer must first determine the 10 ft (3.0 m) area of exclusion. Once the area of exclusion is determined, an installer must then determine the horizontal flow distance. This is the horizontal distance along the ceiling from the closest edge of the cooking appliance to the smoke alarm or detector. The horizontal distance can consist of line segments due to impediments, such as interior partitions. Once an impediment is met, the measurement of the distance will then continue along the new horizontal path segment until the distance requirement is met or another impediment is encountered. Figure A.29.8.3.4(4)(b) provides an example for placement outside a kitchen in a nearby hallway. Figure A.29.8.3.4(4)(c) provides another example of appropriate placement outside of a kitchen in an adjacent room.

At a horizontal flow path distance of greater than 20 ft (6.1 m), any type of smoke alarm or smoke detector can be installed.

In rare cases, a residential dwelling can be of such size and configuration that an area of exclusion of 10 ft (3.0 m) from a stationary or fixed cooking appliance excludes the placement of a smoke alarm or smoke detector required by other areas of this Code. In these cases, a smoke alarm or smoke detector using photoelectric detection can be installed at least 72 in. (1.83 m) from the fixed or stationary cooking appliance. Fig-

ure A.29.8.3.4(4)(d) provides an example of this situation in practice where a smoke alarm or smoke detector is required outside of the sleeping area, but the space is in close proximity to the kitchen space.

A.29.8.3.4(6) Studies indicate that smoke alarms and smoke detectors that use ionization detection, photoelectric detection, or a combination of ionization and photoelectric detection, are susceptible to nuisance alarms caused by steam. Little research has been done on the comparative response of these types of detection to steam. Steam particles, in general, are visible, reflect light easily, and are typically produced in a size range that would be more likely to activate a photoelectric sensor. Thus, it is required that smoke alarms and smoke detectors be installed greater than 36 in. (910 mm) from the bathroom door where possible. Increasing the distance between the smoke alarm or smoke detector and the bathroom door can reduce the frequency of nuisance alarms from bathroom steam. Frequent nuisance alarms can result in the occupant disabling the smoke alarm. Each incremental increase in separation, up to 10 ft (3.0 m), between the bathroom door and the smoke alarm or smoke detector is expected to reduce the frequency of nuisance alarms.

A.29.8.3.4(11) Figure A.29.8.3.4(11) illustrates acceptable smoke alarm or smoke detector mounting locations for tray-shaped ceilings.

A.29.8.4 While Chapter 29 does not require heat alarms or heat detectors as part of the basic protection scheme, it is recommended that the householder consider the use and placement of additional heat detectors for the same reasons presented under A.29.8.3. For example, additional heat alarms or heat detectors could be considered, but not limited to, the following areas: kitchen, dining room, attic (finished or unfinished), furnace room, utility room, basement, and integral or attached garage.

The placement of the heat alarm or heat detector is critical where maximum speed of fire detection is desired. Thus, a logical location for a heat alarm or heat detector is the center of the ceiling. At this location, the heat alarm or heat detector is closest to all areas of the room.

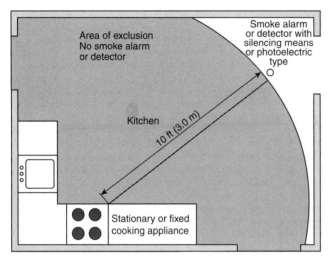

FIGURE A.29.8.3.4(4)(a) Example of Zone of Exclusion (gray area) Within Typical Residential Kitchen.

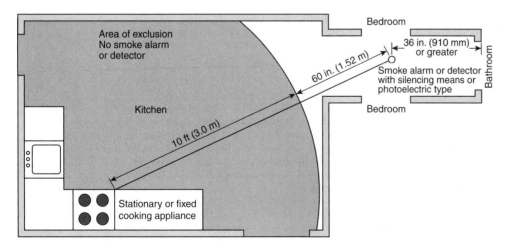

FIGURE A.29.8.3.4(4)(b) Example of Smoke Alarm or Smoke Detector Placement Between 10 ft (3.0 m) and 20 ft (6.1 m) Away in Hallway from Center of Stationary or Fixed Cooking Appliance.

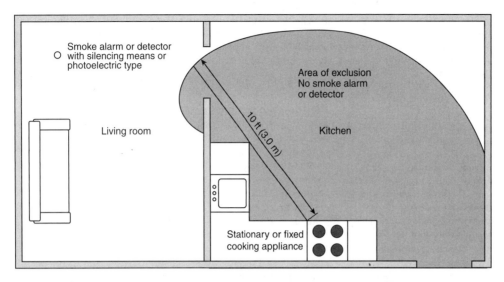

FIGURE A.29.8.3.4(4)(c)   Example of Smoke Alarm or Smoke Detector Placement Between 10 ft (3.0 m) and 20 ft (6.1 m) Away in Hallway from Center of Stationary or Fixed Cooking Appliance.

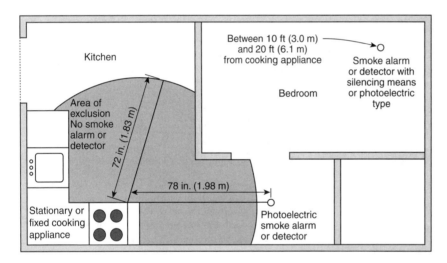

FIGURE A.29.8.3.4(4)(d)   Example of Exception Placement of Photoelectric Smoke Alarm or Smoke Detector at 72 in. (1.83 m) from Stationary or Fixed Cooking Appliance.

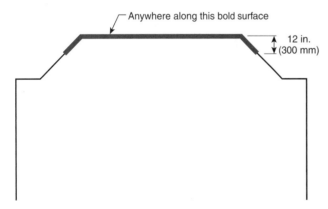

FIGURE A.29.8.3.4(11)   Locations Permitted for Smoke Alarms and Smoke Detectors on Tray-Shaped Ceilings.

A.29.8.4.1   *Heat Alarm or Heat Detector Mounting — Dead Air Space.* Heat from a fire rises to the ceiling, spreads out across the ceiling surface, and begins to bank down from the ceiling. The corner where the ceiling and the wall meet is an air space into which heat has difficulty penetrating. In most fires, this dead air space measures about 4 in. (100 mm) along the ceiling from the corner and about 4 in. (100 mm) down the wall as shown in Figure A.17.6.3.1.3.1. Heat alarm or heat detectors should not be placed in this dead air space.

A.29.8.4.2   Figure A.29.8.3.2 illustrates acceptable heat alarm or heat detector mounting locations for sloped ceilings.

A.29.8.4.3   *Spacing of Detectors.* Where a room is too large for protection by a single heat alarm or heat detector, multiple alarms or detectors should be used. It is important that they be properly located so all parts of the room are covered. *(For further information on the spacing of detectors, see Chapter 17.)*

Where the Distance Between Detectors Should Be Further Reduced. The distance between detectors is based on data obtained from the spread of heat across a smooth ceiling. Where the ceiling is not smooth, the placement of the heat alarm or heat detector should be tailored to the situation.

Figure A.17.6.3.1.3.1 illustrates acceptable heat alarms or heat detector mounting locations for smooth ceilings and sidewalls.

A.29.8.4.5 Refer to Figure A.29.8.4.5, where the distance between heat alarms or heat detectors should be further reduced.

For instance, with open wood joists, heat travels freely down the joist channels so that the maximum distance between the heat alarm or heat detectors [(50 ft) 15.2 m] can be used. However, heat has trouble spreading across the joists, so the distance in this direction should be one-half the distance allowed between detectors, as shown in Figure A.29.8.4.5, and the distance to the wall is reduced to 12.5 ft (3.8 m). Since one-half of 50 ft (15.2 m) is 25 ft (7.6 m), the distance between heat alarms or detectors across open wood joists should not exceed 25 ft (7.6 m), as shown in Figure A.29.8.4.5, and the distance to the wall is reduced [one-half of 25 ft (7.6 m)] to 12.5 ft (3.8 m). Paragraph 29.8.4.4 requires that a heat alarm or heat detectors be mounted on the bottom of the joists and not up in joist channels.

Walls, partitions, doorways, ceiling beams, and open joists interrupt the normal flow of heat, thus creating new areas to be protected.

In addition to the special requirements for heat detectors installed on ceilings with exposed joists, reduced spacing also might be required due to other structural characteristics of the protected area, possible drafts, or other conditions that could affect heat alarm or detector operation.

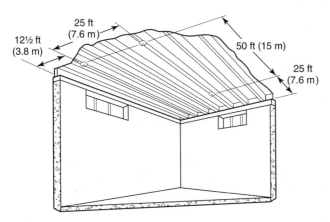

FIGURE A.29.8.4.5 Open Joists, Attics, and Extra-High Ceilings are Some Areas that Require Special Knowledge for Installation.

Annex B Engineering Guide for Automatic Fire Detector Spacing

This annex is not a part of the requirements of this NFPA document but is included for informational purposes only.

Users of Annex B should refer back to the text of NFPA 72 to familiarize themselves with the limitations of the design methods summarized herein.

Section B.2, and particularly B.2.2 and B.2.3, are largely based on the work of Custer and Meacham as found in "Performance-Based Fire Safety Engineering: An Introduction of Basic Concepts" (Meacham and Custer 1995) and Introduction to Performance-Based Fire Safety (Custer and Meacham 1997). [25]

The National Fire Protection Association and the Technical Committee on Initiating Devices for Fire Alarm Systems gratefully acknowledge the technical contributions of the Society of Fire Protection Engineers, Richard Custer, and Brian Meacham to performance-based design and this annex.

B.1 Introduction.

B.1.1 Scope. Annex B provides information intended to supplement Chapter 17. It includes a procedure for determining detector spacing based on the objectives set for the system, size, and rate of growth of fire to be detected, various ceiling heights, ambient temperatures, and response characteristics of the detectors. In addition to providing an engineering method for the design of detection systems using plume-dependent detectors, heat detectors, and smoke detectors, this annex also provides guidance on the use of radiant energy–sensing detectors.

B.1.2 General.

B.1.2.1 In the 1999 edition Annex B was revised in its entirety from previous editions. The correlations originally used to develop the tables and graphs for heat and smoke detector spacings in the earlier editions have been updated to be consistent with current research. These revisions correct the errors in the original correlations. In earlier editions, the tables and graphs were based on an assumed heat of combustion of 20,900 kJ/kg (8986 Btu/lb). The effective heat of combustion for common cellulosic materials is usually taken to be approximately 12,500 kJ/kg (5374 Btu/lb). The equations in this annex were produced using test data and data correlations for cellulosic (wood) fuels that have a total heat of combustion of about 12,500 kJ/kg (5374 Btu/lb).

B.1.2.2 In addition to the revisions undertaken in 1999, the concept of performance-based design was further expanded on. This included, to a large extent, additional material taken from the work of Custer and Meacham. Since this time, the industry continues to develop additional codes, standards, and guides to further assist in undertaking a performance-based assessment. This includes the work of SFPE [40, 49], NFPA [50, 51, 52], and ICC [53].

B.1.2.3 For the purposes of this annex, the heat produced by a fire is manifested either as convective heat or radiant heat. It is assumed that conductive heat transfer is of little consequence during the early stages of the development of a fire, where this annex is relevant. A convective heat release rate fraction equal to 75 percent of the total heat release rate has been used in this annex. Users should refer to references 12 and 13 in G.1.2.13 for fuels or burning conditions that are substantially different from these conditions.

B.1.2.4 The design methods for plume-dependent fire detectors provided in this annex are based on full-scale fire tests funded by the Fire Detection Institute in which all fires were geometrically growing flaming fires. *(See Environments of Fire Detectors — Phase 1: Effect of Fire Size, Ceiling Height and Material; Measurements Vol. I and Analysis Vol. II [10].)*

B.1.2.5 The guidance applicable to smoke detectors is limited to a theoretical analysis based on the flaming fire test data and is not intended to address the detection of smoldering fires.

B.1.2.6 The design methods for plume-dependent fire detectors do not address the detection of steady-state fires.

B.1.2.7 The design methods for plume-dependent fire detectors used in this annex are only applicable when employed in the context of applications where the ceiling is smooth and level. They cannot be used for ceilings where there are beams, joists, or bays formed by beams and purlins. The research upon which the following methods have been based did not consider the effect of beams, joists, and bays in sufficient detail to justify the use of this annex to those applications.

B.1.3 Purpose.

B.1.3.1 The purpose of Annex B is to provide a performance basis for the location and spacing of fire detection–initiating devices. The sections for heat and smoke detectors provide an alternative design method to the prescriptive approach presented in Chapter 17 (i.e., based on their listed spacings). The section on radiant energy–sensing detectors elaborates on the performance-based criteria already existing in Chapter 17. A performance-based approach allows one to consider potential fire growth rates and fire signatures, the individual compartment characteristics, and damageability characteristics of the targets (e.g., occupants, equipment, contents, structures, and so on) in order to determine the location of a specific type of detector to meet the objectives established for the system.

B.1.3.2 Under the prescriptive approach, heat detectors are installed according to their listed spacing. The listed spacing is determined in a full-scale fire test room. The fire test room used for the determination of listed spacing for heat detectors has a ceiling height of 4.8 m (15 ft 9 in.). A steady-state, flammable liquid fire with a heat release rate of approximately 1137 kW (1200 Btu/sec), located 0.9 m (3 ft) above the floor, is used as the test fire. Special 71°C (160°F) test sprinklers are installed on a 3 m × 3 m (10 ft × 10 ft) spacing array such that the fire is in the center of the sprinkler array. The heat detectors being tested are installed in a square array with increasing spacing centered about the fire location. The elevation of the test fire is adjusted during the test to produce the temperature versus time curve at the test sprinkler heads to yield actuation of the heads in 2.0 minutes ±10 seconds. The largest heat detector spacing that achieves alarm before the actuation of the sprinkler heads in the test becomes the listed spacing for the heat detector. See Figure A.17.6.3.1.1(c). If the room dimensions, ambient conditions, and fire and response characteristics of the detector are different from above, the response of the heat detector must be expected to be different as well. Therefore, the use of an installed detector spacing that is different from the listed spacing might be warranted through the use of a performance-based approach if the conditions are as follows:

(1) The design objectives are different from designing a system that operates at the same time as a sprinkler in the approval test.
(2) Faster response of the device is desired.
(3) A response of the device to a smaller fire than used in the approved test is required.

(4) Accommodation to room geometry that is different from that used in the listing process.
(5) Other special considerations, such as ambient temperature, air movement, ceiling height, or other obstruction, are different from or are not considered in the approval tests.
(6) A fire other than a steady state 1137 kW (1200 Btu/sec) fire is contemplated.

B.1.3.3 The designer of fire alarm systems needs to be knowledgeable in the applicable areas associated with undertaking a performance-based design, including fire dynamics, performance-based design, detector response, and so forth, and apply these principles judiciously. In addition, the majority of jurisdictions consider the design of fire alarm systems as "engineering work." They therefore require licensed engineers to perform such work. Other jurisdictions allow technologists to lay out fire alarm systems as long as they follow the appropriate prescriptive requirements. Designers who are using a performance-based design approach need to review the relevant engineering licensure laws in the jurisdictions in which they are practicing, as performance-based designs might very likely be deemed engineering and of the type that requires licensure of a professional engineer.

B.2 Performance-Based Approach to Designing and Analyzing Fire Detection Systems.

B.2.1 Overview. Subsection B.2.1 provides an overview of a systematic approach to conducting a performance-based design or analysis of a fire detection system. The approach has been outlined by Custer and Meacham and the SFPE *Engineering Guide to Performance Based Fire Protection Analysis and Design* [40] and is summarized below in the context of design and analysis of fire detection systems. *(Refer to Figure B.2.1.)* This approach has been divided into two phases: defining goals and objectives and system design and evaluation.

B.2.2 Phase 1 — Defining Goals and Objectives.

B.2.2.1 Define Scope of Project.

B.2.2.1.1 The initial step of this approach is to identify information relative to the overall scope of work on the project, including characteristics of the building, design intent, design and construction team organization, constraints on design and project schedule, proposed building construction and features, relevant hazards, how the building functions, occupant characteristics, and so forth. Additional information that one might want to consider could also include characteristics of the fire departments, historic preservation, building management, and applicable regulations.

B.2.2.1.2 While defining the project's scope, the designer will identify which of the three situations in Table B.2.2.1.2 best describes the project at hand (i.e., a performance-based analysis of an existing detection system in an existing building).

B.2.2.2 Identify Goals.

B.2.2.2.1 Fire protection assets are acquired in order to attain one or more of the following four goals:

(1) To provide life safety (occupants, employees, fire fighters, and so forth)
(2) To protect property and heritage (structure, contents, and so forth)

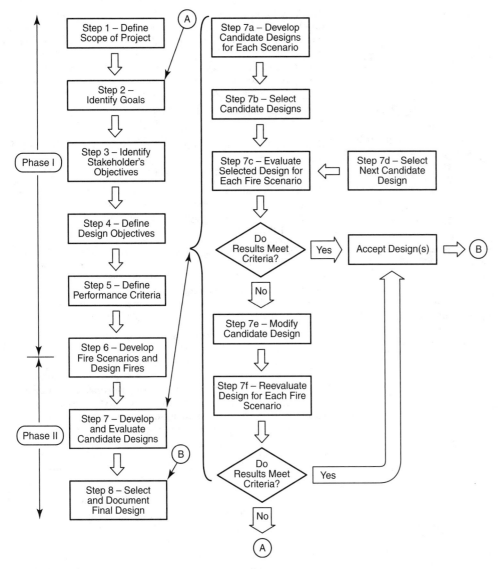

FIGURE B.2.1 Overview of the Performance-Based Design Process. [25]

Table B.2.2.1.2 Design/Analysis Situation

Building Type	System Type	Design/Analysis
New	New	Design
Existing	New	Design
Existing	Existing	Analysis

(3) To provide for continuity of operations (protect stake-holder's mission, operating capability, and so forth)

(4) To limit the environmental impact of fire (toxic products, fire-fighting water run-off, and so forth)

B.2.2.2.2 Fire protection goals are like other goals in that they are generally easy to agree on, are qualitative, and are noncontroversial in nature. They express the desired overall outcome to be achieved, that is, to provide life safety to the building occupants.

B.2.2.2.3 When starting the performance-based process, the various parties — including the stakeholders (i.e., the architect, building owner, insurance carrier, building or fire officials, and so forth), the authority having jurisdiction, and the design engineer — work together to prioritize the basic fire protection goals. Prioritizing is based on the stakeholder's objective and the building and occupancy involved. For example, life safety is a high priority in a hospital or stadium, while property protection might have an equally high priority in a large warehouse or historic building.

B.2.2.3 Identify Stakeholder's Objectives.

B.2.2.3.1 Each stakeholder must explicitly state her or his objectives in terms of acceptable loss for the various goals previously stated.

B.2.2.3.2 Stakeholder objectives specify how much safety the stakeholder wants, needs, or can afford. "No loss of life within the room of origin" is a sample stakeholder objective or statement of the stakeholder's maximum acceptable loss.

B.2.2.3.3 The stakeholder's objectives are generally not stated in fire protection engineering terms.

B.2.2.3.4 Note that in a performance-based code environment, the Code will most likely define a performance objective or stakeholder objective.

B.2.2.4 Define Design Objectives.

B.2.2.4.1 The stakeholder's objective must then be explicitly stated and quantified in fire protection engineering terms that describe how the objective will be achieved. This demands that the design objectives be expressed quantitatively. See Table B.2.2.4.1(a) through Table B.2.2.4.1(c).

Table B.2.2.4.1(a) Defining Goals and Objectives — Life Safety

Fire protection goal	Provide life safety
Stakeholder's objective	No loss of life within compartment of origin
Design objective	Maintain tenable conditions within the compartment of origin
Performance criteria	Maintain: Temperatures below $xx°$C ($°$F) Visibility above yy m (ft) CO concentration below zz ppm for tt minutes

Table B.2.2.4.1(b) Defining Goals and Objectives — Property Protection

Fire protection goal	Provide protection of property
Stakeholder's objective	No fire damage outside compartment of origin
Design objective	Limit the spread of flame to the compartment of origin
Performance criteria	Maintain upper layer temperature below $xx°$C ($°$F) and radiation level to the floor below yy kW/m^2 (Btu/sec·ft^2) to prevent flashover

Table B.2.2.4.1(c) Defining Goals and Objectives — Continuity of Operations

Fire protection goal	Provide continuity of operations
Stakeholder's objective	Prevent any interruption to business operations in excess of 2 hours
Design objective	Limit the temperature and the concentration of HCl to within acceptable levels for continued operation of the equipment
Performance criteria	Provide detection such that operation of a gaseous suppression system will maintain temperatures below $xx°$C ($°$F) and HCl levels below yy ppm

B.2.2.4.2 The design objective provides a description of how the stakeholder's objective will be achieved in general fire protection engineering terms prior to this description being quantified. The general objective is then reduced to explicit and quantitative fire protection engineering terms. The explicit fire protection engineering objectives provide a performance benchmark against which the predicted performance of a candidate design is evaluated.

B.2.2.5 Define Performance Criteria.

B.2.2.5.1 Once the design objective has been established, specific, quantitatively expressed criteria that indicate attainment of the performance objective are developed.

B.2.2.5.2 Performance criteria provide a yardstick or threshold values that can measure a potential design's success in meeting stakeholder objectives and their associated design objectives. [25]

B.2.2.5.3 Quantification of the design objectives into performance criteria involves determination of the various fire-induced stresses that are a reflection of the stated loss objectives. Performance criteria can be expressed in various terms, including temperature, radiant flux, a rate of heat release, or concentration of a toxic or corrosive species that must not be exceeded.

B.2.2.5.4 Once the design performance criteria are established, appropriate safety factors are applied to obtain the working design criteria. The working design criteria reflect the performance that must be achieved by the detection system. This performance level must allow appropriate actions to be undertaken (e.g., activate suppression systems, occupants' egress, notify fire department, and so forth) to meet the objectives. An acceptable fire detection system design provides the detection of the fire sufficiently early in its development to permit the other fire protection systems to meet or exceed the relevant performance criteria established for those systems.

B.2.2.5.5 Throughout the process identified as Phase I and II, communication should be maintained with the authorities having jurisdiction (AHJs) to review and develop consensus on the approach being taken. It is recommended that this communication commence as early in the design process as possible. The AHJ should also be involved in the development of performance criteria. Often the acceptance of a performance-based design in lieu of a design based on a prescriptive approach relies on demonstrating equivalence. This is called the comparative method, where the designer demonstrates that the performance-based design responds at least as well as, if not better than, a system designed using a prescriptive approach.

B.2.3 Phase II — System Design and Evaluation.

B.2.3.1 Develop Fire Scenarios.

B.2.3.1.1 General.

B.2.3.1.1.1 A fire scenario defines the development of a fire and the spread of combustion products throughout a compartment or building. A fire scenario represents a set of fire conditions that are deemed a threat to a building and its occupants and/or contents, and, therefore, should be addressed in the design of the fire protection features of the structure. [25]

B.2.3.1.1.2 The process of developing a fire scenario is a combination of hazard analysis and risk analysis. The hazard analysis identifies potential ignition sources, fuels, and fire development. Risk is the probability of occurrence multiplied by the consequences of that occurrence. The risk analysis looks at the impact of the fire to the surroundings or target items.

B.2.3.1.1.3 The fire scenario should include a description of various conditions, including building characteristics, occupant characteristics, and fire characteristics. [25, 40]

B.2.3.1.2 Building Characteristics. Building characteristics include the following:

(1) Configuration (area; ceiling height; ceiling configuration, such as flat, sloped beams; windows and doors, and thermodynamic properties)
(2) Environment (ambient temperature, humidity, background noise, and so forth)
(3) Equipment (heat-producing equipment, HVAC, manufacturing equipment, and so forth)
(4) Functioning characteristics (occupied, during times, days, and so forth)
(5) Target locations
(6) Potential ignition sources
(7) Aesthetic or historic preservation considerations

(Note target items — that is, areas associated with stakeholder objectives — along the expected route of spread for flame, heat, or other combustion products.)

B.2.3.1.3 Occupant Characteristics. Occupant characteristics include the following:

(1) Alertness (sleeping, awake, and so forth)
(2) Age
(3) Mobility
(4) Quantity and location within the building
(5) Sex
(6) Responsiveness
(7) Familiarity with the building
(8) Mental challenges

Human behavior plays a key role in life safety, as well as with the other fire safety goals. (*See SFPE Engineering Guide to Human Behavior in Fire.*) The possible actions that could be taken upon detecting a fire as well as how one reacts once they hear an alarm need to be considered. These actions can include alerting and rescuing other family members, gathering belongings, interpreting or verifying the message, shutting down processes. They should also include a look at how individuals respond on their own as well as in group situations.

Once these occupant characteristics and their behavior have been analyzed, one might also want to determine evacuation times. Numerous factors again need to be considered, including number of occupants, distribution throughout the building, pre-movement times, motivation, state of wakefulness, familiarity, capacity, and layout of the means of egress.

Due to the nature of human behavior, it is difficult to accurately quantify the movements and evacuation times of occupants from a building. Thus, particular attention should be given to assumptions and uncertainties assigned to these occupant characteristics.

B.2.3.1.4 Fire Characteristics.

B.2.3.1.4.1 Fire characteristics include the following:

(1) Ignition sources — temperature, energy, time, and area of contact with potential fuels
(2) Initial fuels
  (a) *State.* Fuels can come in various states (i.e., solid, liquid, or gas). Each state can have very different combustion characteristics (i.e., a solid block of wood versus wood shavings versus wood dust)
  (b) *Type and quantity of fuel.* A fire's development and duration depends also on what is burning. Cellulosic-based materials burn quite differently compared to plastics, or flammable liquids, in terms of producing different fire growth rates, heat release rates, and products of combustion.
  (c) *Fuel configuration.* The geometrical arrangement of the fuel can also influence the fire growth rate and heat release rate. A wood block will burn very differently from a wood crib, as there is more surface area and ventilation, and radiation feedback between the combustible materials is increased.
  (d) *Fuel location.* The location of the fuel (i.e., against wall, in corner, in open, against the ceiling) will influence the development of the fire. Fires in the corner of a room or against a wall will typically grow faster than a fire located in the center of a room.
  (e) *Heat release rate.* The rate at which heat is released depends on the fuel's heat of combustion, the mass loss rate, the combustion efficiency, and the amount of incident heat flux. The mass loss rate also directly relates to the production rate of smoke, toxic gases, and other products of combustion.
  (f) *Fire growth rate.* Fires grow at various rates that are dependent on type of fuel, configuration, and amount of ventilation. Some fires such as confined flammable liquid fires might not be growing fires as their burning area is fixed. These are referred to as steady state fires. The faster a fire develops, the faster the temperature rises, and the faster the products of combustion are produced.
  (g) *Production rate of combustion products (smoke, CO, CO_2, etc.).* As the characteristics of various fuels vary, so will the type of quantity of materials generated during combustion. Species production rates can be estimated with species yields, which are representative of the mass of species produced per mass of fuel loss.
(3) Secondary fuels — proximity to initial fuels; amount; distribution, ease of ignitibility (*see initial fuels*); and extension potential (beyond compartment, structure, area, if outside)

B.2.3.1.4.2 An example of a fire scenario in a computer room might be as follows.

The computer room is 9.1 m × 6 m (30 ft × 20 ft) and 2.8 m (8 ft) high. It is occupied 12 hours a day, 5 days a week. The occupants are mobile and familiar with the building. There are no fixed fire suppression systems protecting this location. The fire department is capable of responding to the scene in 6 minutes, and an additional 15 minutes for fire ground evolution is needed.

Overheating of a resistor leads to the ignition of a printed circuit board and interconnecting cabling. This leads to a fire that quickly extends up into the above ceiling space containing power and communications cabling. The burning of this cabling produces large quantities of dense, acrid smoke and corrosive products of combustion that spread throughout the computer suite. This causes the loss of essential computer and telecommunications services for 2 months.

B.2.3.2 Develop Design Fires.

B.2.3.2.1 General.

B.2.3.2.1.1 The design fire is the fire the system is intended to detect. When specifying a design fire, the specifics regarding the ignition, growth, steady-state output (if appropriate), and decay of the fire are expressed quantitatively.

There are numerous analysis techniques available to identify fire scenarios. These can typically fall into one of two categories: probabilistic or deterministic.

Probabilistic approaches typically relate to the statistical likelihood that ignition will occur, and the resultant outcome if a fire does occur. Probabilistic approaches could use the following as sources of data:

(1) Fire statistics (ignition, first items ignited, and so on)
(2) Past history
(3) Hazard/failure analysis
(4) Failure modes and effects analysis (FMEA)
(5) Event trees
(6) Fault trees
(7) HAZOP studies
(8) Cause-consequence analysis

Deterministic approaches use analysis or engineering judgment that is based on chemistry, physics, or correlations based on experimental data.

The selection of the design fire scenario and the supporting analysis techniques should be appropriate to the premise or processes. Inappropriate scenario selection or analysis can result in conservative designs that are not economical or designs with unacceptably high risks.

B.2.3.2.1.2 Fire development varies depending on the combustion characteristics of the fuel or fuels involved, the physical configuration of the fuels, the availability of combustion air, and the influences due to the compartment. Once a stable flame is attained, most fires grow in an accelerating pattern *(see Figure B.2.3.2.3.5)*, reach a steady state characterized by a maximum heat release rate, and then enter into a decay period as the availability of either fuel or combustion air becomes limited. Fire growth and development are limited by factors such as quantity of fuel, arrangement of fuel, quantity of oxygen, and the effect of manual and automatic suppression systems.

For design fires with a smoldering period, very little data are available. The design engineer should, therefore, be careful in specifying the duration of this period. The fire growth rate of flaming fires is determined by a variety of factors, including the following:

(1) Type of fuel and ease of ignition
(2) Fuel configuration and orientation
(3) Location of secondary fuel packages
(4) Proximity of fire to walls and corners
(5) Ceiling height
(6) Ventilation

It is important to note when using heat release data that the fuel burning as well as the compartment in which it is burning need to be considered together. A couch can produce sufficient heat to cause flashover in a small compartment, whereas this same couch placed in a large compartment with high ceilings can cause a limited fire and never reach flashover.

Several sources for developing design fires should be reviewed, including *SFPE Handbook of Fire Protection Engineering* [41]; *NFPA 101, Life Safety Code; NFPA 5000, Building Construction and Safety Code;* and *SFPE Engineering Guide to Performance Based Fire Protection Analysis and Design of Buildings* [40].

B.2.3.2.1.3 Designers might also need to consider fires that might be related to extreme events. These can either be fires used to trigger extreme events, or post-extreme-event-induced fires. If these are deemed credible, then designers should take these into consideration as design fires and also with respect to the overall reliability, redundancy, and robustness of the detection system to function during these types of events. [54]

B.2.3.2.2 Heat Release Rates.

B.2.3.2.2.1 Fires can be characterized by their rate of heat release, measured in terms of the number of kW (Btu/sec) of heat liberated. Typical maximum heat release rates (Q_m) for a number of different fuels and fuel configurations are provided in Table B.2.3.2.6.2(a) and Table B.2.3.2.6.2(c). The heat release rate of a fire can be described as a product of a heat release density and fire area using the following equation:

$$Q_m = qA \qquad \text{(B.1)}$$

where:
Q_m = maximum or peak heat release rate [kW (Btu/sec)]
q = heat release rate density per unit floor area [kW/m^2 (Btu/sec·ft^2)]
A = floor area of the fuel [m^2 (ft^2)]

B.2.3.2.2.2 The following example is provided: A particular hazard analysis is to be based on a fire scenario involving a 3.05 m × 3.05 m (10 ft × 10 ft) stack of wood pallets stored 1.5 m (5 ft) high. Approximately what peak heat release rate can be expected?

From Table B.2.3.2.6.2(a), the heat release rate density (q) for 1.5 m (5 ft) high wood pallets is approximately 3745 kW/m^2 (330 Btu/sec·ft^2).

The area is 3.05 m × 3.05 m (10 ft × 10 ft), or 9.29 m^2 (100 ft^2). Using equation B.1 to determine the heat release rate yields the following:

3745 × 9.29 = 34,791 kW (330 × 100 = 33,000 Btu/sec)

As indicated in the Table B.2.3.2.6.2(a), this fire generally produces a medium to fast fire growth rate, reaching 1055 kW (1000 Btu/sec) in approximately 90 to 190 seconds.

B.2.3.2.3 Fire Growth Rate.

B.2.3.2.3.1 Fires can also be defined by their growth rate or the time (t_g) it takes for the fire to reach a given heat release rate. Previous research [16] has shown that most fires grow exponentially and can be expressed by what is termed the "power law fire growth model":

$$Q \cong t^p \qquad \text{(B.2)}$$

where:
Q = heat release rate (kW or Btu/sec)
t = time (seconds)
p = 2

B.2.3.2.3.2 In fire protection, fuel packages are often described as having a growth time (t_g). This is the time necessary after the ignition with a stable flame for the fuel package to attain a heat release rate of 1055 kW (1000 Btu/sec). The following equations describe the growth of design fires:

$$Q = \frac{1055}{t_g^2} t^2 \quad \text{(for SI units)} \qquad \text{(B.3a)}$$

or

$$Q = \frac{1000}{t_g^2}t^2 \quad \text{(for inch-pound units)} \quad \textbf{(B.3b)}$$

and thus

$$Q = \alpha t^2 \quad \textbf{(B.4)}$$

where:
Q = heat release rate [kW or (Btu/sec)]
α = fire growth rate [$1055/t_g^2$ (kW/sec^2) or $1000/t_g^2$
      (Btu/sec^3)]
t_g = fire growth time to reach 1055 kW (1000
      Btu/sec) after established burning
t = time after established burning occurs (seconds)

B.2.3.2.3.3 Table B.2.3.2.6.2(a) and Table B.2.3.2.6.2(e) provide values for t_g, the time necessary to reach a heat release rate of 1055 kW (1000 Btu/sec), for a variety of materials in various configurations.

B.2.3.2.3.4 Test data from 40 furniture calorimeter tests, as indicated in Table B.2.3.2.6.2(e), have been used to independently verify the power law fire growth model, $Q = \alpha t^2$. [14] For reference, the table contains the test numbers used in the original NIST reports.

The virtual time of origin (t_v) is the time at which a stable flame had appeared and the fires began to obey the power law fire growth model. Prior to t_v, the fuels might have smoldered but did not burn vigorously with an open flame. The model curves are then predicted by the following equations:

$$Q = \alpha\left(t - t_v\right)^2 \quad \textbf{(B.5)}$$

and

$$Q = \left(\frac{1055}{t_g^2}\right)\left(t - t_v\right)^2 \quad \text{(for SI units)} \quad \textbf{(B.6a)}$$

or

$$Q = \left(\frac{1000}{t_g^2}\right)\left(t - t_v\right)^2 \quad \text{(for inch-pound units)} \quad \textbf{(B.6b)}$$

where:
Q = heat release rate [kW or (Btu/sec)]
α = fire growth rate [$1055/t_g^2$ (kW/sec^2) or $1000/t_g^2$
      (Btu/sec^3)]
t_g = fire growth time to reach 1055 kW
      (1000 Btu/sec)
t = time after established burning occurs (seconds)
t_v = virtual time of origin (seconds)

B.2.3.2.3.5 Figure B.2.3.2.3.5 is an example of actual test data with a power law curve superimposed.

B.2.3.2.3.6 For purposes of this annex, fires are classified as being either slow-, medium-, or fast-developing from the time that established burning occurs until the fire reaches a heat release rate of 1055 kW (1000 Btu/sec). Table B.2.3.2.3.6 results from using the relationships discussed earlier. *[See also Table B.2.3.2.6.2(a).]*

B.2.3.2.4 Flame Height.

B.2.3.2.4.1 There are a number of flame height to heat release rate correlations available that can be used to determine an appropriate design fire. The differences in the various correlations arise from the different data sets and curve-fitting methods used by the researchers. One such correlation is

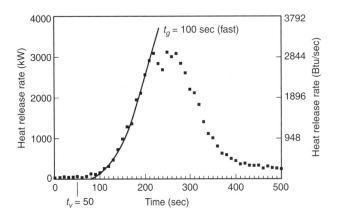

FIGURE B.2.3.2.3.5   Test 38, Foam Sofa. *(Courtesy of R. P. Schifiliti Associates, Inc.)*

shown in Figure B.2.3.2.4.1. It indicates that flame height and fire heat release rate are directly related. [2] The lines in Figure B.2.3.2.4.1 were derived from the following equation:

$$h_f = 0.182\left(kQ\right)^{2/5} \quad \text{(for SI units)} \quad \textbf{(B.7a)}$$

or

$$h_f = 0.584\left(kQ\right)^{2/5} \quad \text{(for inch-pound units)} \quad \textbf{(B.7b)}$$

where:
h_f = flame height (m or ft)
k = wall effect factor
Q = heat release rate (kW or Btu/sec)

Where there are no nearby walls, use $k = 1$.
Where the fuel package is near a wall, use $k = 2$.
Where the fuel package is in a corner, use $k = 4$.

B.2.3.2.4.2 The following example is provided: What is the average flame height of a fire with a heat release rate of 1055 kW (1000 Btu/sec) located in the middle of a compartment?

From Figure B.2.3.2.4.1, find the heat release rate on the abscissa and read estimated flame height from the ordinate, or use equation B.7a or B.7b:

$h_f = 0.182(kQ)^{2/5}$ (for SI units) or
$h_f = 0.584(kQ)^{2/5}$ (for inch-pound units)
$h_f = 0.182(1 \times 1055 \text{ kW})^{2/5}$ or
$h_f = 0.584(1 \times 1000 \text{ Btu/sec})^{2/5}$
$h_f = 2.8 \text{ m (9.25 ft)}$

Another correlation has been derived by Drysdale [42]:

$$I = 0.235\, Q_c^{2/5} - 1.02D$$

where:
I = the flame height (m)
Q_c = the convective heat release rate (kW)
D = the diameter of the fuel bed

These correlations will not produce the same prediction when used for exactly the same input data. There is inherent uncertainty in the calculated flame height due to the fact that the flaming combustion in the diffusion regime is a dynamic phenomenon. The designer should run multiple predictions with bounding values to address the inherent uncertainty of the correlations.

Table B.2.3.2.3.6 Power Law Heat Release Rates

Fire Growth Rate	Growth Time (t_g)	α (kW/sec^2)	α (Btu/sec^3)
Slow	$t_g \geq 400$ sec	$\alpha \leq 0.0066$	$\alpha \leq 0.0063$
Medium	$150 \leq t_g < 400$ sec	$0.0066 < \alpha \leq 0.0469$	$0.0063 < \alpha \leq 0.0445$
Fast	$t_g < 150$ sec	$\alpha > 0.0469$	$\alpha > 0.0445$

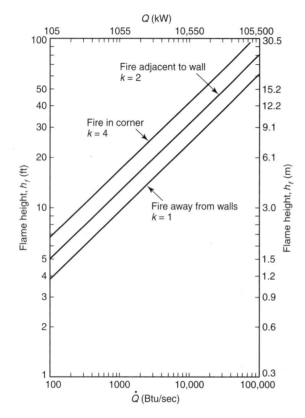

FIGURE B.2.3.2.4.1 Heat Release Rate vs. Flame Height.

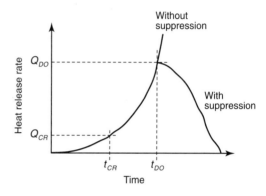

FIGURE B.2.3.2.5 Critical and Design Objective Heat Release Rates vs. Time.

B.2.3.2.5 Selection of Critical Fire Size. Because all fire control means require a finite operation time, there is a critical difference between the time at which the fire must be detected and the time at which it achieves the magnitude of the design fire. Even though a fire has been detected, this does not mean that it stops growing. Fires typically grow exponentially until they become ventilation controlled, and limited by the availability of fuel, or until some type of fire suppression or extinguishment is commenced. Figure B.2.3.2.5 shows that there can be a significant increase in the heat release rate with only a small change in time due to the exponential growth rate of fire.

B.2.3.2.5.1 Once the design objectives and the design fire have been established, the designer will need to establish two points on the design fire curve: Q_{DO} and Q_{CR}.

B.2.3.2.5.2 Q_{DO} represents the heat release rate, or product release rate, which produces conditions representative of the design objective. This is the "design fire." However, Q_{DO} does not represent the point in time at which detection is needed. Detection must occur sufficiently early in the development of the fire to allow for any intrinsic reaction time of the detection as well as

the operation time for fire suppression or extinguishing systems. There will be delays in both detection of the fire as well as the response of equipment, or persons, to the alarm.

B.2.3.2.5.3 A critical fire size (Q_{CR}) is identified on the curve that accounts for the delays in detection and response. This point represents the maximum permissible fire size at which detection must occur that allows appropriate actions to be taken to keep the fire from exceeding the design objective (Q_{DO}).

B.2.3.2.5.4 Delays are inherent in both the detection system as well as in the response of the equipment or people that need to react once a fire is detected. Delays associated with the detection system include a lag in the transport of combustion products from the fire to the detector and response time lag of the detector, alarm verification time, processing time of the detector, and processing time of the control unit. Delays are also possible with an automatic fire extinguishing system(s) or suppression system(s). Delay can be introduced by alarm verification or crossed zone detection systems, filling and discharge times of preaction systems, delays in agent release required for occupant evacuation (e.g., CO_2 systems), and the time required to achieve extinguishment.

B.2.3.2.5.5 Occupants do not always respond immediately to a fire alarm. The following must be accounted for when evaluating occupant safety issues:

(1) Time expected for occupants to hear the alarm (due to sleeping or manufacturing equipment noise)
(2) Time to decipher the message (e.g., voice alarm system)
(3) Time to decide whether to leave (get dressed, gather belongings, call security)
(4) Time to travel to an exit

B.2.3.2.5.6 Response of the fire department or fire brigade to a fire incident involves several different actions that need to occur sequentially before containment and extinguishment efforts of the fire can even begin. These actions should also be taken into account to properly design detection systems that meet the design objectives. These actions typically include the following:

(1) Detection (detector delays, control unit delays, and so forth)
(2) Notification to the monitoring station (remote, central station, proprietary, and so forth)
(3) Notification of the fire department
(4) Alarm handling time at the fire department
(5) Turnout time at the station
(6) Travel time to the incident
(7) Access to the site
(8) Set-up time on site
(9) Access to building
(10) Access to fire floor
(11) Access to area of involvement
(12) Application of extinguishant on the fire

B.2.3.2.5.7 Unless conditions that limit the availability of combustion air or fuel exist, neither the growth of the fire nor the resultant damage stop until fire suppression begins. The time needed to execute each step of the fire response sequence of actions must be quantified and documented. When designing a detection system, the sum of the time needed for each step in the response sequence (t_{delay}) must be subtracted from the time at which the fire attains the design objective (t_{DO}) in order to determine the latest time and fire size (Q_{CR}) in the fire development at which detection can occur and still achieve the system design objective.

B.2.3.2.5.8 The fire scenarios and design fires selected should include analysis of best and worst-case conditions and their likelihood of occurring. It is important to look at different conditions and situations and their effects on response.

B.2.3.2.6 Data Sources.

B.2.3.2.6.1 To produce a design fire curve, information is needed regarding the burning characteristics of the object(s) involved. Data can be obtained from either technical literature or by conducting small or large scale calorimeter tests.

B.2.3.2.6.2 Some information is contained in Figure B.2.3.2.6.2 and Table B.2.3.2.6.2(a) through Table B.2.3.2.6.2(e).

Table B.2.3.2.6.2(a) Maximum Heat Release Rates — Warehouse Materials

Warehouse Materials	Growth Time (t_g) (sec)	Heat Release Density (q) kW/m²	Heat Release Density (q) Btu/sec·ft²	Classification
1. Wood pallets, stack, 0.46 m (1½ ft) high (6%–12% moisture)	150–310	1,248	110	fast–medium
2. Wood pallets, stack, 1.52 m (5 ft) high (6%–12% moisture)	90–190	3,745	330	fast
3. Wood pallets, stack, 3.05 m (10 ft) high (6%–12% moisture)	80–110	6,810	600	fast
4. Wood pallets, stack, 4.88 m (16 ft) high (6%–12% moisture)	75–105	10,214	900	fast
5. Mail bags, filled, stored 1.52 m (5 ft) high	190	397	35	medium
6. Cartons, compartmented, stacked 4.57 m (15 ft) high	60	2,270	200	fast
7. Paper, vertical rolls, stacked 6.10 m (20 ft) high	15–28	—	—	*
8. Cotton (also PE, PE/cot, acrylic/nylon/PE), garments in 3.66 m (12 ft) high racks	20–42	—	—	*
9. Cartons on pallets, rack storage, 4.57 m–9.14 m (15 ft–30 ft) high	40–280	—	—	fast–medium
10. Paper products, densely packed in cartons, rack storage, 6.10 m (20 ft) high	470	—	—	slow
11. PE letter trays, filled, stacked 1.52 m (5 ft) high on cart	190	8,512	750	medium
12. PE trash barrels in cartons, stacked 4.57 m (15 ft) high	55	2,837	250	fast
13. FRP shower stalls in cartons, stacked 4.57 m (15 ft) high	85	1,248	110	fast
14. PE bottles, packed in item 6	85	6,242	550	fast
15. PE bottles in cartons, stacked 4.57 m (15 ft) high	75	1,929	170	fast
16. PE pallets, stacked 0.91 m (3 ft) high	130	—	—	fast
17. PE pallets, stacked 1.83 m–2.44 m (6 ft–8 ft) high	30–55	—	—	fast
18. PU mattress, single, horizontal	110	—	—	fast
19. PE insulation board, rigid foam, stacked 4.57 m (15 ft) high	8	1,929	170	*
20. PS jars, packed in item 6	55	13,619	1,200	fast
21. PS tubs nested in cartons, stacked 4.27 m (14 ft) high	105	5,107	450	fast
22. PS toy parts in cartons, stacked 4.57 m (15 ft) high	110	2,042	180	fast
23. PS insulation board, rigid, stacked 4.27 m (14 ft) high	7	3,291	290	*
24. PVC bottles, packed in item 6	9	3,405	300	*
25. PP tubs, packed in item 6	10	4,426	390	*
26. PP and PE film in rolls, stacked 4.27 m (14 ft) high	40	3,972	350	*
27. Distilled spirits in barrels, stacked 6.10 m (20 ft) high	23–40	—	—	*
28. Methyl alcohol	—	738	65	—
29. Gasoline	—	2,270	200	—
30. Kerosene	—	2,270	200	—
31. Diesel oil	—	2,043	180	—

PE: Polyethylene. PS: Polystyrene. PVC: Polyvinyl chloride. PP: Polypropylene. PU: Polyurethane.
FRP: Fiberglass-reinforced polyester.
Note: The heat release rates per unit floor area are for fully involved combustibles, assuming 100 percent combustion efficiency. The growth times shown are those required to exceed 1000 Btu/sec heat release rate for developing fires, assuming 100 percent combustion efficiency.
*Fire growth rate exceeds design data.

Table B.2.3.2.6.2(b) Maximum Heat Release Rates from Fire Detection Institute Analysis

Materials	Approximate Values	
	kW	Btu/sec
Medium wastebasket with milk cartons	105	100
Large barrel with milk cartons	148	140
Upholstered chair with polyurethane foam	369	350
Latex foam mattress (heat at room door)	1265	1200
Furnished living room (heat at open door)	4217–8435	4000–8000

Table B.2.3.2.6.2(c) Unit Heat Release Rates for Fuels Burning in the Open

Commodity	Heat Release Rate	
	kW	Btu/sec
Flammable liquid pool	$3291/m^2$	$290/ft^2$ of surface
Flammable liquid spray	557/Lpm	2000/gpm of flow
Pallet stack	3459/m	1000/ft of height
Wood or PMMA* (vertical)		
0.6 m (2 ft) height	104/m	30/ft of width
1.8 m (6 ft) height	242/m	70/ft of width
2.4 m (8 ft) height	623/m	180/ft of width
3.7 m (12 ft) height	1038/m	300/ft of width
Wood or PMMA*		
Top of horizontal surface	$715/m^2$	$63/ft^2$ of surface
Solid polystyrene (vertical)		
0.6 m (2 ft) height	218/m	63/ft of width
1.8 m (6 ft) height	450/m	130/ft of width
2.4 m (8 ft) height	1384/m	400/ft of width
3.7 m (12 ft) height	2352/m	680/ft of width
Solid polystyrene (horizontal)	$1362/m^2$	$120/ft^2$ of surface
Solid polypropylene (vertical)		
0.6 m (2 ft) height	218/m	63/ft of width
1.8 m (6 ft) height	346/m	100/ft of width
2.4 m (8 ft) height	969/m	280/ft of width
3.7 m (12 ft) height	1626/m	470/ft of width
Solid polypropylene (horizontal)	$795/m^2$	$70/ft^2$ of surface

*Polymethyl methacrylate (Plexiglas™, Lucite™, Acrylic).
[**92B:** Table B.1, 1995.]

Table B.2.3.2.6.2(d) Characteristics of Ignition Sources

	Typical Heat Output		Burn Time[a]	Maximum Flame Height		Flame Width		Maximum Heat Flux	
	W	Btu/sec	(sec)	mm	in.	mm	in.	kW/m²	Btu/sec · ft²
Cigarette 1.1 g (not puffed, laid on solid surface)									
Bone dry	5	0.0047	1200	—	—	—	—	42	3.7
Conditioned to 50% relative humidity	5	0.0047	1200	—	—	—	—	35	3.1
Methenamine pill, 0.15 g (0.0053 oz)	45	0.043	90	—	—	—	—	4	0.35
Match, wooden, laid on solid surface	80	0.076	20–30	30	1.18	14	0.092	18–20	1.59–1.76
Wood cribs, BS 5852 Part 2									
No. 4 crib, 8.5 g (0.3 oz)	1,000	0.95	190	—	—	—	—	15[d]	1.32
No. 5 crib, 17 g (0.6 oz)	1,900	1.80	200	—	—	—	—	17[d]	1.50
No. 6 crib, 60 g (2.1 oz)	2,600	2.46	190	—	—	—	—	20[d]	1.76
No. 7 crib, 126 g (4.4 oz)	6,400	6.07	350	—	—	—	—	25[d]	2.20
Crumpled brown lunch bag, 6 g (0.21 oz)	1,200	1.14	80	—	—	—	—	—	—
Crumpled wax paper, 4.5 g (0.16 oz) (tight)	1,800	1.71	25	—	—	—	—	—	—
Crumpled wax paper, 4.5 g (0.16 oz) (loose)	5,300	5.03	20	—	—	—	—	—	—
Folded double-sheet newspaper, 22 g (0.78 oz) (bottom ignition)	4,000	3.79	100	—	—	—	—	—	—
Crumpled double-sheet newspaper, 22 g (0.78 oz) (top ignition)	7,400	7.02	40	—	—	—	—	—	—
Crumpled double-sheet newspaper, 22 g (0.78 oz) (bottom ignition)	17,000	16.12	20	—	—	—	—	—	—
Polyethylene wastebasket, 285 g (10.0 oz), filled with 12 milk cartons [390 g (13.8 oz)]	50,000	47.42	200[b]	550	21.7	200	7.9	35[c]	3.08
Plastic trash bags, filled with cellulosic trash [1.2–14 kg (42.3–493 oz)][e]	120,000–350,000	113.81–331.96	200[b]	—	—	—	—	—	—

Note: Based on Table B.5.3(b) of NFPA 92, 2012 edition.
[a]Time duration of significant flaming.
[b]Total burn time in excess of 1800 seconds.
[c]As measured on simulation burner.
[d]Measured from 25 mm away.
[e]Results vary greatly with packing density.

Table B.2.3.2.6.2(e) Furniture Heat Release Rates [3, 14, 16]

Test No.	Item/Description/Mass	Growth Time (t_g) (sec)	Classification	Fuel Fire Intensity Coefficient (α) kW/sec^2	Btu/sec^3	Virtual Time (t_v) (sec)	Maximum Heat Release Rates kW	Btu/sec
15	Metal wardrobe, 41.4 kg (91.3 lb) (total)	50	fast	0.4220	0.4002	10	750	711
18	Chair F33 (trial love seat), 29.2 kg (64.4 lb)	400	slow	0.0066	0.0063	140	950	901
19	Chair F21, 28.15 kg (62.01 lb) (initial)	175	medium	0.0344	0.0326	110	350	332
19	Chair F21, 28.15 kg (62.01 lb) (later)	50	fast	0.4220	0.4002	190	2000	1897
21	Metal wardrobe, 40.8 kg (90.0 lb) (total) (initial)	250	medium	0.0169	0.0160	10	250	237
21	Metal wardrobe, 40.8 kg (90.0 lb) (total) (average)	120	fast	0.0733	0.0695	60	250	237
21	Metal wardrobe, 40.8 kg (90.0 lb) (total) (later)	100	fast	0.1055	0.1001	30	140	133
22	Chair F24, 28.3 kg (62.4 lb)	350	medium	0.0086	0.0082	400	700	664
23	Chair F23, 31.2 kg (68.8 lb)	400	slow	0.0066	0.0063	100	700	664
24	Chair F22, 31.2 kg (68.8 lb)	2000	slow	0.0003	0.0003	150	300	285
25	Chair F26, 19.2 kg (42.3 lb)	200	medium	0.0264	0.0250	90	800	759
26	Chair F27, 29.0 kg (63.9 lb)	200	medium	0.0264	0.0250	360	900	854
27	Chair F29, 14.0 kg (30.9 lb)	100	fast	0.1055	0.1001	70	1850	1755
28	Chair F28, 29.2 kg (64.4 lb)	425	slow	0.0058	0.0055	90	700	664
29	Chair F25, 27.8 kg (61.3 lb) (later)	60	fast	0.2931	0.2780	175	700	664
29	Chair F25, 27.8 kg (61.3 lb) (initial)	100	fast	0.1055	0.1001	100	2000	1897
30	Chair F30, 25.2 kg (55.6 lb)	60	fast	0.2931	0.2780	70	950	901
31	Chair F31 (love seat), 39.6 kg (87.3 lb)	60	fast	0.2931	0.2780	145	2600	2466
37	Chair F31 (love seat), 40.4 kg (89.1 lb)	80	fast	0.1648	0.1563	100	2750	2608
38	Chair F32 (sofa), 51.5 kg (113.5 lb)	100	fast	0.1055	0.1001	50	3000	2845
39	½ in. plywood wardrobe with fabrics, 68.5 kg (151.0 lb)	35	*	0.8612	0.8168	20	3250	3083
40	½ in. plywood wardrobe with fabrics, 68.32 kg (150.6 lb)	35	*	0.8612	0.8168	40	3500	3320
41	⅛ in. plywood wardrobe with fabrics, 36.0 kg (79.4 lb)	40	*	0.6594	0.6254	40	6000	5691
42	⅛ in. plywood wardrobe with fire-retardant interior finish (initial growth)	70	fast	0.2153	0.2042	50	2000	1897
42	⅛ in. plywood wardrobe with fire-retardant interior finish (later growth)	30	*	1.1722	1.1118	100	5000	4742
43	Repeat of ½ in. plywood wardrobe, 67.62 kg (149.08 lb)	30	*	1.1722	1.1118	50	3000	2845
44	⅛ in. plywood wardrobe with fire-retardant latex paint, 37.26 kg (82.14 lb)	90	fast	0.1302	0.1235	30	2900	2751
45	Chair F21, 28.34 kg (62.48 lb)	100	*	0.1055	0.1001	120	2100	1992
46	Chair F21, 28.34 kg (62.48 lb)	45	*	0.5210	0.4941	130	2600	2466
47	Chair, adj. back metal frame, foam cushions, 20.82 kg (45.90 lb)	170	medium	0.0365	0.0346	30	250	237
48	Easy chair CO7, 11.52 kg (25.40 lb)	175	medium	0.0344	0.0326	90	950	901
49	Easy chair F34, 15.68 kg (34.57 lb)	200	medium	0.0264	0.0250	50	200	190
50	Chair, metal frame, minimum cushion, 16.52 kg (36.42 lb)	200	medium	0.0264	0.0250	120	3000	2845
51	Chair, molded fiberglass, no cushion, 5.28 kg (11.64 lb)	120	fast	0.0733	0.0695	20	35	33

(continues)

Table B.2.3.2.6.2(e)   *Continued*

Test No.	Item/Description/Mass	Growth Time (t_g) (sec)	Classification	Fuel Fire Intensity Coefficient (α)		Virtual Time (t_v) (sec)	Maximum Heat Release Rates	
				kW/sec²	Btu/sec³		kW	Btu/sec
52	Molded plastic patient chair, 11.26 kg (24.82 lb)	275	medium	0.0140	0.0133	2090	700	664
53	Chair, metal frame, padded seat and back, 15.54 kg (34.26 lb)	350	medium	0.0086	0.0082	50	280	266
54	Love seat, metal frame, foam cushions, 27.26 kg (60.10 lb)	500	slow	0.0042	0.0040	210	300	285
56	Chair, wood frame, latex foam cushions, 11.2 kg (24.69 lb)	500	slow	0.0042	0.0040	50	85	81
57	Love seat, wood frame, foam cushions, 54.6 kg (120.37 lb)	350	medium	0.0086	0.0082	500	1000	949
61	Wardrobe, ¾ in. particleboard, 120.33 kg (265.28 lb)	150	medium	0.0469	0.0445	0	1200	1138
62	Bookcase, plywood with aluminum frame, 30.39 kg (67.00 lb)	65	fast	0.2497	0.2368	40	25	24
64	Easy chair, molded flexible urethane frame, 15.98 kg (35.23 lb)	1000	slow	0.0011	0.0010	750	450	427
66	Easy chair, 23.02 kg (50.75 lb)	76	fast	0.1827	0.1733	3700	600	569
67	Mattress and box spring, 62.36 kg (137.48 lb) (later)	350	medium	0.0086	0.0082	400	500	474
67	Mattress and box spring, 62.36 kg (137.48 lb) (initial)	1100	slow	0.0009	0.0009	90	400	379

Note: For tests 19, 21, 29, 42, and 67, different power law curves were used to model the initial and the latter realms of burning. In examples such as these, engineers should choose the fire growth parameter that best describes the realm of burning to which the detection system is being designed to respond.

*Fire growth exceeds design data.

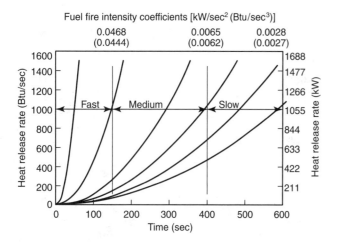

Fuel fire intensity coefficients [kW/sec² (Btu/sec³)]

FIGURE B.2.3.2.6.2   Power Law Heat Release Rates.

B.2.3.2.6.3 Graphs of heat release data from the 40 furniture calorimeter tests can be found in *Investigation of a New Sprinkler Sensitivity Approval Test: The Plunge Test* [8]. Best fit power law fire growth curves have been superimposed on the graphs. Data from these curves can be used with this guide to design or analyze fire detection systems that are intended to respond to similar items burning under a flat ceiling. Table B.2.3.2.6.2(e) is a summary of the data.

B.2.3.2.6.4 In addition to heat release rate data, the original NIST reports [8] contain data on particulate conversion and radiation from the test specimens. These data can be used to determine the threshold fire size (heat release rate) at which tenability becomes endangered or the point at which additional fuel packages might become involved in the fire.

B.2.3.2.6.5 The *NFPA Fire Protection Handbook* [22], SFPE *Handbook of Fire Protection Engineering*, and *Upholstered Furniture Heat Release Rates Measured with a Furniture Calorimeter* [3] contain further information on heat release rates and fire growth rates.

B.2.3.2.6.6 Technical literature searches can be performed using a number of resources including FIREDOC, a document base of fire literature that is maintained by NIST.

B.2.3.2.6.7 A series of design fire curves are included as part of the "Fastlite" computer program available from NIST.

B.2.3.2.6.8 In addition, there are various organizations conducting tests and posting results of various test data on their websites, including the UK's British Research Establishment (BRE), Worcester Polytechnic Institute, and NIST's FASTData Fire Test Database.

B.2.3.3 Develop and Evaluate Candidate Fire Detection Systems.

B.2.3.3.1 Once the design objectives, the potential fire scenarios, and the room characteristics are well understood, the designer can select an appropriate detection strategy to detect the fire before its critical fire size (Q_{CR}) is reached. Important factors to consider include the type of detector, its sensitivity to expected fire signatures, its alarm threshold level and required duration at that threshold, expected installed location (e.g., distance from fire, or below ceiling), and freedom from nuisance response to expected ambient conditions. *(See Chapter 17 and Annex A.)*

B.2.3.3.2 Reliability of the detection system and individual components should be computed and included in the selection and evaluation of the candidate fire detection system. A performance-based alternative design cannot be deemed performance-equivalent unless the alternative design provides comparable reliability to the prescriptive design it is intended to replace.

Reliability studies can be part of RAMS studies (i.e., reliability, availability, maintainability, and safety). RAMS is a tool that is used to manage dependability in "mission critical" systems. These are all factors that should be considered to ensure the system will continue to operate as designed, as well as ensure ease of and safety during maintenance.

The basis of RAMS is a systematic process, based on the system life cycle and tasks within it, that does the following:

(1) Assists the client to specify system requirements, in terms of dependability, from a general mission statement to availability targets for systems and subsystems, components (including software)
(2) Assesses proposed designs, using formal RAMS techniques, to see how targets are met and where objectives are not achieved
(3) Provides a means to make recommendations to designers and a system of hazard logging, to record and eventually "check off" identified necessary actions

The technical concepts of availability and reliability are based on a knowledge of and means to assess the following:

(1) All possible system failure modes in the specified application environment
(2) The probability (or rate) of occurrence of a system failure mode
(3) The cause and effect of each failure mode on the functionality of the system
(4) Efficient failure detection and location
(5) The efficient restorability of the failed system
(6) Economic maintenance over the required life cycle of the system
(7) Human factors issues regarding safety during inspection, testing, and maintenance

B.2.3.3.3 Various methods are available to evaluate whether a candidate design will achieve the previously established performance criteria. Some methods are presented in Section B.3.

B.2.3.3.4 Candidate designs developed in the context of comparison evaluation might require comparing the response of the detection system designed using a performance-based approach to that of a prescriptive-based design. It could also be evaluated against acceptance criteria previously established with applicable stakeholders.

In addition to the preceding operational and response characteristics that need to be considered, there might be limitations set on the amount of disruption, visibility, or the impact the system will have on the space in which it is to be installed. This is particularly important in heritage-type buildings where one would want these to be as unobtrusive as possible, yet not require ripping down ornate ceilings to install.

B.2.3.4 Select and Document Final Design.

B.2.3.4.1 The last step in the process is the preparation of design documentation and equipment and installation specifications.

B.2.3.4.2 These documents should encompass the following information [25]:

(1) Participants in the process — persons involved, their qualifications, function, responsibility, interest, and contributions.
(2) Scope of work — purpose of conducting the analysis or design, part of the building evaluated, assumptions, and so forth.
(3) Design approach — approach taken, where and why assumptions were made, and engineering tools and methodologies applied.
(4) Project information — hazards, risks, construction type, materials, building use, layout, existing systems, occupant characteristics, and so forth.
(5) Goals and objectives — agreed upon goals and objectives, how they were developed, who agreed to them and when.
(6) Performance criteria — clearly identify performance criteria and related objective(s), including any safety, reliability, or uncertainty factors applied, and support for these factors where necessary.
(7) Fire scenarios and design fires — description of fire scenarios used, bases for selecting and rejecting fire scenarios, assumptions, and restrictions.
(8) Design alternative(s) — describe design alternative(s) chosen, basis for selecting and rejecting design alternative(s), heat release rate, assumptions, and limitations. [This step should include the specific design objective (Q_{DO}) and the critical heat release rate (Q_{CR}) used, comparison of results with the performance criteria and design objectives, and a discussion of the sensitivity of the selected design alternative to changes in the building use, contents, fire characteristics, occupants, and so forth.]
(9) Engineering tools and methods used — description of engineering tools and methods used in the analysis or design, including appropriate references (literature, date, software version, and so forth), assumptions, limitations, engineering judgments, input data, validation data or procedures, and sensitivity analyses.
(10) Drawings and specifications — detailed design and installation drawings and specification.
(11) Test, inspection, and maintenance requirements *(see Chapter 14)*.
(12) Fire safety management concerns — allowed contents and materials in the space in order for the design to function properly, training, education, and so forth.
(13) References — software documentation, technical literature, reports, technical data sheets, fire test results, and so forth.
(14) Critical design assumptions — should include all assumptions that need to be maintained throughout the life cycle of the building so that the design functions as intended. Critical design features — should include the design features and parameters that need to be maintained throughout the life of the building so that the design functions as intended.

(15) Operations and maintenance manual — an operation and maintenance manual should be developed that clearly states the requirements for ensuring that the components of the performance-based design are correctly in place and functioning as designed. All subsystems should be identified, as well as their operation and interaction with the fire detection system. It should also include maintenance and testing frequencies, methods, and forms. The importance of testing interconnected systems should be detailed (i.e., elevator recall, suppression systems, HVAC shutdown, and so on).

(16) Inspection, testing, maintenance, and commissioning — requirements for commissioning of systems and any special procedures or test methods — should be documented as well as inspection, testing, and maintenance procedures to address the design as well as any pertinent features or systems that need to be assessed.

B.2.3.5 Management. It is important to ensure that the systems are designed, installed, commissioned, maintained, and tested on regular intervals as indicated in Chapter 14. In addition, the person conducting the testing and inspections should be aware of the background of the design and the need to evaluate not only the detector and whether it operates but also be aware of changing conditions including the following:

(1) Changes in hazard being protected
(2) Location of the hazard changes
(3) Other hazards introduced into the area
(4) Ambient environment
(5) Invalidity of any of the design assumptions

B.3 Evaluation of Heat Detection System Performance.

B.3.1 General. Section B.3 provides a method for determining the application spacing for both fixed-temperature heat detectors (including sprinklers) and rate-of-rise heat detectors. This method is valid only for use when detectors are to be placed on a large, flat ceiling. It predicts detector response to a geometrically growing flaming fire at a specific fire size. This method takes into account the effects of ceiling height, radial distance between the detector and the fire, threshold fire size [critical heat release rate (Q_{CR})], rate of fire development, and detector response time index. For fixed-temperature detectors, the ambient temperature and the temperature rating of the detector are also considered. This method also allows for the adjustment of the application spacing for fixed-temperature heat detectors to account for variations in ambient temperature (T_a) from standard test conditions.

B.3.1.1 This method can also be used to estimate the fire size at which detection will occur, given an existing array of listed heat detectors installed at a known spacing, ceiling height, and ambient conditions.

B.3.1.2 The effect of rate of fire growth and fire size of a flaming fire, as well as the effect of ceiling height on the spacing and response of smoke detectors, can also be determined using this method.

B.3.1.3 The methodology contained herein uses theories of fire development, fire plume dynamics, and detector performance. These are considered the major factors influencing detector response. This methodology does not address several lesser phenomena that, in general, are considered unlikely to have a significant influence. A discussion of ceiling drag, heat loss to the ceiling, radiation to the detector from a fire, re-radiation of heat from a detector to its surroundings, and the heat of fusion of eutectic materials in fusible elements of heat detectors and their possible limitations on the design method are provided in References 4, 11, 16, and 18 in G.1.2.13.

B.3.1.4 The methodology in Section B.3 does not address the effects of ceiling projections, such as beams and joists, on detector response. While it has been shown that these components of a ceiling have a significant effect on the response of heat detectors, research has not yet resulted in a simplified method for quantifying this effect. The prescriptive adjustments to detector spacing in Chapter 17 should be applied to application spacings derived from this methodology. Computational fluid dynamics (CFD) programs are available and can assist in analyzing the fire and development and spread of heat and smoke, as well as the potential effects of varying ceiling configurations and characteristics including sloped and beamed ceilings.

B.3.2 Considerations Regarding Input Data.

B.3.2.1 Required Data. The following data are necessary in order to use the methods in this annex for either design or analysis.

B.3.2.1.1 Design. Data required to determine design include the following:

(1) Ceiling height or clearance above fuel (H)
(2) Threshold fire size at which response must occur (Q_d) or the time to detector response (t_d)
(3) Response time index (RTI) for the detector (heat detectors only) or its listed spacing
(4) Ambient temperature (T_a)
(5) Detector operating temperature (T_s) (heat detectors only)
(6) Rate of temperature change set point for rate-of-rise heat detectors (T_s/min)
(7) Fuel fire intensity coefficient (α) or the fire growth time (t_g)

B.3.2.1.2 Analysis. Data required to determine analysis include the following:

(1) Ceiling height or clearance above fuel (H)
(2) Response time index (RTI) for the detector (heat detectors only) or its listed spacing
(3) Actual installed spacing (S) of the existing detectors
(4) Ambient temperature (T_a)
(5) Detector operating temperature (T_s) (heat detectors only)
(6) Rate of temperature change set point for rate-of-rise heat detectors (T_s/min)
(7) Fuel fire intensity coefficient (α) or the fire growth time (t_g)

B.3.2.2 Ambient Temperature Considerations.

B.3.2.2.1 The maximum ambient temperature expected to occur at the ceiling will directly affect the choice of temperature rating for a fixed-temperature heat detector application. However, the minimum ambient temperature likely to be present at the ceiling is also very important. When ambient temperature at the ceiling decreases, more heat from a fire is needed to bring the air surrounding the detector's sensing element up to its rated (operating) temperature. This results in slower response when the ambient temperature is lower. In the case of a fire that is growing over time, lower ambient temperatures result in a larger fire size at the time of detection.

B.3.2.2.2 Therefore, selection of the minimum ambient temperature has a significant effect on the calculations. The designer should decide what temperature to use for these calculations and document why that temperature was chosen. Because the response time of a given detector to a given fire is dependent only on the detector's time constant and the temperature difference between ambient and the detector rating, the use of the lowest anticipated ambient temperature for the space results in the most conservative design. For unheated spaces, a review of historical weather data would be appropriate. However, such data might show extremely low temperatures that occur relatively infrequently, such as every 100 years. Depending on actual design considerations, it might be more appropriate to use an average minimum ambient temperature. In any case, a sensitivity analysis should be performed to determine the effect of changing the ambient temperature on the design results.

B.3.2.2.3 In a room or work area that has central heating, the minimum ambient temperature would usually be about $20°C$ ($68°F$). On the other hand, certain warehouse occupancies might be heated only enough to prevent water pipes from freezing and, in this case, the minimum ambient temperature can be considered to be $2°C$ ($35°F$), even though, during many months of the year, the actual ambient temperature can be much higher.

B.3.2.3 Ceiling Height Considerations.

B.3.2.3.1 A detector ordinarily operates sooner if it is nearer to the fire. Where ceiling heights exceed 4.9 m (16 ft), ceiling height is the dominant factor in the detection system response.

B.3.2.3.2 As flaming combustion commences, a buoyant plume forms. The plume is comprised of the heated gases and smoke rising from the fire. The plume assumes the general shape of an inverted cone. The smoke concentration and temperature within the cone varies inversely as a variable exponential function of the distance from the source. This effect is very significant in the early stages of a fire, because the angle of the cone is wide. As a fire intensifies, the angle of the cone narrows and the significance of the effect of height is lessened.

B.3.2.3.3 As the ceiling height increases, a larger-size fire is necessary to actuate the same detector in the same length of time. In view of this, it is very important that the designer consider the size of the fire and rate of heat release that might develop before detection is ultimately obtained.

B.3.2.3.4 The procedures presented in this section are based on analysis of data for ceiling heights up to 9.1 m (30 ft). No data were analyzed for ceiling heights greater than 9.1 m (30 ft). In spaces where the ceiling heights exceed this limit, this section offers no guidance. [40]

B.3.2.3.5 The relationships presented here are based on the difference between the ceiling height and the height of the fuel item involved in the fire. It is recommended that the designer assume the fire is at floor level and use the actual distance from floor to ceiling for the calculations. This will yield a design that is conservative, and actual detector response can be expected to exceed the needed speed of response in those cases where the fire begins above floor level.

B.3.2.3.6 Where the designer desires to consider the height of the potential fuel in the room, the distance between the base of the fuel and the ceiling should be used in place of the ceiling height. This design option is appropriate only if the minimum height of the potential fuel is always constant and the concept is approved by the authority having jurisdiction.

B.3.2.4 Operating Temperature.

B.3.2.4.1 The operating temperature, or rate of temperature change, of the detector required for response is obtained from the manufacturer's data and is determined during the listing process.

B.3.2.4.2 The difference between the rated temperature of a fixed-temperature detector (T_s) and the maximum ambient-temperature (T_a) at the ceiling should be as small as possible. However, to reduce unwanted alarms, the difference between operating temperature and the maximum ambient temperature should be not less than $11°C$ ($20°F$). *(See Chapter 17.)*

B.3.2.4.3 If using combination detectors incorporating both fixed temperature and rate-of-rise heat detection principles to detect a geometrically growing fire, the data contained herein for rate-of-rise detectors should be used in selecting an installed spacing, because the rate-of-rise principle controls the response. The fixed-temperature set point is determined from the maximum anticipated ambient temperature.

B.3.2.5 Time Constant and Response Time Index (RTI). The flow of heat from the ceiling jet into a heat detector sensing element is not instantaneous. It occurs over a period of time. A measure of the speed with which heat transfer occurs, the thermal response coefficient is needed to accurately predict heat detector response. This is currently called the detector time constant (τ_0). The time constant is a measure of the detector's sensitivity. The sensitivity of a heat detector, τ_0 or RTI, should be determined by validated test. Research by FM Global [43,44,45] has shown that such a correlation exists and has resulted in a test method to determine RTI. This test method is documented in FM Approval Standard 3210, *Heat Detectors for Automatic Fire Alarm Signaling*. Heat detectors should be listed with their RTI so that heat detector spacing can be appropriately determined for various objectives and applications. For older or existing detectors, given the detector's listed spacing and the detector's rated temperature (T_s), Table B.3.2.5, developed in part by Heskestad and Delichatsios [10], can be used to find the detector time constant.

B.3.2.6 Fire Growth Rate.

B.3.2.6.1 Fire growth varies depending on the combustion characteristics and the physical configuration of the fuels involved. After ignition, most fires grow in an accelerating pattern. Information regarding the fire growth rate for various fuels has been provided previously in this annex.

B.3.2.6.2 If the heat release history for a particular fire is known, the α or t_g can be calculated using curve fitting techniques for implementation into the method detailed herein. [16]

B.3.2.6.3 In most cases, the exact fuel(s) and growth rates will not be known. Engineering judgment should therefore be used to select α or t_g that is expected to approximate the fire. Sensitivity analysis should also be performed to determine the effect on response from changes in the expected fire growth rate. In some analyses the effect on response will be negligible. Other cases might show that a more thorough analysis of potential fuels and fire scenarios is necessary.

B.3.2.7 Threshold Fire Size. The user should refer to previous sections regarding discussions on determining threshold fire sizes (Q_{DO} and Q_{CR}) to meet the design objectives.

B.3.3 Heat Detector Spacing.

B.3.3.1 Fixed-Temperature Heat Detector Spacing. The following method can be used to determine the response of fixed-temperature heat detectors for designing or analyzing heat detection systems.

Table B.3.2.5 Time Constants (τ_0) for Any Listed Heat Detector [at a reference velocity of 1.5 m/sec (5 ft/sec)]

Listed Spacing		Underwriters Laboratories Inc.						Factory Mutual Research Corporation (All Temperatures)
m	ft	53.3°C (128°F)	57.2°C (135°F)	62.8°C (145°F)	71.1°C (160°F)	76.7°C (170°F)	91.1°C (196°F)	
3.05	10	400	330	262	195	160	97	196
4.57	15	250	190	156	110	89	45	110
6.10	20	165	135	105	70	52	17	70
7.62	25	124	100	78	48	32	—	48
9.14	30	95	80	61	36	22	—	36
12.19	40	71	57	41	18	—	—	—
15.24	50	59	44	30	—	—	—	—
21.34	70	36	24	9	—	—	—	—

Notes:
(1) These time constants are based on an analysis [10] of the Underwriters Laboratories Inc. and Factory Mutual listing test procedures.
(2) These time constants can be converted to response time index (RTI) values by using the equation RTI = τ_0 (5.0 ft/sec)$^{1/2}$. *(See also B.3.3.)*

B.3.3.1.1 The objective of designing a detection system is to determine the spacing of detectors required to respond to a given set of conditions and goals. To achieve the objectives, detector response must occur when the fire reaches a critical heat release rate, or in a specified time.

B.3.3.1.2 When analyzing an existing detection system, the designer is looking to determine the size of the fire at the time that the detector responds.

B.3.3.2 Theoretical Background. [26, 28] The design and analysis methods contained in Annex B are the joint result of extensive experimental work and of mathematical modeling of the heat and mass transfer processes involved. The original method was developed by Heskestad and Delichatsios [9, 10], Beyler [4], and Schifiliti [16]. It was recently updated by Marrion [28] to reflect changes in the original correlations as discussed in work by Heskestad and Delichatsios [11] and Marrion [27]. Additional research has been conducted by FM Global [43, 44, 45]. Paragraph B.3.3.2 outlines methods and data correlations used to model the heat transfer to a heat detector, as well as velocity and temperature correlations for growing fires at the location of the detector. Only the general principles are described here. More detailed information is available in References 4, 9, 10, 16, and 28 in G.1.2.13.

B.3.3.3 Heat Detector Correlations. The heat transfer to a detector can be described by the following equation:

$$Q_{\text{total}} = Q_{\text{cond}} + Q_{\text{conv}} + Q_{\text{rad}} \qquad \textbf{(B.8)}$$

where:
Q_{total} = total heat transfer to a detector (kW or Btu/sec)
Q_{cond} = conductive heat transfer
Q_{conv} = convective heat transfer
Q_{rad} = radiative heat transfer

B.3.3.3.1 Because detection typically occurs during the initial stages of a fire, the radiant heat transfer component (Q_{rad}) can be considered negligible. In addition, because the heat-sensing elements of most of the heat detectors are thermally isolated from the rest of the detection unit, as well as from the ceiling, it can be assumed that the conductive portion of the heat release rate (Q_{cond}) is also negligible, especially when compared to the convective heat transfer rate. Because the majority of the heat transfer to the detection element is via

convection, the following equation can be used to calculate the total heat transfer:

$$Q = Q_{\text{conv}} = H_c A \left(T_g - T_d \right) \qquad \textbf{(B.9)}$$

where:
Q_{conv} = convective heat transfer (kW or Btu/sec)
H_c = convective heat transfer coefficient for the detector (kW/m²·°C or Btu/ft²·sec·°F)
A = surface area of the detector's element (m² or ft²)
T_g = temperature of fire gases at the detector (°C or °F)
T_d = temperature rating, or set point, of the detector (°C or °F)

B.3.3.3.2 Assuming the detection element can be treated as a lumped mass (m) (kg or lbm), its temperature change can be defined as follows:

$$\frac{dT_d}{dt} = \frac{Q}{mc} \qquad \textbf{(B.10)}$$

where:
dT_d/dt = change in temperature of detection element (deg/sec)
Q = heat release rate (kW or Btu/sec)
m = detector element's mass (kg or lbm)
c = detector element's specific heat (kJ/kg·°C or Btu/lbm·°F)

B.3.3.3.3 Substituting this into the previous equation, the change in temperature of the detection element over time can be expressed as follows:

$$\frac{dT_d}{dt} = \frac{H_c A \left(T_g - T_d \right)}{mc} \qquad \textbf{(B.11)}$$

Note that the variables are identified in Section B.7.

B.3.3.3.4 The use of a time constant (τ) was proposed by Heskestad and Smith [8] in order to define the convective heat transfer to a specific detector's heat-sensing element. This time constant is a function of the mass, specific heat, convective heat transfer coefficient, and area of the element and can be expressed as follows:

$$\tau = \frac{mc}{H_c A} \qquad \textbf{(B.12)}$$

where:
- m = detector element's mass (kg or lbm)
- c = detector element's specific heat (kJ/kg·°C or Btu/lbm ·°F)
- H_c = convective heat transfer coefficient for the detector (kW/m²·°C or Btu/ft²·sec·°F)
- A = surface area of the detector's element (m² or ft²)
- τ = detector time constant (seconds)

B.3.3.3.5 As seen in the equation B.12, τ is a measure of the detector's sensitivity. By increasing the mass of the detection element, the time constant, and thus the response time, increases.

B.3.3.3.6 Substituting into equation B.11 produces the following:

$$\frac{dT_d}{dt} = \frac{T_g - T_d}{\tau} \qquad \textbf{(B.13)}$$

Note that the variables are identified in Section B.7.

B.3.3.3.7 Research has shown [24] that the convective heat transfer coefficient for sprinklers and heat detection elements is similar to that of spheres, cylinders, and so forth, and is thus approximately proportional to the square root of the velocity of the gases passing the detector. As the mass, thermal capacity, and area of the detection element remain constant, the following relationship can be expressed as the response time index (RTI) for an individual detector:

$$\tau u^{1/2} \sim \tau_0 u_0^{1/2} = \text{RTI} \qquad \textbf{(B.14)}$$

where:
- τ = detector time constant (seconds)
- u = velocity of fire gases (m/sec or ft/sec)
- u_0 = instantaneous velocity of fire gases (m/sec or ft/sec)
- RTI = response time index

B.3.3.3.8 If τ_0 is measured at a given reference velocity (u_0), τ can be determined for any other gas velocity (u) for that detector. A plunge test is the easiest way to measure τ_0. It has also been related to the listed spacing of a detector through a calculation. Table B.3.2.5 presents results from these calculations [10]. The RTI value can then be obtained by multiplying τ_0 values by $u_0^{1/2}$.

B.3.3.3.9 It has become customary to refer to the time constant using a reference velocity of u_0 = 1.5 m/sec (5 ft/sec). For example, where u_0 = 1.5 m/sec (5 ft/sec), a τ_0 of 30 seconds corresponds to an RTI of 36 sec$^{1/2}$/m$^{1/2}$ (or 67 sec$^{1/2}$/ft$^{1/2}$). On the other hand, a detector that has an RTI of 36 sec$^{1/2}$/m$^{1/2}$ (or 67 sec$^{1/2}$/ft$^{1/2}$) would have a τ_0 of 23.7 seconds, if measured in an air velocity of 2.4 m/sec (8 ft/sec).

B.3.3.3.10 The following equation can therefore be used to calculate the heat transfer to the detection element and thus determine its temperature from its local fire-induced environment:

$$\frac{dT_d}{dt} = \frac{u^{1/2}\left(T_g - T_d\right)}{\text{RTI}} \qquad \textbf{(B.15)}$$

Note that the variables are identified in Section B.7.

B.3.3.4 Temperature and Velocity Correlations. [26, 28] In order to predict the operation of any detector, it is necessary to characterize the local environment created by the fire at the location of the detector. For a heat detector, the important variables are the temperature and velocity of the gases at the detector. Through a program of full-scale tests and the use of mathematical modeling techniques, general expressions for temperature and velocity at a detector location have been developed by Heskestad and Delichatsios *(refer to references 4, 9, 10, and 16 in G.1.2.13)*. These expressions are valid for fires that grow according to the following power law relationship:

$$Q = \alpha t^p \qquad \textbf{(B.16)}$$

where:
- Q = theoretical convective fire heat release rate (kW or Btu/sec)
- α = fire growth rate (kW/sec² or Btu/sec³)
- t = time (seconds)
- p = positive exponent

Several other ceiling jet correlations [41] have been developed over the years that the designer should also review as to their applicability to the particular design case. Sensitivity analyses should also be conducted with the analysis.

B.3.3.4.1 Relationships have been developed by Heskestad and Delichatsios [9] for temperature and velocity of fire gases in a ceiling jet. These have been expressed as follows [26]:

$$U_p^* = \frac{u}{A^{1/(3+p)} u^{1/(3+p)} H^{(p-1)/(3+p)}} = f\left(t_p^*, \frac{r}{H}\right) \qquad \textbf{(B.17)}$$

$$\Delta T_p^* = g\left(t_p^*, \frac{r}{H}\right) = \frac{\Delta T}{A^{2/(3+p)}\left(\dfrac{T_a}{g}\right)\alpha^{2/(3+p)} H^{-(5-p)/(3+p)}} \qquad \textbf{(B.18)}$$

where:

$$t_p^* = \frac{t}{A^{-1/(3+p)}\alpha^{-1/(3+p)} H^{4/(3+p)}} \qquad \textbf{(B.19)}$$

and

$$A = \frac{g}{C_p T_a \rho_0} \qquad \textbf{(B.20)}$$

Note that the variables are identified in Section B.7.

B.3.3.4.2 Using the preceding correlations, Heskestad and Delichatsios [9], and with later updates from another paper by Heskestad [11], the following correlations were presented for fires that had heat release rates that grew according to the power law equation, with $p = 2$. As previously discussed [10, 18], the $p = 2$ power law fire growth model can be used to model the heat release rate of a wide range of fuels. These fires are therefore referred to as *t-squared* fires.

$$t_{2f}^* = 0.861\left(1 + \frac{r}{H}\right) \qquad \textbf{(B.21)}$$

$$\Delta T_2^* = 0 \qquad \text{for } t_2^* < t_{2f}^* \qquad \textbf{(B.22)}$$

$$\Delta T_2^* = \left(\frac{t_2^* - t_{2f}^*}{0.146 + 0.242 r/H}\right)^{4/3} \qquad \text{for } t_2^* \geq t_{2f}^* \qquad \textbf{(B.23)}$$

$$\frac{u_2^*}{\left(\Delta T_2^*\right)^{1/2}} = 0.59\left(\frac{r}{H}\right)^{-0.63} \tag{B.24}$$

Note that the variables are identified in Section B.7.

B.3.3.4.3 Work by Beyler [4] determined that the preceding temperature and velocity correlations could be substituted into the heat transfer equation for the detector and integrated. His analytical solution is as follows:

$$T_d(t) - T_d(0) = \left(\frac{\Delta T}{\Delta T_2^*}\right)\Delta T_2^*\left[\frac{1-\left(1-e^{-Y}\right)}{Y}\right] \tag{B.25}$$

$$\frac{dT_d(t)}{dt} = \frac{\left(\frac{4}{3}\right)\left(\frac{\Delta T}{\Delta T_2^*}\right)\left(\Delta T_2^*\right)^{1/4}\left(1-e^{-Y}\right)}{\left(\frac{t}{t_2^*}\right)D} \tag{B.26}$$

where:

$$Y = \left(\frac{3}{4}\right)\left(\frac{u}{u_2^*}\right)^{1/2}\left(\frac{u_2^*}{\Delta T_2^{*1/2}}\right)^{1/2}\left(\frac{\Delta T_2^*}{RTI}\right)\left(\frac{t}{t_2^*}\right)D \tag{B.27}$$

and

$$D = 0.146 + 0.242\, r/H \tag{B.28}$$

Note that the variables are identified in Section B.7.

B.3.3.4.4 The steps involved in solving these equations for either a design or analysis situation are presented in Figure B.3.3.4.4 [28].

B.3.3.5 Limitations. [26]

B.3.3.5.1 [26] If velocity and temperature of the fire gases flowing past a detector cannot be accurately determined, errors will be introduced when calculating the response of a detector. The graphs presented by Heskestad and Delichatsios indicate the errors in the calculated fire–gas temperatures and velocities [10]. A detailed analysis of these errors is beyond the scope of this annex; however, some discussion is warranted. In using the method as previously described, the user should be aware of the limitations of these correlations, as outlined in Reference 26. The designer should also refer back to the original reports.

Graphs of actual and calculated data show that errors in T_2^* can be as high as 50 percent, although generally there appears to be much better agreement. The maximum errors occur at r/H values of about 0.37. All other plots of actual and calculated data, for various r/H, show much smaller errors. In terms of the actual change in temperature over ambient, the maximum errors are on the order of 5°C to 10°C (9°F to 18°F). The larger errors occur with faster fires and lower ceilings.

At $r/H = 0.37$, the errors are conservative when the equations are used in a design problem. That is, the equations predicted lower temperatures. Plots of data for other values of r/H indicate that the equations predict slightly higher temperatures.

Errors in fire–gas velocities are related to errors in temperatures. The equations show that the velocity of the fire gases is proportional to the square root of the change in temperatures of the fire gases. In terms of heat transfer to a detector, the detector's change in temperature is proportional to the change in gas temperature and the square root of the fire–gas velocity. Hence, the expected errors bear the same relationships.

Based on the preceding discussion, errors in predicted temperatures and velocities of fire gases will be greatest for fast fires and low ceilings. Sample calculations simulating these conditions show errors in calculated detector spacings on the order of plus or minus one meter, or less.

B.3.3.5.2 The procedures presented in this annex are based on an analysis of test data for ceiling heights up to 9.1 m (30 ft). No data were analyzed for ceilings greater than 9.1 m (30 ft). The reader should refer to Reference 40 for additional insight.

B.3.3.6 Design Examples.

B.3.3.6.1 Define Project Scope. A fire detection system is to be designed for installation in an unsprinklered warehouse building. The building has a large, flat ceiling that is approximately 4 m (13.1 ft) high. The ambient temperature inside is normally 10°C (50°F). The municipal fire service has indicated that it can begin putting water on the fire within 5.25 minutes of receiving the alarm.

B.3.3.6.2 Identify Goals. Provide protection of property.

B.3.3.6.3 Define Stakeholder's Objective. No fire spread from initial fuel package.

B.3.3.6.4 Define Design Objective. Prevent radiant ignition of adjacent fuel package.

B.3.3.6.5 Develop Performance Criteria. After discussions with the plant fire brigade with regard to their capability and analyzing the radiant energy levels necessary to ignite adjacent fuel packages, it was determined that the fire should be detected and suppression activities started prior to its reaching 10,000 kW (9478 Btu/sec).

B.3.3.6.6 Develop Fire Scenarios and the Design Fire. Evaluation of the potential contents to be warehoused identified the areas where wood pallets are stored to be one of the highest fire hazards.

B.3.3.6.6.1 The fire scenario involving the ignition of a stack of wood pallets will therefore be evaluated. The pallets are stored 0.5 m (1.5 ft) high. Fire test data *[see Table B.2.3.2.6.2(a)]* indicate that this type of fire follows the t^2 power law equation with a t_g equal to approximately 150 to 310 seconds. To be conservative, the faster fire growth rate will be used. Thus, using equation B.16,

$$Q = \alpha t^p$$
$$1055\text{ kW} = \left(\alpha\text{ kW/sec}^2\right)\left(150\text{ sec}\right)^2$$
$$\alpha = 0.047\text{ kW/sec}^2$$

or

$$Q = \alpha t^p$$
$$1000\text{ Btu/sec} = \left(\alpha\text{ Btu/sec}^3\right)\left(150\text{ sec}\right)^2$$
$$\alpha = 0.044\text{ Btu/sec}^3$$

Note that the variables are identified in Section B.7.

Fire Detection Design and Analysis Worksheet [28]
Design Example

1.	Determine ambient temperature (T_a) ceiling height or height above fuel (H).	$T_a = $ _____ °C + 273 = _____ K $H = $ _____ m
2.	Determine the fire growth characteristic (α or t_g) for the expected design fire.	$\alpha = $ _____ kW/sec^2 $t_g = $ _____ sec
3a.	Define the characteristics of the detectors.	$T_s = $ _____ °C + 273 = ___ K RTI = ___ m$^{1/2}$sec$^{1/2}$ $\dfrac{dT_d}{dt} = $ _____ °C/min $\tau_0 = $ _____ sec
3b. or	*Design* — Establish system goals (t_{CR} or Q_{CR}) and make a first estimate of the distance (r) from the fire to the detector.	$t_{CR} = $ _____ sec $r = $ _____ m $Q_{CR} = $ _____ kW
3b.	*Analysis* — Determine spacing of existing detectors and make a first estimate of the response time or the fire size at detector response ($Q = \alpha t^2$).	$r = $ _____ *1.41 = _____ = S (m) $Q = $ _____ kW $t_d = $ _____ sec
4.	Using equation B.21, calculate the nondimensional time (t_{2f}^*) at which the initial heat front reaches the detector.	$t_{2f}^* = 0.861\left(1 + \dfrac{r}{H}\right)$ $t_{2f}^* = $
5.	Calculate the factor A defined by the relationship for A in equation B.20.	$A = \dfrac{g}{C_p T_a \rho_0}$ $A = $
6.	Use the required response time (t_{CR}) along with the relationship for t_p^* in equation B.19 and $p = 2$ to calculate the corresponding value of t_2^*.	$t_2^* = \dfrac{t_{CR}}{A^{-1/(3+p)}\,\alpha^{-1/(3+p)}\,H^{4/(3+p)}}$ $t_2^* = $
7.	If $t_2^* > t_{2f}^*$, continue to step 8. If not, try a new detector position (r) and return to step 4.	
8.	Calculate the ratio $\dfrac{u}{u_2^*}$ using the relationship for U_p^* in equation B.17.	$\dfrac{u}{u_2^*} = A^{1/(3+p)}\,\alpha^{1/(3+p)}\,H^{(p-1)/(3+p)}$ $\dfrac{u}{u_2^*} = $
9.	Calculate the ratio $\dfrac{\Delta T}{\Delta T_2^*}$ using the relationship for ΔT_p^* in equation B.18.	$\dfrac{\Delta T}{\Delta T_2^*} = A^{2/(3+p)}(T_a/g)\,\alpha^{2/(3+p)}\,H^{-(5-p)/(3+p)}$ $\dfrac{\Delta T}{\Delta T_2^*} = $
10.	Use the relationship for ΔT_2^* in equation B.23 to calculate ΔT_2^*.	$\Delta T_2^* = \left[\dfrac{t_2^* - t_{2f}^*}{(0.146 + 0.242 r/H)}\right]^{4/3}$ $\Delta T_2^* = $
11.	Use the relationship for $\dfrac{u_2^*}{(\Delta T_2^*)^{1/2}}$ in equation B.24 to calculate the ratio $\dfrac{u_2^*}{(\Delta T_2^*)^{1/2}}$.	$\dfrac{u_2^*}{(\Delta T_2^*)^{1/2}} = 0.59\left(\dfrac{r}{H}\right)^{-0.63}$ $\dfrac{u_2^*}{(\Delta T_2^*)^{1/2}} = $
12.	Use the relationships for Y and D in equations B.27 and B.28 to calculate Y.	$Y = \left(\dfrac{3}{4}\right)\left(\dfrac{u}{u_2^*}\right)^{1/2}\left[\dfrac{u_2^*}{(\Delta T_2^*)^{1/2}}\right]^{1/2}\left(\dfrac{\Delta T_2^*}{\text{RTI}}\right)\left(\dfrac{t}{t_2^*}\right)D$ $Y = $
13.	*Fixed Temperature HD* — Use the relationship for $T_d(t) - T_d(0)$ in equation B.25 to calculate the resulting temperature of the detector $T_d(t)$.	$T_d(t) = \left(\dfrac{\Delta T}{\Delta T_2^*}\right)\Delta T_2^*\left[1 - \dfrac{(1-e^{-Y})}{Y}\right] + T_d(0)$ $T_d(t) = $
14.	*Rate of Rise HD* — Use the relationship for $\dfrac{dT_d(t)}{dt}$ in equation B.26.	$dT_d = \left[\left(\dfrac{4}{3}\right)\left(\dfrac{\Delta T}{\Delta T_2^*}\right)(\Delta T_2^*)^{1/4}\dfrac{(1-e^{-Y})}{[(t/t_2^*)D]}\right]dt$ $dT_d = $

	Repeat Procedure Using	
If: 1. $T_d > T_s$ 2. $T_d < T_s$ 3. $T_d = T$	Design 1. a larger r 2. a smaller r 3. $s = 1.41 \times r = $ _____ m	Analysis 1. a larger t_r 2. a smaller t_r 3. $t_r = $ _____ sec

FIGURE B.3.3.4.4 Fire Detection Design and Analysis Worksheet. [28]

B.3.3.6.6.2 Using the power law growth equation with $p = 2$, the time after open flaming until the fire grows to 10,000 kW (9478 Btu/sec) can be calculated as follows:

$$Q = \left(\frac{1055}{t_c^2}\right) t_{DO}^2 = \alpha t^2 \quad \text{(for SI units)} \quad \textbf{(B.29a)}$$

or

$$Q = \left(\frac{1000}{t_c^2}\right) t_{DO}^2 = \alpha t^2 \quad \text{(for inch-pound units)} \quad \textbf{(B.29b)}$$

$$t_{DO} = 461 \text{ seconds}$$

Note that the variables are identified in Section B.7.

B.3.3.6.6.3 The critical heat release rate and time to detection can therefore be calculated as follows, assuming $t_{respond}$ equals the 5.25 minutes necessary for the fire brigade to respond to the alarm and begin discharging water:

$$t_{CR} = t_{DO} - t_{respond} \quad \textbf{(B.30)}$$

$$t_{CR} = 461 - 315 = 146 \text{ seconds}$$

and thus

$$Q_{CR} = \alpha t_{CR}^2 \quad \textbf{(B.31)}$$

$$Q_{CR} = 1000 \text{ kW } (948 \text{ Btu/sec})$$

Note that the variables are identified in Section B.7.

B.3.3.7 Develop Candidate Designs.

B.3.3.7.1 Fixed-temperature heat detectors have been selected for installation in the warehouse with a 57°C (135°F) operating temperature and a UL-listed spacing of 9.1 m (30 ft). From Table B.3.2.5, the time constant is determined to be 80 seconds when referenced to a gas velocity of 1.5 m/sec (5 ft/sec). When used with equation B.14, the detector's RTI can be calculated as follows:

$$RTI = \tau_0 u_0^{1/2} \quad \textbf{(B.32)}$$

$$RTI = 98 \text{ m}^{1/2} \text{ sec}^{1/2}$$

or

$$RTI = 179 \text{ ft}^{1/2} \text{ sec}^{1/2}$$

B.3.3.7.2 To begin calculations, it will be necessary to make a first guess at the required detector spacing. For this example, a first estimate of 4.7 m (15.3 ft) is used. This correlates to a radial distance of 3.3 m (10.8 ft).

B.3.3.8 Evaluate Candidate Designs. These values can then be entered into the design and analysis worksheet shown in Figure B.3.3.8 in order to evaluate the candidate design.

B.3.3.8.1 After 146 seconds, when the fire has grown to 1000 kW (948 Btu/sec) and at a radial distance of 3.3 m (10.8 ft) from the center of the fire, the detector temperature is calculated to be 57°C (135°F). This is the detector actuation temperature. If the calculated temperature of the detector were higher than the actuation temperature, the radial distance could be increased. The calculation would then be repeated until the calculated detector temperature is approximately equal to the actuation temperature.

B.3.3.8.2 The last step is to use the final calculated value of r with the equation relating spacing to radial distance. This will determine the maximum installed detector spacing that will result in detector response within the established goals.

$$S = 2^{1/2} r \quad \textbf{(B.33)}$$

$$S = 4.7 \text{ m } (15.3 \text{ ft})$$

where:
S = spacing of detectors
r = radial distance from fire plume axis (m or ft)

B.3.3.8.3 The following example of analysis is provided.

B.3.3.8.3.1 The following example shows how an existing heat detection system or a proposed design can be analyzed to determine the response time or fire size at response. The scenario that was analyzed in the previous example will be used again, with the exception that the warehouse building has existing heat detectors. The fire, building, and detectors have the same characteristics as the previous example with the exception of spacing. The detectors are spaced evenly on the ceiling at 9.1 m (30 ft) intervals.

B.3.3.8.3.2 The following equation is used to determine the maximum radial distance from the fire axis to a detector:

$$S = 1.414r \quad \textbf{(B.34)}$$

or

$$r = \frac{S}{1.414}$$

$$r = 6.5 \text{ m } (21.2 \text{ ft})$$

where:
S = spacing of detectors
r = radial distance from fire plume axis (m or ft)

B.3.3.8.3.3 Next, the response time of the detector or the fire size at response is estimated. In the preceding design, the fire grew to 1000 kW (948 Btu/sec) in 146 seconds when the detector located at a distance of 3.3 m (10.8 ft) responded. As the radial distance in this example is larger, a slower response time and thus a larger fire size at response is expected. A first approximation at the response time is made at 3 minutes. The corresponding fire size is found using the power law fire growth equation B.16 with $p = 2$ and α from B.3.3.6.6.1:

$$Q = \alpha t^p$$

$$Q = (0.047 \text{ kW/sec}^2)(180 \text{ sec})^2$$

$$Q = 1523 \text{ kW}$$

or

$$Q = (0.044 \text{ Btu/sec}^3)(180 \text{ sec})^2$$

$$Q = 1426 \text{ Btu/sec}$$

B.3.3.8.3.4 These data can be incorporated into the fire detection design and analysis worksheet shown in Figure B.3.3.8.3.4 in order to carry out the remainder of the calculations.

Fire Detection Design and Analysis Worksheet [28]
Design Example

#	Description	Values / Equations
1.	Determine ambient temperature (T_a) ceiling height or height above fuel (H).	$T_a =$ __10__ °C + 273 = __283__ K $H =$ __4__ m
2.	Determine the fire growth characteristic (α or t_g) for the expected design fire.	$\alpha =$ __0.047__ kW/sec^2 $t_g =$ __150__ sec
3a.	Define the characteristics of the detectors.	$T_s =$ __57__ °C + 273 = __330__ K RTI = __98__ m$^{1/2}$sec$^{1/2}$ $\dfrac{dT_d}{dt} =$ _____ °C/min $\tau_0 =$ _____ sec
3b. or	*Design* — Establish system goals (t_{CR} or Q_{CR}) and make a first estimate of the distance (r) from the fire to the detector.	$t_{CR} =$ __146__ sec $r =$ __3.3__ m $Q_{CR} =$ __1000__ kW
3b.	*Analysis* — Determine spacing of existing detectors and make a first estimate of the response time or the fire size at detector response $(Q = \alpha t^2)$.	$r =$ _____ *1.41 = _____ = S (m) $Q =$ _____ kW $t_d =$ _____ sec
4.	Using equation B.21, calculate the nondimensional time $\left(t^*_{2f}\right)$ at which the initial heat front reaches the detector.	$t^*_{2f} = 0.861\left(1 + \dfrac{r}{H}\right)$ $t^*_{2f} = 1.57$
5.	Calculate the factor A defined by the relationship for A in equation B.20.	$A = \dfrac{g}{C_p T_a \rho_0}$ $A = 0.030$
6.	Use the required response time (t_{CR}) along with the relationship for t^*_p in equation B.19 and $p = 2$ to calculate the corresponding value of t^*_2.	$t^*_2 = \dfrac{t_{CR}}{A^{-1/(3+p)}\alpha^{-1/(3+p)}H^{4/(3+p)}}$ $t^*_2 = 12.98$
7.	If $t^*_2 > t^*_{2f}$, continue to step 8. If not, try a new detector position (r) and return to step 4.	
8.	Calculate the ratio $\dfrac{u}{u^*_p}$ using the relationship for U^*_p in equation B.17.	$\dfrac{u}{u^*_2} = A^{1/(3+p)}\alpha^{1/(3+p)}H^{(p-1)/(3+p)}$ $\dfrac{u}{u^*_2} = 0.356$
9.	Calculate the ratio $\dfrac{\Delta T}{\Delta T^*_p}$ using the relationship for ΔT^*_p in equation B.18.	$\dfrac{\Delta T}{\Delta T^*_2} = A^{2/(3+p)}(T_a/g)\,\alpha^{2/(3+p)}H^{-(5-p)/(3+p)}$ $\dfrac{\Delta T}{\Delta T^*_2} = 0.913$
10.	Use the relationship for ΔT^*_2 in equation B.23 to calculate ΔT^*_2.	$\Delta T^*_2 = \left[\dfrac{t^*_2 - t^*_{2f}}{(0.146 + 0.242r/H)}\right]^{4/3}$ $\Delta T^*_2 = 105.89$
11.	Use the relationship for $\dfrac{u^*_2}{(\Delta T^*_2)^{1/2}}$ in equation B.24 to calculate the ratio $\dfrac{u^*_2}{(\Delta T^*_2)^{1/2}}$.	$\dfrac{u^*_2}{(\Delta T^*_2)^{1/2}} = 0.59\left(\dfrac{r}{H}\right)^{-0.63}$ $\dfrac{u^*_2}{(\Delta T^*_2)^{1/2}} = 0.66$
12.	Use the relationships for Y and D in equations B.27 and B.28 to calculate Y.	$Y = \left(\dfrac{3}{4}\right)\left(\dfrac{u}{u^*_2}\right)^{1/2}\left[\dfrac{u^*_2}{(\Delta T^*_2)^{1/2}}\right]^{1/2}\left(\dfrac{\Delta T^*_2}{RTI}\right)\left(\dfrac{t}{t^*_2}\right)D$ $Y = 1.533$
13.	*Fixed Temperature HD* — Use the relationship for $T_d(t) - T_d(0)$ in equation B.25 to calculate the resulting temperature of the detector $T_d(t)$.	$T_d(t) = \left(\dfrac{\Delta T}{\Delta T^*_2}\right)\Delta T^*_2\left[1 - \dfrac{(1-e^{-Y})}{Y}\right] + T_d(0)$ $T_d(t) = 57.25$
14.	*Rate of Rise HD* — Use the relationship for $\dfrac{dT_d(t)}{dt}$ in equation B.26.	$dT_d = \left[\left(\dfrac{4}{3}\right)\left(\dfrac{\Delta T}{\Delta T^*_2}\right)(\Delta T^*_2)^{1/4}\dfrac{(1-e^{-Y})}{[(t/t^*_2)D]}\right]dt$ $dT_d =$
15.	If: 1. $T_d > T_s$ 2. $T_d < T_s$ 3. $T_d = T$	Repeat Procedure Using Design Analysis 1. a larger r 1. a larger t_r 2. a smaller r 2. a smaller t_r 3. $s = 1.41 \times r =$ __4.7__ m 3. $t_r =$ _____ sec

FIGURE B.3.3.8 Fire Detection Design and Analysis Worksheet [28] — Design Example.

Fire Detection Design and Analysis Worksheet [28]
Design Analysis 2

#	Description	Values / Equations	
1.	Determine ambient temperature (T_a) ceiling height or height above fuel (H).	$T_a =$ __10__ °C + 273 = __283__ K $H =$ __4__ m	
2.	Determine the fire growth characteristic (α or t_g) for the expected design fire.	$\alpha =$ __0.047__ kW/sec^2 $t_g =$ __150__ sec	
3a.	Define the characteristics of the detectors.	$T_s =$ __57__ °C + 273 = __330__ K RTI = __98__ m$^{1/2}$sec$^{1/2}$ $\dfrac{dT_d}{dt} =$ _____ °C/min $\tau_0 =$ _____ sec	
3b. or	*Design* — Establish system goals (t_{CR} or Q_{CR}) and make a first estimate of the distance (r) from the fire to the detector.	$t_{CR} =$ _____ sec $r =$ _____ m $Q_{CR} =$ _____ kW	
3b.	*Analysis* — Determine spacing of existing detectors and make a first estimate of the response time or the fire size at detector response ($Q = \alpha t^2$).	$r =$ __6.5__ *1.41 = __9.2__ = S (m) $Q =$ __1,523__ kW $t_d =$ __180__ sec	
4.	Using equation B.21, calculate the nondimensional time (t^*_{2f}) at which the initial heat front reaches the detector.	$t^*_{2f} = 0.861\left(1 + \dfrac{r}{H}\right)$ $t^*_{2f} =$ **2.26**	
5.	Calculate the factor A defined by the relationship for A in equation B.20.	$A = \dfrac{g}{C_p T_a \rho_0}$ $A =$ **0.030**	
6.	Use the required response time (t_{CR}) along with the relationship for t^*_p in equation B.19 and $p = 2$ to calculate the corresponding value of t^*_2.	$t^*_2 = \dfrac{t_{CR}}{A^{-1/(3+p)}\,\alpha^{-1/(3+p)}\,H^{4/(3+p)}}$ $t^*_2 =$ **16**	
7.	If $t^*_2 > t^*_{2f}$, continue to step 8. If not, try a new detector position (r) and return to step 4.		
8.	Calculate the ratio $\dfrac{u}{u^*_2}$ using the relationship for U^*_p in equation B.18.	$\dfrac{u}{u^*_2} = A^{1/(3+p)}\,\alpha^{1/(3+p)}\,H^{(p-1)/(3+p)}$	$\dfrac{u}{u^*_2} =$ **0.356**
9.	Calculate the ratio $\dfrac{\Delta T}{\Delta T^*_2}$ using the relationship for ΔT^*_p in equation B.18.	$\dfrac{\Delta T}{\Delta T^*_2} = A^{2/(3+p)}(T_a/g)\,\alpha^{2/(3+p)}\,H^{-(5-p)/(3+p)}$	$\dfrac{\Delta T}{\Delta T^*_2} =$ **0.913**
10.	Use the relationship for ΔT^*_2 in equation B.23 to calculate ΔT^*_2.	$\Delta T^*_2 = \left[\dfrac{t^*_2 - t^*_{2f}}{(0.146 + 0.242r/H)}\right]^{4/3}$	$\Delta T^*_2 =$ **75.01**
11.	Use the relationship for $\dfrac{u^*_2}{(\Delta T^*_2)^{1/2}}$ in equation B.24 to calculate the ratio $\dfrac{u^*_2}{(\Delta T^*_2)^{1/2}}$.	$\dfrac{u^*_2}{(\Delta T^*_2)^{1/2}} = 0.59\left(\dfrac{r}{H}\right)^{-0.63}$	$\dfrac{u^*_2}{(\Delta T^*_2)^{1/2}} =$ **0.435**
12.	Use the relationships for Y and D in equations B.27 and B.28 to calculate Y.	$Y = \left(\dfrac{3}{4}\right)\left(\dfrac{u}{u^*_2}\right)^{1/2}\left[\dfrac{u^*_2}{(\Delta T^*_2)^{1/2}}\right]^{1/2}\left(\dfrac{\Delta T^*_2}{\text{RTI}}\right)\left(\dfrac{t}{t^*_2}\right)D$	$Y =$ **1.37**
13.	*Fixed Temperature HD* — Use the relationship for $T_d(t) - T_d(0)$ in equation B.25 to calculate the resulting temperature of the detector $T_d(t)$.	$T_d(t) = \left(\dfrac{\Delta T}{\Delta T^*_2}\right)\Delta T^*_2\left[1 - \dfrac{(1-e^{-Y})}{Y}\right] + T_d(0)$	$T_d(t) =$ **41**
14.	*Rate of Rise HD* — Use the relationship for $\dfrac{dT_d(t)}{dt}$ in equation B.26.	$dT_d = \left[\left(\dfrac{4}{3}\right)\left(\dfrac{\Delta T}{\Delta T^*_2}\right)(\Delta T^*_2)^{1/4}\dfrac{(1-e^{-Y})}{[(t/t^*_2)D]}\right]dt$	$dT_d =$
15.	If: 1. $T_d > T_s$ 2. $T_d < T_s$ 3. $T_d = T$	Repeat Procedure Using **Design** 1. a larger r 2. a smaller r 3. $s = 1.41 \times r =$ _____ m	**Analysis** 1. a larger t_r 2. a smaller t_r 3. $t_r =$ _____ sec

FIGURE B.3.3.8.3.4   Fire Detection Design and Analysis Worksheet [28] — Analysis Example 2.

B.3.3.8.3.5 Using a radial distance of 6.5 m (21 ft) from the axis of this fire, the temperature of the detector is calculated to be 41°C (106°F) after 3 minutes of exposure. The detector actuation temperature is 57°C (135°F). Thus, the detector response time is more than the estimated 3 minutes. If the calculated temperature were more than the actuation temperature, then a smaller t would be used. As in the previous example, calculations should be repeated varying the time to response until the calculated detector temperature is approximately equal to the actuation temperature. For this example, the response time is estimated to be 213 seconds. This corresponds to a fire size at response of 2132 kW (2022 Btu/sec).

B.3.3.8.4 The preceding examples assume that the fire continues to follow the t-squared fire growth relationship up to detector activation. These calculations do not check whether this will happen, nor do they show how the detector temperature varies once the fire stops following the power law relationship. The user should therefore determine that there will be sufficient fuel, since the preceding correlations do not perform this analysis. If there is not a sufficient amount of fuel, then there is the possibility that the heat release rate curve will flatten out or decline before the heat release rate needed for actuation is reached.

B.3.3.8.5 Table B.3.3.8.5(a) through Table B.3.3.8.5(k) provide a comparison of heat release rates, response times, and spacings when variables characteristic of the fires, detectors, and room are changed from the analysis example.

Table B.3.3.8.5(a) Operating Temperature Versus Heat Transfer Rate [S = 9.1 m (30 ft)]

Operating Temperature		Heat Release Rate/ Response Time	
°C	°F	kW/sec	Btu/sec/sec
57	135	2132/213	2022/213
74	165	2798/244	2654/244
93	200	3554/275	3371/275

Table B.3.3.8.5(b) Operating Temperature Versus Spacing [Q_d = 1000 kW (948 Btu/sec)]

Operating Temperature		Spacing	
°C	°F	m	ft
57	135	4.7	15.4
74	165	3.5	11.5
93	200	2.5	8.2

Table B.3.3.8.5(c) RTI Versus Heat Release Rate [S = 9.1 m (30 ft)]

RTI		Heat Release Rate/ Response Time	
$m^{1/2}$ $sec^{1/2}$	$ft^{1/2}$ $sec^{1/2}$	kW/sec	Btu/sec/sec
50	93	1609/185	1526/185
150	280	2640/237	2504/237
300	560	3898/288	3697/288

Table B.3.3.8.5(d) RTI Versus Spacing [Q_d = 1000 kW (948 Btu/sec)]

RTI		Spacing	
$m^{1/2}$ $sec^{1/2}$	$ft^{1/2}$ $sec^{1/2}$	m	ft
50	93	6.1	20.0
150	280	3.7	12.1
300	560	2.3	7.6

Table B.3.3.8.5(e) Ambient Temperature Versus Heat Release Rate [S = 9.1 m (30 ft)]

Ambient Temperature		Heat Release Rate/ Response Time	
°C	°F	kW/sec	Btu/sec/sec
0	32	2552/233	2420/233
20	68	1751/193	1661/193
38	100	1058/150	1004/150

Table B.3.3.8.5(f) Ambient Temperature Versus Spacing [Q_d = 1000 kW (948 Btu/sec)]

Ambient Temperature		Spacing	
°C	°F	m	ft
0	32	3.8	12.5
20	68	5.7	18.7
38	100	8.8	28.9

Table B.3.3.8.5(g) Ceiling Height Versus Heat Release Rate [S = 9.1 m (30 ft)]

Ceiling Height		Heat Release Rate/ Response Time	
m	ft	kW/sec	Btu/sec/sec
2.4	8	1787/195	1695/195
4.9	16	2358/224	2237/224
7.3	24	3056/255	2899/255

Table B.3.3.8.5(h) Ceiling Height Versus Spacing [Q_d = 1000 kW (948 Btu/sec)]

Ceiling Height		Spacing	
m	ft	m	ft
2.4	8	5.8	19.0
4.9	16	4.0	13.1
7.3	24	2.1	6.9

Table B.3.3.8.5(i) Detector Spacing Versus Heat Release Rate [S = 9.1 m (30 ft)]

Detector Spacing		Heat Release Rate/ Response Time	
m	ft	kW/sec	Btu/sec/sec
4.6	15	1000/146	949/146
9.1	30	2132/213	2022/213
15.2	50	4146/297	3932/297

Table B.3.3.8.5(j) Fire Growth Rate Versus Heat Release Rate [S = 9.1 m (30 ft)]

Fire Growth Rate	Heat Release Rate/ Response Time	
	kW/sec	Btu/sec/sec
Slow t_g = 400 sec	1250/435	1186/435
Medium t_g = 250 sec	1582/306	1499/306
Fast t_g = 100 sec	2769/162	2626/162

Table B.3.3.8.5(k) Fire Growth Rate Versus Spacing [Q_d = 1000 kW (948 Btu/sec)]

Fire Growth Rate	Spacing	
	m	ft
Slow, t_g = 400 sec	8.2	26.9
Medium, t_g = 250 sec	6.5	21.3
Fast, t_g = 100 sec	3.7	12.1

B.3.3.9 Rate-of-Rise Heat Detector Spacing.

B.3.3.9.1 The preceding procedure can be used to estimate the response of rate-of-rise heat detectors for either design or analysis purposes. In this case, it is necessary to assume that the heat detector response can be modeled using a lumped mass heat transfer model.

B.3.3.9.2 In step 3 of Figure B.3.3.4.4, Figure B.3.3.8, and Figure B.3.3.8.3.4, the user must determine the rate of temperature rise (dT_d/dt) at which the detector will respond from the manufacturer's data. [Note that listed rate-of-rise heat detectors are designed to activate at a nominal rate of temperature rise of 8°C (15°F) per minute.] The user must use the relationship for $dT_d(t)/dt$ in equation B.26 instead of the relationship for $T_d(t) - T_d(0)$ in equation B.25 in order to calculate the rate of change of the detector temperature. This value is then compared to the rate of change at which the chosen detector is designed to respond.

NOTE: The assumption that heat transfer to a detector can be modeled as a lumped mass might not hold for rate-of-rise heat detectors. This is due to the operating principle of this type of detector, in that most rate-of-rise detectors operate when the expansion of air in a chamber expands at a rate faster than it can vent through an opening. To accurately model the response of a rate-of-rise detector would require

modeling the heat transfer from the detector body to the air in the chamber, as well as the air venting through the hole.

B.3.3.10 Rate Compensation–Type Heat Detectors. Rate-compensated detectors are not specifically covered by Annex B. However, a conservative approach to predicting their performance is to use the fixed-temperature heat detector guidance contained herein.

B.4 Smoke Detector Spacing for Flaming Fires.

B.4.1 Introduction.

B.4.1.1 The listing investigation for smoke detectors does not yield a "listed spacing" as it does for heat detectors. Instead, the manufacturers recommend a spacing. Because the largest spacing that can be evaluated in the full-scale fire test room is 7.6 m (25 ft), it has become common practice to recommend 9.1 m (30 ft) spacing for smoke detectors when they are installed on flat, smooth ceilings. Reductions in smoke detector spacing are made empirically to address factors that can affect response, including ceiling height, beamed or joisted ceilings, and areas that have high rates of air movement.

B.4.1.2 The placement of smoke detectors, however, should be based on an understanding of fire plume and ceiling jet flows, smoke production rates, particulate changes due to aging, and the operating characteristics of the particular detector being used. The heat detector spacing information presented in Section B.3 is based on knowledge of plume and jet flows. An understanding of smoke production and aging lags considerably behind an understanding of heat production. In addition, the operating characteristics of smoke detectors in specific fire environments are not often measured or made generally available for other than a very few number of combustible materials. Therefore, the existing knowledge base precludes the development of complete engineering design information for smoke detector location and spacing.

B.4.1.3 In design applications where predicting the response of smoke detectors is not critical, the spacing criteria presented in Chapter 17 should provide sufficient information to design a very basic smoke detection system. However, if the goals and objectives established for the detection system require detector response within a certain amount of time, optical density, heat release rate, or temperature rise, then additional analysis might be needed. For these situations, information regarding the expected fire characteristics (fuel and its fire growth rate), transport characteristics, detector characteristics, and compartment characteristics is required. The following information regarding smoke detector response and various performance-based approaches to evaluating smoke detector response is therefore provided.

B.4.2 Response Characteristics of Smoke Detectors. To determine whether a smoke detector will respond to a given Q_{CR}, a number of factors need to be evaluated. These factors include smoke characteristics, smoke transport, and detector characteristics.

B.4.3 Smoke Characteristics.

B.4.3.1 Smoke characteristics are a function of the fuel composition, the mode of combustion (smoldering or flaming), and the amount of mixing with the ambient air (dilution). These factors are important for determining the characteristics of the products of combustion, such as particle size, distribution, composition, concentration, refractive index, and so on. The significance of these features with regard to smoke detector response is well documented. [29, 30]

B.4.3.2 Whether smoke detectors detect by sensing scattered light, loss of light transmission (light extinction), or reduction of ion current, they are particle detectors. Thus, particle concentration, size, color, size distribution, and so forth, affect each sensing technology differently. It is generally accepted that a flaming, well-ventilated, energetic fire produces smoke having a larger proportion of the sub-micron diameter particulates as opposed to a smoldering fire that produces smoke with a predominance of large, super-micron particulates. It is also known that as the smoke cools, the smaller particles agglomerate, forming larger ones as they age, and are carried away from the fire source. More research is necessary to provide sufficient data to allow the prediction of smoke characteristics at the source, as well as during transport. Furthermore, response models must be developed that can predict the response of a particular detector to different kinds of smoke as well as smoke that has aged during the flow from the fire to the detector location.

B.4.4 Transport Considerations.

B.4.4.1 All smoke detection relies on the plume and ceiling jet flows to transport the smoke from the locus of the fire to the detector. Various considerations must be addressed during this transport time, including changes to the characteristics of the smoke that occur with time and distance from the source, and transport time of smoke from the source to the detector.

B.4.4.2 The smoke characteristic changes that occur during transport relate mainly to the particle size distribution. Particle size changes during transport occur mainly as a result of sedimentation and agglomeration.

B.4.4.3 Transport time is a function of the characteristics of the travel path from the source to the detector. Important characteristics that should be considered include ceiling height and configuration (e.g., sloped, beamed), intervening barriers such as doors and beams, as well as dilution and buoyancy effects such as stratification that might delay or prevent smoke in being transported to the detector.

B.4.4.4 In smoldering fires, thermal energy provides a force for transporting smoke particles to the smoke sensor. However, usually in the context of smoke detection, the rate of energy (heat) release is small and the rate of growth of the fire is slow. Consequently, other factors such as ambient airflow from HVAC systems, differential solar heating of the structure, and wind cooling of the structure can have a dominant influence on the transport of smoke particles to the smoke sensor when low-output fires are considered.

B.4.4.5 In the early stages of development of a growing fire, the same interior environmental effects, including ambient airflow from HVAC systems, differential solar heating of the structure, and wind cooling of the structure, can have a dominant influence on the transport of smoke. This is particularly important in spaces having high ceilings. Greater thermal energy release from the fire is necessary to overcome these interior environmental effects. Because the fire must attain a sufficiently high level of heat release before it can overcome the interior environmental airflows and drive the smoke to the ceiling-mounted detectors, the use of closer spacing of smoke detectors on the ceiling might not significantly improve the response of the detectors to the fire. Therefore, when considering ceiling height alone, smoke detector spacing closer than

9.1 m (30 ft) might not be warranted, except in instances where an engineering analysis indicates additional benefit will result. Other construction characteristics also should be considered. (*Refer to the appropriate sections of Chapter 17 dealing with smoke detectors and their use for the control of smoke spread.*)

B.4.5 Smoke Dilution. Smoke dilution causes a reduction in the quantity of smoke per unit of air volume of smoke reaching the detector. Dilution typically occurs either by entrainment of air in the plume or the ceiling jet or by effects of HVAC systems. Forced ventilation systems with high air change rates typically cause the most concern, particularly in the early stages of fire development, when smoke production rate and plume velocity are both low. Airflows from supply as well as return vents can create defined air movement patterns within a compartment, which can either keep smoke away from detectors that are located outside of these paths or can inhibit smoke from entering a detector that is located directly in the airflow path. [26]

There currently are no quantitative methods for estimating either smoke dilution or airflow effects on locating smoke detectors. These factors should therefore be considered qualitatively. The designer should understand that the effects of airflow become larger as the fire size at detection (Q_{CR}) gets smaller. Depending on the application, the designer might find it useful to obtain airflow and velocity profiles within the room or to even conduct small-scale smoke tests under various conditions to assist in the design of the system.

B.4.6 Stratification.

B.4.6.1 The potential for the stratification of smoke is another concern in designing and analyzing the response of detectors. This is of particular concern with the detection of low-energy fires and fires in compartments with high ceilings.

B.4.6.2 The upward movement of smoke in the plume depends on the smoke being buoyant relative to the surrounding air. Stratification occurs when the smoke or hot gases flowing from the fire fail to ascend to the smoke detectors mounted at a particular level (usually on the ceiling) above the fire due to the loss of buoyancy. This phenomenon occurs due to the continuous entrainment of cooler air into the fire plume as it rises, resulting in cooling of the smoke and fire plume gases. The cooling of the plume results in a reduction in buoyancy. Eventually the plume cools to a point where its temperature equals that of the surrounding air and its buoyancy diminishes to zero. Once this point of equilibrium is reached, the smoke will cease its upward flow and form a layer, maintaining its height above the fire, regardless of the ceiling height, unless and until sufficient additional thermal energy is provided from the fire to raise the layer due to its increased buoyancy. The maximum height to which plume fluid (smoke) will ascend, especially early in the development of a fire, depends on the convective heat release rate of the fire and the ambient temperature in the compartment.

B.4.6.3 Because warm air rises, there will usually be a temperature gradient in the compartment. Of particular interest are those cases where the temperature of the air in the upper portion of the compartment is greater than at the lower level before the ignition. This can occur as a result of solar load where ceilings contain glazing materials. Computational methods are available to assess the potential for intermediate stratification for the following two cases, depicted in Figure B.4.6.3(a).

Case 1. The temperature of the ambient is relatively constant up to a height above which there is a layer of warm air at uniform temperature. This situation can occur if the upper portion of a mall, atrium, or other large space is unoccupied and the air is left unconditioned.

Case 2. The ambient interior air of the compartment has a constant and uniform temperature gradient (temperature change per unit height) from floor to ceiling. This case is generally encountered in industrial and storage facilities that are normally unoccupied.

The analysis of intermediate stratification is presented in Figure B.4.6.3(b). Plume centerline temperatures from two fires, 1000 kW (948 Btu/sec) and 2000 kW (1896 Btu/sec), are graphed based on estimates from correlations presented in this section. In Case 1, a step function is assumed to indicate a 30°C/m (16.5°F/ft) change in temperature 15 m (49.2 ft) above the floor due to the upper portion of the atrium being unconditioned. For Case 2, a temperature gradient of 1.5°C/m (0.82°F/ft) is arbitrarily assumed in an atrium that has a ceiling height of 20 m (65.6 ft).

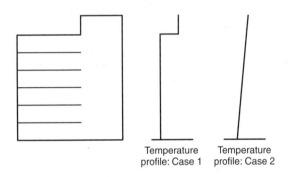

Temperature profile: Case 1   Temperature profile: Case 2

FIGURE B.4.6.3(a) Pre-Fire Temperature Profiles.

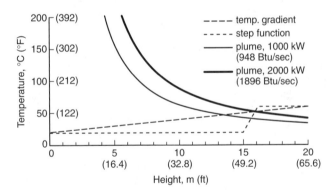

FIGURE B.4.6.3(b) Indoor Air and Plume Temperature Profiles with Potential for Intermediate Stratification.

B.4.6.3.1 Step Function Temperature Gradient Spaces. If the interior air temperature exhibits a discrete change at some elevation above the floor, the potential for stratification can be assessed by applying the plume centerline temperature correlation. If the plume centerline temperature is equal to the ambient temperature, the plume is no longer buoyant, loses its upward momentum, and stratifies at that height. The plume centerline temperature can be calculated by using the following equation:

$$T_c = 25\,Q_c^{2/3} z^{-5/3} + 20 \quad \text{(for SI units)} \tag{B.35a}$$

$$T_c = 316\,Q_c^{2/3} z^{-5/3} + 70 \quad \text{(for inch-pound units)} \tag{B.35b}$$

where:
T_c = plume centerline temperature (°C or °F)
Q_c = convective portion of fire heat release rate (kW or Btu/sec)
z = height above the top of the fuel package involved (m or ft)

B.4.6.3.2 Linear Temperature Gradient Spaces. To determine whether or not the rising smoke or heat from an axisymmetric fire plume will stratify below detectors, the following equation can be applied where the ambient temperature increases linearly with increasing elevation:

$$Z_m = 5.54\,Q_c^{1/4}\left(\frac{\Delta T_0}{dZ}\right)^{-3/8} \quad \text{(for SI units)} \tag{B.36a}$$

or

$$Z_m = 14.7\,Q_c^{1/4}\left(\frac{\Delta T_0}{dZ}\right)^{-3/8} \quad \text{(for inch-pound units)} \tag{B.36b}$$

where:
Z_m = maximum height of smoke rise above the fire surface (m or ft)
ΔT_0 = difference between the ambient temperature at the location of detectors and the ambient temperature at the level of the fire surface (°C or °F)
Q_c = convective portion of the heat release rate (kW or Btu/sec)

B.4.6.3.2.1 The convective portion of the heat release rate (Q_c) can be estimated as 70 percent of the heat release rate.

B.4.6.3.2.2 As an alternative to using the noted expression to directly calculate the maximum height to which the smoke or heat will rise, Figure B.4.6.3.2.2 can be used to determine Z_m for given fires. Where Z_m, as calculated or determined graphically, is greater than the installed height of detectors, smoke or heat from a rising fire plume is predicted to reach the detectors. Where the compared values of Z_m and the installed height of detectors are comparable heights, the prediction that smoke or heat will reach the detectors might not be a reliable expectation.

B.4.6.3.2.3 Assuming the ambient temperature varies linearly with the height, the minimum Q_c required to overcome the ambient temperature difference and drive the smoke to the ceiling ($Z_m = H$) can be determined from the following equation:

$$Q_c = 0.0018 H^{5/2}\Delta T_0^{3/2} \quad \text{(for SI units)} \tag{B.37a}$$

or

$$Q_c = 2.39\times10^{-5} H^{5/2}\Delta T_0^{3/2} \quad \text{(for inch-pound units)} \tag{B.37b}$$

Note that the variables are identified in Section B.7.

B.4.6.3.2.4 The theoretical basis for the stratification calculation is based on the works of Morton, Taylor, and Turner [15] and Heskestad [9]. For further information regarding the derivation of the expression defining Z_m, the user is referred to the work of Klote and Milke [13] and NFPA 92, *Standard for Smoke Control Systems.*

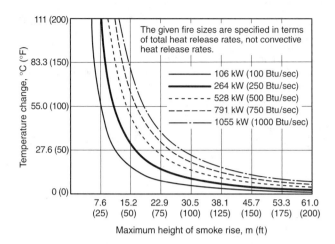

FIGURE B.4.6.3.2.2 Temperature Change and Maximum Height of Smoke Rise for Given Fire Sizes.

B.4.7 Detector Characteristics.

B.4.7.1 General. Once smoke is transported to the detector, additional factors become important in determining whether response will occur. These include the aerodynamic characteristics of the detector and the type of sensor within the detector. The aerodynamics of the detector relate to how easily smoke can pass through the detector housing and enter the sensor portion of the unit. Additionally, the location of the entry portion to the sensor with respect to the velocity profile of the ceiling jet is also an important factor. Finally, different sensing methods (e.g., ionization or photoelectric) will respond differently, depending on the smoke characteristics (smoke color, particle size, optical density, and so forth). Within the family of photoelectric devices, there will be variations depending on the wavelengths of light and the scattering angles employed. The following paragraphs discuss some of these issues and various calculation methods.

B.4.7.2 Resistance to Smoke Entry.

B.4.7.2.1 All spot-type smoke detectors require smoke to enter the detection chamber in order to be sensed. This requires additional factors to be taken into consideration when attempting to estimate smoke detector response, as smoke entry into the detection chamber can be affected in several ways, for example, insect screens, sensing chamber configuration, and location of the detector with respect to the ceiling.

B.4.7.2.2 In trying to quantify this, Heskestad [32] developed the idea of smoke detector lag to explain the difference in optical density outside (D_{ur}) versus inside (D_{uo}) of a detector when the detector activates. It was demonstrated that this difference could be explained by the use of a correction factor D_{uc} using the following relationship:

$$D_{uc} = \frac{L \dfrac{d(D_u)}{dt}}{V} \qquad \text{(B.38)}$$

where:
L = characteristic length for a given detector design, represents the ease of smoke entry into the sensing chamber
$d(D_u)/dt$ = rate of increase of optical density outside the detector
V = velocity of the smoke at the detector

B.4.7.2.3 Various studies regarding this correlation have provided additional insight regarding smoke entry and associated lags [33, 34, 34a, 34b, 34c, 34d, 34e]; however, the difficulty in quantifying L for different detectors and relating it to spacing requirements can have limited usefulness, and the concept of critical velocity (u_c) could be more applicable. [21]

B.4.7.3 Critical Velocity. A smoke detector's critical velocity refers to the minimum velocity of the smoke necessary to enter the sensing chamber to cause an alarm without significant delays due to smoke entry lag. Alarms can occur at velocities less than the critical velocity value, but their response can be delayed or require greater smoke concentrations than would normally be necessary. Flow across a detector causes a pressure differential between the upstream and downstream sides of the detector. This pressure differential is the principal driving force for the smoke entering the unit.

Experimental work has indicated that the critical velocity is approximately 0.15 m/sec (0.49 ft/sec) for the ionization detectors tested in one particular study. [21] Once velocities were reduced below this level, the smoke concentration level outside the detector before an alarm condition increased dramatically when compared to smoke concentration levels when the velocity was above the critical value. Another study found that measured velocities at the time of alarm for ionization and photoelectric detectors in full-scale flaming fire tests generally supported this velocity value, with a mean value of 0.13 m/sec (0.43 ft/sec) and a standard deviation of 0.07 m/sec (0.23 ft/sec) [46]. Estimating the critical velocity can therefore be useful for design and analysis.

It is interesting to note that this critical velocity value (0.15 m/sec or 0.49 ft/sec) is close to that at which a smoke detector must respond in the UL smoke detector sensitivity chamber in order to become listed. [35] The location in the ceiling jet where this velocity occurs for a given fire and ceiling height might therefore be considered as a first approximation for locating detectors. This again assumes a horizontal, smooth ceiling. Care should also be taken when using this correlation, such that consideration is given to potential effects of coagulation and agglomeration, and settling of the smoke within the ceiling jet as it moves away from the fire source and loses its buoyancy. The velocity for smoke entry might be present, but the concentration of smoke might not be sufficient to activate the detector.

B.4.7.4 Response to Smoke Color. Smoke detectors that use an optical means to detect smoke respond differently to smokes of different colors.

B.4.7.4.1 Manufacturers currently provide limited information regarding the response of smoke detectors in their specifications as well as in the information contained on the labels on the backs of the detectors. This response information indicates only their nominal response values with respect to gray smoke, not to black, and is often provided with a response range instead of an exact response value. This range is in accordance with ANSI/UL 268, *Standard for Smoke Detectors for Fire Alarm Systems.*

B.4.7.4.2 The response ranges allowable by UL for gray smoke are shown in Table B.4.7.4.2. Older editions of ANSI/UL 268 contained response ranges for black smoke and are also shown for comparison.

Table B.4.7.4.2 ANSI/UL 268 Smoke Detector Test Acceptance Criteria for Different Colored Smoke [35]

Color of Smoke	Acceptable Response Range	
	%/m	%/ft
Gray	1.6–12.5	0.5–4.0
Black	5.0–29.2	1.5–10.0

B.4.7.4.3 Detectors respond at different optical density levels to different fuels and different types of smoke. Examples of this are shown in Table B.4.7.4.3, which contains values of optical density at response recommended by Heskestad and Delichatsios [10] based on their test.

Note the large variations in response not only to materials producing relatively the same color of smoke but also to smoke of different color, which is much more pronounced. Also note that there was variation in the optical density at response values for a given material in the test conducted by Heskestad and Delichatsios, which is not shown in Table B.4.7.4.3. The values cited in Table B.4.7.4.3 are provided as an example of the variation in optical density at response, but these values are not necessarily appropriate for all analyses. For example, the results presented for polyurethane and PVC involved relatively large, rapidly developing fires, and fires with smaller growth rates could result in smaller values of optical density at response [10]. More information on the variation of optical density at response is available from Geiman and Gottuk [48] and Geiman [46].

B.4.7.5 Optical Density and Temperature. During a flaming fire, smoke detector response is affected by ceiling height and the size and rate of fire growth in much the same way as heat detector response. The thermal energy of the flaming fire transports smoke particles to the sensing chamber just as it does heat to a heat sensor. While the relationship between the amount of smoke and the amount of heat produced by a fire is highly dependent on the fuel and the way it is burning, research has shown that the relationship between temperature and the optical density of smoke remains somewhat constant within the fire plume and on the ceiling in the proximity of the plume.

B.4.7.5.1 These results were based on the work by Heskestad and Delichatsios [10] and are indicated in Table B.4.7.5.1. Note that for a given fuel, the optical density to temperature rise ratio between the maximum and minimum levels is 10 or less.

B.4.7.5.2 In situations where the optical density at detector response is known and is independent of particle size distribution, the detector response can be approximated as a function of the heat release rate of the burning fuel, the fire growth rate, and the ceiling height, assuming that the preceding correlation exists.

B.4.7.5.3 When Appendix C of NFPA 72E (no longer in print) was first published in 1984, a 13°C (20°F) temperature rise was used to indicate detector response. Schifiliti and Pucci [18] have combined some of the data from Heskestad and Delichatsios [10] to produce Table B.4.7.5.3 showing the temperature rise at detector response. Note that the temperature rise associated with detector response varies significantly depending on the detector type and fuel.

Table B.4.7.4.3 Values of Optical Density at Response for Flaming Fires [18]

Material	Optical Density at Response				Relative Smoke Color
	D_{ur}(m^{-1})		D_{ur}(ft^{-1})		
	Ionization	Photoelectric	Ionization	Photoelectric	
Wood crib	0.016	0.049	0.005	0.015	Light
Cotton fabric	0.002	0.026	0.0005	0.008	Light
Polyurethane foam	0.164	0.164	0.05	0.05	Dark
PVC	0.328	0.328	0.1	0.1	Dark
Variation			200:1	12.5:1	

Table B.4.7.5.1 Ratio of Optical Density to Temperature Rise

Material	$D_u/\Delta T$ [(m°C)$^{-1}$]		$D_u/\Delta T$ [(ft°F)$^{-1}$]		Maximum: Minimum
	Representative Value	Value Range	Representative Value	Value Range	
Wood (sugar pine, 5% moist)	1.20E-03	8.9E-4–3.2E-3	2.00E-04	1.5E–5.5E-4	3.7:1
Cotton (unbleached muslin fabric)	5.9E-4/1.2E-3	3.0E-4–1.8E-3	1.0E-04/2.0–4	5.0E-5–3.0E-4	6:1
Paper (in trash can)	1.80E-03	Data not available	3.00E-04	Data not available	—
Polyurethane foam	2.40E-03	1.2E-2–3.2E-2	4.00E-04	2.0E-3–5.5E-3	2.8:1
Polyester fiber (bed pillow)	1.80E-02	Data not available	5.0E-3/1.0E-2	Data not available	—
PVC (wire insulation)	3.0E-2/5.9E-2	5.9E-3–5.9E-2	3.00E-03	1.0E-3–1.0E-2	10:1
Foam rubber PU (sofa cushion)	7.70E-02	Data not available	1.30E-02	Data not available	—
Average	2.10E-02	3.0E-4–7.7E-2	3.60E-03	5.0E-05–1.3E-2	260:1

Also note that the values in Table B.4.7.5.3 are not based on temperature measurements taken at the detector response times, but were calculated by Heskestad and Delichatsios [10] from their recommended values of optical density at response (Table B.4.7.4.3) and their recommended ratios of optical density to temperature rise (Table B.4.7.5.1).

Table B.4.7.5.3 Temperature Rise for Detector Response [18]

Material	Ionization Temperature Rise		Scattering Temperature Rise	
	°C	°F	°C	°F
Wood	13.9	25	41.7	75
Cotton	1.7	3	27.8	50
Polyurethane	7.2	13	7.2	13
PVC	7.2	13	7.2	13
Average	7.8	14	21.1	38

Several experimental studies have cited temperature rises at detection as low as 1°C to 3°C (1.8°F to 5.4°F). Of particular note, Geiman [46] found that for flaming fires, 80 percent of the ionization detectors examined in full-scale smoke detection tests alarmed at measured temperature rises less than or equal to 3°C (5.4°F).

B.4.8 Methods for Estimating Smoke Detector Response.

B.4.8.1 General. There are various methods to estimate smoke detector response. Research is still needed in this area to reflect smoke production, transport to the detector, response of the detector, and performance metrics of the smoke detector. Designers should be aware of the advantages and disadvantages, as well as limitations, of these methods and undertake sensitivity analyses and use of multiple methods where applicable.

B.4.8.1.1 Method 1 — Optical Density Versus Temperature.

B.4.8.1.2 It is intended to determine whether an existing fire detection system can detect a fire in part of a warehouse used to store wardrobes in sufficient time to prevent radiant ignition of adjacent wardrobes. The area under review has a large, flat ceiling, 5 m (16.5 ft) high. The ambient temperature within the compartment is 20°C (68°F). The compartment is not sprinklered. The wardrobes are constructed mainly of particleboard. The detectors are ionization-type smoke detectors spaced 6.1 m (20 ft) on center. The design objective is to keep the maximum heat release rate (Q_{DO}) below 2 MW (1897 Btu/sec) in order to ensure that radiant ignition of the wardrobes in the adjacent aisle will not occur. There is an on-site fire brigade that can respond to and begin discharging water on the fire within 90 seconds of receiving the alarm. It can be assumed that there are no other delays between the time the detector reaches its operating threshold and the time to notification of the fire brigade. Given this information, would the existing system be sufficient?

B.4.8.1.3 The following assumptions are made for this example:

$$\alpha = 0.047 \text{ kW/sec}^2 \left(0.044 \text{ Btu/sec}^3\right)$$

$$\text{RTI} = 25 \text{ m}^{1/2}\text{sec}^{1/2} \left(45 \text{ ft}^{1/2} \text{ sec}^{1/2}\right)$$

Temperature rise for response = 14°C (25°F)

Refer to Table B.4.7.5.3 for temperature rise to response of an ionization smoke detector for a wood fire.

B.4.8.1.4 Using the power law equation, the design objective response time is calculated as follows:

$$Q_{DO} = \alpha t_{DO}^2 \qquad \textbf{(B.39)}$$

$$2000 \text{ kW} = 0.047 \text{ kW/sec}^2 \, (t_{DO}^2)$$

$$t_{DO} = 210 \text{ sec}$$

or

$$1897 \text{ Btu/sec} = 0.044 \text{ Btu/sec}^3 \, (t_{DO}^2)$$

$$t_{DO} = 210 \text{ sec}$$

B.4.8.1.5 Next, subtract the time for the fire brigade to respond to determine what time after ignition that detection should occur. Note that a 30-second safety factor has been added to the fire brigade's response time.

$$t_{CR} = 210 \text{ sec} - 120 \text{ sec} = 90 \text{ sec} \qquad \textbf{(B.40)}$$

B.4.8.1.6 Then calculate the critical heat release rate at which detection should occur as follows:

$$Q_{CR} = \alpha t_{CR}^2 \qquad \textbf{(B.41)}$$

$$Q_{CR} = 0.047 \text{ kW/sec}^2 \left(90 \text{ sec}\right)^2 = 380 \text{ kW}$$

or

$$Q_{CR} = 0.044 \text{ Btu/sec}^3 \left(90 \text{ sec}\right)^2 = 360 \text{ Btu/sec}$$

B.4.8.1.7 Using the numbers in the fire detection design and analysis worksheet at 90 seconds into the fire when the heat release rate is 380 kW (360 Btu/sec), the temperature rise at the detector is calculated to be approximately 17°C (30.6°F). This, therefore, might be a reasonable approximation to show that the detector might respond.

B.4.8.2 Method 2 — Mass Optical Density.

B.4.8.2.1 Data regarding smoke characteristics for given fuels can be used as another method to evaluate detector response.

B.4.8.2.2 The following example is provided.

The design objective established for this scenario is to detect the smoke from a flaming 400 g (1.0 lb) polyurethane chair cushion in less than 2 minutes. The chair is placed in a compartment that is 40 m² (431 ft²). The ceiling height is 3.0 m (10 ft). It has been determined that the burning rate of the cushion is a steady rate of 50 g/min (0.09 lb/min). Determine whether the design objective will be met.

B.4.8.2.3 The total mass loss of the cushion due to combustion at 2 minutes is 100 g (0.22 lb). Therefore, the optical density in the room produced by the burning cushion can be calculated from the following equation: [5]

$$D = \frac{D_m M}{V_c} \qquad \text{(B.42)}$$

where:
D_m = mass optical density (m^2/g) [26]
M = mass (g)
V_c = volume of the compartment
D = [(0.22 m^2/g)(100 g)]/(40 m^2)(3 m) = 0.183 m^{-1}

or

where:
D_m = mass optical density (ft^2/lb) [26]
M = mass (lb)
V_c = volume of the compartment
D = [(1075 ft^2/lb)(0.22 lb)]/(431 ft^2)(9.8 ft) = 0.056 ft^{-1}

B.4.8.2.4 If it is assumed that the detector responds at an optical density of 0.15 m^{-1} (0.046 ft^{-1}), the maximum black smoke optical density allowed in a previous edition of the ANSI/UL 268 sensitivity test [35], it can be assumed that the detector will respond within 2 minutes.

B.4.8.2.5 It should be noted that this method presents a very simplified approach, and that various assumptions would need to be made including that the smoke is confined to the room, is well mixed, can reach the ceiling, and can enter the detector.

B.4.8.2.6 The preceding estimation assumes that the smoke is evenly distributed throughout the entire compartment volume. This is rarely the case but establishes a very conservative limit. For design purposes, one can model the smoke layer as a cylindrical volume centered about the fire plume having a depth equivalent to the ceiling jet thickness or some multiple of it. Refer to Figure B.4.8.2.6.

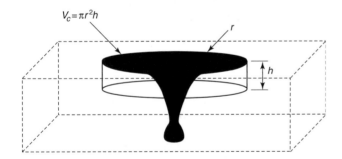

FIGURE B.4.8.2.6 Smoke Layer Volume Model.

The volume of the cylinder can now be used as the solution volume:

$$D = \frac{D_m M}{V_c} \qquad \text{(B.43)}$$

is used with the substitution of

$$V_c = \pi r^2 h \qquad \text{(B.44)}$$

To obtain the maximum radius from the fire plume centerline at which detector response is expected, the nominal 0.14 m^{-1} optical density criterion is substituted into the relation and an explicit relation for r is obtained,

$$r = \left(\frac{D_m M}{0.14 \pi h} \right)^{1/2} \qquad \text{(B.45)}$$

Note that the results of this calculation are highly dependent upon the assumed layer thickness, h. The designer must carefully document the value used for the ceiling jet thickness for this reason. This method does not assume any minimum velocity across the detector, nor does it provide for any delay due to smoke entry. Finally, it assumes uniform smoke concentration throughout the solution volume. Failure to use prudently selected values for ceiling jet thickness and use of this relation outside the limitations imposed by the assumptions can lead to invalid designs.

B.4.8.2.7 The mass optical density method also enables the designer to analyze existing systems. When we accept the assumption that smoke detectors listed by UL will respond at an optical density of 0.14 m^{-1}, we can write the relation:

$$D_A = 0.14 = \frac{D_m M}{V_c} \qquad \text{(B.46)}$$

and thus

$$M = D_A \pi r^2 h / D_m \qquad \text{(B.47)}$$

for a cylindrical solution volume.

Since $H(t) = M \Delta H_c$ and $H(t) = (\alpha t^3)/3$, we can write the relation

$$M = \frac{(\alpha t^3)}{3 \Delta H_c} \qquad \text{(B.48)}$$

Substituting, this leads to the relation

$$\frac{(\alpha t^3)}{3 \Delta H_c} = \frac{D_A \pi r^2 h}{D_m} \qquad \text{(B.49)}$$

This relation is reorganized to be explicit in t,

$$t = \left(\frac{3 D_A \pi r^2 h \Delta H_c}{\alpha D_m} \right)^{1/3} \qquad \text{(B.50)}$$

This time estimate must be corrected for the lag time produced by the resistance to smoke entry of the detector. Currently, this time delay, which is a function of detector design and ceiling jet velocity, is not quantified in the listing process. Consequently, the designer must make an estimate of the time delay due to smoke entry, t_e. Thus, the response time estimate becomes:

$$t = \left(\frac{3 D_A \pi r^2 h \Delta H_c}{\alpha D_m} \right)^{1/3} + t_e \qquad \text{(B.51)}$$

This relation predicts the time at which the mass optical density attains the detector alarm threshold in the solution volume derived from the detector spacing and an assumed ceiling jet thickness. Again, the results of this calculation are highly dependent upon the assumed ceiling jet layer thickness. However, once time, t, is known, if the fire can be characterized as a t-square fire, the fire size can be calculated from the relation

$$Q = \alpha t^2 \qquad \text{(B.52)}$$

Consequently, substitution of this relation into the preceding relation yields the final analytical relation for the heat release rate at alarm, Q_a:

$$Q_a = \alpha \left[\left(\frac{3D_A \pi r^2 h \Delta H_c}{\alpha D_m} \right)^{1/3} + t_e \right]^2 \quad \textbf{(B.53)}$$

This relation provides an estimate of detector response subject to the assumptions and values selected or the relevant parameters. The estimate can be no better than the data used to generate it.

B.4.8.3 Critical Velocity Method. Research shows that a minimum critical velocity is necessary before smoke can enter the sensing chamber of the smoke detector. *(See B.4.7.3.)* This method assumes that, if this critical velocity has been attained, sufficient smoke concentration is in the ceiling jet gas flow to produce an alarm signal. Ceiling jet velocity correlations exist for steady-state fires, not *t*-square fires. However, a *t*-square fire can be modeled as a succession of steady-state fires for slow and medium growth rate fires. In the UL smoke box test, the minimum flow velocity at the detector is 0.152 m/sec (30 ft/minute). The correlation

$$\frac{0.195 \left(Q^{1/3} H^{1/2} \right)}{r^{5/6}} \quad \text{for } r/h \geq 0.15 \quad \textbf{(B.54)}$$

is used. U_r is set to equal 0.152 m/sec. With this substitution the relation becomes:

$$r \leq \left(1.28 Q_c^{1/3} H^{1/2} \right)^{6/5} \quad \textbf{(B.55)}$$

This relation is solved to obtain the maximum distance between the fire plume centerline and the detector at which the critical jet velocity is expected to be obtained for the given convective heat release rate and ceiling height.

B.4.9 Projected Beam Smoke Detection.

B.4.9.1 Projected beam smoke detection is often used in large open spaces with high ceilings where the use of spot-type detectors is impractical due to the problems of smoke stratification. In these spaces, there is questionable basis for the use of the prescriptive spacings presented in Section 17.7. However, beams can be installed such that, regardless of the fire origin, the plume will intersect at least one beam. To employ this strategy, the plume divergence is calculated as a function of the altitude at which the projected beam detectors are installed. The region of relatively uniform temperature and smoke density in a buoyant plume diverges at an angle of approximately 22 degrees, as shown in Figure B.4.9.1.

Another method involves assessing the smoke obstruction through the plume to determine the reduction in light from the receiver to the transmitter of the beam-type smoke detector to determine whether the detector might respond. [47]

B.4.10 Effects of HVAC Systems. The requirement to address the effects of HVAC systems on the performance of smoke detectors was historically reduced to a "3-foot rule." However, research conducted under the auspices of the Fire Protection Research Foundation showed that such a simple rule was not adequate in many cases.

Theoretically, the effect of HVAC flows on the performance of smoke detectors can be implemented by calculating the flow velocity and smoke concentration at the detector as a function of fire growth and HVAC operating parameters. With

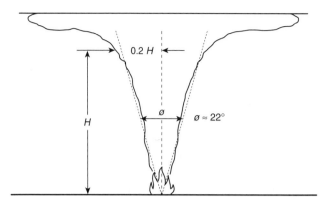

FIGURE B.4.9.1 The Plume Divergence of an Unconstrained Fire.

complex ceilings this often requires the use of computational fluid dynamics models running in computers. One such model is FDS, developed and supported by NIST.

However, for simple, planar ceilings at heights customarily encountered in conventional construction, the effects of HVAC system can be estimated using a simplified calculation derived from well-known correlations to identify where a problem is likely. These simple calculations are not a substitute for a fully modeled scenario, but they provide the advantage of being easily executed in a short time frame.

Ceiling-mounted HVAC system supply and return registers are designed to produce specific airflow patterns. The exact shape of the velocity and flow volume profiles is determined by the physical design of the register. A commercially available register might exhibit a flow profile as shown in Figure B.4.10.

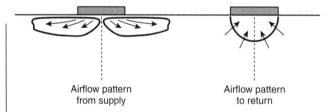

Airflow pattern   Airflow pattern
from supply   to return

FIGURE B.4.10 Typical HVAC Flow Patterns in Mercantile and Business Occupancies.

This section considers two cases. The first is where the ceiling jet is being acted upon by an HVAC system supply. The second is where the ceiling jet is being acted upon by an HVAC system return. Each case is considered in its bounding value condition to provide a worst-case estimate of the resulting velocity at the detector.

In the first case, the flow of air from the ceiling supply can divert, impede, and dilute the ceiling jet flow, retarding detector response. This effect can be estimated using a one-dimensional vector analysis of the velocity produced by the HVAC system versus that produced by the fire. The velocity profile produced by the HVAC supply register is determined by the design of the register and the flow volume supplied to it. The velocity at the detector produced by the fire is an artifact of the ceiling jet. The sum of these two velocities versus the minimum velocity for response can be used to determine if sufficient ceiling jet velocity exists at the detector to initiate an alarm.

In the second case, the HVAC return pulls air up from lower elevations in the compartment, diluting the smoke density in the ceiling jet in the vicinity of the HVAC return. This case is much more difficult to evaluate because it implies a flow volume analysis to determine when the flow to ceiling-mounted HVAC returns will distort the concentration profile of the ceiling jet to the point that it adversely affects detector response. Unfortunately, the listings of smoke detectors do not include an explicit measurable value for detector sensitivity in terms that can relate to the design fire.

B.4.10.1 Effects of HVAC Ceiling Supply Registers. This method makes use of the finding that there is a critical minimum velocity necessary for reliable smoke detector response. The use of the 30 ft/min (0.15 m/sec) flow velocity in the UL 268 and 217 smoke detector sensitivity test for spot-type smoke detectors has led to the evolution of spot-type smoke detectors that are optimized for that flow velocity. In listing investigations, it has been learned that when the ceiling jet velocity is less than the nominal 30 ft/min (0.15 m/sec) commercially available, listed spot-type smoke detector, performance begins to suffer. *(See B.4.7.3.)*

For the prediction of spot-type smoke detector response we assume that the ceiling jet velocity at the detector must exceed this critical velocity, 0.15 m/sec (30 ft/min), at the detector. The flow from an HVAC system supply register also produces a flow velocity. When a fire occurs in a room equipped with ceiling-mounted HVAC system supply, the velocity at the detector is the vector sum of the velocity due to the HVAC system supply and the fire ceiling jet.

To estimate the resultant flow velocity at a smoke detector, the flow velocity from the ceiling supply is determined as a function of register design, flow volume, and distance from the supply register. The velocity produced by the ceiling jet is calculated as a function of distance from the fire plume. The worst-case limit condition is where the detector location is where the ceiling jet flow is directly opposite in direction to the flow from the HVAC supply register. Consequently, it is assumed that the ceiling jet is flowing in the opposite direction of the flow from the ceiling register.

The flow of air into a compartment via the HVAC system can be estimated by the flow volume and a flow factor that is related to the flow characteristics of the supply register. See Figure B.4.10.1(a) for an example of such characteristics.

The manufacturer of the ceiling supply register provides a velocity diagram that depicts flow velocity as a function of flow volume for each register it produces. In the U.S., these diagrams generally use conventional feet per minute (FPM) and cubic feet per minute (CFM) units. Since fire protection engineering correlations are generally expressed in metric units, it is necessary to convert the flow volume and flow velocity from the HVAC system to metric units. Replacing CFM with flow volume per unit time this relation becomes:

$$v_r = k(V)/d^2 \text{ m/sec} \tag{B.56}$$

Where v_r is the velocity due to the register.

The ceiling jet velocity can be modeled with the relation for critical velocity developed by Alpert.

$$v_d = 0.195\left(Q_c^{1/3}H^{1/2}\right)r^{5/6} \text{ m/sec} \tag{B.57}$$

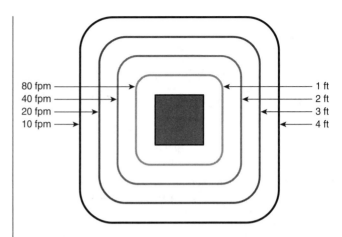

$v = k(\text{CFM})/d^2$ (converted to metric units)

FIGURE B.4.10.1(a)   Typical HVAC Velocity Versus Flow Volume Diagram that Might be Used to Describe Operation of Supply Register.

The flow at the detector is the sum of the velocity from the ceiling jet and the ceiling supply register. Since the worst-case scenario is where the fire is located such that the flow of the ceiling jet is directly opposed to the flow from the HVAC supply register, this scenario forms the basis for the analysis as shown in Figure B.4.10.1(b).

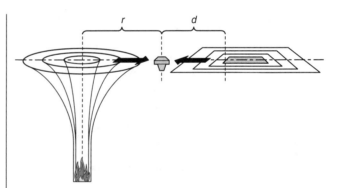

FIGURE B.4.10.1(b)   Ceiling Jet Flow in Opposition to Flow from HVAC System.

The velocity from the ceiling jet is derived from Alpert's correlations.

$$v_d = 0.195\left(Q_c^{1/3}H^{1/2}\right)r^{5/6} \tag{B.58}$$

where:
v_d = ceiling jet velocity at the detector
Q_c = convective heat release, 0.65 Q
H = ceiling height
r = radius, distance between plume centerline and the detector

All in metric units.

In the case of opposing flows, the resultant velocity at the detector is the ceiling jet velocity minus the velocity due to the flow from the HVAC supply. The relation becomes:

$$v_d = 0.195\left(Q_c^{1/3}H^{1/2}\right)/r^{5/6} - k(V)/d^2 \tag{B.59}$$

Smoke detector response can be expected to be consistent with its listing when the value of v_d is greater than or equal to 0.15 m/sec. Thus the relation becomes:

$$0.15 \text{ m/sec} \leq 0.195\left(Q^{1/3}H^{1/2}\right)/r^{5/6} - k(CFM)/d^2 \quad \textbf{(B.60)}$$

If the right-hand side of the equation B.60 exceeds the left, the airflow from the HVAC register should not be sufficient to reduce the ceiling jet flow from the fire plume to the point where response by a smoke detector would not be expected. On the other hand, if the calculated resultant velocity is less than the 0.15 m/sec threshold, adjustments should be made to the design to locate the smoke detector where there will be sufficient ceiling jet velocity to predict alarm response.

B.4.10.2 Effects of HVAC Returns. When detectors are in close proximity to ceiling-mounted HVAC return grilles, the flow of air upward toward the return grille tends to dilute and cool the ceiling jet. This tends to retard the response of detectors. Unfortunately the geometry is more complex in this case. The ceiling jet is moving horizontally across the ceiling while the flow toward a ceiling-mounted return grille is essentially moving vertically.

Most ceiling return grilles usually exhibit a flow velocity profile that is roughly hemispherical in shape, centered on the duct centerline. Figure B.4.10.2 illustrates this flow velocity profile.

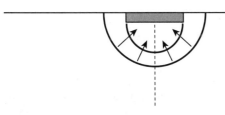

FIGURE B.4.10.2 Velocity Profile for Ceiling-Mounted Return Grille.

As the radial distance from the HVAC return increases, the velocity drops off quite rapidly, proportional to 4π times the square of the increase in distance. The relative velocity contributions could be again used to calculate the relative effect, but in this case an explicit sensitivity parameter that relates to the design fire is not available. Percent per foot obscuration cannot be reliably used.

However, the bounding value, worst-case scenario is where the upward velocity is modeled as if it is flowing directly opposite to that of the ceiling jet. This reduces to the same analysis as for the ceiling supply.

These calculations do NOT replace CFD modeling. They are limited only for level ceilings of heights normally encountered in commercial construction. In that limited context they can be used to predict smoke detector performance.

B.5 Radiant Energy Detection.

B.5.1 General.

B.5.1.1 Electromagnetic Radiation. Electromagnetic radiation is emitted over a broad range of the spectrum during the combustion process. The portion of the spectrum in which radiant energy–sensing detectors operate has been divided into three bands: ultraviolet (UV), visible, or infrared (IR). These wavelengths are defined with the following wavelength ranges: [3]

(1) Ultraviolet 0.1–0.35 microns
(2) Visible 0.35–0.75 microns
(3) Infrared 0.75–220 microns

B.5.1.2 Wavelength. These wavelength ranges correspond to the quantum-mechanical interaction between matter and energy. Photonic interactions with matter can be characterized by wavelength as shown in Table B.5.1.2.

Table B.5.1.2 Wavelength Ranges

Wavelength	Photonic Interaction
$\lambda < 50$ micron	Gross molecular translations
$50 \ \mu m < \lambda < 1.0 \ \mu m$	Molecular vibrations and rotations
$1.0 \ \mu m < \lambda < 0.05 \ \mu m$	Valence electron bond vibrations
$0.3 \ \mu m < \lambda < 0.05 \ \mu m$	Electron stripping and recombinations

B.5.1.3 Photon Transfer. When a fuel molecule is oxidized in the combustion process, the combustion intermediate molecule must lose energy to become a stable molecular species. This energy is emitted as a photon with a unique wavelength determined by the following equation:

$$e = \frac{hc}{\lambda} \quad \textbf{(B.61)}$$

where:
e = energy (joules)
h = Planck's constant (6.63E-23 joule-sec)
c = speed of light (m/sec)
λ = wavelength (microns)

[1.0 joule = 5.0345E+18(λ), where λ is measured in microns.]

B.5.1.4 Type of Detector. The choice of the type of radiant energy–sensing detector to use is determined by the type of emissions that are expected from the fire radiator.

B.5.1.4.1 Fuels that produce a flame, a stream of combustible or flammable gases involved in the combustion reaction with a gaseous oxidizer, radiate quantum emissions. These fuels include flammable gases, flammable liquids, combustible liquids, and solids that are burning with a flame.

B.5.1.4.2 Fuels that are oxidized in the solid phase or radiators that are emitting due to their internal temperature (sparks and embers) radiate Planckian emissions. These fuels include carbonaceous fuels such as coal, charcoal, wood, and cellulosic fibers that are burning without an established flame, as well as metals that have been heated due to mechanical impacts and friction.

B.5.1.4.3 Almost all combustion events produce Planckian emissions, emissions that are the result of the thermal energy in the fuel mass. Therefore, spark/ember detectors that are designed to detect these emissions are not fuel specific. Flame detectors detect quantum emissions that are the result of changes in molecular structure and energy state in the gas phase. These emissions are uniquely associated with particular molecular structures. This can result in a flame detector that is very fuel specific.

B.5.1.5 Effects of Ambient. The choice of radiant energy–sensing detector is also limited by the effect of ambient conditions. The design must take into account the radiant energy absorption of the atmosphere, presence of non-fire-related radiation sources that might cause nuisance alarms, the electromagnetic energy of the spark, ember, or fire to be detected, the distance from the fire source to the sensor, and characteristics of the sensor.

B.5.1.5.1 Ambient Non-Fire Radiators. Most ambients contain non-fire radiators that can emit at wavelengths used by radiant energy–sensing detectors for fire detection. The designer should make a thorough evaluation of the ambient to identify radiators that have the potential for producing unwarranted alarm response from radiant energy–sensing detectors. Since radiant energy–sensing detectors use electronic components that can act as antennas, the evaluation should include radio band, microwave, infrared, visible, and ultraviolet sources.

B.5.1.5.2 Ambient Radiant Absorbance. The medium through which radiant energy passes from fire source to detector has a finite transmittance. Transmittance is usually quantified by its reciprocal, absorbance. Absorbance by atmospheric species varies with wavelength. Gaseous species absorb at the same wavelengths that they emit. Particulate species can transmit, reflect, or absorb radiant emission, and the proportion that is absorbed is expressed as the reciprocal of its emissivity, ε.

B.5.1.5.3 Contamination of Optical Surfaces. Radiant energy can be absorbed or reflected by materials contaminating the optical surfaces of radiant energy–sensing detectors. The designer should evaluate the potential for surface contamination and implement provisions for keeping these surfaces clean. Extreme caution must be employed when considering the use of surrogate windows. Common glass, acrylic, and other glazing materials are opaque at the wavelengths used by most flame detectors and some spark/ember detectors. Placing a window between the detector and the hazard area that has not been listed by a nationally recognized testing laboratory (NRTL) for use with the detector in question is a violation of the detector listing and will usually result in a system that is incapable of detecting a fire in the hazard area.

B.5.1.5.4 Design Factors. These factors are important for several reasons. First, a radiation sensor is primarily a line-of-sight device, and must "see" the fire source. If there are other radiation sources in the area, or if atmospheric conditions are such that a large fraction of the radiation could be absorbed in the atmosphere, the type, location, and spacing of the sensors could be affected. In addition, the sensors react to specific wavelengths, and the fuel must emit radiation in the sensor's bandwidth. For example, an infrared detection device with a single sensor tuned to 4.3 microns (the CO_2 emission peak) cannot be expected to detect a non-carbon-based fire. Furthermore, the sensor needs to be able to respond reliably within the required time, especially when activating an explosion suppression system or similar fast-response extinguishing or control system.

B.5.1.6 Detector Response Model. The response of radiant energy–sensing detectors is modeled with a modified inverse square relationship as shown in the following equation [5]:

$$S = \frac{kPe^{-\zeta d}}{d^2} \tag{B.62}$$

where:
S = radiant power reaching the detector (W or Btu/sec) sufficient to produce alarm response
k = proportionality constant for the detector

P = radiant power emitted by the fire (W or Btu/sec)
ζ = extinction coefficient of air at detector operating wavelengths
d = distance between the fire and the detector (m or ft)

This relationship models the fire as a point source radiator, of uniform radiant output per steradian, some distance (d) from the detector. This relationship also models the effect of absorbance by the air between the fire and the detector as being a uniform extinction function. The designer must verify that these modeling assumptions are valid for the application in question.

B.5.2 Design of Flame Detection Systems.

B.5.2.1 Detector Sensitivity. Flame detector sensitivity is traditionally quantified as the distance at which the unit can detect a fire of given size. The fire most commonly used by the NRTLs in North America is a 0.9 m^2 (1.0 ft^2) fire fueled with regular grade, unleaded gasoline. Some special-purpose detectors are evaluated using 150 mm (6 in.) diameter fires fueled with isopropanol.

B.5.2.1.1 This means of sensitivity determination does not take into account that flames can best be modeled as an optically dense radiator in which radiant emissions radiated from the far side of the flame toward the detector are re-absorbed by the flame. Consequently, the radiated power from a flame is not proportional to the area of the fire but to the flame silhouette, and hence to the height and width of the fire.

B.5.2.1.2 Because flame detectors detect the radiant emissions produced during the formation of flame intermediates and products, the radiant intensity produced by a flame at a given wavelength is proportional to the relative concentration of the specific intermediate or product in the flame and that portion of the total heat release rate of the fire resulting from the formation of that specific intermediate or product. This means that the response of a detector can vary widely as different fuels are used to produce a fire of the same surface area and flame width.

B.5.2.1.3 Many flame detectors are designed to detect specific products such as water (2.5 microns) and CO_2 (4.35 microns). These detectors cannot be used for fires that do not produce these products as a result of the combustion process.

B.5.2.1.4 Many flame detectors use time variance of the radiant emissions of a flame to distinguish between non-fire radiators and a flame. Where a deflagration hazard exists, the designer must determine the sample time period for such flame detectors and how such detectors will operate in the event of a deflagration of fuel vapor or fuel gases.

B.5.2.2 Design Fire. Using the process outlined in Section B.2, determine the fire size (kW or Btu/sec) at which detection must be achieved.

B.5.2.2.1 Compute the surface area the design fire is expected to occupy from the correlations in Table B.2.3.2.6.2(a) or other sources. Use the flame height correlation to determine the height of the flame plume:

$$h_f = 0.182(kQ)^{2/5} \quad \text{(for SI units)} \tag{B.63a}$$

or

$$h_f = 0.584\left(kQ\right)^{2/5} \quad \text{(for inch-pound units)} \quad \textbf{(B.63b)}$$

where:
h_f = flame height (m or ft)
Q = heat release rate (kW or Btu/sec)
k = wall effect factor

Where there are no nearby walls, use $k = 1$.

Where the fuel package is near a wall, use $k = 2$.

Where the fuel package is in a corner, use $k = 4$.

Determine the minimum anticipated flame area width (w_f). Where flammable or combustible liquids are the fuel load and are unconfined, model the fuel as a circular pool. Compute the radiating area (A_r) using the following equation:

$$A_r = \frac{1}{2h_f w_f} \quad \textbf{(B.64)}$$

where:
A_r = radiating area (m² or ft²)
h_f = flame height (m or ft)
w_f = flame width (m or ft)

B.5.2.2.2 The radiant power output of the fire to the detector can be approximated as being proportional to the radiating area (A_r) of the flame:

$$P = cA_r \quad \textbf{(B.65)}$$

where:
A_r = radiating area (m² or ft²)
c = power per unit area proportionality constant
P = radiated power (W or Btu/sec)

B.5.2.3 Calculate Detector Sensitivity. Using equation B.58a or B.58b compute the radiating area of the test fire used by the NRTL in the listing process (A_t). The radiant power output of the test fire to the detector in the listing process is proportional to the radiating area (A_t) of the listing test flame.

B.5.2.4 Calculate Detector Response to Design Fire. Because the sensitivity of a flame detector is fixed during the manufacturing process, the following is the relationship that determines the radiant power reaching the detector sufficient to produce an alarm response:

$$S = \frac{kcA_t e^{-\zeta d}}{d^2} \quad \textbf{(B.66)}$$

where:
S = radiant power reaching the detector (W or Btu/sec) sufficient to produce alarm response
k = proportionality constant for the detector
A_t = radiant area of the listing test fire (m² or ft²)
ζ = extinction coefficient of air at detector operating wavelengths
d = distance between the fire and the detector during the listing fire test (m or ft)
c = emitted power per unit flame radiating area correlation

Because the sensitivity of the detector is constant over the range of ambients for which it is listed:

$$S = \frac{kcA_r e^{-\zeta d'}}{d'^2} \quad \textbf{(B.67)}$$

where:
S = radiant power reaching the detector (W or Btu/sec) sufficient to produce alarm response
k = proportionality constant for the detector
c = emitted power per unit flame radiating area correlation
A_r = radiant area of the design fire (m² or ft²)
ζ = extinction coefficient of air at detector operating wavelengths
d' = distance between the design fire and the detector (m or ft)

Therefore, use the following equation to determine the following:

$$\frac{kcA_t e^{-\zeta d}}{d^2} = \frac{kcA_r e^{-\zeta d'}}{d'^2} \quad \textbf{(B.68)}$$

To solve for d' use the following equation:

$$\left(\frac{d^2 A_r e^{-\zeta d'}}{A_t e^{-\zeta d}}\right)^{1/2} = d' \quad \textbf{(B.69)}$$

This relation is solved iteratively for d', the distance at which the detector can detect the design fire.

B.5.2.5 Correction for Angular Displacement.

B.5.2.5.1 Most flame detectors exhibit a loss of sensitivity as the fire is displaced from the optical axis of the detector. This correction to the detector sensitivity is shown as a polar graph in Figure A.17.8.3.2.3.

B.5.2.5.2 When the correction for angular displacement is expressed as a reduction of normalized detection distance, the correction is made to detection distance (d').

B.5.2.5.3 When the correction for angular displacement is expressed as a normalized sensitivity (fire size increment), the correction must be made to A_r, prior to calculating response distance (d').

B.5.2.6 Corrections for Fuel. Most flame detectors exhibit some level of fuel specificity. Some manufacturers provide "fuel factors" that relate detector response performance to a fire of one fuel to the response performance of a benchmark fuel. Other manufacturers provide performance criteria for a list of specific fuels. Unless the manufacturer's published instructions, bearing the listing mark, contain explicit instructions for the application of the detector for fuels other than those used in the listing process, the unit cannot be deemed listed for use in hazard areas containing fuels different from those employed in the listing process.

B.5.2.6.1 When the fuel factor correction is expressed as a detection distance reduction, the correction should be applied after the detection distance has been computed.

B.5.2.6.2 When the fuel factor correction is expressed as a function of normalized fire size, the correction must be made prior to calculating detection distance.

B.5.2.7 Atmospheric Extinction Factors.

B.5.2.7.1 Because the atmosphere is not infinitely transmittent at any wavelength, all flame detectors are affected by atmospheric absorption to some degree. The effect of atmospheric extinction on the performance of flame detectors is determined to some degree by the wavelengths used for sensing and the detector electronic architecture. Values for the atmospheric extinction coefficient (ζ) should be obtained from the detector manufacturer's published instructions.

B.5.2.7.2 The numerical value of ζ can be determined experimentally for any flame detector. The detector must be tested with two different sized test fires to determine the distance at which each of the fires can be detected by the detector in question. The larger the difference between the sizes of the flaming fires, the more precise the determination of ζ. Ideally, one test fire would be approximately 4 times the heat release rate (surface area) of the other. The data are then used in the relation:

$$\zeta = \frac{\ln\left[\left(d_1^2 A_2\right)/\left(d_2^2 A_1\right)\right]}{d_2 - d_1} \quad \textbf{(B.70)}$$

where:
"1" = subscripts referring to the first test fire
"2" = subscripts referring to the second test fire
d = maximum distance between the flame detector and the fire at which the fire is detected
A = the radiating area of the test fire as determined per B.5.2.2.1

This relation allows the designer to determine the value of ζ for detectors that are already installed or for those that were evaluated for listing before the inclusion of the requirement for the publishing of ζ appeared in ANSI/FM-3260.

B.5.3 Design of Spark/Ember Detection Systems.

B.5.3.1 Design Fire. Using the process outlined in Section B.2, determine the fire size (kW or Btu/sec) at which detection must be achieved.

B.5.3.1.1 The quantification of the fire is generally derived from the energy investment per unit time sufficient to propagate combustion of the combustible particulate solids in the fuel stream. Because energy per unit time is power, expressed in watts, the fire size criterion is generally expressed in watts or milliwatts.

B.5.3.1.2 The radiant emissions, integrated over all wavelengths, from a non-ideal Planckian radiator is expressed with the following form of the Stefan–Boltzmann equation:

$$P = \varepsilon A \sigma T^4 \quad \textbf{(B.71)}$$

where:
P = radiant power (W or Btu/sec)
ε = emissivity, a material property expressed as a fraction between 0 and 1.0
A = area of radiator (m^2 or ft^2)
σ = Stefan–Boltzmann constant 5.67E-8 W/m^{2}K^4
T = temperature (K or R)

B.5.3.1.3 This models the spark or ember as a point source radiator.

B.5.3.2 Fire Environment. Spark/ember detectors are usually used on pneumatic conveyance system ducts to monitor combustible particulate solids as they flow past the detector(s). This environment puts large concentrations of combustible particulate solids between the fire and the detector. A value for ζ must be computed for the monitored environment. The simplifying assumption that absorbance at visible levels is equal to

or greater than that at infrared wavelengths yields conservative designs and is used.

B.5.3.3 Calculate Detector Response to Design Fire. Because the sensitivity of a spark/ember detector is fixed during the manufacturing process,

$$S = \frac{kPe^{-\zeta d}}{d^2} \quad \textbf{(B.72)}$$

where:
S = radiant power reaching the detector (W or Btu/sec) sufficient to produce alarm response
k = proportionality constant for the detector
P = radiant power emitted by test spark (W or Btu/sec)
ζ = extinction coefficient of air at detector operating wavelengths
d = distance between the fire and the detector during the listing fire test (m^2 or ft^2)

Because the sensitivity of the detector is constant over the range of ambients for which it is listed,

$$S = \frac{kP'e^{-\zeta d'}}{d'^2} \quad \textbf{(B.73)}$$

where:
S = radiant power reaching the detector (W or Btu/sec) sufficient to produce alarm response
k = proportionality constant for the detector
P' = radiant power from the design fire (W or Btu/sec)
ζ = the extinction coefficient of air at detector operating wavelengths
d' = the distance between the design fire and the detector (m^2 or ft^2)

Therefore, use the following equation to solve for

$$\frac{kPe^{-\zeta d}}{d^2} = \frac{kP'e^{-\zeta d'}}{d'^2} \quad \textbf{(B.74)}$$

To solve for d',

$$d' = \left(\frac{d^2 P' e^{-\zeta d'}}{P e^{-\zeta d}}\right)^{1/2} \quad \textbf{(B.75)}$$

This relation is solved iteratively for d', the distance at which the detector can detect the design fire.

B.5.3.4 Correction for Angular Displacement.

B.5.3.4.1 Most spark/ember detectors exhibit a loss of sensitivity as the fire is displaced from the optical axis of the detector. This correction to the detector sensitivity is shown as a polar graph in Figure A.17.8.3.2.3.

B.5.3.4.2 When the correction for angular displacement is expressed as a reduction of normalized detection distance, the correction is made to detection distance (d').

B.5.3.4.3 When the correction for angular displacement is expressed as a normalized sensitivity (fire size increment), the correction must be made to P' prior to calculating response distance (d').

B.5.3.5 Corrections for Fuel. Because spark/ember detectors respond to Planckian emission in the near infrared portion of the spectrum, corrections for fuels are rarely necessary.

B.6 Computer Fire Models. Several special application computer models are available to assist in the design and analysis of both heat detectors (e.g., fixed-temperature, rate-of-rise, sprinklers, fusible links) and smoke detectors. These computer models typically run on personal computers and are available from NIST website http://fire.nist.gov.

B.6.1 DETACT — T^2. DETACT — T^2 (DETector ACTuation — time squared) calculates the actuation time of heat detectors (fixed-temperature and rate-of-rise) and sprinklers to user-specified fires that grow with the square of time. DETACT — T^2 assumes the detector is located in a large compartment with an unconfined ceiling, where there is no accumulation of hot gases at the ceiling. Thus, heating of the detector is only from the flow of hot gases along the ceiling. Input data include H, τ_0, RTI, T_s, S, and α. The program calculates the heat release rate at detector activation, as well as the time to activation.

B.6.2 DETACT — QS. DETACT — QS (DETector ACTuation — quasi-steady) calculates the actuation time of heat detectors and sprinklers in response to fires that grow according to a user-defined fire. DETACT — QS assumes the detector is located in a large compartment with unconfined ceilings, where there is no accumulation of hot gases at the ceiling. Thus, heating of the detector is only from the flow of hot gases along the ceiling. Input data include H, τ_0, RTI, T_s, the distance of the detector from the fire's axis, and heat release rates at user-specified times. The program calculates the heat release rate at detector activation, the time to activation, and the ceiling jet temperature.

DETACT — QS can also be found in HAZARD I, FIRE-FORM, FPETOOL. A comprehensive evaluation of DETACT QS can be found in the *SFPE Engineering Guide: Evaluation of the Computer Fire Model DETACT QS*. This guide provides information on the theoretical basis, mathematical robustness, sensitivity of output to input, and an evaluation of the predictive ability of the model.

B.6.3 LAVENT. LAVENT (Link Actuated VENT) calculates the actuation time of sprinklers and fusible link-actuated ceiling vents in compartment fires with draft curtains. Inputs include the ambient temperature, compartment size, thermophysical properties of the ceiling, fire location, size and growth rate, ceiling vent area and location, RTI, and temperature rating of the fusible links. Outputs of the model include the temperatures and release times of the links, the areas of the vents that have opened, the radial temperature distribution at the ceiling, and the temperature and height of the upper layer.

B.6.4 JET is a single-compartment, two-zone computer model. It has been designed to calculate the centerline temperature of the plume, the ceiling jet temperature, and the ceiling jet velocity. JET can model ceiling-mounted fusible links, as well as link-actuated ceiling vents. JET evolved from the model platform used for LAVENT and contains many of the same features. Some of the major differences between them include the ceiling jet temperature and velocity algorithms, the fusible link algorithm, and the use of a variable radiative fraction. [57]

B.6.5 References.

(1) Alpert, R. "Ceiling Jets," *Fire Technology*, Aug. 1972.

(2) "Evaluating Unsprinklered Fire Hazards," *SFPE Technology Report* 83-2.

(3) Babrauskas, V., Lawson, J. R., Walton, W. D., and Twilley, W. H. "Upholstered Furniture Heat Release Rates Measured with a Furniture Calorimeter," (NBSIR 82-2604) (Dec. 1982). National Institute of Standards and Technology (formerly National Bureau of Standards), Center for Fire Research, Gaithersburg, MD 20889.

(4) Beyler, C. "A Design Method for Flaming Fire Detection," *Fire Technology*, Vol. 20, No. 4, Nov. 1984.

(5) DiNenno, P., ed. Chapter 31, *SFPE Handbook of Fire Protection Engineering*, by R. Schifiliti, Sept. 1988.

(6) Evans, D. D. and Stroup, D. W. "Methods to Calculate Response Time of Heat and Smoke Detectors Installed Below Large Unobstructed Ceilings," (NBSIR 85-3167) (Feb. 1985, issued Jul. 1986). National Institute of Standards and Technology (formerly National Bureau of Standards), Center for Fire Research, Gaithersburg, MD 20889.

(7) Heskestad, G. "Characterization of Smoke Entry and Response for Products-of-Combustion Detectors" Proceedings, 7th International Conference on Problems of Automatic Fire Detection, Rheinish-Westfalischen Technischen Hochschule Aachen (Mar. 1975).

(8) Heskestad, G. "Investigation of a New Sprinkler Sensitivity Approval Test: The Plunge Test," FMRC Tech. Report 22485, Factory Mutual Research Corporation, 1151 Providence Turnpike, Norwood, MA 02062.

(9) Heskestad, G. and Delichatsios, M. A. "The Initial Convective Flow in Fire: Seventeenth Symposium on Combustion," The Combustion Institute, Pittsburgh, PA (1979).

(10) Heskestad, G. and Delichatsios, M. A. "Environments of Fire Detectors — Phase 1: Effect of Fire Size, Ceiling Height and Material," Measurements Vol. I (NBS-GCR-77-86), Analysis Vol. II (NBS-GCR-77-95). National Technical Information Service (NTIS), Springfield, VA 22151.

(11) Heskestad, G. and Delichatsios, M. A. "Update: The Initial Convective Flow in Fire," *Fire Safety Journal*, Vol. 15, No. 5, 1989.

(12) International Organization for Standardization, *Audible Emergency Evacuation Signal*, ISO 8201, 1987.

(13) Klote, J. and Milke, J. "Principles of Smoke Management," American Society of Heating, Refrigerating and Air Conditioning Engineers, Atlanta, GA, 2002.

(14) Lawson, J. R., Walton, W. D., and Twilley, W. H. "Fire Performance of Furnishings as Measured in the NBS Furniture Calorimeter, Part 1," (NBSIR 83-2787) (Aug. 1983). National Institute of Standards and Technology (formerly National Bureau of Standards), Center for Fire Research, Gaithersburg, MD 20889.

(15) Morton, B. R., Taylor, Sir Geoffrey, and Turner, J. S. "Turbulent Gravitational Convection from Maintained and Instantaneous Sources," Proc. Royal Society A, 234, 1–23, 1956.

(16) Schifiliti, R. "Use of Fire Plume Theory in the Design and Analysis of Fire Detector and Sprinkler Response," Master's Thesis, Worcester Polytechnic Institute, Center for Firesafety Studies, Worcester, MA, 1986.

(17) Title 47, Code of Federal Regulations, Communications Act of 1934 Amended.

(18) Schifiliti, R. and Pucci, W. "Fire Detection Modelling, State of the Art," 6 May, 1996 sponsored by the Fire Detection Institute, Bloomfield, CT.

(19) Forney, G., Bukowski, R., Davis, W. "Field Modelling: Effects of Flat Beamed Ceilings on Detector and Sprinkler Response," Technical Report, Year 1. International Fire Detection Research Project, Fire Protection Research Foundation, Quincy, MA. October, 1993.

(20) Davis, W., Forney, G., Bukowski, R. "Field Modelling: Simulating the Effect of Sloped Beamed Ceilings on Detector and Sprinkler Response," Year 1. International Fire Detection

Research Project Technical Report, Fire Protection Research Foundation, Quincy, MA. October, 1994.

(21) Brozovski, E. "A Preliminary Approach to Siting Smoke Detectors Based on Design Fire Size and Detector Aerosol Entry Lag Time," Master's Thesis, Worcester Polytechnic, Worcester, MA, 1989.

(22) Cote, A. NFPA Fire Protection Handbook, 20th edition, National Fire Protection Association, Quincy, MA, 2008.

(23) Tewarson, A., "Generation of Heat and Chemical Compounds in Fires," SFPE Handbook of Fire Protection Engineering, Second Edition, NFPA and SFPE, 1995.

(24) Hollman, J. P. Heat Transfer, McGraw-Hill, New York, 1976.

(25) Custer, R. L. P., and Meacham, B. "Introduction to Performance Based Fire Safety," SFPE, 1997.

(26) Schifiliti, R. P., Meacham B., Custer, R. L. P. "Design of Detection Systems," SFPE Handbook of Fire Protection Engineering.

(27) Marrion, C. "Correction Factors for the Heat of Combustion in NFPA 72," Appendix B, Fire Protection Engineering, SFPE, 1998.

(28) Marrion, C. "Designing and Analyzing the Response of Detection Systems: An Update to Previous Correlations," 1988.

(29) Custer, R. and Bright, R. "Fire Detection: The State-of-the-Art," NBS Tech. Note 839, National Bureau of Standards, Washington, 1974.

(30) Meacham, Brian J. "Characterization of Smoke from Burning Materials for the Evaluation of Light Scattering-Type Smoke Detector Response," MS Thesis, WPI Center for Firesafety Studies, Worcester, MA, 1991.

(31) Delichatsios, M. A. "Categorization of Cable Flammability, Detection of Smoldering, and Flaming Cable Fires," Interim Report, Factory Mutual Research Corporation, Norwood, MA, NP-1630, Nov. 1980.

(32) Heskestad, G. FMRC Serial Number 21017, Factory Mutual Research Corp., Norwood, MA, 1974.

(33) Marrion, C. E. "Lag Time Modeling and Effects of Ceiling Jet Velocity on the Placement of Optical Smoke Detectors," MS Thesis, WPI Center for Firesafety Studies, Worcester, MA, 1989.

(34) Kokkala, M. et al. "Measurements of the Characteristic Lengths of Smoke Detectors," Fire Technology, Vol. 28, No. 2, National Fire Protection Association, Quincy, MA, 1992.

(34a) Yamauchi et al. "A Calculation Method for Predicting Heat and Smoke Detector's Response."

(34b) Cleary et al. "Particulate Entry Lag in Spot Type Smoke Detectors," IAFSS Proceedings, Boston, MA 2000.

(34c) Keski-Rahkonen, "Revisiting Modeling of Fluid Penetration into Smoke Detectors," AUBE 2001.

(34d) Bjoerkman et al. "Determination of Dynamic Model Parameters of Smoke Detectors," Fire Safety Journal, No 37, pp. 395–407, 2002.

(34e) Keski-Rahkonen, "A New Model for Time Lag of Smoke Detectors," International Collaborative Project to Evaluate Fire Models for Nuclear Power Plant Application, Gaithersburg, MD May 2002.

(35) UL 268, Standard for Smoke Detectors for Fire Alarm Signaling Systems, Underwriters Laboratories, Inc., Northbrook, IL, 2009.

(36) Deal, Scott. "Technical Reference Guide for FPEtool Version 3.2," NISTIR 5486, National Institute for Standards and Technology, U.S. Department of Commerce, Gaithersburg, MD, Aug. 1994.

(37) Mowrer, F. W. "Lag Times Associated with Detection and Suppression," Fire Technology, Vol. 26, No. 3, pp. 244–265, 1990.

(38) Newman, J. S. "Principles for Fire Detection," Fire Technology, Vol. 24, No. 2, pp. 116–127, 1988.

(39) Custer, R., Meacham, B., Wood, C. "Performance Based Design Techniques for Detection and Special Suppression Applications," Proceedings of the SFPE Engineering Seminars on Advances in Detection and Suppression Technology, 1994.

(40) SFPE Engineering Guide to Performance Based Fire Protection Analysis and Design, 2007, SFPE, Bethesda, MD.

(41) SFPE Handbook of Fire Protection Engineering, Fourth Edition, SFPE, Bethesda, MD, 2008.

(42) Drysdale, Dougal, An Introduction to Fire Dynamics, John Wiley & Sons, New York, NY, 1998, ISBN 0 471 90613 1, Second Edition.

(43) Nam S., Donovan L.P. and Kim S.G., Establishing Heat Detectors Thermal Sensitivity Through Bench Scale Tests; Fire Safety Journal, Volume 39, Number 3, 191–215; April 2004.

(44) Nam S., Thermal Response Coefficient TRC of Heat Detectors and Its Field Applications, Fire Detection and Research Applications Symposium, NFPA Research Foundation, January 2003.

(45) Nam S., Performance-Based Heat Detector Spacing, Interflam 2004, pp. 883–892.

(46) Geiman, J. A., "Evaluation of Smoke Detector Response Estimation Methods," Master of Science Thesis, University of Maryland, College Park, MD, December 2003.

(47) Projected Beam Smoke Detectors — More Than Just a Substitute for Spot Detectors, Fire Protection Engineering, Summer 2004, SFPE.

(48) Geiman, J. A., and Gottuck, D.T., "Alarm Thresholds for Smoke Detector Modeling," Fire Safety Science — Proceeding of the Seventh International Symposium, 2003, pp. 197–208.

(49) The SFPE Code Official's Guide to Performance-based Design Review and Analysis of Buildings, Society of Fire Protection Engineers, Bethesda, MD, 2004.

(50) NFPA 101, Life Safety Code, National Fire Protection Association, Quincy, MA, 2009.

(51) NFPA 909, Code for the Protection of Cultural Resource Properties — Museums, Libraries, and Places of Worship, National Fire Protection Association, Quincy, MA, 2010.

(52) NFPA 914, Code for Fire Protection of Historic Structures, National Fire Protection Association, Quincy, MA, 2010.

(53) Performance-based Building Design Concepts, International Code Council, Washington DC, 2004.

(54) Extreme Event Mitigation In Buildings — Analysis and Design, Meacham, National Fire Protection Association, Quincy MA, 2006.

(55) Geiman, Gottuk, and Milke, "Evaluation of Smoke Detector Response Estimation Methods: Optical Density, Temperature Rise and Velocity at Alarm," Journal of Fire Protection Engineering, 2006.

(56) Su et al., "Kemano Fire Studies — Part 1: Response of Residential Smoke Alarms," Research Report 108, NRCC, April 2003.

(57) Davis, W., The Zone Model Jet, "A Model for the Prediction of Detector Activation and Gas Temperature in the Presence of a Smoke Layer," NISTIR 6324, NIST, May 1999.

B.7 Nomenclature. The nomenclature used in Annex B is defined in Table B.7.

Table B.7 Nomenclature

α	=	fire intensity coefficient (kW/sec^2 or Btu/sec^3)
A	=	area (m^2 or ft^2)
A_0	=	$g/(C_p T_a \rho)$ [m^4/(sec^{2}kJ) or ft^4/(sec^{2}Btu)]
A_r	=	radiating area (m^2 or ft^2)
A_t	=	radiating area of test fire
C	=	specific heat of detector element (kJ/kg·°C or Btu/lbm·°F)
c	=	speed of light (m/sec or ft/sec)
C_p	=	specific heat of air [kJ/(kg K) or Btu/lbm R (1.040 kJ/kg K)]
D_m	=	mass optical density (m^2/g or ft^2/lb)
d	=	distance between fire and radiant energy–sensing detector
d'	=	distance between fire and detector
$d(Du)/dt$	=	rate of increase of optical density outside the detector
D	=	$0.146 + 0.242 r/H$
Δt	=	change in time (seconds)
ΔT	=	increase above ambient in temperature of gas surrounding a detector (°C or °F)
Δt_d	=	increase above ambient in temperature of a detector (°C or °F)
Δt_p^*	=	change in reduced gas temperature
e	=	energy (joules or Btu)
f	=	functional relationship
g	=	gravitational constant (9.81 m/sec^2 or 32 ft/sec^2)
h	=	Planck's constant (6.63E-23 joule-sec)
H	=	ceiling height or height above fire (m or ft)
H_c	=	convective heat transfer coefficient (kW/m^2·°C or Btu/ft^2·sec·°F)
ΔH_c	=	heat of combustion (kJ/mol)
h_f	=	flame height (m or ft)
H_f	=	heat of formation (kJ/mol)
L	=	characteristic length for a given detector design
k	=	detector constant, dimensionless
m	=	mass (kg or lbm)
p	=	positive exponent
P	=	radiant power (watts or Btu/sec)
q	=	heat release rate density per unit floor area (watts/m^2 or Btu/sec·ft^2)
Q	=	heat release rate (kW or Btu/sec)
Q_c	=	convection portion of fire heat release rate (kW or Btu/sec)
Q_{cond}	=	heat transferred by conduction (kW or Btu/sec)
Q_{conv}	=	heat transferred by convection (kW or Btu/sec)
Q_d	=	threshold fire size at which response must occur
Q_{rad}	=	heat transferred by radiation (kW or Btu/sec)
Q_{total}	=	total heat transfer (kW or Btu/sec)
Q_{CR}	=	critical heat release rate (kW or Btu/sec)

Q_{DO}	=	design heat release rate (kW or Btu/sec)
Q_m	=	maximum heat release rate (kW or Btu/sec)
Q_p	=	predicted heat release rate (kW or Btu/sec)
Q_T	=	threshold heat release rate at response (kW or Btu/sec)
r	=	radial distance from fire plume axis (m or ft)
ρ_0	=	density of ambient air [kg/m^3 or lb/ft^3 (1.1 kg/m^3)]
RTI	=	response time index (m$^{1/2}$sec$^{1/2}$ or ft$^{1/2}$ sec$^{1/2}$)
S	=	spacing of detectors or sprinkler heads (m or ft)
S	=	radiant energy
t_{DO}	=	time at which the design objective heat release rate (Q_{DO}) is reached (seconds)
t_{CR}	=	time at which the critical heat release rate (Q_{CR}) is reached (seconds)
t	=	time (seconds)
t_c	=	critical time — time at which fire would reach a heat release rate of 1055 kW (1000 Btu/sec) (seconds)
t_d	=	time to detector response
t_g	=	fire growth time to reach 1055 kW (1000 Btu/sec) (seconds)
t_r	=	response time (seconds)
$t_{respond}$	=	time available, or needed, for response to an alarm condition (seconds)
t_v	=	virtual time of origin (seconds)
t_{2f}	=	arrival time of heat front (for $p = 2$ power law fire) at a point r/H (seconds)
t_{2f}^*	=	reduced arrival time of heat front (for $p = 2$ power law fire) at a point r/H (seconds)
t_p^*	=	reduced time
T	=	temperature (°C or °F)
T_a	=	ambient temperature (°C or °F)
T_c	=	plume centerline temperature (°C or °F)
T_d	=	detector temperature (°C or °F)
T_g	=	temperature of fire gases (°C or °F)
T_s	=	rated operating temperature of a detector or sprinkler (°C or °F)
u_0	=	instantaneous velocity of fire gases (m/sec or ft/sec)
u	=	velocity (m/sec or ft/sec)
u_c	=	critical velocity
U_p^*	=	reduced gas velocity
V	=	velocity of smoke at detector
w_f	=	flame width (m or ft)
Y	=	defined in equation B.27
z	=	height above top of fuel package involved (m or ft)
λ	=	wavelength (microns)
Z_m	=	maximum height of smoke rise above fire surface (m or ft)
τ	=	detector time constant $mc/H_c A$ (seconds)
τ_0	=	detector time constant measured at reference velocity u_0 (seconds)
ε	=	emissivity, a material property expressed as a fraction between 0 and 1.0

Annex C   System Performance and Design Guide

This annex is not a part of the requirements of this NFPA document but is included for informational purposes only.

C.1 Scope. The requirements of the protected premises Chapter 23 provide for minimum levels of protection for fire alarm systems to protect life and property, regardless of the building characteristics, contents, or use. This System Performance and Design Guide provides additional considerations for users of the NFAC when planning, designing, and installing protected premises fire alarm systems for buildings that might be unusual in scale, mission, use, symbolism, or other critical or high-profile characteristics.

This guidance suggests potential system characteristics to enhanced system performance for protection of life, mission, and property in high-profile and other critical buildings, including signaling path integrity, redundancies, survivability, backup fire control stations, nonerasable logs, multiple information stations, and the benefits of networked and peer-to-peer configurations.

C.2 Building Scale. The size of a building to be protected influences fire alarm system operating characteristics, control functions, circuit integrity, annunciation, and other factors for protection of life, property, or the mission of the building.

C.2.1 Fire Service Response Location(s).

C.2.1.1 Location(s). Determine the fire service response location(s) by inquiry to the responding fire department (and building operating personnel, if appropriate).

C.2.1.2 Quantity. The fire service might desire more than one response location. Building operators might desire redundancies for security or operations under emergency conditions.

C.2.1.3 Functions. The primary response location is the normally expected location of the fire command center (FCC). In general, the fire command center provides information and control functions for the entire building. One or more redundant or abbreviated fire command centers might be desired for security or operations under emergency conditions.

C.2.1.3.1 Information. Nonprimary response locations might be intended to provide annunciation equipment to provide information for the entire building, or for a portion of the building associated with the response location.

C.2.1.3.2 Control. Nonprimary response locations might be intended to provide a partial or complete fire command center to provide control functions for the entire building, or for a portion of the building associated with the response location.

C.2.2 System Operational Characteristics.

C.2.2.1 On-Premises Response. Determine an alarm response plan considering the requirements of NFAC, local codes and regulations, the availability and responsibility of building operating personnel, and the mobility of occupants.

C.2.2.1.1 Investigation. Building security or operating personnel should investigate every alarm signal, and the alarm response plan might include investigation of initial alarm signals prior to activating a general alarm or the evacuation or relocation of occupants.

C.2.2.1.2 Communication. Determine appropriate methods to provide alarm information, and instructions when required, to building security and operating personnel, supervisory and management personnel, and building occupants.

Consider the need for predetermined messages, single- or multiple-channel communications systems, and coordination of communications system coverage and zoning with building subdivisions, including smoke compartments and automatic suppression system coverage and zoning. Consider the need for multiple languages in emergency communications.

C.2.2.1.3 Evacuation/Relocation. Determine the extent to which the emergency egress plan is based on total evacuation, relocation and partial evacuation, areas of rescue assistance and/or defending in place.

C.2.2.1.4 Survivability. Consider means to harden the fire notification circuits/paths to attack by fire for a period of time necessary to notify building operating personnel and occupants of a fire emergency and/or provide instructions if appropriate.

C.2.2.1.5 Control. Fire alarm system control units can be arranged to activate other building systems and to condition passive fire barriers to enhance fire safety in the building.

C.2.2.1.6 Building Systems. Consider activation or release of building systems and elements including, but not limited to, closing fire/smoke doors and dampers, recall of elevators, unlocking stairway doors, activating smoke control systems and or shut-down fans to prevent recirculation of smoke.

C.2.2.1.7 Fire Scene Operations. Compartmentation, water supply, fire fighter access, and communication links are important for manual fire-fighting operations. Fire alarm system monitoring, reporting, display, and control functions that enhance the maintenance and operation of these elements that enhance fire scene operations should be considered in the design, installation, and maintenance of protected premises fire alarm systems. An example would be a flashing light over the fire department connection.

C.2.2.2 External Response.

C.2.2.2.1 Resources Available. Determine the availability and responsibility of fire service resources. An example of the use of this information might be determining how to stage evacuation.

C.2.2.2.2 Time Required. Consider the time required for fire service response to the building. Consider travel time at various times of day and seasons of year.

C.2.2.2.3 Notification. Determine one or more acceptable means of automatic and manual notification of the fire service to initiate response to the building. Consider the extent of information that might be transmitted to the responding fire service to enhance response to the building and to provide incident information prior to its arrival.

C.2.2.2.4 Evacuation/Relocation. Consider system operational characteristics that might enhance coordination of control and direction to building operating personnel and occupants. Consider means of control and shift in control of evacuation or relocation direction from building operating personnel to fire service command.

C.2.2.2.5 Knowledge of Premises. Harmonize system operating characteristics to pre-incident planning with fire service and building operating and security personnel.

C.2.2.2.6 Communications and Control. Provide for fire-fighter communications through dedicated two-way fire-fighter communication systems, or consider a means to provide enhanced operation of fire service radio communications in the protected premises.

C.3 Premises Mission/Use/Property Protection. The loss of use or mission of a facility to the effects of accidental fire can have a very significant impact on the community or organization served by the facility. In such a case, it is appropriate to enhance functional characteristics of the protected premises system. Considerations include the following:

(1) Criticality/Mission Continuity
    (a) Community — Loss of operations of the facility might affect the community beyond the facility. Consider the sensitivity of fire detection and the effectiveness of alarm processing, emergency response, and fire suppression to minimize effects on the community served due to facility impairment by fire.
    (b) Operations
        i. On-premises — Fire might result in business interruption or reduced effectiveness.
        ii. Elsewhere — Services provided by the facility to remote locations might cease or be reduced.
(2) Life Safety
    (a) Evacuation/Relocation — Size, distribution, and mobility of the occupant population should be considered with knowledge of facility emergency planning and availability of emergency response resources to determine the extent to which people movement might be managed during a fire incident.
    (b) Defend In Place — A protected premises system might be used to activate facility fire safety elements necessary to defend occupants in place or to enhance rescue assistance.
(3) Property
    (a) Value — Cost, availability, and time required to reestablish facility contents should be considered when determining the sensitivity of fire detection and the effectiveness of alarm processing, emergency response, and fire suppression.
    (b) Replacement — Availability and time required to replace damaged facility contents should be considered when determining the sensitivity of fire detection and the effectiveness of alarm processing emergency response and fire suppression.
    (c) Redundancy — Duplication of facility contents in separate locations might reduce the need for sensitivity of fire detection or other property protection system capabilities.

C.4 Protected Premises Signaling System Features.

C.4.1 Event Logs. Computer processor–based systems are capable of assembling logs of system events by date and time, including alarm history. Such logs are an important resource in assessing system performance or malfunctions and in understanding or reconstructing a fire event after the fact. It is imperative that such logs are preserved and protected against deletion until it is affirmed that no further need for a log exists. Caution is recommended to secure system history logs when system software changes are made.

C.4.2 Network Configuration. Systems that use digital means to transfer signal information might provide benefits in economy of installation and distribution of information to multiple locations to enable rigorous alarm processing and response. Transmission of digital alarm information to remote locations might assist responding personnel by providing incident information prior to arrival at the location of the fire.

C.4.3 Peer to Peer Data Communication. Systems that duplicate the operating and history data bases in multiple network control units provide redundant monitoring and control points on a system that can enhance the reliability of the system and the operation of the system during emergency or degraded conditions.

Annex D   Speech Intelligibility

This annex is not a part of the requirements of this NFPA document but is included for informational purposes only.

Users of Annex D should refer back to the text of NFPA 72 to familiarize themselves with the specific requirements for the planning, design, installation, and testing of voice communication systems.

D.1 Introduction.

D.1.1 This annex is intended to provide guidance on the planning, design, installation, and testing of voice communication systems. The majority of this annex contains recommendations for testing of the intelligibility of voice systems.

D.1.2 As with most systems, proper system performance is related to good planning, design, installation, and maintenance. Similarly, test results are a valuable feedback mechanism for persons planning, designing, and installing systems.

D.1.3 This annex describes when, where, and how to test for speech intelligibility. It is also not the intent of this test protocol to describe how to interpret results or how to correct systems or environments that contribute to poor speech intelligibility.

D.1.4 For occupancies that do not yet exist, the designer should have an understanding of the acoustic characteristics of the architectural design, as well as the acoustic performance properties of available loudspeakers. Architecturally, this includes the physical size and shape of the space, as well as the acoustic properties of the walls, floors, ceilings, and interior furnishings. A proper design analysis can sometimes reveal that an intelligible system is not achievable unless some features of the architectural design are changed. The designer should be prepared to defend such conclusions and, if necessary, refuse to certify the installation of such a system. While "hand calculations" and experience work well for simpler installations, more complex designs are frequently better and more cost-effectively analyzed using one of a number of readily available computer-based design programs.

D.1.5 The designer and the authority having jurisdiction should both be aware that the acoustic performance parameters of the chosen loudspeakers, as well as their placement in the structure, play a major role in determining how many appliances are necessary for adequate intelligibility. The numerical count of appliances for a given design and protected space cannot, by itself, be used to determine the adequacy of the design. Sometimes, the acoustic problems of certain placement constraints can be satisfactorily overcome through the careful selection of loudspeakers with the requisite performance characteristics, rather than by increasing their number.

D.2 Fundamentals of Test Protocol.

D.2.1 Measurement Method.

D.2.1.1 STI/STIPA.

D.2.1.1.1 Where the method for measuring speech intelligibility is the Speech Transmission Index (STI), this test protocol should be followed.

D.2.1.1.2 There are several methods that measure the STI. One method common to the emergency communications system industry uses a test signal referred to as STIPA — STI-Public Address.

D.2.1.2 Other Methods. Where the method for measuring speech intelligibility is the Phonetically Balanced Word test (PB), Modified Rhyme Test (MRT), or Speech Intelligibility Index (SII) method, the same methods for determining measurement locations should be used.

D.2.2 References.

D.2.2.1 IEC 60268-16, *Sound system equipment — Part 16: Objective rating of speech intelligibility by speech transmission index*, International Electrotechnical Commission, Geneva, Switz., 22 May 2003.

D.2.2.2 ISO 7240-19, *Fire Detection and Alarm Systems — Part 19: Design, Installation, Commissioning and Service of Sound Systems for Emergency Purposes*, International Organization for Standardization, Geneva, Switz., 1st edition, 15 Aug 2007.

D.2.2.3 NEMA Standards Publication SB 50-2008, *Emergency Communications Audio Intelligibility Applications Guide*, National Electrical Manufacturers Association, Rosslyn VA, 2008.

D.2.3 Terminology.

D.2.3.1 Acoustically Distinguishable Space (ADS).

D.2.3.1.1 An acoustically distinguishable space (ADS) can be an emergency communication system notification zone, or subdivision thereof, that can be an enclosed or otherwise physically defined space, or that can be distinguished from other spaces because of different acoustical, environmental, or use characteristics such as reverberation time and ambient sound pressure level. The ADS might have acoustical design features that are conducive for voice intelligibility, or it might be a space where voice intelligibility could be difficult or impossible to achieve.

D.2.3.1.2 All parts of a building or area intended to have occupant notification are subdivided into ADSs as defined. Some ADSs might be designated to have voice communication capability and require that those communications be intelligible. Other spaces might not require voice intelligibility or might not be capable of reliable voice intelligibility. Each is still referred to as an ADS.

D.2.3.1.3 In smaller areas, such as those under 400 ft² (40 m²), walls alone will define the ADS. In larger areas, other factors might have to be considered. In spaces that might be subdivided by temporary or movable partitions, such as ballrooms and meeting rooms, each individual configuration should be considered a separate ADS. Physical characteristics such as a change in ceiling height of more than 20 percent or change in acoustical finish, such as carpet in one area and tile in another, would require those areas to be treated as separate ADSs. In larger areas there might be noise sources that require a section to be treated as a separate ADS. Any significant change in ambient sound pressure level or frequency might necessitate an area be considered a separate ADS.

D.2.3.1.4 In areas of 85 dBA or greater ambient sound pressure level, meeting the pass/fail criteria for intelligibility might not be possible and other means of communication

might be necessary. So, for example, the space immediately surrounding a printing press or other high noise machine might be designated as a separate ADS and the design might call for some form of effective notification but not necessarily require the ability to have intelligible voice communication. The aisles or operator's control stations might be separate ADSs where intelligible voice communication might be desired.

D.2.3.1.5 Significant differences in furnishings, for example, an area with tables, desks, or low dividers adjacent to an area with high shelving, would require separate consideration. The entire desk area could be a single acoustic zone whereas each area between shelving could be a unique zone. Essentially, any noteworthy change in the acoustical environment within an area will mandate consideration of that portion of the area to be treated as an acoustic zone. Hallways and stairwells will typically be considered as individual acoustic zones.

D.2.3.1.6 Spaces confined by walls with carpeting and acoustical ceilings can be deemed to be one ADS. An ADS should be an area of consistent size and material. A change of materials from carpet to hard tile, the existence of sound sources such as decorative waterfalls, large expanses of glass, and changes in ceiling height are all factors that might separate one ADS from another.

D.2.3.1.7 Each ADS might require different components and design features to achieve intelligible voice communication. For example, two ADSs with similar acoustical treatments and noise levels might have different ceiling heights. The ADS with the lower ceiling height might require more ceiling-mounted speakers to ensure that all listeners are in a direct sound field. See Figure D.2.3.1.7. Other ADSs might benefit from the use of alternate speaker technologies such as line arrays to achieve intelligibility.

D.2.3.1.8 An ADS that differs from another because of the frequency and level of ambient sound pressure level might require the use of speakers and system components that have a wider frequency bandwidth than conventional emergency communications equipment. However, designers should not use higher bandwidth speakers in all locations unless needed to overcome certain acoustic and ambient conditions. This is because the higher bandwidth appliance will require more energy to perform properly. This increases amplifier and wire size and power supply requirements.

D.2.3.1.9 In some spaces it might be impractical to achieve intelligibility, and in such a case alternatives to voice evacuation might be required within such areas.

D.2.3.1.10 There might be some areas of a facility where there are several spaces of the same approximate size and with the same acoustic properties. For example, there might be an office space with multiple individual offices, each with one speaker. If one or two are satisfactorily tested, there is no need to test all of them for speech intelligibility.

D.2.3.2 Audibility Test. Measurement of the sound pressure level of a tone signal in accordance with the requirements of *NFPA 72*.

D.2.3.3 Intelligibility Test. A test method used to predict how well speech is understood by a listener.

D.2.3.4 Occupied Ambient Sound Pressure Level. The period of time when the building involved in the test is occupied and is reasonably close to having maximum background noise. For

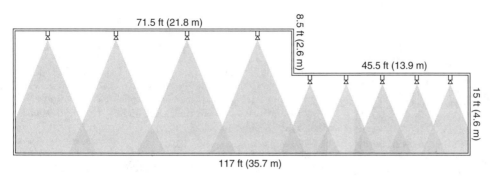

FIGURE D.2.3.1.7 Illustration Demonstrating Effect of Ceiling Height.
(Source: R. P. Schifiliti Associates, Inc.)

example, this might involve the operation of HVAC equipment, an industrial process, or a maximum number of occupants such as might occur in a place of public assembly.

D.2.3.5 STI or STIPA Test Signal.

D.2.3.5.1 A special audio signal that is played over the emergency communications system being tested.

D.2.3.5.2 Instruments that measure STI using a STIPA signal use a special signal that consists of signals in seven octave bands. The sound in each octave band is modulated using two (separate) modulation frequencies. The STI and STIPA have been standardized in IEC 60268. However, at the present time, the implementation of the measurement software and correlations with the test signal can differ between instrument manufacturers. Therefore, until there is further standardization, only the test signal recommended by the instrument manufacturer should be used with their instrument. Although the STIPA test signals can sound similar, there might be speed or other differences that affect results if one manufacturer's test signal is used with another manufacturer's instrument.

D.2.3.6 Talkbox. An instrument usually consisting of a high quality audio speaker and a CD player or other method used to play an STI or STIPA test signal.

D.2.3.7 Unoccupied Ambient Sound Pressure Level. The period of time when the primary occupants of the facility are not present, or when ambient sound pressure level is not at its highest level.

D.2.4 Acceptability Criteria.

D.2.4.1 The intelligibility of an emergency communication system is considered acceptable if at least 90 percent of the measurement locations within each ADS have a measured STI of not less than 0.45 (0.65 CIS) and an average STI of not less than 0.50 STI (0.70 CIS).

D.2.4.2 Speech intelligibility is not a physical quantity like meters, feet, amperes, volts, or even decibels. It is a benchmark of the degree to which we understand spoken language, and as such is a complex phenomenon affected by many variables (Ref: Jacob, K. & Tyson, T., "Computer-Based Prediction of Speech Intelligibility for Mass Notification Systems," SUPDET 2008, Fire Protection Research Foundation, Mar 2008). There are two basic categories of intelligibility testing: (1) subject (human) based testing and (2) instrument based test methods. Test methods that use human subjects are only statistical predictions of how well speech might be understood at any other time for any other

group of listeners. Several subject based test methods have been extensively researched, tested for reliability, and standardized. Examples include the Phonetically Balanced (PB) word scores (256 words or 1000 words) and Modified Rhyme Test (MRT). (Ref: ANSI S3.2-1989 revised 2009, "Method for Measuring the Intelligibility of Speech over Communication Systems." Ref: ISO/TR 4870, "Acoustics — The Construction and Calibration of Speech Intelligibility Tests").

D.2.4.3 Subject based test methods can gauge how much of the spoken information is correctly understood by a person or group of persons for that particular test. When properly done, that resulting value is a prediction of how much of the spoken word will be correctly understood by others at some other time. Therefore, the results of speech intelligibility testing are usually described as predictions, not measurements. However, most users of the instruments refer to the results as measurements, not as predictions. Since the use of portable instruments is the more common method in the alarm and emergency communications industries, in this document the results will be referred to as measurements to avoid confusion. However, in scientific and general acoustic literature, readers can see the measured values correctly referred to as predictions.

D.2.4.4 Several instrument based methods for predicting speech intelligibility have been extensively researched and tested for accuracy and repeatability, and the methods have been standardized, most notably the Speech Intelligibility Index (SII) (formerly the Articulation Index, AI), Speech Transmission Index (STI), and Speech Transmission Index for Public Address (STIPA) (Ref: IEC 60268-16, "Sound system equipment — Part 16: Objective rating of speech intelligibility by speech transmission index", 2003. Ref: ANSI/ASA S3.5, "American National Standard Methods for Calculation of the Speech Intelligibility Index", 1997). Accuracy is how close the meter corresponds to actual human test results. Thus, even though an instrument is used, the results are subjective in that they correlate with how humans perceive the quality of speech.

D.2.4.5 Each of the established methods for measuring speech intelligibility has its own scale. The Common Intelligibility Scale (CIS) was developed in 1995 to show the relationship between the different methods and to permit codes and standards to require a certain level of performance while permitting any of the accepted measurement methods to be employed (Ref: Barnett, P.W. and Knight, A.D., "The Common Intelligibility Scale," Proceedings of the Institute of Acoustics, Vol. 17, Part 7, 1995). The Speech Transmission Index (STI) is widely used and has been implemented in portable equipment using a modified method called STIPA (STI Public Address). For this reason, the performance metrics cited in this document use units of STI with units of CIS in parentheses. The relationship between the two is: CIS = 1+log (STI). Relationships between other methods can be found in the literature (Ref: IEC 60849, Annex B, Sound Systems for Emergency Purposes, Feb 1998).

D.2.4.6 If an ADS is small enough to only require one measurement location (see the requirements for measurement point spacing), the result should be 0.50 STI (0.70 CIS) or more for the ADS to pass the requirement for speech intelligibility. This is based on the requirement for an average of 0.50 STI (0.70 CIS) or more in that ADS. Therefore, a single measurement of 0.45 STI (0.65 CIS) would not be considered acceptable, because that one measurement would be below the minimum required average of 0.50 STI (0.70 CIS) in that ADS.

D.2.4.7 If the value at that one measurement location were less than 0.50 STI (0.70 CIS), additional measurements could be taken at that same single measurement location. As with simple sound pressure level measurements, intelligibility measurements at any point will vary. If the average of all the measurements at that location were 0.50 STI (0.70 CIS) or more, the ADS would pass the requirement for speech intelligibility.

D.2.4.8 Some ADSs might require multiple measurement points due to their larger size. (See the requirements for measurement point spacing.) However, even in a small ADS where one measurement point would be permitted, a designer might intend that multiple measurements be made because of conditions that might result in specific points having intelligibility scores below the minimum. Where an ADS has multiple measurement locations, the requirement is that at least 90 percent of the measurement locations have values not less than 0.45 STI, (0.65 CIS) and that all measurement points average to 0.50 STI (0.70 CIS) or greater.

D.2.4.9 The use of an average intelligibility score as a part of the requirement permits a wider range of measured values within an ADS than would a simple minimum requirement. A range of permitted values is not appropriate since there is no need for an upper limit for intelligibility — prefect intelligibility is certainly acceptable.

D.2.4.10 The requirement that only 90 percent of the measured points in the ADS meet the minimum and that the average for the entire ADS be 0.50 STI (0.70 CIS) or greater recognizes that in any space, with any system and any set of acoustic conditions, there can be points where the intelligibility score might be below the minimum. See also the discussion on the definition of an ADS and how some ADSs might be designated to not require speech intelligibility at all. For example, in a room that is otherwise similar from an acoustics standpoint, the space around a loud machine might be one ADS while the rest of the room is a separate ADS. The ADS surrounding the machine might be designed to have some form of occupant notification, but not to have intelligible voice communications. This type of ADS designation permits the remainder of the room to be scored without being penalized by the fact that intelligible communication near some loud sound sources might not be possible.

D.2.4.11 The intelligibility performance requirement cited herein intentionally uses two decimal points. Portable instruments that use the STIPA method for measuring the Speech

Transmission Index (STI) generally have a precision on the order of 0.02 to 0.03 (Ref: Sander J. van Wijngaarden and Jan A. Verhave, Past Present and Future of the Speech Transmission Index, Chapter 9, Measurement and Prediction of Speech Intelligibility in Traffic Tunnels Using the STI, p113, TNO Human Factors, The Netherlands, 2002). Other methods that measure STI can have a greater measurement precision. Other measurement methods, such as Modified Rhyme Test (MRT), Phonetically Balanced Word (PB) lists, and Speech Intelligibility Index (SII), also have levels of precision in the hundredths when properly conducted and scored. However, there might be slight variations in measured values between any two meters or between any two persons taking measurements with the same instrument, or between any two listener panels when using subject based test methods. This is true for any measurement method or instrument, including simple scales for measuring length or mass.

D.2.4.12 Measurements should be made and recorded using two decimal places. Averages can be calculated to three decimal points and rounded. The calculated average value should be rounded to the nearest five-hundredths (0.05) to reflect possible measurement errors and the intent of the requirement (Ref: Mapp, P., "Systematic & Common Errors in Sound System STI and Intelligibility Measurements," Convention Paper 6271, Audio Engineering Society, 117th Convention, San Fran, CA, 28–31 Oct 2004. Ref: Peter Mapp, Past Present and Future of the Speech Transmission Index, Chapter 8, Practical Application of STI to Assessing Public Address and Emergency Sound Systems, TNO Human Factors, The Netherlands, 2002). For example, averages of 0.47–0.525 STI would all be rounded to report an average of 0.50 STI (0.70 CIS). The minimum value permitted for all but 10 percent of the measurement locations in an ADS should be 0.45 STI (0.65 CIS) or greater. For example, values of 0.44 STI are below the minimum; they are not rounded up to 0.45 STI.

D.2.5 Limitations of Test Method.

D.2.5.1 Equipment designed in accordance with UL 864 and fire alarm speakers designed in accordance with UL 1480 are only tested for and only required to produce frequencies of 400 to 4000 Hz. Speech, however, includes a wider range of frequencies. Speech intelligibility measurements using STI and STIPA include octave band measurements that range from 125 Hz to 8000 Hz. STI results are most dependent on the 2000, 1000, 500, and 4000 Hz octave bands (in order of weighting) and to a lesser extent the 8000 and 250 Hz octave bands and to an even lesser extent, the 125 Hz band (again, in order of weighting).

D.2.5.2 While the lower and higher octave bands in STI calculations are weighted much less than the others, under certain acoustic conditions, systems that do not produce the highs and the lows can produce speech intelligibility that is less than desired. This does not imply that all systems should use equipment capable of greater bandwidth sound reproduction. While the larger frequency response will probably sound better and be more intelligible to a listener, it might not be necessary for the minimum desired performance. The use of equipment with higher bandwidth will require an increase in power supplies, amplifiers, and wire sizes to drive the speaker appliances.

D.2.5.3 Areas of high ambient sound pressure levels ("noise") might be incapable of meeting the acceptability criteria in D.2.4.

D.2.5.4 In areas where the ambient sound pressure level exceeds 90 dBA, speech satisfactory speech intelligibility is difficult to achieve with conventional communications equipment and design practice. A better system design might include alternate communications methods, such as signs and displays, or might involve providing occupant notification but not communication at that location.

D.2.5.5 Impulse sounds made during measurements can impact measurement accuracy or cause instrument error.

D.2.5.6 Impulse sounds such as accidentally tapping the meter microphone, or a nearby door slamming can cause a measurement error. Some meters will display an error message. If an impulse sound occurs during the measurement, consider taking another measurement to check the results. This process is analogous to ignoring temporary sound sources, as permitted by *NFPA 72* when taking sound pressure level measurements.

D.2.5.7 Natural variation in ambient sound pressure level levels can affect the results.

D.2.6 General Requirements.

D.2.6.1 The qualified staff should be identified on the system design documents. Acceptable evidence of qualifications or certification should be provided when requested by the authority having jurisdiction. Qualified personnel should include, but not be limited to, one or more of the following:

(1) Personnel who are factory trained and certified for fire alarm system design of the specific type and brand of system addressed by this test protocol
(2) Personnel who are certified by a nationally recognized certification organization acceptable to the authority having jurisdiction
(3) Personnel who are registered, licensed, or certified by a state or local authority

D.2.6.2 All necessary precautions should be taken with the facility owner to work with appropriately qualified staff when handling or performing any function with the emergency communications system control unit.

D.2.6.3 Testing impairment and record keeping requirements of *NFPA 72*, Chapter 14 should apply.

D.2.6.4 Test measurements and other documentation should be maintained as required by the authority having jurisdiction.

D.2.6.5 Impairment management procedures of *NFPA 72*, Section 10.21 should be followed.

D.2.6.6 Test Participants. The test participants should include representatives of and/or coordination with the following: building owners; the organizations responsible for the fire alarm or emergency communications system design and installation; system equipment supplier and/or manufacturer; and the authority having jurisdiction.

D.3 Pre-Planning.

D.3.1 Facility Occupancy and Use.

D.3.1.1 Occupancy/Use Types. Prior to testing, the pre-planning effort should identify the occupancy or use type to better minimize disruption to the facility occupants during the test.

D.3.1.2 Normal Operational Time Periods. Prior to testing, pre-planning efforts should identify the operational time periods when the occupied ambient sound pressure level and the unoccupied ambient sound pressure level are most likely to occur.

D.3.1.3 Testing Before Building Furnishing Completion. It might be necessary to perform testing to permit partial use before the building is in its final acoustic configuration. The results of intelligibility testing at this stage can differ from the final performance of the system. It might be necessary to work with the authority having jurisdiction to develop a testing plan. For example, until acoustical treatments such as carpeting, ceiling tiles, and other furnishings are in place, the system can be partially tested to meet audibility requirements but not necessarily intelligibility requirements. Other test plans or mitigating procedures might be permitted.

D.3.1.4 Facility Construction and Condition. Construction in the facility to be tested should be completed for areas that will be subject to intelligibility testing. This specifically requires that the command center and all locations of system microphones to be tested should be completed. Any location of remote system microphones not tested during this time should be noted, and said locations should be fully tested with positive results within 90 days of area occupancy or as required by the authority having jurisdiction. Also, all building systems such as environmental conditioning systems should be completed and operational, as they both produce noise and provide acoustic noise travel paths. In addition, all floor treatments and any acoustical wall or ceiling treatments should be in place.

D.3.1.5 System Under Test Status. The system under test should be completed for all areas where intelligibility testing will be done.

D.3.1.6 System Under Test Power. System under test should be on permanent primary power source as defined in *NFPA 72*.

D.3.1.7 System Under Test Secondary Power. Secondary power, where required and/or provided for the system under test, should be fully functional. If batteries are used for this purpose, batteries should be fully charged for a minimum of 48 hours prior to the commencement of any testing.

D.3.2 Emergency Communication Equipment.

D.3.2.1 As discussed in D.2.3.1, not all ADSs will require or be capable of intelligible voice communications. It is the designer's job to define areas that will have voice communication versus those that might have tone-only signaling, as well as which spaces will have strobes, textual signage, or other forms of notification and/or communication. This document intends that "notification" mean any form of notification, not just voice communication, whether audible, visual, or using some other human sense.

D.3.2.2 There might be applications where not all spaces will require intelligible voice signaling (Ref: NFPA 72, *National Fire Alarm Code*, 2007, Section A.7.4.1.4). For example, in a residential occupancy such as an apartment, the authority having jurisdiction and the designer might agree to a system that achieves the required audibility throughout but does not result in intelligible voice signaling in the bedrooms. The system would be sufficient to awaken and alert. However, intelligibility might not be achieved in the bedrooms with the doors closed and the sounder in the adjacent hallway or room. In some cases this can require that messages repeat a sufficient number of times to ensure that occupants can reach a location where the system is sufficiently intelligible to be understood. Systems that use tone signaling in some areas and voice signaling in other areas would not require voice intelligibility in those areas only covered by the tone.

D.3.2.3 Emergency Communications System Control Panel. The system under test for the emergency communications system should be located and identified prior to testing, and its operation features necessary for the testing clarified. Personnel who are authorized to access and service the control panel are necessary for the testing and should be included within the team performing the tests. If necessary, notification to locations beyond the facility that is being tested (e.g., fire department or a supervising station) should be notified of the tests, and if appropriate, their automatic notification feature disabled. Upon completion of the tests the emergency communications system should be returned to its normal operating condition.

D.3.2.4 Test Set-up. The function and operation of the emergency communication system control unit should be reviewed with personnel authorized to access and operate this equipment. Information should be acquired on the functioning of the voice notification portion of the system, and whether it has zone capabilities that will allow minimal disruption to building occupants by testing each zone individually. The test plan should also specify whether other functions of the system, such as elevator recall and air handler control, will be disabled during the testing of the emergency communications system.

D.3.2.5 System Under Test Calibration. The complete system under test audio path should be fully calibrated in accordance with manufacturer's instructions. On systems with adjustable technology, if manufacturer's instructions are not provided, the alternate calibration procedure offered below can be employed to calibrate the system under test.

D.3.2.5.1 Alternate Calibration Procedure.

D.3.2.5.1.1 This calibration is to be performed with the system under test on normal AC power, then checked with the system on secondary power (if so equipped).

D.3.2.5.1.2 The system under test amplifier output or the circuit being calibrated should have a minimum of a 1-watt load during the calibration process.

D.3.2.5.1.3 Perform pre-test occupant and remote monitoring station notification requirements specified in NFPA 72-2013, Chapter 14.

D.3.2.5.1.4 Introduce a 1 kHz sine-wave tone (± 100 Hz) at 90 dBA-fast 4" (4 in.) to the system microphone on-axis, perpendicular to the face of the microphone.

D.3.2.5.1.5 Place the system under test into manual paging mode (microphone "live" and connected to amplifier circuitry with notification appliance circuits active).

D.3.2.5.1.6 Using a 4-digit accuracy RMS meter, set on AC scale, set the output of the System Under Test audio notification appliance circuits to between 24 and 26 Vrms for 25.2 volt systems or between 69 and 71 Vrms for 70.7 volt systems.

D.3.2.5.1.7 Once system under test manual paging mode has been calibrated, pre-recorded tone (if so equipped) should then be tested by playing it through the system under test to ensure that there is no more than a 3 dBA difference between manual paging using the system microphone and the pre-recorded message. The dBA measurement should be made using an integrating/averaging meter and averaged over approximately

10 seconds of voice announcement to compensate for voice amplitude modulation.

D.3.2.5.1.8 On a system under test with more than one emergency paging microphone and/or pre-recorded message units, the primary units should be calibrated, then secondary units tested to ensure that they produce signals throughout the system under test at the same amplitude as the primary units.

D.3.3 Plans and Specifications.

D.3.3.1 The approved plans and specifications for the system should be used to plan and document the tests.

D.3.3.2 Testing is best accomplished using large scale plans showing all notification appliances.

D.3.3.3 The plans should show the different system notification zones.

D.3.3.4 The type and location of the notification appliances used in the emergency communication system should be identified prior to testing.

D.3.3.5 Notification appliance symbols should differentiate the type of appliance where more than one type is used.

D.3.3.6 Notification appliance symbols should include the design wattage for each speaker appliance.

D.3.3.7 The plans should show the ambient sound pressure levels used as a basis for the system design.

D.3.4 Calculating Percentage of Articulation Loss of Consonants (%AL$_{CONS}$). There are occasions in which a space may not be available to take test measurements in prior to the design being completed. One method of calculation for the Speech Intelligibly Index is by calculating percentage of articulation loss of consonants (%AL$_{CONS}$). The formula is:

$$\%AL_{CONS} = 656 D_2{}^2 RT_{60}{}^2 (N) / VQM$$

where:

D_2 = distance from the loudspeaker to the farthest listener
RT_{60} = reverberation time (seconds)
N = power ratio of L_W causing L_D to the L_W of all devices except those causing L_D
V = volume of the room (ft^3)
Q = directivity index (ratio)
M = D_C modifier (usually 1)

As point of reference, D_C is the critical distance.

N is further defined as:

L_W = sound power level (dB)
L_D = total direct energy
L_W = 10log ($W_a/10^{-12}W$)
W_a = acoustic watts
10^{-12} = specified reference
$L_D = L_W + 10\log (Q/4\pi r^2) + 10.5$

The conversion factor from %AL$_{CONS}$ to STI:

STI = [−0.1845 × ln(%AL$_{CONS}$)] + 0.9482

D.3.5 Assignment of Acoustically Distinguishable Spaces.

D.3.5.1 ADSs should be assigned prior to the test, and be subject to review by all test participants.

D.3.5.2 ADS assignments should be a part of the original design process. See the discussion in D.2.3.1.

D.3.5.3 The design drawings should be used to plan and show the limits of each ADS where there is more than one.

D.3.5.4 All areas that are intended to have audible occupant notification, whether by tone only or by voice are to be designated as one or more ADSs. See D.2.3.1.

D.3.5.5 The drawings or a table listing all ADSs should be used to indicate which ADSs will require intelligible voice communications and which will not. The same drawings or table could be used to list audibility requirements where tones are used and to list any forms of visual or other notification or communications methods being employed in the ADS.

D.3.5.6 ADS layouts that differ from the original, approved design documents should be approved by the authority having jurisdiction.

D.3.6 Spaces Not Requiring Testing.

D.3.6.1 Buildings and areas of buildings that are not acoustically challenging such as traditional office environments, hotel guest rooms, dwelling units, and spaces with carpeting and furnishings generally meet intelligibility levels if the audibility levels are consistent with the requirements of *NFPA 72, National Fire Alarm and Signaling Code.* Performing intelligibility testing might not be necessary in these areas. Areas of a typical building that can be acoustically challenging could include vehicle parking levels and large lobby areas with hard floors and wall surfaces, stairs, and other spaces with high reverberation. Intelligibility meeting the requirements in this document can be difficult to achieve throughout these spaces. Specialized sound system design procedures, principles, and equipment might be necessary to achieve speech intelligibility in high noise areas or areas with challenging acoustics. Alternatively, intelligibility could be provided near exits and within specific areas (elevator lobby of a parking level) where occupants can obtain clear instructions after being alerted. This is done, in part, by the proper planning and designation of ADSs.

D.3.6.2 Factors that influence the decision to measure speech intelligibility include:

D.3.6.2.1 Possible reasons not to test speech intelligibility include the following:

(1) Distance listener to speaker less than 30 ft (9.1 m) in the room (assuming proper audibility and low reverberation)
(2) Ambient sound level is less than 50 dBA and the average SPL of the voice message is 10–15 dBA fast greater
(3) No appreciable hard surfaces (e.g., glass, marble, tile, metal, etc.)
(4) No appreciable high ceilings (i.e., ceiling height equals speaker spacing at a ratio of 1:1 optimal or 1:2 max)

D.3.6.2.2 Possible reasons not to test intelligibility, except possibly for spot sample testing include the following:

(1) Space has been acoustically designed by individuals having skills sufficient to properly design a voice/alarm system for the occupancy to be protected (e.g., space has been designed using commercially available computer modeling software acceptable to authority having jurisdiction)

D.3.6.2.3 Possible reasons to test include the following:

(1) Appreciable hard surfaces (e.g., glass, marble, tile, metal, etc.)
(2) Appreciable high ceilings (e.g., atriums, multiple ceiling heights)

D.3.6.3 In situations where there are several ADSs that have the exact same physical and system configuration, it might be possible to test only a representative sample and then just check the others to confirm system and appliance operation — for example, hotel rooms with similar layouts or offices of similar size and furnishings where each has a speaker appliance. In these cases there would be no expected difference in system intelligibility. The only possible problem would be one where an appliance was not operational or tapped at the incorrect wattage. These problems would be apparent by a basic "listening" test.

D.3.6.4 Not all ADSs will require speech intelligibility testing. Some areas might be designed for notification, but not for voice communication. Notification can be accomplished by tone-only signaling or by a pre-alert tone preceding a voice message. See D.3.5.5.

D.3.6.5 By definition, an ADS is relatively uniform in acoustic characteristics. However, speech intelligibility will vary at different points within an ADS depending primarily on distance to noise sources and distance to speaker appliances. Generally, in smaller spaces up to about 40 ft × 40 ft (12.2 m × 12.2 m), one measurement location will be sufficient. The location should not be directly in front of a wall mounted speaker or directly under a ceiling mounted speaker. Neither should it be in the far corner right next to walls or windows. Generally, try to stay about 5 to 10 ft (1.5 to 3.0 m) away from vertical surfaces that reflect sound. In larger spaces, a grid of about 40 ft × 40 ft (12.2 m × 12.2 m) can be used as a starting guide, then adjusted for the locations of machines and other obstructions and for speaker appliance locations. See D.2.4 for additional discussion on measuring points and the averaging of results in an ADS.

D.3.6.6 Of the ADSs that do require intelligible voice communications, some will require speech intelligibility testing and others might only require audibility testing.

D.3.6.7 Testing of intelligibility might not be required in buildings and areas of buildings that are not acoustically challenging and that meet the audibility requirements of NFPA 72. Spaces that are not considered to be acoustically challenging include traditional office environments, hotel guest rooms, spaces with carpeting and furnishings that reduce reverberation, and other, smaller spaces where a speaker appliance is installed in the space.

D.3.7 Measurement Points Within ADS.

D.3.7.1 Measurements should be taken at an elevation of 5 ft (1.5 m) or at any other elevation deemed appropriate based on occupancy (e.g., elevated walkways, child-height, sitting height, work area height, etc.) or test instrument instructions.

D.3.7.2 The number and location of measurement points in each ADS should be planned and based on the area and volume of the space and the speaker appliance location within the space. The location of noise sources, egress paths, and the locations of personnel in the space should also be considered.

D.3.7.3 Testing when the area is occupied and when the ambient sound level is at or near its expected maximum is preferred because it is easier. However, it does involve playing of a test signal through the emergency communications system for the duration of the test. When testing using the STIPA signal, the signal is a continuous noise signal. Other methods that measure STI use a swept tone that should be repeated for each measurement location. The alternate procedure is to test and save the STI measurement data during unoccupied times, measure and save the unoccupied sound level, and then take and save sound level measurements during occupied times. The three data sets are combined by software to calculate the corrected STI for the area. Testing using this method requires three measurements at each measurement location, but does not subject occupants to constant test signals. The choice of testing occupied versus unoccupied for intelligibility is the same as for audibility testing of tone signaling systems and is based on convenience versus disruption of normal use of the space. However, unlike audibility testing, intelligibility testing is less likely to contribute to the Cry Wolf Syndrome because the test signal is not the same as the evacuation tone, which would be sounded throughout testing of a tone signaling system. [Ref: Schifiliti, Robert P., "Fire Alarm Testing Strategies Can Improve Occupant Response and Reduce the "Cry Wolf" Syndrome," NEMA Supplement in Fire Protection Engineering, Society of Fire Protection Engineers, Bethesda, MD 20814, Fall 2003.] and [Ref: Brezntiz, S., "Cry Wolf: The Psychology of False Alarms," Lawrence Erlbaum Associates, Hillsdale, NJ, February 1984.]

D.3.7.4 If multiple measurement points are required within an ADS, they should be separated by about 40 ft (12.2 m).

D.3.7.5 No more than one third of the measurement points within an ADS should be on the axis of a speaker.

D.3.7.6 See D.2.4 for the requirements for averaging the results at different measurement points within an ADS.

D.3.7.7 Measurement points should be shown on plans or otherwise described in a way that permits future testing at the same locations.

D.3.8 Test Method — Occupied versus Unoccupied.

D.3.8.1 It is possible to conduct STI measurements when the area is occupied or when it is not occupied. In this document "occupied" versus "unoccupied" is intended to be consistent with the definitions in D.2.3 for occupied ambient sound pressure level and for unoccupied ambient sound pressure level.

D.3.8.2 The preferred procedure is to conduct the STI/STIPA test in the presence of the occupied ambient sound pressure level. See D.6.4.

D.3.8.3 Where the test method is measuring the STI using the STIPA test signal, the STIPA test signal can be played through the system and the STI can be measured and the data saved by the test instrument when the area is either not occupied or when the background ambient conditions are not the occupied ambient sound pressure level. It is also necessary to measure and save the unoccupied ambient sound level at each measurement location. Then, during occupied times, take and save ambient sound level measurements. The three data sets are combined by software to calculate the corrected STI for the area. See D.6.5.6.

D.4 Test Equipment Calibration for Testing Using STIPA Test Signal.

D.4.1 General.

D.4.1.1 The calibration of the STI test instrument is done in accordance with this section using a talkbox or in accordance with manufacturer's instructions.

D.4.1.2 The Intelligibility Test System consists of a talkbox and STIPA test meter (analyzer) all from one manufacturer. Units from other manufacturers should not be interchanged unless said units have been tested by a recognized testing laboratory for compatibility *(see D.2.3.5.2).*

D.4.1.3 Prior to performing any intelligibility testing or intelligibility system calibration, verify that the test meter's microphone, talkbox, and analyzer are within calibration date as listed on the unit's calibration tag.

D.4.1.4 All audio test equipment, including ANSI Type 2 sound pressure level meters required by *NFPA 72* for audibility testing, require regular calibration to known, traceable standards. The portable meters used to measure STI using the STIPA test signal should meet or exceed ANSI Type 2 meter requirements. In addition, the STIPA test signal and the meter algorithm for measuring the received signal and calculating the modulation transfer function to arrive at the STI should be tested by a certifying laboratory for accuracy to the IEC standard for STI.

D.4.2 Calibration Procedure.

D.4.2.1 The following procedures should be performed at the commencement and conclusion of intelligibility testing. If the following procedure differs from that recommended by the manufacturer of the test equipment, follow their calibration test procedure.

D.4.2.2 Perform these calibration procedures in a quiet room (45 dBA or less) without any extraneous sounds or any talking, music, etc.

D.4.2.3 Start STIPA test tone as instructed by the manufacturer.

D.4.2.4 Apply power to the talkbox and then activate the STIPA test signal.

D.4.2.5 Turn on the analyzer and set it to SPL A fast measurement mode.

D.4.2.6 Place the analyzer's microphone approximately 1 in., on axis, from the talkbox. Do not place the analyzer microphone against any hard surface — this can lead to induced noise and affect the calibration.

D.4.2.7 Adjust the talkbox volume so that the STI analyzer's reading is approximately 92 dBA.

D.4.2.8 Keeping the analyzer in approximately the same position, measure the STI. Note that some meters display STI measurements using the CIS scale while some can display results in either STI or CIS units. See D.2.4 for an explanation of the CIS scale.

D.4.2.9 The equipment is working properly if the reading is greater than 0.91 STI or 0.96 CIS. Up to three tests can be performed. If the system does not pass after three tests, it should be returned to the manufacturer for repair or recalibration.

D.5 Talkbox Set-up.

D.5.1 Input Test Signal.

D.5.1.1 The input test signal should be configured to produce the proper level by utilizing either the microphone input method or the direct input injection method.

D.5.1.2 Most emergency communications systems have microphones for manual voice communication and should be tested using the microphone test method. Systems that do not have microphones and that only play pre-recorded voice announcements can be tested using the direct input injection method.

D.5.1.3 By putting the STI or STIPA test signal into the system via the system microphone, the ECS system is being tested from end to end. If an ECS system has the test signal pre-recorded in its hardware, playback of that test signal would not be testing the microphone and the part that feeds the microphone signal into the system.

D.5.1.4 Direct Input Injection Method for Test Signals.

D.5.1.4.1 With this method the STI or STIPA test signals are pre-recorded in the emergency communications system hardware in the same way as the pre-recorded voice messages and at the same input levels. Alternately, the test signal can input to the system via input jacks or terminals.

D.5.1.4.2 The input level of the test signal should be tested by the ECS listing agency as being the same as the pre-recorded voice levels or should be calibrated using the ECS equipment manufacturer's instructions.

D.5.1.4.3 For ECS systems that permit voice messages to be custom recorded, the equivalent sound level *(see A.18.4.3.1)* L_{eq} of the recorded voice over a period of 10 seconds or the length of the voice message should be measured and should be within 3 dB of the prerecorded STI or STIPA test signal to ensure that it is at the correct level.

D.5.1.4.4 Field measurements of the STI are made using the procedure in Section D.5.

D.5.1.5 Microphone Input Method for Test Signals.

D.5.1.5.1 With this method a recording of the STI or STIPA test signals are played into the system microphone using a talkbox.

D.5.1.5.2 The talkbox is set up and calibrated per D.5.2, and field measurements of the STI are made using the procedure in Section D.6.

D.5.2 Calibrating the Input Test Signal for Microphone Input Method.

D.5.2.1 Of the two methods for setting the test signal input to the system microphone, the method that sets the level to match that of a person speaking into the microphone is the one required by IEC 60268-16, *Sound system equipment — Part 16: Objective rating of speech intelligibility by speech transmission index,* the standard that defines STI and STIPA.

D.5.2.2 In theory, the two methods for setting up the talkbox should result in the talkbox being set at approximately the same sound level. The ECS should be designed and configured so that input to the microphone results in the same output level that any pre-recorded announcements would produce.

D.5.2.3 General.

D.5.2.3.1 There are two methods for setting the level of the STI or STIPA test signal at the input microphone.

D.5.2.3.2 Method 1 sets the volume of the input test signal so that the dBA output in the area under test is the same as that for a pre-recorded message.

D.5.2.3.3 Method 2 sets the volume of the input test signal to match that of speech level under normal conditions.

D.5.2.3.4 The room where the talkbox and system under test microphone are located should be quiet.

D.5.2.3.5 An emergency command center or fire command center will not be free of noise during an actual emergency. However, for testing purposes, the room should be relatively free of extraneous noises that could affect the results. The purpose of the tests is to establish the baseline capability of the system and acoustic environment to support intelligible communications. Good design practice for an emergency command center is to isolate the space so that only emergency command personnel have access. In addition, the location of the microphone for manual input should be such that background discussions and noise are minimized.

D.5.2.3.6 Set up the talkbox in accordance with the manufacturer's instructions.

D.5.2.4 Method 1 — Matching Recorded Message Level.

D.5.2.4.1 The intent of this method is to set the talkbox or audio source input level into the emergency communications system microphone so that the output at a location in the area under test is the same as the level of prerecorded messages played by the system.

D.5.2.4.2 The sound pressure level produced by the talkbox while playing the STI or STIPA test signal should be matched with the sound pressure level of the pre-recorded voice message.

D.5.2.4.3 Two people will be needed to perform the calibration procedure. One person needs to be present at the talkbox while the other person needs to operate the analyzer at a typical location in the facility.

D.5.2.4.4 At a typical location in the facility, position the analyzer it so its microphone is approximately 5 ft (1.5 m) above the finished floor.

D.5.2.4.5 Set the analyzer (meter) to measure sound pressure level, A-weighted, fast.

D.5.2.4.6 Activate the pre-recorded voice message from the ECS.

D.5.2.4.7 The decibel reading at the analyzer will be somewhat erratic due to the nature of speech signals.

D.5.2.4.8 Record the highest dB reading the system produces.

D.5.2.4.9 Do not move the analyzer from the test location.

D.5.2.4.10 Turn off the pre-recorded voice message.

D.5.2.4.11 Place the microphone of the emergency communications system at a distance from the talkbox as recommended by the microphone or ECS manufacturer.

D.5.2.4.12 Start the talkbox STI or STIPA test signal.

D.5.2.4.13 Adjust the talkbox sound level until the field measurement of the test signal is ±3 dB of the level generated when the pre-recorded voice message was played and measured. This setting should not change for the remainder of the testing.

D.5.2.4.14 Begin field testing in accordance with Section D.6.

D.5.2.5 Method 2 — Matching Speech Level.

D.5.2.5.1 The intent of this method is to set the talkbox or audio source input level to the emergency communications system microphone to match that of an average person speaking into the microphone.

D.5.2.5.2 Set the analyzer (meter) to measure sound pressure level, A-weighted, fast.

D.5.2.5.3 Start the STI or STIPA test signal and hold the meter at a distance of 39.4 in. (1.0 m) on-axis from the talkbox or audio source.

D.5.2.5.4 Set the talkbox volume (level) so that the meter registers 65 dBA at a distance of 39.4 in. (1.0 m). This setting should not change for the remainder of the testing.

D.5.2.5.5 The distance from the microphone to the talkbox should be documented so that future tests can be set up consistently. Most microphone manufacturers or ECS equipment manufacturers will state a recommended distance for a person to hold the microphone when talking. Some microphone use chin guards or some physical means to help users know when they are holding the microphone at the correct distance. If the manufacturer has not recommended a talking distance, 4 in. (100 mm) is recommended as a guide.

D.5.2.5.6 Place the microphone of the emergency communications system at a distance from the talkbox as recommended by the microphone or ECS manufacturer.

D.5.2.5.7 A level of 60 dBA at one meter is required by IEC 60268-16, *Sound system equipment — Part 16: Objective rating of speech intelligibility by speech transmission index*, the standard that defines STI and STIPA and is considered a normal speech level. While 60 dBA at 1 m is documented as "normal" speech, in areas where there is background noise, the Lombard effect causes a person to talk at an elevated volume. For this document, the committee chose to use 65 dBA as more representative of speech levels during emergency situations. It is recommended that at least one field STI measurement be made at both 60 dBA and 70 dBA at one meter talking level to test the effects of elevated voice level.

D.5.2.5.8 Sound pressure level increases 6 dB whenever the distance is halved. So, the test could be set up so that the talkbox level achieves 65 + 6 = 71 dBA at a distance of 19.7 in. (0.50 m). Table D.5.2.5.8 shows different dB levels at distances that would be equivalent to 65 dBA at 39.4 in. (1.0 m).

Table D.5.2.5.8 Audibility Equivalent to 65 dBA at 1-m Distance

r (in.)	r (m)	L_P (dB)	r (in.)	r (m)	L_P (dB)	r (in.)	r (m)	L_P (dB)
0.1	0	117	4	0.10	85	11	0.28	76
0.2	0.01	111	5	0.13	83	12	0.30	75
0.5	0.01	103	6	0.15	81	20	0.50	71
1.0	0.03	97	7	0.18	80	24	0.61	69
1.5	0.04	93	8	0.20	79	39.37	1.00	65
2.0	0.05	91	9	0.23	78	78.8	2.00	59
3.0	0.08	87	10	0.25	77			

D.5.2.5.9 Begin field testing in accordance with Section D.6.

D.6 STI/STIPA Test Procedure.

D.6.1 General. This test procedure permits testing during either occupied conditions or during unoccupied conditions. See D.3.8.

D.6.2 Power. The system under test should be tested on secondary power for a minimum of 15 minutes and then on primary power for the remainder of the testing.

D.6.3 System Operation. Where two ADSs are adjacent to each other and not separated by physically barriers that significantly prevent noise penetration from one ADS to another, the notification appliances in both ADSs should be operating

during the testing. It is acceptable for intelligibility testing to silence or disable other notification zones that would not potentially interfere with each other. However, regular testing per *NFPA 72* would require that all circuits be operated simultaneously at one point to ensure proper operation and to verify power requirements.

D.6.4 Occupied Testing.

D.6.4.1 Testing should be done during a period of time when the area is occupied and is reasonably close to having maximum background noise.

D.6.4.2 Set up the talkbox in accordance with Section D.4 and start the STI or STIPA test signal.

D.6.4.3 At each measurement point in each ADS measure the STI.

D.6.4.4 Document the results on plans or forms in a way that accurately describes the measurement point and that permits future testing at the same locations.

D.6.5 Unoccupied Testing.

D.6.5.1 General. Testing of speech intelligibility in the presence of the occupied ambient sound pressure level is the preferred method. However, for various reasons, including disruption of normal work, it might be desirable to only do "silent" testing during occupied periods and to do testing with the STI or STIPA test signal during unoccupied or less occupied conditions.

D.6.5.2 Number of Tests. This test method requires three different measurements at each measurement point, typically made during two site visits. The data for each measurement is saved in a format in accordance with the instrument manufacturer's requirements. The three data files are then post-processed to arrive at the final corrected STI.

D.6.5.3 Occupied Ambient Sound Pressure Level Measurement.

D.6.5.3.1 At each measurement point in each ADS measure the occupied ambient sound pressure level.

D.6.5.3.2 Save the measurement data in accordance with the instrument manufacturer's requirements to permit post-processing of the data.

D.6.5.3.3 Document the results in writing on plans or forms in a way that accurately describes the measurement point and that permits future testing at the same locations.

D.6.5.4 Unoccupied Ambient Sound Pressure Level Measurement.

D.6.5.4.1 At each measurement point in each ADS measure the unoccupied ambient sound pressure level.

D.6.5.4.2 Save the measurement data in accordance with the instrument manufacturer's requirements to permit post-processing of the data.

D.6.5.4.3 Document the results in writing on plans or forms in a way that accurately describes the measurement point and that permits future testing at the same locations.

D.6.5.5 Unoccupied STI Measurement.

D.6.5.5.1 Set up the talkbox in accordance with Section D.4 and start the STI or STIPA test signal.

D.6.5.5.2 At each measurement point in each ADS measure the uncorrected STI.

D.6.5.5.3 Save the measurement data in accordance with the instrument manufacturer's requirements to permit post-processing of the data.

D.6.5.5.4 Document the results in writing on plans or forms in a way that accurately describes the measurement point and that permits future testing at the same locations.

D.6.5.6 Post Processing.

D.6.5.6.1 The corrected STI is arrived at by post-processing of the occupied ambient sound pressure level measurement, the unoccupied ambient sound pressure level measurement, and the unoccupied STI measurement. In effect, the measured STI (uncorrected) is being corrected by adding in the effects the actual expected (occupied) ambient sound pressure level.

D.6.5.6.2 The post processing procedure or software provided by the instrument manufacturer should be used to calculate the final corrected STI for each measurement point.

D.6.5.6.3 Document the results in writing on plans or forms in a way that accurately describes the measurement point and that permits future testing at the same locations.

D.6.5.6.4 Documentation of the final results for each point should include the results of all three measurements and the final corrected STI value. The manufacturer's software revision should also be included in the results documentation.

D.7 Post Test Procedures.

D.7.1 Test Closure. Upon completion of all testing, the emergency communications system should be returned to its normal operating condition.

D.7.2 Results.

D.7.2.1 It is also not the intent of this test protocol to describe how to interpret results or how to correct systems or environments that contribute to poor speech intelligibility. However, depending on the instrument used, it might be possible to have data retained by the instrument to determine possible causes and their effects on STI results. Consult with the instrument manufacturer to determine if the instrument has the capability to display or save the intermediate STI modulation indices and octave band measurement results and for instructions on how to interpret those data.

D.7.2.2 For each ADS, summarize the results in accordance with the performance requirements of D.2.4.

D.7.2.3 For an ADS that had multiple measurement points or that had multiple measurements at only one measurement point, calculate the average per D.2.4 and list the average and the minimum measurement per D.2.4 in the results summary.

D.7.3 Documentation.

D.7.3.1 The test results should be fully documented and provided to the building owner, the emergency communications system contractor, the system designer, the authority having jurisdiction, and any other individual or organization deemed appropriate.

D.7.3.2 In addition to the requirements for test documentation contained in *NFPA 72*, Chapter 10, the test results should include:

(1) Building location and related descriptive facility information
(2) Names, titles, and contact information for individuals involved in test

(3) Dates and times of tests
(4) A list of testing instruments, including manufacturer's name, model, serial number, and date of most recent calibration
(5) Technical description of emergency communications system
(6) Identification of ADSs
(7) Locations of specific measurement points (in a list or on a set of drawings)
(8) Site definition of ambient sound pressure levels
(9) STI/STIPA measurements at each measurement point
(10) Final corrected STI/STIPA values where the post-processing procedure is used
(11) Indication of whether or not the test met the pass/fail criteria
(12) Record of system restoration
(13) Any additional information to assist with future evaluation of system performance

D.7.3.3 If appropriate, the plans and specifications addressed in D.3.3 should be updated based on the results of the test.

Annex E   Sample Ordinance Adopting *NFPA 72*

This annex is not a part of the requirements of this NFPA document but is included for informational purposes only.

E.1 The following sample ordinance is provided to assist a jurisdiction in the adoption of this Code and is not part of this Code.

ORDINANCE NO. _____

An ordinance of the *[jurisdiction]* adopting the 2013 edition of *NFPA 72, National Fire Alarm and Signaling Code*, and documents listed in Chapter 2 of that Code; prescribing regulations governing conditions hazardous to life and property from fire or explosion; providing for the issuance of permits and collection of fees; repealing Ordinance No. _____ of the *[jurisdiction]* and all other ordinances and parts of ordinances in conflict therewith; providing a penalty; providing a severability clause; and providing for publication; and providing an effective date.

BE IT ORDAINED BY THE *[governing body]* OF THE *[jurisdiction]*:

SECTION 1 That the *NFPA 72, National Fire Alarm and Signaling Code*, and documents adopted by Chapter 2, three (3) copies of which are on file and are open to inspection by the public in the office of the *[jurisdiction's keeper of records]* of the *[jurisdiction]*, are hereby adopted and incorporated into this ordinance as fully as if set out at length herein, and from the date on which this ordinance shall take effect, the provisions thereof shall be controlling within the limits of the *[jurisdiction]*. The same are hereby adopted as the Code of the *[jurisdiction]* for the purpose of prescribing regulations governing conditions hazardous to life and property from fire or explosion and providing for issuance of permits and collection of fees.

SECTION 2 Any person who shall violate any provision of this code or standard hereby adopted or fail to comply therewith; or who shall violate or fail to comply with any order made thereunder; or who shall build in violation of any detailed statement of specifications or plans submitted and approved thereunder; or fail to operate in accordance with any certificate or permit issued thereunder; and from which no appeal has been taken; or who shall fail to comply with such an order as affirmed or modified by a court of competent jurisdiction, within the time fixed herein, shall severally for each and every such violation and noncompliance, respectively, be guilty of a misdemeanor, punishable by a fine of not less than $ _____ nor more than $_____ or by imprisonment for not less than _____ days nor more than _____ days or by both such fine and imprisonment. The imposition of one penalty for any violation shall not excuse the violation or permit it to continue; and all such persons shall be required to correct or remedy such violations or defects within a reasonable time; and when not otherwise specified the application of the above penalty shall not be held to prevent the enforced removal of prohibited conditions. Each day that prohibited conditions are maintained shall constitute a separate offense.

SECTION 3 Additions, insertions, and changes — that the 2013 edition of *NFPA 72, National Fire Alarm and Signaling Code* is amended and changed in the following respects:

List Amendments

SECTION 4 That ordinance No. _____ of *[jurisdiction]* entitled *[fill in the title of the ordinance or ordinances in effect at the present time]* and all other ordinances or parts of ordinances in conflict herewith are hereby repealed.

SECTION 5 That if any section, subsection, sentence, clause, or phrase of this ordinance is, for any reason, held to be invalid or unconstitutional, such decision shall not affect the validity or constitutionality of the remaining portions of this ordinance. The *[governing body]* hereby declares that it would have passed this ordinance, and each section, subsection, clause, or phrase hereof, irrespective of the fact that any one or more sections, subsections, sentences, clauses, and phrases be declared unconstitutional.

SECTION 6 That the *[jurisdiction's keeper of records]* is hereby ordered and directed to cause this ordinance to be published.

[NOTE: An additional provision may be required to direct the number of times the ordinance is to be published and to specify that it is to be in a newspaper in general circulation. Posting may also be required.]

SECTION 7 That this ordinance and the rules, regulations, provisions, requirements, orders, and matters established and adopted hereby shall take effect and be in full force and effect *[time period]* from and after the date of its final passage and adoption.

Annex F   Wiring Diagrams and Guide for Testing Fire Alarm Circuits

This annex is not a part of the requirements of this NFPA document but is included for informational purposes only.

Annex F provides guidance for testing of the various classes of circuits identified in Chapter 12 of this edition of NFPA 72. Earlier editions of NFPA 72 have used different designations for these circuits. Designations found in previous editions (located in Annex C of NFPA 72, 2007 edition or earlier) can be compared with these corresponding diagrams.

F.1 Circuit class designations in this edition of the Code are Class A, B, C, D, E, R, S, and X. Definitions can be found in Chapter 12. Additionally, special circuits unique to supervising stations are designated as Types 4, 5, 6, and 7 and definitions can be found in Chapter 26.

The wiring diagrams depicted in Figure F.2.1.1 through Figure F.3.14(k) are representative of typical circuits encountered in the field and are not intended to be all-inclusive.

The noted symbols are as indicated in NFPA 170, *Standard for Fire Safety and Emergency Symbols.*

An individual point-identifying (addressable) fire alarm initiating device operates on a signaling line circuit and is designated as a Class A, Class B, or Class X initiating device circuit. All fire alarm circuits must test free of grounds because metallic conductors will cause failure of the circuit when a second ground condition occurs on the same power source.

Nonmetallic circuit paths, such as wireless and fiber-optic may still be designated as Class A, B, or X if they meet the other performance requirements of those pathways.

Ground-fault detection is not required for all circuits that might be interconnected with the fire alarm system. Therefore, tests for ground-fault detection should be limited to those circuits equipped with ground-fault detection. The Class R designation is for a redundant circuit that can use metallic conductors, but is not concerned with ground fault detection. Class S is a single path supervised circuit that can use metallic conductors, but is not concerned with ground fault detection.

The following initiating device circuits are illustrative of either alarm or supervisory signaling. Alarm-initiating devices and supervisory initiating devices are not permitted to have identical annunciation at the fire alarm control unit.

Directly connected system smoke detectors, commonly referred to as two-wire detectors, should be listed as being electrically and functionally compatible with the fire alarm control unit and the specific subunit or module to which they are connected. If the detectors and the units or modules are not compatible, it is possible that, during an alarm condition, the detector's visible indicator will illuminate, but no change of state to the alarm condition will occur at the fire alarm control unit. Incompatibility can also prevent proper system operation at extremes of operating voltage, temperature, and other environmental conditions.

Where two or more two-wire detectors with integral relays are connected to a single initiating device circuit, and their relay contacts are used to control essential building functions (e.g., fan shutdown, elevator recall), it should be clearly noted that the circuit might be capable of supplying only enough energy to support one detector/relay combination in an alarm mode. If control of more than one building function is required, each detector/relay combination used to control separate functions should be connected to separate initiating device circuits, or they should be connected to an initiating device circuit that provides adequate power to allow all the detectors connected to the circuit to be in the alarm mode simultaneously. During acceptance and reacceptance testing, this feature should always be tested and verified.

A speaker is an alarm notification appliance, and, if used as shown in the diagrams in Section F.2, the principle of operation and supervision is the same as for other audible alarm notification appliances (e.g., bells and horns).

The testing of supervised remote relays is to be conducted in the same manner as for notification appliances.

F.2 Wiring Diagrams and Testing. When testing circuits, the correct wiring size, insulation type, and conductor fill should be verified in accordance with the requirements of *NFPA 70, National Electrical Code.*

F.2.1 Testing Nonpowered, Hard-Wired Class A, B, or C Initiating Device Circuits. Disconnect conductor at device or control unit, then reconnect. Temporarily connect a ground to either leg of conductors, then remove ground. Both operations should indicate audible and visual trouble with subsequent restoration at control unit.

F.2.1.1 Hard-Wired Alarm Initiating or Supervisory Initiating Devices. Hard-wired alarm initiating devices (e.g., manual station or valve supervisory switch), by their intended function, initiate alarm upon a conductor-to-conductor short. See Figure F.2.1.1.

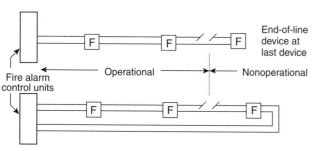

End-of-line device within the control unit

FIGURE F.2.1.1 Nonpowered Alarm Initiating or Supervisory Initiating Devices Connected to Hard-Wired and Class B Initiating Device Circuits.

F.2.2 Nonpowered Class A Circuits. Disconnect a conductor at a device at midpoint in the circuit. Operate a device on either side of the device with the disconnected conductor. Reset fire alarm control unit and reconnect conductor. Repeat test with a ground applied to either conductor in place of the disconnected conductor. Both operations should indicate audible and visual trouble, then alarm or supervisory indication with subsequent restoration.

F.2.3 Circuit-Powered (Two-Wire) Smoke Detectors for Class A or B Initiating Device Circuits. Remove smoke detector where installed with plug-in base or disconnect conductor from fire alarm control unit beyond first device. Activate smoke detector per manufacturer's published instructions between fire alarm control unit and circuit break. Restore detector or circuit, or both. Fire alarm control unit should indicate trouble when fault occurs and alarm when detectors are activated between the break and the fire alarm control unit. See Figure F.2.3.

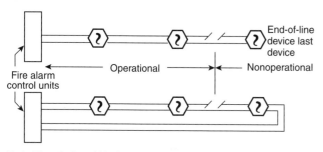

End-of-line device within the control unit

FIGURE F.2.3 Circuit-Powered (Two-Wire) Smoke Detectors for Class A or B Initiating Device Circuits.

F.2.4 Circuit-Powered (Two-Wire) Smoke Detectors for Class A Initiating Device Circuits. Disconnect conductor at a smoke detector or remove where installed with a plug-in base at midpoint in the circuit. Operate a device on either side of the device with the fault. Reset control unit and reconnect

conductor or detector. Repeat test with a ground applied to either conductor in place of the disconnected conductor or removed device. Both operations should indicate audible and visual trouble, then alarm indication with subsequent restoration. See Figure F.2.4.

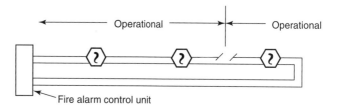

FIGURE F.2.4 Circuit-Powered (Two-Wire) Smoke Detectors for Class A Initiating Device Circuits.

F.2.5 Combination Alarm Initiating Device and Notification Appliance Circuits. Disconnect a conductor either at indicating or initiating device. Activate initiating device between the fault and the fire alarm control unit. Activate additional smoke detectors between the device first activated and the fire alarm control unit. Restore circuit, initiating devices, and fire alarm control unit. Confirm that all notification appliances on the circuit operate from the fire alarm control unit up to the fault and that all smoke detectors tested and their associated ancillary functions, if any, operate. See Figure F.2.5.

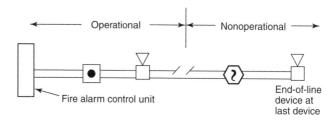

FIGURE F.2.5 Combination Alarm Initiating Device and Notification Appliance Circuits.

F.2.6 Combination Alarm Initiating Device and Notification Appliance Circuits Arranged for Operation with Single Open or Ground Fault. Testing of the circuit is similar to that described in F.2.5. Confirm that all notification appliances operate on either side of fault. See Figure F.2.6.

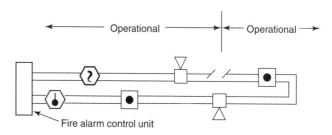

FIGURE F.2.6 Combination Alarm Initiating Device and Notification Appliance Circuits Arranged for Operation with Single Open or Ground Fault.

F.2.7 Class A or B Circuits with Four-Wire Smoke Detectors and End-of-Line Power Supervision Relay. Testing of the circuit is similar to that described in F.2.3 and F.2.4. Disconnect a leg of the power supply circuit beyond the first device on the circuit. Activate initiating device between the fault and the fire alarm control unit. Restore circuits, initiating devices, and fire alarm control unit. Audible and visual trouble should indicate at the fire alarm control unit where either the initiating or power circuit is faulted. All initiating devices between the circuit fault and the fire alarm control unit should activate. In addition, removal of a smoke detector from a plug-in-type base can also break the power supply circuit. Where circuits contain various powered and nonpowered devices on the same initiating circuit, verify that the nonpowered devices beyond the power circuit fault can still initiate an alarm. A return loop should be brought back to the last powered device and the power supervisory relay to incorporate into the end-of-line device. See Figure F.2.7.

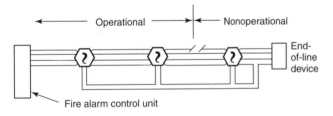

FIGURE F.2.7 Class B Circuits with Four-Wire Smoke Detectors and End-of-Line Power Supervision Relay.

F.2.8 Class B Initiating Device Circuits with Four-Wire Smoke Detectors That Include Integral Individual Supervision Relays. Testing of the circuit is similar to that described in F.2.3 with the addition of a power circuit. See Figure F.2.8.

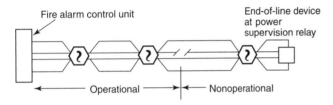

FIGURE F.2.8 Class B Initiating Device Circuits with Four-Wire Smoke Detectors That Include Integral Individual Supervision Relays.

F.2.9 Alarm Notification Appliances Connected Class B (Two-Wire) Circuits. Testing of the notification appliances connected as Class B is similar to that described in F.2.3. See Figure F.2.9.

F.2.10 Alarm Notification Appliances Connected to Class A (Four-Wire) Circuits. Testing of the notification appliances connected as Class A is similar to that described in F.2.4. See Figure F.2.10.

F.2.11 System with Supervised Audible Notification Appliance Circuit and Unsupervised Visible Notification Appliance Circuit. Testing of the notification appliances connected to Class B is similar to that described in F.2.4. See Figure F.2.11.

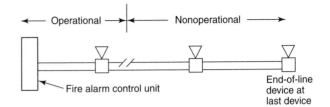

FIGURE F.2.9 Alarm Notification Appliances Connected to Class B (Two-Wire) Circuits.

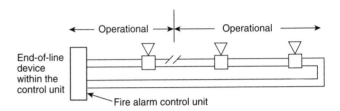

FIGURE F.2.10 Alarm Notification Appliances Connected to Class A (Four-Wire) Circuits.

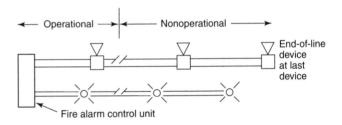

FIGURE F.2.11 Supervised Audible Notification Appliance Circuit and Unsupervised Visible Notification Appliance Circuit.

F.2.12 System with Supervised Audible and Visible Notification Appliance Circuits. Testing of the notification appliances connected to Class B is similar to that described in F.2.4. See Figure F.2.12.

F.2.13 Series Notification Appliance Circuit That No Longer Meets Requirements of *NFPA 72*. An open fault in the circuit wiring should cause a trouble condition. See Figure F.2.13.

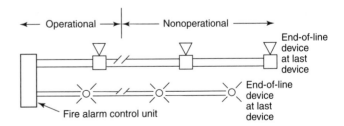

FIGURE F.2.12 Supervised Audible and Visible Notification Appliance Circuits.

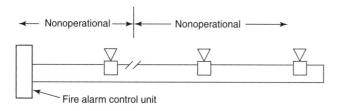

FIGURE F.2.13 Series Notification Appliance Circuit.

F.2.14 Supervised Series Supervisory Initiating Circuit with Sprinkler Supervisory Valve Switches Connected That No Longer Meets Requirements of *NFPA 72.* An open fault in the circuit wiring or operation of the valve switch (or any supervisory signal device) should cause a trouble condition. The classification of this circuit is now designated as Class D because the intended operation is performed. When the circuit fails, the indication at the fire control unit is the same as if the supervisory switch were to open. Fire alarm initiating devices, including supervisory inputs, are no longer allowed to annunciate as trouble conditions. See Figure F.2.14.

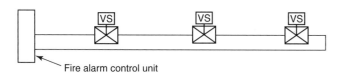

FIGURE F.2.14 Supervised Series Supervisory Initiating Circuit with Sprinkler Supervisory Valve Switches Connected.

F.2.15 Initiating Device Circuit with Parallel Waterflow Alarm Switches and Series Supervisory Valve Switch That No Longer Meets Requirements of *NFPA 72.* An open fault in the circuit wiring or operation of the valve switch should cause a trouble signal. See Figure F.2.15.

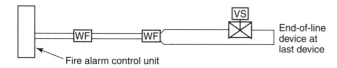

FIGURE F.2.15 Initiating Device Circuit with Parallel Waterflow Alarm Switches and Series Supervisory Valve Switch.

F.2.16 System Connected to Municipal Fire Alarm Master Box Circuit. Disconnect a leg of municipal circuit at master box. Verify alarm sent to public communications center. Disconnect leg of auxiliary circuit. Verify trouble condition on control unit. Restore circuits. Activate control unit and send alarm signal to communications center. Verify control unit in trouble condition until master box reset. See Figure F.2.16.

F.2.17 Auxiliary Circuit Connected to Municipal Fire Alarm Master Box. For operation with a master box, an open or ground fault (where ground detection is provided) on the circuit should result in a trouble condition at the fire alarm control unit. A trouble signal at the fire alarm control unit should persist until the master box is reset. For operation with a shunt trip master box, an open fault in the auxiliary circuit should cause an alarm on the municipal system. See Figure F.2.17.

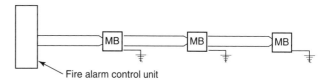

FIGURE F.2.16 System Connected to Municipal Fire Alarm Master Box Circuit.

FIGURE F.2.17 Auxiliary Circuit Connected to Municipal Fire Alarm Master Box.

F.3 Circuit Classes. Some testing laboratories and authorities having jurisdiction permitted systems to be classified as Class X by the application of two circuits operating in tandem. An example of this is to take two series circuits, Class B, and operate them in tandem. The logic was that if a condition occurs on one of the circuits, the other series circuit remained operative.

To understand the principles of the circuit, alarm receipt capability should be performed on a single circuit, and the Class type, based on the performance, should be indicated on the record of completion.

F.3.1 Style 0.5. This signaling circuit operates as a series circuit in performance. This is identical to the historical series audible signaling circuits. Any type of break or ground in one of the conductors, or the internal of the multiple interface device, and the total circuit is rendered inoperative.

To test and verify this type of circuit, either a conductor should be lifted or an earth ground should be placed on a conductor or a terminal point where the signaling circuit attaches to the multiplex interface device.

F.3.2 Style 0.5(a) (Class B) Series That No Longer Meets Requirements of *NFPA 72.* Style 0.5(a) functions so that, when a box is operated, the supervisory contacts open, making the succeeding devices nonoperative while the operating box sends a coded signal. Any alarms occurring in any successive devices will not be received at the receiving station during this period. See Figure F.3.2.

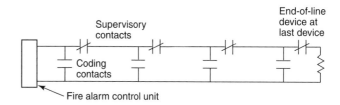

FIGURE F.3.2 Style 0.5(a) Series.

F.3.3 Style 0.5(b) Shunt That No Longer Meets Requirements of *NFPA 72.* The contact closures when the device is operated (and remains closed) to shunt out the remainder of the system until the code is complete. See Figure F.3.3.

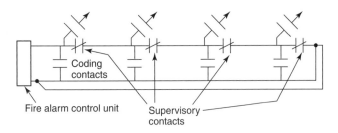

FIGURE F.3.3   Style 0.5(b) Shunt.

F.3.4 Style 0.5(c) Positive Supervised Successive That No Longer Meets Requirements of *NFPA 72.* An open or ground fault on the circuit should cause a trouble condition at the control unit. See Figure F.3.4.

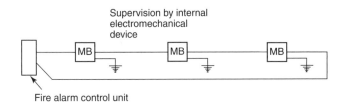

FIGURE F.3.4   Style 0.5(c) Positive Supervised Successive.

F.3.5 Style 1.0 That No Longer Meets Requirements of *NFPA 72.* This is a series circuit identical to the diagram for Style 0.5, except that the fire alarm system hardware has enhanced performance. *[See Figure F.3.5(a) and Figure F.3.5(b).]* A single earth ground can be placed on a conductor or multiplex interface device, and the circuit and hardware will still have alarm operability.

If a conductor break or an internal fault occurs in the pathway of the circuit conductors, the entire circuit becomes inoperative.

To verify alarm receipt capability and the resulting trouble signal, place an earth ground on one of the conductors or at the point where the signaling circuit attaches to the multiplex interface device. One of the transmitters or an initiating device should then be placed into alarm.

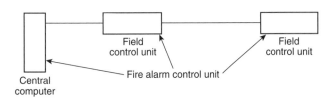

FIGURE F.3.5(a)   Style 1.0 (Class B).

F.3.6 Typical McCulloh Loop. This is the central station McCulloh redundant-type circuit and has alarm receipt capability on either side of a single break. See Figure F.3.6.

F.3.6.1 To test, lift one of the conductors and operate a transmitter or initiating device on each side of the break. This activity should be repeated for each conductor.

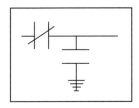

FIGURE F.3.5(b)   Typical Transmitter Layout.

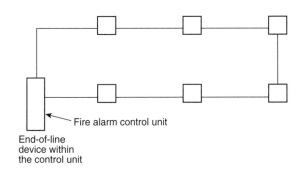

FIGURE F.3.6   Typical McCulloh Loop.

F.3.6.2 Place an earth ground on a conductor and operate a single transmitter or initiating device to verify alarm receipt capability and trouble condition for each conductor.

F.3.6.3 Repeat the instructions of F.3.6.1 and F.3.6.2 at the same time, verify alarm receipt capability, and verify that a trouble condition results.

F.3.7 Class B (Formerly Style 3.0). This is a parallel circuit in which multiplex interface devices transmit signal and operating power over the same conductors. *(See Figure F.3.7.)* The multiplex interface devices might be operable up to the point of a single break. Verify by lifting a conductor and causing an alarm condition on one of the units between the central alarm unit and the break. Either lift a conductor to verify the trouble condition or place an earth ground on the conductors. Test for all the valuations shown on the signaling table.

On ground-fault testing, verify alarm receipt capability by actuating a multiplex interface initiating device or a transmitter.

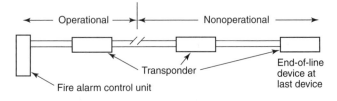

FIGURE F.3.7   Class B (Formerly Style 3.0).

F.3.8 Style 3.5 That No Longer Meets Requirements of *NFPA 72.* Follow the instructions for Class B (formerly Style 3.0) and verify the trouble conditions by either lifting a conductor or placing a ground on the conductor. See Figure F.3.8.

F.3.9 Class B (Formerly Style 4.0). Follow the instructions for Class B (formerly Style 3.0) and include a loss of carrier where the signal is being used. See Figure F.3.9.

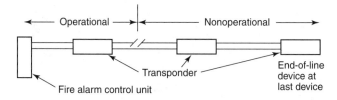

FIGURE F.3.8 Style 3.5.

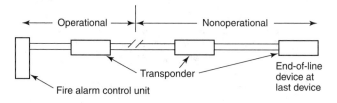

FIGURE F.3.9 Class B (Formerly Style 4.0).

F.3.10 Style 4.5 That No Longer Meets Requirements of *NFPA 72.* Follow the instructions for Style 3.5. Verify alarm receipt capability while lifting a conductor by actuating a multiple interface device or transmitter on each side of the break. See Figure F.3.10.

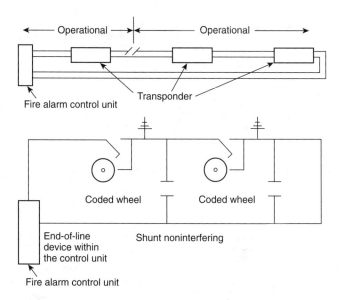

FIGURE F.3.10 Style 4.5 (Class B).

F.3.11 Class A (Formerly Style 5.0). Verify the alarm receipt capability and trouble annunciation by lifting a conductor and actuating a multiplex interfacing device or a transmitter on each side of the break.

F.3.11.1 Ground Test on Class A (Formerly Style 5.0) Circuit. For the earth ground verification, place an earth ground and certify alarm receipt capability and trouble annunciation by actuating a single multiplex interfacing device or a transmitter. See Figure F.3.11.

F.3.12 Class A (Formerly Style 6.0). Follow the instructions from F.3.11. Verify the trouble annunciation for the various combinations. See Figure F.3.12.

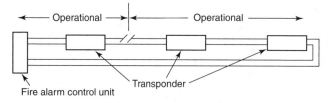

FIGURE F.3.11 Class A (Formerly Style 5.0).

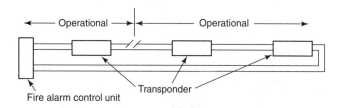

FIGURE F.3.12 Style 6.0 (Class A).

F.3.13 Class A with Circuit Isolators. For the portions of the circuits electrically located between the monitoring points of circuit isolators, follow the instructions for a Class X circuit. It should be clearly noted that the alarm receipt capability for remaining portions of the circuit protection isolators is not the capability of the entire circuit but is permitted with enhanced system capabilities. See Figure F.3.13.

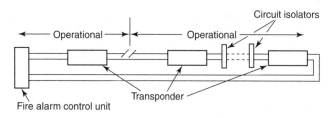

FIGURE F.3.13 Class A with Circuit Isolators.

F.3.14 Class X (Formerly Style 7.0). Follow the instructions for testing of Class A (formerly Style 6.0) for alarm receipt capability and trouble annunciation. See Figure F.3.14(a) through Figure F.3.14(k).

NOTE: Some manufacturers of this type of equipment have isolators as part of the base assembly. Therefore, in the field, this component might not be readily observable without the assistance of the manufacturer's representative.

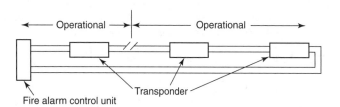

FIGURE F.3.14(a) Class X (Formerly Style 7.0).

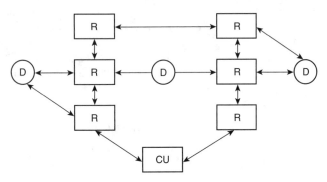

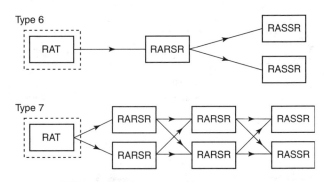

RAT   = Radio alarm transmitter
RARSR = Radio alarm repeater station receiver
RASSR = Radio alarm supervising station receiver

FIGURE F.3.14(e)   One-Way Radio Alarm System (Type 6 and Type 7).

CU = Wireless control unit
       (with power supply and standby power)
R = Wireless repeater
       (with power supply and standby power)
D = Wireless initiating, indicating, and control device
       (either primary battery or primary standby battery)

FIGURE F.3.14(b)   Low-Power Radio (Wireless) Fire Alarm System.

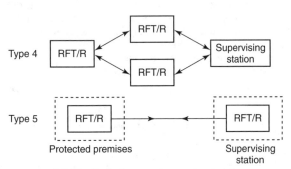

RFT/R = Radio frequency transmitter/receiver

FIGURE F.3.14(c)   Two-Way RF Multiplex Systems.

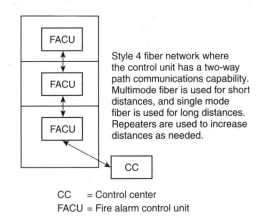

Style 4 fiber network where the control unit has a two-way path communications capability. Multimode fiber is used for short distances, and single mode fiber is used for long distances. Repeaters are used to increase distances as needed.

CC   = Control center
FACU = Fire alarm control unit

FIGURE F.3.14(f)   Style 4 Fiber Network.

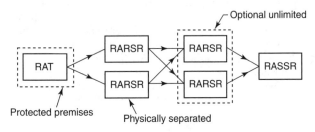

RAT   = Radio alarm transmitter
RARSR = Radio alarm repeater station receiver
RASSR = Radio alarm supervising station receiver

FIGURE F.3.14(d)   One-Way Radio Alarm System.

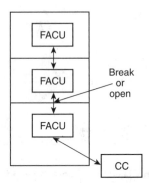

Style 4 fiber network where the control unit has a two-way path communications capability. A single break separates the system into two LANs, both with Style 4 capabilities.

CC   = Control center
FACU = Fire alarm control unit

FIGURE F.3.14(g)   Style 4 Fiber Network (Single Break).

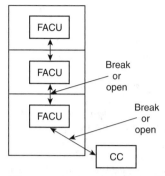

Style 4 fiber network where the control unit has a two-way path communications capability. A double break isolates the control units and the control center in this case. There is one LAN and one isolated control unit operating on its own. Control center is isolated completely with no communications with the network.

CC   = Control center
FACU = Fire alarm control unit

FIGURE F.3.14(h)   Style 4 Fiber Network (Double Break).

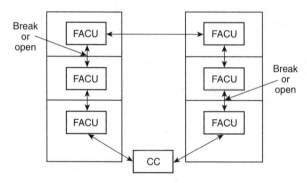

Style 7 fiber network where the control unit has a two-way path communications capability with the two breaks now breaking into two LANs, both functioning as independent networks with the same Style 7 capabilities.

CC   = Control center
FACU = Fire alarm control unit

FIGURE F.3.14(i)   Style 7 Fiber Network (Two LANs).

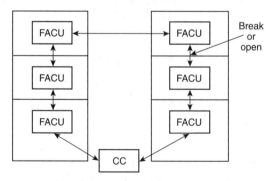

Style 7 fiber network where the control unit has a two-way path communications capability, with one break. System remains as one LAN and meets Style 7.

CC   = Control center
FACU = Fire alarm control unit

FIGURE F.3.14(j)   Style 7 Fiber Network (One LAN).

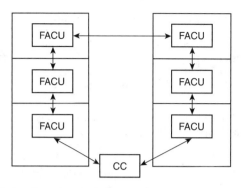

Style 7 fiber network where the control unit has a two-way path communications capability.

CC   = Control center
FACU = Fire alarm control unit

FIGURE F.3.14(k)   Style 7 Fiber Network.

F.4 Batteries. To maximize battery life, nickel-cadmium batteries should be charged as in Table F.4(a).

To maximize battery life, the battery voltage for lead-acid cells should be maintained within the limits shown in Table F.4(b).

The following procedure is recommended for checking the state of charge for nickel-cadmium batteries:

(1) The battery charger should be switched from float to high-rate mode.
(2) The current, as indicated on the charger ammeter, will immediately rise to the maximum output of the charger, and the battery voltage, as shown on the charger voltmeter, will start to rise at the same time.
(3) The actual value of the voltage rise is unimportant, because it depends on many variables. The length of time it takes for the voltage to rise is the important factor.
(4) If, for example, the voltage rises rapidly in a few minutes, then holds steady at the new value, the battery is fully charged. At the same time, the current will drop to slightly above its original value.
(5) In contrast, if the voltage rises slowly and the output current remains high, the high-rate charge should be continued until the voltage remains constant. Such a condition is an indication that the battery is not fully charged, and the float voltage should be increased slightly.

Table F.4(a) Voltage for Nickel-Cadmium Batteries

Float voltage	1.42 volts/cell +0.01 volt
High-rate voltage	1.58 volts/cell +0.07 volt −0.00 volt

Note: High- and low-gravity voltages are (+) 0.07 volt and (−) 0.03 volt, respectively.

Table F.4(b) Voltage for Lead-Acid Batteries

Float Voltage	High-Gravity Battery (Lead Calcium)	Low-Gravity Battery (Lead Antimony)
Maximum	2.25 volts/cell	2.17 volts/cell
Minimum	2.20 volts/cell	2.13 volts/cell
High-rate voltage	—	2.33 volts/cell

Annex G   Informational References

G.1 Referenced Publications. The documents or portions thereof listed in this annex are referenced within the informational sections of this Code and are not part of the requirements of this document unless also listed in Chapter 2 for other reasons.

G.1.1 NFPA Publications. National Fire Protection Association, 1 Batterymarch Park, Quincy, MA 02169-7471.

NFPA 3, *Recommended Practice for Commissioning and Integrated Testing of Fire Protection and Life Safety Systems*, 2012 edition.

NFPA 10, *Standard for Portable Fire Extinguishers*, 2010 edition.

NFPA 11, *Standard for Low-, Medium-, and High-Expansion Foam*, 2010 edition.

NFPA 12, *Standard on Carbon Dioxide Extinguishing Systems*, 2011 edition.

NFPA 12A, *Standard on Halon 1301 Fire Extinguishing Systems*, 2009 edition.

NFPA 13, *Standard for the Installation of Sprinkler Systems*, 2013 edition.

NFPA 14, *Standard for the Installation of Standpipe and Hose Systems*, 2010 edition.

NFPA 15, *Standard for Water Spray Fixed Systems for Fire Protection*, 2012 edition.

NFPA 17, *Standard for Dry Chemical Extinguishing Systems*, 2009 edition.

NFPA 17A, *Standard for Wet Chemical Extinguishing Systems*, 2009 edition.

NFPA 25, *Standard for the Inspection, Testing, and Maintenance of Water-Based Fire Protection Systems*, 2011 edition.

NFPA 70®, National Electrical Code®, 2011 edition.

NFPA 80, *Standard for Fire Doors and Other Opening Protectives*, 2013 edition.

NFPA 90A, *Standard for the Installation of Air-Conditioning and Ventilating Systems*, 2012 edition.

NFPA 90B, *Standard for the Installation of Warm Air Heating and Air-Conditioning Systems*, 2012 edition.

NFPA 92, *Standard for Smoke Control Systems*, 2012 edition.

NFPA *101®, Life Safety Code®*, 2012 edition.

NFPA 105, *Standard for Smoke Door Assemblies and Other Opening Protectives*, 2013 edition.

NFPA 170, *Standard for Fire Safety and Emergency Symbols*, 2012 edition.

NFPA 551, *Guide for the Evaluation of Fire Risk Assessments*, 2010 edition.

NFPA 720, *Standard for the Installation of Carbon Monoxide (CO) Detection and Warning Equipment*, 2012 edition.

NFPA 730, *Guide for Premises Security*, 2011 edition.

NFPA 750, *Standard on Water Mist Fire Protection Systems*, 2010 edition.

NFPA 909, *Code for the Protection of Cultural Resource Properties — Museums, Libraries, and Places of Worship*, 2010 edition.

NFPA 914, *Code for Fire Protection of Historic Structures*, 2010 edition.

NFPA 1221, *Standard for the Installation, Maintenance, and Use of Emergency Services Communications Systems*, 2013 edition.

NFPA 1600®, Standard on Disaster/Emergency Management and Business Continuity Programs, 2010 edition.

NFPA 5000®, Building Construction and Safety Code®, 2012 edition.

Fire Protection Research Foundation, *Optimizing Fire Alarm Notification for High Risk Groups*, 2007.

G.1.2 Other Publications.

G.1.2.1 ANSI Publications. American National Standards Institute, Inc., 25 West 43rd Street, 4th floor, New York, NY 10036.

ANSI/ASME A17.1/CSA B44, *Safety Code for Elevators and Escalators*, 2010.

ANSI/FM 3260, *American National Standard for Energy-Sensing Fire Detectors for Automatic Fire Alarm Signaling*, 2004.

ANSI S3.2, *Method for Measuring the Intelligibility of Speech Over Communications Systems*, 1989, revised 2009.

ANSI S3.41, *American National Standard Audible Emergency Evacuation Signal*, 1990, reaffirmed 2008.

ANSI/UL 268, *Standard for Smoke Detectors for Fire Alarm Systems*, 2009.

ANSI/UL 864, *Standard for Control Units and Accessories for Fire Alarm Systems*, 2003, revised 2011.

ANSI/UL 1638, *Standard for Visual Signaling Appliances — Private Mode Emergency and General Utility Signaling*, 2001, revised 2008.

ANSI/UL 1971, *Standard for Signaling Devices for the Hearing Impaired*, 2002, revised 2008.

G.1.2.2 ASME Publication. American Society of Mechanical Engineers, Three Park Avenue, New York, NY 10016-5990.

ASME A.17.2, *Guide for Inspection of Elevators, Escalators and Moving Walks*, 2010.

G.1.2.3 FEMA Publications. FEMA Headquarters, 500 C Street, SW, Washington DC, 20472.

FEMA Publication CPG-17, *Outdoor Warning Systems Guide*, March, 1980.

G.1.2.4 FM Publications. FM Global, 1301 Atwood Avenue, P.O. Box 7500, Johnston, RI 02919.

FM 3210, *Heat Detectors for Automatic Fire Alarm Signaling*, 2007.

G.1.2.5 IEC Publications. International Electrotechnical Commission, 3 rue de Varembé, P.O. Box 131, CH-1211 Geneva 20, Switzerland. IEC documents are available through ANSI.

IEC 60268, *Sound system equipment — Part 16: Objective rating of speech intelligibility by speech transmission index*, second edition, 1998.

G.1.2.6 IES Publication. Illuminating Engineering Society of North America, 120 Wall Street, 17th floor, New York, NY 10005.

Lighting Handbook Reference and Application, 2008.

G.1.2.7 ISO Publications. Standards Secretariat, Acoustical Society of America, 335 East 45th Street, New York, NY 10017-3483.

ISO/TR 4870, *Acoustics — The Construction and Calibration of Speech Intelligibility Tests*, 1991.

ISO 7240-19, *Fire Detection and Alarm Systems — Part 19: Design, Installation, Commissioning, and Service of Sound Systems for Emergency Purposes*, 2007.

ISO 8201, *Audible Emergency Evacuation Signal*, 1990, revised 2008.

G.1.2.8 NEMA Publication. 1300 North 17th Street, Suite 1752, Rosslyn, VA 22209.

NEMA SB-30, *Fire Service Annunciator and Interface*, 2005.

NEMA SB-40, *Communications Systems for Life Safety in Schools*, 2008.

NEMA SB-50, *Emergency Communications Audio Intelligibility Applications Guide*, 2008.

G.1.2.9 OASIS Publication. Organization for the Advancement of Structured Information Standards (OASIS), 25 Corporate Drive, Suite 103, Burlington, MA 01803.

OASIS Standard CAP-V1.2, *OASIS Common Alerting Protocol*, Version 1.2.

G.1.2.10 SFPE Publications. Society of Fire Protection Engineers, 7315 Wisconsin Avenue, #620E, Bethesda, MD 20814.

Guide to Performance Based Design.

SFPE Engineering Guide: Evaluation of the Computer Fire Model DETACT QS, 2002.

SFPE Engineering Guide to Human Behavior in Fire, 2003.

SFPE Engineering Guide to Performance Based Fire Protection Analysis and Design of Buildings, 2000.

SFPE Handbook of Fire Protection Engineering, 3rd Edition, 2002.

Keating, John P. and Loftus, Elizabeth F., "People Care in Fire Emergencies — Psychological Aspects, 1975," SFPE, 1975.

G.1.2.11 U.S. Government Publications. U.S. Government Printing Office, Washington, DC 20402.

ADA-ABA-AG, *Americans with Disabilities Act and Architectural Barriers Act Accessibility Guidelines,* 2004.

Title 29, Code of Federal Regulations, Part 1910.5.

Title 47, Code of Federal Regulations, Part 15.

NIST Technical Note 1455–1, *Performance of Home Smoke Alarms, Analysis of the Response of Several Available Technologies in Residential Fire Settings,* February 2008.

G.1.2.12 References Associated with Annex A.

G.1.2.12.1 Reference to A.18.4.7.2. http://www.aip.org/pt/nov99/locsound.html.

G.1.2.12.2 References to A.24.3.11.

(1) *CARVER — Target Analysis and Vulnerability Assessment Methodology,* Washington, DC: U.S. Department of Defense (see Field Manual 34-36, Special Operation Forces Intelligence and Electronics Warfare Operation, Sept. 30, 1991), www.defense.gov

(2) *General Security Risk Assessment Guidelines.* Alexandria, VA: American Society for Industrial Security International, www.asisonline.org

(3) *NFPA 1600, Standard on Disaster/Emergency Management and Business Continuity Programs,* Quincy, MA: National Fire Protection Association, www.nfpa.org

(4) NFPA 730, *Guide for Premises Security,* Quincy, MA: National Fire Protection Association, www.nfpa.org

(5) *Responsible Care Code,* Washington, DC: American Chemistry Council, www.americanchemistry.com

(6) *Risk and Resilience Management of Water & Wastewater Systems,* Denver, CO: American Water Works Association, www.awwa.org

(7) *VAMCAP® Vulnerability Assessment Methodology for Critical Asset Protection,* Wilmington, DE: SafePlace Corporation, www.safeplace.com

(8) *Vulnerability Assessment Methodologies,* Albuquerque, NM: Sandia National Laboratories, www.sandia.gov

G.1.2.12.3 References to A.24.4.1.2.

(1) Cherry, E.C., Some Experiments on the Recognition of Speech, With One and With Two Ears. *Journal of Acoustical Society of America,* 1953, 25, 975–979.

(2) Cherry, E.C. and Taylor, W.K., Some Further Experiments on the Recognition of Speech With One and Two Ears. *Journal of Acoustical Society of America,* 1954, 26, 554–559.

(3) Michelle Ball and Dorothy Bruck, "The Salience of Fire Alarm Signals for Sleeping Individuals: A Novel Approach to Signal Design," 3rd International Symposium on Human Behaviour in Fire 2004. Belfast: Interscience Communications and Ulster University, 2004, pp. 303–314.

(4) Dorothy Bruck and Ian Thomas, Comparison of the Effectiveness of Different Fire Notification Signals in Sleeping Older Adults, *Fire Technology,* Volume 44, Number 1, 15–38.

(5) M. Ball and D. Bruck, "The Effect of Alcohol Upon Response to Fire Alarm Signals in Sleeping Young Adults,", in Proceedings of the Third International Symposium on Human Behaviour in Fire (Belfast), J. Shields (ed.), Interscience Communications, London, UK, 2004, pp. 291–302.

(6) Lars Benthorn and Hakan Frantzich, Fire Alarm in a Public Building: How do People Evaluate Information and Choose an Evacuation Exit? *Fire and Materials* 23, 311–315 (1999)

(7) Proulx, G., Occupant Behaviour and Evacuation Proceedings of the 9th International Fire Protection Symposium, Munich, May 25–26, 2001, pp. 219-232.

(8) Zhang, L., Sun, X., Zhang, K., A Research of Speech Signal on Fire Information Display Interface. *China Safety Science Journal* 16(4), 13–18 (2006).

(9) Alla Keselman, Laura Slaughter and Vimla L. Patel, Toward a framework for understanding lay public's comprehension of disaster and bioterrorism information, *Journal of Biomedical Informatics* Volume 38, Issue 4, August 2005, pp. 331–344.

(10) Sabrina Koreimann, Sabine Strauß, Oliver Vitouch, Inattentional Deafness Under Dynamic Musical Conditions, Proceedings of the 7th Triennial Conference of European Society for the Cognitive Sciences of Music (ESCOM 2009) Jyväskylä, Finland, pp. 246–249.

(11) Maha Nasrallah, David Carmel, Nilli Lavie, Murder, She Wrote: Enhanced Sensitivity to Negative Word Valence, *Emotion,* 2009, Vol. 9, No. 5, 609–618.

(12) J.T. Siegel, J.K. Burgoon, Expectancy theory approaches to prevention: Violating adolescent expectations to increase the effectiveness of public service announcements in William D. Crano, Michael Burgoon Mass media and drug prevention: classic and contemporary theories and research.

(13) Timothy R. Levine, Lori N. Anders, John Banas, Karie Leigh Baum, Keriane Endo, Allison D. S. Hu, Norman C. H. Wong, Norms, expectations, and deception: A norm violation model of veracity judgments, *Communication Monographs,* Volume 67, Issue 2 June 2000, pp 123–137.

(14) Mirjam Broersma and Kees de Bot, Triggered codeswitching: A corpus-based evaluation of the original triggering hypothesis and a new alternative, *Bilingualism: Language and Cognition* 9 (1), 2006, 1–13.

(15) Mirjam Broersma, Triggered codeswitching between cognate languages, *Bilingualism: Language and Cognition* 12 (4), 2009, 447–462.

(16) J.E. Driskell, R.P. Willis, C. Copper, Effect of overlearning on retention, *Journal of Applied Psychology* 1992, Vol. 77, No. 5, 615–622.

G.1.2.12.4 References to A.24.4.2.8.

(1) Schifiliti, R.P., "To Leave or Not to Leave — That is the Question!", National Fire Protection Association, World Fire Safety Congress & Exposition, May 16, 2000, Denver, CO.

(2) Ramachandran, G., "Informative Fire Warning Systems," *Fire Technology,* Volume 47, Number 1, February 1991, National Fire Protection Association, 66–81.

(3) J. Bryan, "Psychological Variables That May Affect Fire Alarm Design," *Fire Protection Engineering,* Society of Fire Protection Engineers, Issue No. 11, Fall 2001.

(4) Proulx, G., "Cool Under Fire," *Fire Protection Engineering,* Society of Fire Protection Engineers, Issue No. 16, Fall 2002.

(5) General Services Administration, Proceedings of the Reconvened International Conference on Fire Safety in High Rise Buildings, Washington, D.C., October 1971.

(6) Proulx, G., "Strategies for Ensuring Appropriate Occupant Response to Fire Alarm Signals," National Research

Council of Canada, Ottawa, Ontario, *Construction Technology Update*, No. 43, 1–6, December 2000.

G.1.2.12.5 References to A.29.2.

(1) "A Few Fire Facts at the Household Level," NFPA Fire Analysis Division, *Fire Journal*, May 1986.

(2) "Fire Loss in the United States during 2007," Michael J. Karter, NFPA Fire Analysis and Research Division.

(3) "Home Structure Fires," Marty Ahrens, NFPA Fire Analysis and Research Division, February 2007.

G.1.2.12.6 References to A.29.3.7.

CSE NIH report, 2005; Bruck and Thomas, 2009; Bruck, Thomas, and Ball, NFPA RF report, 2007.

G.1.2.12.7 References to A.29.5.1.

(1) NBS GCR 75-51, *Detector Sensitivity and Siting Requirements for Dwellings*, 1975.

(2) NBS GCR 77-82, *Detector Sensitivity and Siting Requirements for Dwellings Phase 2*, 1977.

(3) NIST Technical Note 1455-1, *Performance of Home Smoke Detectors Analysis of the Response of Several Available Technologies in a Residential Setting*, 2007.

G.1.2.13 References Associated with Annex B.

(1) Alpert, R. "Ceiling Jets," *Fire Technology*, Aug. 1972.

(2) "Evaluating Unsprinklered Fire Hazards," *SFPE Technology Report* 83-2.

(3) Babrauskas, V., Lawson, J. R., Walton, W. D., and Twilley, W. H. "Upholstered Furniture Heat Release Rates Measured with a Furniture Calorimeter," (NBSIR 82-2604) (Dec. 1982). National Institute of Standards and Technology (formerly National Bureau of Standards), Center for Fire Research, Gaithersburg, MD 20889.

(4) Beyler, C. "A Design Method for Flaming Fire Detection," *Fire Technology*, Vol. 20, No. 4, Nov. 1984.

(5) DiNenno, P., ed. Chapter 31, *SFPE Handbook of Fire Protection Engineering*, by R. Schifiliti, Sept. 1988.

(6) Evans, D. D. and Stroup, D. W. "Methods to Calculate Response Time of Heat and Smoke Detectors Installed Below Large Unobstructed Ceilings," (NBSIR 85-3167) (Feb. 1985, issued Jul. 1986). National Institute of Standards and Technology (formerly National Bureau of Standards), Center for Fire Research, Gaithersburg, MD 20889.

(7) Heskestad, G. "Characterization of Smoke Entry and Response for Products-of-Combustion Detectors" Proceedings, 7th International Conference on Problems of Automatic Fire Detection, Rheinish-Westfalischen Technischen Hochschule Aachen (Mar. 1975).

(8) Heskestad, G. "Investigation of a New Sprinkler Sensitivity Approval Test: The Plunge Test," FMRC Tech. Report 22485, Factory Mutual Research Corporation, 1151 Providence Turnpike, Norwood, MA 02062.

(9) Heskestad, G. and Delichatsios, M. A. "The Initial Convective Flow in Fire: Seventeenth Symposium on Combustion," The Combustion Institute, Pittsburgh, PA (1979).

(10) Heskestad, G. and Delichatsios, M. A. "Environments of Fire Detectors — Phase 1: Effect of Fire Size, Ceiling Height and Material," Measurements Vol. I (NBS-GCR-77-86), Analysis Vol. II (NBS-GCR-77-95). National Technical Information Service (NTIS), Springfield, VA 22151.

(11) Heskestad, G. and Delichatsios, M. A. "Update: The Initial Convective Flow in Fire," *Fire Safety Journal*, Vol. 15, No. 5, 1989.

(12) International Organization for Standardization, *Audible Emergency Evacuation Signal*, ISO 8201, 1987.

(13) Klote, J. and Milke, J. "Principles of Smoke Management," American Society of Heating, Refrigerating and Air Conditioning Engineers, Atlanta, GA, 2002.

(14) Lawson, J. R., Walton, W. D., and Twilley, W. H. "Fire Performance of Furnishings as Measured in the NBS Furniture Calorimeter, Part 1," (NBSIR 83-2787) (Aug. 1983). National Institute of Standards and Technology (formerly National Bureau of Standards), Center for Fire Research, Gaithersburg, MD 20889.

(15) Morton, B. R., Taylor, Sir Geoffrey, and Turner, J. S. "Turbulent Gravitational Convection from Maintained and Instantaneous Sources," Proc. Royal Society A, 234, 1–23, 1956.

(16) Schifiliti, R. "Use of Fire Plume Theory in the Design and Analysis of Fire Detector and Sprinkler Response," Master's Thesis, Worcester Polytechnic Institute, Center for Firesafety Studies, Worcester, MA, 1986.

(17) Title 47, Code of Federal Regulations, Communications Act of 1934 Amended.

(18) Schifiliti, R. and Pucci, W. "Fire Detection Modelling, State of the Art," 6 May, 1996 sponsored by the Fire Detection Institute, Bloomfield, CT.

(19) Forney, G., Bukowski, R., Davis, W. "Field Modelling: Effects of Flat Beamed Ceilings on Detector and Sprinkler Response," Technical Report, Year 1. International Fire Detection Research Project, National Fire Protection Research Foundation, Quincy, MA. October, 1993.

(20) Davis, W., Forney, G., Bukowski, R. "Field Modelling: Simulating the Effect of Sloped Beamed Ceilings on Detector and Sprinkler Response," Year 1. International Fire Detection Research Project Technical Report, National Fire Protection Research Foundation, Quincy, MA. October, 1994.

(21) Brozovski, E. "A Preliminary Approach to Siting Smoke Detectors Based on Design Fire Size and Detector Aerosol Entry Lag Time," Master's Thesis, Worcester Polytechnic, Worcester, MA, 1989.

(22) Cote, A. *NFPA Fire Protection Handbook*, 20th edition, National Fire Protection Association, Quincy, MA, 2008.

(23) Tewarson, A., "Generation of Heat and Chemical Compounds in Fires," *SFPE Handbook of Fire Protection Engineering*, Second Edition, NFPA and SFPE, 1995.

(24) Hollman, J. P. *Heat Transfer*, McGraw-Hill, New York, 1976.

(25) Custer, R. L. P., and Meacham, B. "Introduction to Performance Based Fire Safety," SFPE, 1997.

(26) Schifiliti, R. P., Meacham B., Custer, R. L. P. "Design of Detection Systems," *SFPE Handbook of Fire Protection Engineering*.

(27) Marrion, C. "Correction Factors for the Heat of Combustion in NFPA 72," Appendix B, Fire Protection Engineering, SFPE, 1998.

(28) Marrion, C. "Designing and Analyzing the Response of Detection Systems: An Update to Previous Correlations," 1988.

(29) Custer, R. and Bright, R. "Fire Detection: The State-of-the-Art," NBS Tech. Note 839, National Bureau of Standards, Washington, 1974.

(30) Meacham, Brian J. "Characterization of Smoke from Burning Materials for the Evaluation of Light Scattering-Type Smoke Detector Response," MS Thesis, WPI Center for Firesafety Studies, Worcester, MA, 1991.

(31) Delichatsios, M. A. "Categorization of Cable Flammability, Detection of Smoldering, and Flaming Cable Fires," Interim Report, Factory Mutual Research Corporation, Norwood, MA, NP-1630, Nov. 1980.

(32) Heskestad, G. FMRC Serial Number 21017, Factory Mutual Research Corp., Norwood, MA, 1974.

(33) Marrion, C. E. "Lag Time Modeling and Effects of Ceiling Jet Velocity on the Placement of Optical Smoke Detectors," MS Thesis, WPI Center for Firesafety Studies, Worcester, MA, 1989.

(34) Kokkala, M. et al. "Measurements of the Characteristic Lengths of Smoke Detectors," *Fire Technology*, Vol. 28, No. 2, National Fire Protection Association, Quincy, MA, 1992.

(34a) Yamauchi et al. "A Calculation Method for Predicting Heat and Smoke Detector's Response."

(34b) Cleary et al. "Particulate Entry Lag in Spot Type Smoke Detectors," IAFSS Proceedings, Boston, MA 2000.

(34c) Keski-Rahkonen, "Revisiting Modeling of Fluid Penetration into Smoke Detectors," AUBE 2001.

(34d) Bjoerkman et al. "Determination of Dynamic Model Parameters of Smoke Detectors," *Fire Safety Journal*, No 37, pp. 395–407, 2002.

(34e) Keski-Rahkonen, "A New Model for Time Lag of Smoke Detectors," International Collaborative Project to Evaluate Fire Models for Nuclear Power Plant Application, Gaithersburg, MD May 2002.

(35) UL 268, *Standard for Smoke Detectors for Fire Alarm Systems*, Underwriters Laboratories, Inc., Northbrook, IL, 2009.

(36) Deal, Scott. "Technical Reference Guide for FPEtool Version 3.2," NISTIR 5486, National Institute for Standards and Technology, U.S. Department of Commerce, Gaithersburg, MD, Aug. 1994.

(37) Mowrer, F. W. "Lag Times Associated with Detection and Suppression," *Fire Technology*, Vol. 26, No. 3, pp. 244–265, 1990.

(38) Newman, J. S. "Principles for Fire Detection," *Fire Technology*, Vol. 24, No. 2, pp. 116–127, 1988.

(39) Custer, R., Meacham, B., Wood, C. "Performance Based Design Techniques for Detection and Special Suppression Applications," Proceedings of the SFPE Engineering Seminars on Advances in Detection and Suppression Technology, 1994.

(40) SFPE *Engineering Guide to Performance Based Fire Protection Analysis and Design of Buildings*, 2007, SFPE, Bethesda, MD.

(41) SFPE *Handbook of Fire Protection Engineering*, Fourth Edition, SFPE, Bethesda, MD, 2008.

(42) Drysdale, Dougal, *An Introduction to Fire Dynamics*, John Wiley & Sons, New York, NY, 1998, ISBN 0 471 90613 1, Second Edition.

(43) Nam S., Donovan L.P. and Kim S.G., Establishing Heat Detectors Thermal Sensitivity Through Bench Scale Tests, *Fire Safety Journal*, Volume 39, Number 3, 191–215, April 2004.

(44) Nam S., Thermal Response Coefficient TRC of Heat Detectors and Its Field Applications, Fire Detection and Research Applications Symposium, NFP Research Foundation, January 2003.

(45) Nam S., Performance-Based Heat Detector Spacing, Interflam 2004, pp 883–892.

(46) Geiman, J. A., "Evaluation of Smoke Detector Response Estimation Methods," Master of Science Thesis, University of Maryland, College Park, MD, December 2003.

(47) Projected Beam Smoke Detectors — More Than Just a Substitute for Spot Detectors; Fire Protection Engineering, Summer 2004, SFPE.

(48) Geiman, J.A., and Gottuck, D.T., "Alarm Thresholds for Smoke Detector Modeling," *Fire Safety Science — Proceeding of the Seventh International Symposium*, 2003, pp. 197–208.

(49) *The SFPE Code Official's Guide to Performance-based Design Review and Analysis of Buildings*, Society of Fire Protection Engineers, Bethesda, MD, 2004.

(50) NFPA *101, Life Safety Code*, National Fire Protection Association, Quincy, MA, 2009.

(51) NFPA 909, *Code for the Protection of Cultural Resource Properties — Museums, Libraries, and Places of Worship*, National Fire Protection Association, Quincy, MA, 2010.

(52) NFPA 914, *Code for Fire Protection of Historic Structures*, National Fire Protection Association, Quincy, MA, 2010.

(53) Performance-based Building Design Concepts, International Code Council, Washington DC, 2004.

(54) *Extreme Event Mitigation In Buildings—Analysis and Design*, Meacham, National Fire Protection Association, Quincy, MA, 2006.

(55) Geiman, Gottuk, and Milke, "Evaluation of Smoke Detector Response Estimation Methods: Optical Density, Temperature Rise and Velocity at Alarm," *Journal of Fire Protection Engineering*, 2006.

(56) Su et al., "Kemano Fire Studies—Part 1: Response of Residential Smoke Alarms," Research Report 108, NRCC, April 2003.

(57) Davis, W., The Zone Model Jet, "A Model for the Prediction of Detector Activation and Gas Temperature in the Presence of a Smoke Layer," NISTIR 6324, NIST, May 1999.

(58) *SFPE Engineering Guide to Human Behavior in Fire*.

G.1.2.14 References Associated with Annex D.

(1) Jacob, K. & Tyson, T., "Computer-Based Prediction of Speech Intelligibility for Mass Notification Systems," SUPDET 2008, Fire Protection Research Foundation, Mar 2008.

(2) IEC 60268-16, "Sound system equipment — Part 16: Objective rating of speech intelligibility by speech transmission index," 2003.

(3) ANSI/ASA S3.5, "American National Standard Methods for Calculation of the Speech Intelligibility Index," 1997.

(4) Barnett, P.W. and Knight, A.D., "The Common Intelligibility Scale," Proceedings of the Institute of Acoustics, Vol. 17, Part 7, 1995.

(5) IEC 60849, Annex B, Sound Systems for Emergency Purposes, Feb 1998.

(6) Sander J. van Wijngaarden and Jan A. Verhave, Past Present and Future of the Speech Transmission Index, Chapter 9, Measurement and Prediction of Speech Intelligibility in Traffic Tunnels Using the STI, p113, TNO Human Factors, The Netherlands, 2002.

(7) Mapp, P., "Systematic & Common Errors in Sound System STI and Intelligibility Measurements," Convention Paper 6271, Audio Engineering Society, 117th Convention, San Fran, CA, 28–31 Oct 2004.

(8) Peter Mapp, Past Present and Future of the Speech Transmission Index, Chapter 8, Practical Application of STI to Assessing Public Address and Emergency Sound Systems, TNO Human Factors, The Netherlands, 2002.

G.2 Informational References. The following documents or portions thereof are listed here as informational resources only. They are not a part of the requirements of this document.

G.2.1 UL Publications. Underwriters Laboratories Inc., 333 Pfingsten Road, Northbrook, IL 60062-2096.

ANSI/UL 2074, *Gas and Vapor Detectors and Sensors*, 2004.

G.3 References for Extracts in Informational Sections.

NFPA 3, *Recommended Practice for Commissioning and Integrated Testing of Fire Protection and Life Safety Systems*, 2012 edition.

NFPA 70®, *National Electrical Code®*, 2011 edition.

NFPA 92, *Standard for Smoke Control Systems*, 2012 edition.

NFPA 92B, *Smoke Management Systems in Malls, Atria, and Large Spaces*, 1995 edition.

NFPA 101®, *Life Safety Code®*, 2012 edition.

NFPA 1221, *Standard for the Installation, Maintenance, and Use of Emergency Services Communications Systems*, 2013 edition.

Sequence of Events Leading to Issuance of this NFPA Committee Document

Step 1: Call for Proposals

•Proposed new Document or new edition of an existing Document is entered into one of two yearly revision cycles, and a Call for Proposals is published.

Step 2: Report on Proposals (ROP)

•Committee meets to act on Proposals, to develop its own Proposals, and to prepare its Report.
•Committee votes by written ballot on Proposals. If two-thirds approve, Report goes forward. Lacking two-thirds approval, Report returns to Committee.
•Report on Proposals (ROP) is published for public review and comment.

Step 3: Report on Comments (ROC)

•Committee meets to act on Public Comments to develop its own Comments, and to prepare its report.
•Committee votes by written ballot on Comments. If two-thirds approve, Report goes forward. Lacking two-thirds approval, Report returns to Committee.
•Report on Comments (ROC) is published for public review.

Step 4: Technical Report Session

•"*Notices of intent to make a motion*" are filed, are reviewed, and valid motions are certified for presentation at the Technical Report Session. ("Consent Documents" that have no certified motions bypass the Technical Report Session and proceed to the Standards Council for issuance.)
•NFPA membership meets each June at the Annual Meeting Technical Report Session and acts on Technical Committee Reports (ROP and ROC) for Documents with "certified amending motions."
•Committee(s) vote on any amendments to Report approved at NFPA Annual Membership Meeting.

Step 5: Standards Council Issuance

•Notification of intent to file an appeal to the Standards Council on Association action must be filed within 20 days of the NFPA Annual Membership Meeting.
•Standards Council decides, based on all evidence, whether or not to issue Document or to take other action, including hearing any appeals.

Committee Membership Classifications

The following classifications apply to Technical Committee members and represent their principal interest in the activity of the committee.

M   *Manufacturer:* A representative of a maker or marketer of a product, assembly, or system, or portion thereof, that is affected by the standard.

U   *User:* A representative of an entity that is subject to the provisions of the standard or that voluntarily uses the standard.

I/M   *Installer/Maintainer:* A representative of an entity that is in the business of installing or maintaining a product, assembly, or system affected by the standard.

L   *Labor:* A labor representative or employee concerned with safety in the workplace.

R/T   *Applied Research/Testing Laboratory:* A representative of an independent testing laboratory or independent applied research organization that promulgates and/or enforces standards.

E   *Enforcing Authority:* A representative of an agency or an organization that promulgates and/or enforces standards.

I   *Insurance:* A representative of an insurance company, broker, agent, bureau, or inspection agency.

C   *Consumer:* A person who is, or represents, the ultimate purchaser of a product, system, or service affected by the standard, but who is not included in the *User* classification.

SE   *Special Expert:* A person not representing any of the previous classifications, but who has a special expertise in the scope of the standard or portion thereof.

NOTES:
1. "Standard" connotes code, standard, recommended practice, or guide.
2. A representative includes an employee.
3. While these classifications will be used by the Standards Council to achieve a balance for Technical Committees, the Standards Council may determine that new classifications of members or unique interests need representation in order to foster the best possible committee deliberations on any project. In this connection, the Standards Council may make appointments as it deems appropriate in the public interest, such as the classification of "Utilities" in the National Electrical Code Committee.
4. Representatives of subsidiaries of any group are generally considered to have the same classification as the parent organization.